AQA Science

Exclusively endorsed and approved by AQA

Teacher's Book

Geoff Carr • Darren Forbes • Sam Holyman • Ruth Miller

Series Editor: Lawrie Ryan

GCSE Additional Science

Nelson Thornes
a Wolters Kluwer business

Published in 2006 by:
Nelson Thornes Ltd
Delta Place
27 Bath Road
CHELTENHAM
GL53 7TH
United Kingdom

07 08 09 10 / 10 9 8 7 6 5

A catalogue record for this book is available from the British Library

ISBN 978 0 7487 9639 7

Cover bubble illustration by Andy Parker
Illustrations by Bede Illustration

Page make-up by Wearset Ltd

Printed in Croatia by Zrinski

The following people have made an invaluable contribution to this
book:

Pauline Anning, Jim Breithaupt, Nigel English, Ann Fullick, Patrick
Fullick, Richard Gott, Keith Hirst, Paul Lister, Niva Miles, John
Scottow, Glenn Toole.

GCSE Additional Science

Contents

B2 Additional biology 2

1 Cells 4
1.1 Animal and plant cells
1.2 Specialised cells
1.3 How do substances get in and out of cells?
1.4 Osmosis
1.5 Cell issues
Summary, Exam-style, How science works answers 14

2 How plants produce food 16
2.1 Photosynthesis
2.2 Limiting factors
2.3 How plants use glucose
2.4 Why do plants need minerals?
2.5 Plant problems?
Summary, Exam-style, How science works answers 26

3 Energy flows 28
3.1 Pyramids of biomass
3.2 Energy losses
3.3 Energy in food production
3.4 Decay
3.5 The carbon cycle
3.6 Farming – intensive or free range?
Summary, Exam-style, How science works answers 40

4 Enzymes 42
4.1 Enzyme structure
4.2 Factors affecting enzyme action
4.3 Aerobic respiration
4.4 Enzymes in digestion
4.5 Speeding up digestion
4.6 Making use of enzymes
4.7 High-tech enzymes
Summary, Exam-style, How science works answers 56

5 Homeostasis 58
5.1 Controlling internal conditions
5.2 Controlling body temperature
5.3 Controlling blood sugar
5.4 Homeostasis matters!
Summary, Exam-style, How science works answers 66

6 Inheritance 68
6.1 Cell division and growth
6.2 Stem cells
6.3 Cell division in sexual reproduction
6.4 From Mendel to DNA
6.5 Inheritance in action
6.6 Inherited conditions in humans
6.7 Stem cells and embryos – an ethical minefield
Summary, Exam-style, How science works answers 82

End of unit exam answers 84

C2 Additional chemistry 86

1 Structures and bonding 88
1.1 Atomic structure
1.2 The arrangement of electrons in atoms
1.3 Chemical bonding
1.4 Ionic bonding
1.5 Covalent bonding
1.6 Bonding in metals
1.7 The history of the atom
Summary, Exam-style, How science works answers 102

2 Structures and properties 104
2.1 Ionic compounds
2.2 Simple molecules
2.3 Giant covalent substances
2.4 Giant metallic structures
2.5 Nanoscience and nanotechnology
Summary, Exam-style, How science works answers 114

3 How much? 116
3.1 Mass numbers
3.2 Masses of atoms and moles
3.3 Percentages and formulae
3.4 Equations and calculations
3.5 Making as much as we want
3.6 Reversible reactions
3.7 Making ammonia – the Haber process
3.8 Aspects of the Haber process
Summary, Exam-style, How science works answers 132

4 Rates of reaction 134
4.1 How fast?
4.2 Collision theory
4.3 The effect of temperature
4.4 The effect of concentration
4.5 The effect of catalysts
4.6 Catalysts in action
Summary, Exam-style, How science works answers 146

5 Energy and reactions 148
5.1 Exothermic and endothermic reactions
5.2 Energy and reversible reactions
5.3 More about the Haber process
5.4 Industrial dilemmas
Summary, Exam-style, How science works answers 156

6 Electrolysis 158
6.1 Electrolysis – the basics
6.2 Changes at the electrodes
6.3 Electrolysing brine
6.4 Purifying copper
6.5 To build or not to build?
Summary, Exam-style, How science works answers 168

7 Acids, alkalis and salts   170

7.1 Acids and alkalis
7.2 Making salts from metals and bases
7.3 Making salts from solutions
7.4 It's all in the soil
Summary, Exam-style, How science works answers   178

End of unit exam answers   180

P2 Additional physics   182

1 Motion   184

1.1 Distance–time graphs
1.2 Velocity and acceleration
1.3 More about velocity–time graphs
1.4 Using graphs
1.5 Transport issues
Summary, Exam-style, How science works answers   194

2 Speeding up and slowing down   196

2.1 Forces between objects
2.2 Resultant force
2.3 Force and acceleration
2.4 On the road
2.5 Falling objects
2.6 Speed limits
Summary, Exam-style, How science works answers   208

3 Work, energy and momentum   210

3.1 Energy and work
3.2 Kinetic energy
3.3 Momentum
3.4 More on collisions and explosions
3.5 Changing momentum
3.6 Forces for safety
Summary, Exam-style, How science works answers   222

4 Static electricity   224

4.1 Electrical charges
4.2 Charge on the move
4.3 Uses and dangers of static electricity
4.4 Static issues
Summary, Exam-style, How science works answers   232

5 Current electricity   234

5.1 Electric circuits
5.2 Resistance
5.3 More current–potential difference graphs
5.4 Series circuits
5.5 Parallel circuits
5.6 Circuits in control
Summary, Exam-style, How science works answers   246

6 Mains electricity   248

6.1 Alternating current
6.2 Cables and plugs
6.3 Fuses
6.4 Electrical power and potential difference
6.5 Electrical energy and charge
6.6 Safety matters
Summary, Exam-style, How science works answers   260

7 Nuclear physics   262

7.1 Nuclear reactions
7.2 The discovery of the nucleus
7.3 Nuclear fission
7.4 Nuclear fusion
7.5 Nuclear energy issues
Summary, Exam-style, How science works answers   272

End of unit exam answers   274

Appendix: How science works   276

Welcome to AQA Science!

AQA Science for GCSE is the only series to be endorsed by AQA. The *GCSE Additional Science* Teacher Book is written by experienced science teachers and is designed to make planning the delivery of the specification easy – everything you need is right here! Information is placed around a reduced facsimile of the Student Book page, allowing you quick reference to features and content that will be used in the lesson.

How science works

This is covered in the section at the beginning of the Student Book, in the main content, in the end of chapter spreads, and in the exam-style questions and 'How Science Works' questions. The corresponding teacher's notes give you detailed guidance on how to integrate 'How Science Works' fully into your lessons and activities.

Exam-Style Questions

There are structured questions for Science B. They are ranked in order of difficulty. All questions are useful to complete, no matter which specification is being taken, as they cover the same content. 'How Science Works' is integrated into some exam-style questions and there are separate 'How Science Works' questions to give additional practice in this area.

Lesson structure

This feature provides ideas for the experienced teacher, support for the newly qualified teacher and structure for cover lessons. Available for every double page lesson spread, it contains a variety of suggestions for how the spread could be taught, including starters and plenaries of varying lengths, as well as suggestions for the main part of the lesson.

LEARNING OBJECTIVES

These tell you what the students should know by the end of the lesson, linking directly to the Learning Objectives in the Student Book, but providing teachers with extra detail. The Learning Objectives for 'How Science Works' are all listed in the Appendix. These should be integrated into the lessons chosen to teach various aspects of 'How Science Works' throughout the course.

LEARNING OUTCOMES

These tell you what the students should be able to do to show they have achieved the Learning Objectives. These are differentiated where appropriate to provide suitable expectations for all your students.

Teaching suggestions

Ideas on how to use features in the Student Book, suggestions for Gifted and Talented, Special Needs, ICT activities and different learning styles are all covered here, and more.

Practical support

For every practical in the Student Book you will find this corresponding feature which gives a list of equipment needed, safety references and further guidance to carry out the practical. A worksheet is provided on the e-Science CD ROM for each practical.

Activity notes

Each activity in the Student Book has background information notes on how to organise it effectively.

Icons

- *appears in the text where opportunities for investigational aspects of 'How Science Works' are signposted in the AQA specification.*

- *appears in the text where AQA have signposted opportunities to cover societal aspects of 'How Science Works' in the specification.*

e-Science CD ROM

This contains a wide range of resources – animations, simulations, photopluses, Powerpoints, activity sheets, practical skill sheets, homework sheets – which are linked to Student Book pages and help deliver the activities suggested in the Teacher Book.

Answers to questions

They're all here! All the questions in the Student Book are answered in the Teacher Book. Each answer is located in the corresponding feature in the Teacher Book. For example, answers to yellow in-text questions in the Student Book can be found in the yellow feature in the Teacher Book.

Key Stage 3 curriculum links:

This expands the 'What you already know' unit opener of the Student Book and gives QCA Scheme of Work references for relevant knowledge that may need revisiting before starting on the unit.

ACTIVITIES & EXTENSIONS

This highlights opportunities to extend a lesson or add activities, providing notes and tips on how to carry them out.

SPECIFICATION LINK-UP

This gives clear references to the AQA specification for the lesson, with additional notes and guidance where appropriate.

KEY POINTS

This feature gives ideas on how to consolidate the key points given in the Student Book, and how to use the key points as a basis for homework, revision or extension work.

B2 | Additional biology

Key Stage 3 curriculum links

The following link to 'What you already know':

* Animal and plant cells can form tissues, and tissues can form organs; the functions of chloroplasts and cell walls in plant cells and the functions of the cell membrane, cytoplasm and nucleus in both plant and animal cells; relate cells and cell functions to life processes in a variety of organisms.

* The principles of digestion, including the role of enzymes in breaking down large molecules into smaller ones; food is used as a fuel during respiration to maintain the body's activity and as a raw material for growth and repair.

* Aerobic respiration involves a reaction in cells between oxygen and food in which glucose is broken down into carbon dioxide and water, summarised in a word equation.

* Plants need carbon dioxide, water and light for photosynthesis, and produce biomass and oxygen, summarised in a word equation. Nitrogen and other elements, in addition to carbon, hydrogen and oxygen, are required for plant growth.

* Plants carry out aerobic respiration.

QCA Scheme of work

7A Cells
8A Food and digestion
8B Respiration
9C Plants and photosynthesis
9D Plants for food

RECAP ANSWERS

1 a) Movement, respiration, sensitivity, growth, reproduction, excretion, nutrition.

   b) Animals move whole body, plants do not; plant cells have cell walls and chloroplasts, animals do not; plants photosynthesise (make their own food), animals cannot.

   c) i) Controls the cell, contains plans for making new cells and new organisms.
      ii) The outer barrier of the cell, it controls substances moving into and out of the cell.
      iii) Jelly (material) where all the important jobs of the cell take place.

2 a) For energy for our cells.

   b) Big molecules need to be broken down to smaller molecules.

   c) Chemical that speeds up reactions.

   d) You cannot use the food for energy until it has been broken down into small molecules.

3 a) It makes the energy from your food available to your body.

   b) glucose + oxygen → energy + carbon dioxide + water

4 a) It would die as it needs light to make food by photosynthesis.

   b) Plants use carbon dioxide to make sugars in photosynthesis. If you talk to them you are breathing air rich in carbon dioxide on to them. They have more carbon dioxide, so they might be able to make more food and therefore grow more.

   c) Minerals, such as nitrates and magnesium, are needed to make other chemicals that they need.

B2 | Additional biology

What you already know

Here is a quick reminder of previous work that you will find useful in this unit:

* Both plant and animal cells have a cell membrane, cytoplasm and a nucleus. Plants cells also have cell walls and chloroplasts.

* Some cells, such as sperm, ova and root hair cells, are specially adapted to carry out particular functions in an organism.

* Enzymes play an important part in breaking down large molecules into smaller ones during digestion.

* Food is used as a fuel during respiration to keep your body activity levels up. You also need it as the raw material for growth and repair of your body cells.

* Plants and animals all carry out aerobic respiration.

* Aerobic respiration involves a reaction in our cells between oxygen and food. Glucose is broken down into carbon dioxide (CO_2) and water (H_2O).

* Plants need carbon dioxide, water and light for photosynthesis. They produce biomass, in the form of new plant material, and oxygen.

* Plants also need nitrogen and other elements to grow.

RECAP QUESTIONS

1 a) Make a list of the things all living things need or do.

   b) Write down three differences between animals and plants.

   c) What are the jobs of:
      i)   the nucleus,
      ii) the cell membrane,
      iii) the cytoplasm,
      in a cell?

2 a) Why do we need food?

   b) What has to happen to the food you eat before it can be useful to your body?

   c) What is an enzyme?

   d) Why are enzymes so important in digestion?

3 a) Respiration takes place in all living cells. Why is it so important?

   b) Write a word equation for what happens during respiration in your cells.

4 a) What would happen if you put a plant in a dark cupboard and left it for several weeks?

   b) There is more carbon dioxide in the air people breathe out than in the air they breathe in. Some people claim that talking to house plants makes them grow better. What might be a scientific explanation for this claim?

   c) Sunlight and water are not enough for plants to grow well.
      What else do they need – and why?

Activity notes

This is a very open-ended activity and students would benefit from some guidelines. It can be done quite simply in a lesson, by asking students to make their individual lists and then compiling a class list, but if more detail is required then research and homework time could be allocated. The more detailed research, particularly with respect to the food that animals eat, could link with subsequent work in Chapter 3.

* **What do we mean by 'food'?** – The students could discuss the term and come to a decision about a definition. Then ask: 'What do we mean by 'different types of food'?' [It could be interpreted in many ways: fast food; energy-giving food; body-building food; baby food etc.] A brainstorming session could come up with a whole range of different types.

* **Different diets (1)** – People in different parts of the world eat different foods. In developing countries, the people rely on one food (a staple food) for a major part of their diet. For example, in SE Asia the staple food is rice and in central Africa it is roots and tubers, such as cassava and sweet potatoes. An interesting project would be to find out about the different staple foods in the world. Ask: 'Why are they the staples? What do they supply in the diet? What other foods are eaten? What can be grown successfully in a particular region?' This suggestion can be more clearly defined into the cereal crops, such as wheat, maize and

SPECIFICATION LINK-UP   Unit: Biology 2

What are animals and plants built from?

All living things are made up of cells. The structures of different types of cell are related to their functions.

How do dissolved substances get into and out of cells?

To get into and out of cells, dissolved substances need to cross cell membranes.

How do plants obtain the food they need to live and grow?

Green plants use light energy to make their own food. They obtain the raw materials they need to make this food from the air and the soil.

What happens to energy and biomass at each stage in a food chain?

By observing the numbers and sizes of the organisms in food chains, we can find out what happens to energy and biomass as it passes along the food chain.

Making connections

The plant production line!

Plants produce food for all the animals that live on Earth, including us. They do this through the process of photosynthesis. They use carbon dioxide, water, and energy from light, to make sugars and oxygen.

Feeding the world

Plants could provide enough material to feed everyone in the world. If everyone understood how pyramids of biomass work, perhaps we would all eat differently and no-one would starve!

Enzymes

The food you eat is made up of big molecules. They can't get out of your gut and into your bloodstream. So they can't reach the cells where they are needed. Fortunately your body makes digestive enzymes. They work in your gut to break your food down into much smaller molecules, which your body can use.

Specialised cells

The cells in your pancreas are very specialised. Some of them (stained pink in this photo) produce enzymes needed to break down your food. Others (stained purple) make the hormone insulin which controls your blood sugar levels.

Food – vital for life!

Balancing blood sugar

After you have eaten and digested a meal, the levels of sugar in your blood shoot up. You need to be able to take this sugar into your cells so they can use it. You also need to store some of the sugar to use later. The hormone insulin is vital for you to balance your blood sugar.

Inheriting problems

Most babies are born with guts that work perfectly. But some inherit genes which mean they can't feed properly. With pyloric stenosis, the baby vomits all its food back. It needs surgery to correct the fault in its gut. In cystic fibrosis the glands that make many of the digestive enzymes get clogged up with thick sticky mucus. Then they don't work at all.

ACTIVITY

Lots of what you will learn in this unit is linked in some way to food. Every living thing needs food to survive. List, draw or find images of as many different types of food as you can.

Think about the food eaten by different types of animals and by different people around the world. There are some amazing sources of energy out there – see how many you can think of!

Chapters in this unit

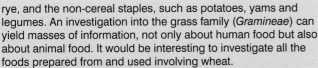

Cells   How plants produce food   Energy flows   Enzymes   Homeostasis   Inheritance

3

---

rye, and the non-cereal staples, such as potatoes, yams and legumes. An investigation into the grass family (*Gramineae*) can yield masses of information, not only about human food but also about animal food. It would be interesting to investigate all the foods prepared from and used involving wheat.

- **Different diets (2)** – Another approach to different diets is to look at what people in different parts of Europe traditionally eat. Students could draw upon their holiday experiences to investigate the 'Mediterranean' diet, what the Greeks eat, why Scandinavian diets include more fish, etc.
- **Food eaten by animals** – There are some animals that have very specific food preferences and requirements (the Giant Panda and bamboo, for example). Some students might like to compile a fact file of such associations. Some research in a library or suitable web sites would need to be done. It could link with work done on why certain species of animals are becoming extinct (Module B1b).
- **Strange foods** – Some of the food we eat comes from strange sources. We get jelly from seaweed, food products from blue-green algae and meat substitutes from a fungus. Students could research food from strange sources. Ask: 'Can it save the world?'
- **Food in history** – Some students might like to investigate how food has changed over time. A comparison of the diet of a medieval peasant with a twenty-first century diet could be quite revealing. At the time of the Roman Conquest, the diet of a Roman soldier was different from the British diet. The Romans are thought to have been responsible for introducing rabbits and they also grew vines to make wine (ask students to think about this in relation to climate change!).

Special needs

These students could find pictures in magazines and newspapers, or draw foods and compile a scrapbook.

Teaching suggestions

- 'What you already know' and the 'Recap questions' review the extent of the students' knowledge of these topics gained from their studies at KS3. The students should understand the structure of cells, the differences between plant and animal cells and that cells are specialised to carry out particular functions. Not all students recognise individual cells and many will not appreciate the differences in size (ova and sperm cells). There could also be some confusion about exactly how much is visible at different magnifications (e.g. mitochondria and other organelles are not visible using a light microscope). The 'Recap questions' are useful to test knowledge and could be expanded by showing a series of pictures of different cells and getting students to name them.
- The roles of enzymes and aerobic respiration are fundamental concepts and necessary for an understanding of many of the processes in the cells of living organisms. At this stage, students should refer to 'glucose' being needed by cells as an energy source and not 'sugar'. The use of the terms 'fuel' and 'burn' are not recommended at this level when explaining the reaction in cells. These are useful analogies to make, but students will gain little credit for explaining respiration in such terms.
- Most students will know the outlines of the process of photosynthesis and its requirements. The misconception that plants get their food from the soil should have been corrected at KS3. The need for minerals, particularly nitrates, was introduced at KS3.
- 'The Recap questions' could be used in a quiz, similar to *Test the Nation*, where the class can be divided up into different groups so that aggregate scores and individual scores can be totalled. Prepared scoring sheets would make life easier when totalling the marks.
- **Making connections** – As indicated in the Student Book, one of the links in this module is 'food'. Using the pictures and boxes on the spread, ask the students to build up a concept map that links them all together and explains the links. Allow them 5–10 minutes to work it out on their own and then bring their ideas together on the board. Not all these pictures and boxes appear to have a direct link with the chapters in this unit – or do they? Encourage students to look ahead and link the references to the topics in the unit. For each box or picture, they could award a mark from 1 (weakest) to 5 (strongest) for its link. For example, Box 1 with its picture would be a 5, linking with Chapter 2 and Photosynthesis, but what about the others? Discuss the award of marks after allowing the students some time to look through on their own or in small groups.

○ Chapters in this unit

○ Cells   ○ Enzymes

○ How plants produce food   ○ Homeostasis

○ Energy flows   ○ Inheritance

B2 1.1

Animal and plant cells

SPECIFICATION LINK-UP   Unit: Biology 2.11.1

- *Most human cells, like most other animal cells, have the following parts:*
  - *a nucleus that controls the activities of the cell*
  - *cytoplasm in which most of the chemical reactions take place*
  - *a cell membrane which controls the passage of substances in and out of the cell*
  - *mitochondria, which is where most energy is released in respiration*
  - *ribosomes, which is where protein synthesis occurs.*
- *Plant cells have a cell wall which strengthens the cell. Plant cells often have:*
  - *chloroplasts, which absorb light energy to make food*
  - *a permanent vacuole filled with cell sap.*
- *The chemical reactions inside cells are controlled by enzymes.*

LEARNING OBJECTIVES

Students should learn:

- The functions of the different parts of animal cells.
- The differences between plant and animal cells.
- That the chemical reactions within cells are controlled by enzymes.

LEARNING OUTCOMES

Most students should be able to:

- Describe the structure of animal cells.
- Describe the functions of the parts of animal cells.
- List the differences between plant and animal cells and state that enzymes control the reactions inside cells.

Some students should also be able to:

- Explain how enzymes control the chemical reactions within cells.

Teaching suggestions

- **Special needs.** Students could be given an outline of an animal cell and a plant cell with labels to stick on.
- **Gifted and talented.** Students could find out more about how an electron microscope works and how it is used to look at cells. (You can find some references in more advanced Biology texts such as *Tools, Techniques and Assessment in Biology*, Adds, Larkcom, Miller and Sutton (Nelson Advanced Science Series).
- **Learning styles**

  Kinaesthetic: Examining plant and animal cells.

  Visual: Drawing and labelling cells.

  Auditory: Explaining functions of parts of cells.

  Interpersonal: Discussing what can be seen in electron micrographs.

  Intrapersonal: Reviewing and deducing functions of cell parts.

Answers to in-text questions

a) Nucleus, cytoplasm, cell membrane, mitochondria, ribosomes.

b) Plant cells have a cell wall, chloroplasts and a permanent vacuole.

c) Protein.

Lesson structure

STARTER

What does it do? – Write up a list of functions of parts of an animal cell on the board, splitting them up so that there is more than one function per part, e.g. 'controls activities' and 'contains chromosomes' for nucleus. Allow students to work through the list by themselves and then check. (5–10 minutes)

Plant or animal? – Show a drawing of a typical plant cell. (Search the web for 'plant cell' images.) Students say whether it is a plant or an animal cell, giving reasons. Get them to suggest labels for the parts and decide whether these are common features of cells or special to plant cells. (10 minutes)

MAIN

- **Seeing more detail** – This exercise is designed to show students that what they can see using a light microscope is limited, and that structures such as mitochondria and ribosomes are only visible using electron microscopy. The students could work in groups, each having light microscopes with slides of stained cheek cells and onion bulb inner epidermal cells and a set of electron micrographs of plant and animal cells (there are plenty in A level text books). They could identify structures in both, and make a comparison of what they can observe from the slides and from the electron micrographs.

- If the magnification of the light microscope is given and the magnification of the electron micrographs known, they can work out how much bigger the latter are. Gather together and discuss the information, particularly with respect to the structures revealed by electron microscopy. Ask: 'Why do they all appear to have membranes around them?'

- **Looking at plant cells** – Plant cells, such as rhubarb petiole epidermis or the inner epidermal cells from onion bulbs, are relatively easy to mount, stain and observe using light microscopes. In order for students to see cell structures, some staining is advisable.

- The procedure, described under 'Practical support,' could be demonstrated to the students and they can then have a go at making their own slides and drawing and labelling some cells.

- **Looking at animal cells** – Using safe, sterile procedures, students could make slides of their own cheek cells. (See 'Practical support'). Some cells could be drawn and labelled.

PLENARIES

A question of size – A typical cell is 20 μm wide (0.002 mm). You might need to talk about scales and the relationship between millimetres and micrometres. Students can then calculate how many cells will fit across the page of their textbook. Give a small prize for the first correct calculation. (5–10 minutes)

Our wonderful world – There are some excellent scanning electron micrographs (SEM) and transmission electron micrographs (TEM) of cells. Show a selection (from www.cellsalive.com) with a 'Guess what this is' attached to each one. This would help students appreciate the complexity of some structures. (10 minutes)

Practical support

Looking at cells

Equipment and materials required

Light microscopes (at least one per group of two or three students), clean microscope slides and cover slips, onion bulbs or rhubarb petiole, scalpels, scissors and mounted needles, dilute iodine solution in dropping bottles (CLEAPSS Hazcard 54), tissues, eye protection.

Details

Cut an onion in half and remove the thin inner epidermis of the leaves with forceps. This can be cut up into small squares about 5 mm square. Place a square of epidermis on a slide, trying to get it as flat as possible, and then place a drop of dilute iodine solution on top to stain the cells. Place a cover slip over the top, lowering it carefully down so that air bubbles are not trapped. Place the slide under the low power of the microscope, focusing carefully. Then switch to high power and focus using the fine adjustment.

- Underground storage organs (onion bulb) and leaf stalks (rhubarb) do not carry out photosynthesis.

For cheek cells

Equipment and materials required

Light microscopes (at least one per group of two or three students), new cotton buds, clean microscope slides and cover slips, dilute methylene blue solution, disinfectant, or another approved way, for disposal of used cotton buds and slides.

Details

The inside of the cheek is gently scraped using a sterile spatula cotton bud and the scrapings smeared on to the middle of a clean microscope slide. A drop of dilute methylene blue is added on top of the cells and covered with a cover slip. The slide can then be observed under the microscope. Some gentle pressure might be needed to spread the cells out so that they are easier to see. When finished place prepared slides and cotton buds in a container of freshly prepared sodium hypochlorite solution. (See CLEAPSS Student Safety Sheet 3 and follow Institute of Biology guidelines.)

ACTIVITY & EXTENSION IDEAS

- Using rhubarb petiole or onion bulb epidermis will not show chloroplasts, so a demonstration of some moss leaf cells or leaves of a water plant such as *Elodea* could be mounted in water and projected. The cells will be live and it is possible that the streaming of the cytoplasm can be observed.

- Showing an electron micrograph of the cellulose cell wall will demonstrate that the cellulose is in fine strands (fibrils) and that there are several layers criss-crossing, so that the cell wall acts like a sieve.

KEY POINTS

The key points about the animal and plant cells can be learnt from clear diagrams. Students should be sure that they know what structures in cells can be observed using a light microscope: ribosomes and mitochondria are only visible in electron micrographs.

BIOLOGY   CELLS

B2 1.1   Animal and plant cells

LEARNING OBJECTIVES

1 What do the different parts of your cells actually do?
2 How do plant cells differ from animal cells?
3 How are all the chemical reactions which go on in your cells controlled?

The Earth is covered with a great variety of living things. The one thing all these living organisms have in common is that they are all made up of cells. Most cells are very small. You can only see them using a microscope.

The **light microscopes** you will use in school may magnify things several hundred times. Scientists have found out even more about cells using **electron microscopes** which can magnify more than a hundred thousand times!

Animal cells – structure and function

All cells have some features in common. We can see these clearly in animal cells. The cells of your body have these features, just like the cells of every other living thing!

- A **nucleus**, which controls all the activities of the cell. It also contains the instructions for making new cells or new organisms.
- The **cytoplasm**, a liquid gel in which most of the chemical reactions needed for life take place. One of the most important of these is respiration.
- The **cell membrane**, which controls the passage of substances in and out of the cell.
- The **mitochondria**, structures in the cytoplasm where oxygen is used and most of the energy is released during respiration.
- **Ribosomes**, where protein synthesis takes place. All the proteins needed in the cell are made here.

a) What are the main features found in all living cells?

Figure 1 A simple animal cell like this shows the features which are common to all living cells

Plant cells – structure and function

Plants are very different from animals, as you may have noticed! They make their own food by photosynthesis and they do not move their whole bodies about. So while plant cells have all the features of a typical animal cell, they also contain structures which are needed for their very different way of life.

All plant cells have:

- a cell wall made of cellulose which strengthens the cell and gives it support.

Many (but not all) plant cells also have these other features:

- chloroplasts, found in all the green parts of the plant. They are green because they contain the green substance chlorophyll which gives the plant its colour. They absorb light to make food by photosynthesis.
- a permanent vacuole (a space in the cytoplasm filled with cell sap), which is important for keeping the cells rigid to support the plant.

b) How do plant cells differ from animal cells?

GET IT RIGHT!

Make sure you can label an animal cell and a plant cell and know the function of each of their parts. Remember that not all plant cells have chloroplasts ... and don't confuse chloroplasts and chlorophyll.

Figure 2 A plant cell has many features in common with an animal cell, but others which are unique to plants

Chemical reactions in cells

Imagine 100 different reactions going on in a laboratory test tube. Chemical chaos and probably a few explosions would be the result! But this is the level of chemical activity going on all the time in your cells.

Cell chemistry works because each reaction is controlled by an enzyme. Each enzyme is a protein which controls the rate of a very specific reaction. It makes sure that the reaction takes place without becoming mixed up with any other reaction.

We find enzymes throughout the structure of a cell, but particularly in the mitochondria (and the chloroplasts in plants).

c) What are enzymes made of?

The enzymes involved in different chemical processes are usually found in different parts of the cell. So, for example, most of the enzymes controlling the reactions of:

- respiration are found in the mitochondria,
- photosynthesis are found in the chloroplasts,
- protein synthesis are found on the surface of the ribosomes.

These cell compartments help to keep your cell chemistry well under control.

PRACTICAL

Looking at cells

Set up a microscope to look at plant cells, e.g. from onions and rhubarb. You should see the cell wall, the cytoplasm and sometimes a vacuole but you won't see chloroplasts.

- Why won't you see any chloroplasts?

Figure 3 Diagrams of cells are much easier to understand than the real thing seen under a microscope. These pictures show a magnified plant cell and animal cell.

DID YOU KNOW?

Although most cells are so small we can only see them under the microscope, the largest cells in the world weigh 1.35kg and are easily visible with the naked eye. The largest single cell is ... an ostrich egg!

SUMMARY QUESTIONS

1 a) List the main structures you would expect to find in an animal cell.
b) You would find all of these things in a plant cell. There are three extra features which are found in plant cells. What are they?
c) What are the main functions of these three extra structures?

2 Root cells in a plant do not have chloroplasts. Why?

3 A nucleus and mitochondria are important structures in almost all cells. Why are they so important?

4 Explain how enzymes control the chemistry of your cells.

KEY POINTS

1 Most animal cells contain a nucleus, cytoplasm, cell membrane, mitochondria and ribosomes.
2 Plant cells contain all the structures seen in animal cells as well as a cell wall and, in many cases, chloroplasts and a permanent vacuole filled with sap.
3 Enzymes control the chemical reactions inside cells.

SUMMARY ANSWERS

1 a) Nucleus, cytoplasm, cell membrane, mitochondria, ribosomes.
  b) Cell wall, chloroplasts, permanent vacuole.
  c) Cell wall provides support and strengthening for the cell and the plant; chloroplasts for photosynthesis; permanent vacuole keeps the cells rigid to support the plant.

2 Root cells do not carry out photosynthesis. They are underground where there is no light.

3 The nucleus controls all the activities of the cell and contains the instructions for making new cells or new organisms. Mitochondria are the site of respiration, so they produce energy for the cell.

4 Each enzyme controls the rate of a very specific reaction and makes sure that it takes place without becoming mixed up with any other reaction. The enzymes involved in different chemical processes are usually found in different parts of the cell (enzymes involved in aerobic respiration are found in the mitochondria).

B2 1.2   Specialised cells

Students should learn that:

- Cells may be specialised to carry out particular functions.

LEARNING OUTCOMES

Most students should be able to:

- Recognise different types of cells.
- Relate the structure of given types of cells to their functions in a tissue or an organ.

Some students should also be able to:

- Relate the structure of novel cells to other functions in a tissue or organ.

Teaching suggestions

- **Special needs.** Use domino-style cards with specialised cells on one side and their special features on the other. Ask the students to play with these as dominoes. Alter the number of cards and the labelling according to ability.

- **Gifted and talented.** Suggest to students that they design a special cell found in an alien or undiscovered species. Ask them to give it an interesting, unusual or gruesome feature and make it scientifically feasible.

- **Learning styles**

  Kinaesthetic: Investigating the root hair cells using microscopes.

  Visual: Examining, drawing and labelling specialised cells.

  Auditory: Listening to the questions and answers in the plenary '20 questions'.

  Interpersonal: Discussing the differences between generalised and specialised cells.

  Intrapersonal: Interpreting specialised features of cells.

SPECIFICATION LINK-UP   Unit: Biology 2.11.1

- *Cells may be specialised to carry out a particular function.*

Lesson structure

STARTER

How big can cells be? – Show a goose egg, explain that it is a single cell and break it on to a plate. They may be able to see the place where the embryo will develop (the germinal disc). Discuss with the students why it is so big and how it is specialised. If possible show an empty ostrich egg. (5–10 minutes)

Do you know what this is? – Project some images of specialised cells – do not label them but give each one a number. Students to name the ones they know and have a guess at the ones they do not. Check the answers at the end. (5–10 minutes)

Key words – Place key words and phrases from this lesson on the board. Ask students to remove and explain what each one means, leaving the rest as 'learning objectives'. (5 minutes)

MAIN

- **Root hair cells** – A few days before the lesson, sow some cress seeds on damp blotting paper or filter paper in Petri dishes. Handle the seeds by the cotyledons using forceps. When ready to use them, remove the lids and cover with cling film to keep the moisture levels high. Place the dishes under a binocular microscope and take digital photographs down the microscope. The photographs can then be stuck in the students' records. This can either be set up as a demonstration or groups of students could work together on the activity.

- If a micrometer eyepiece is inserted in the microscope, the length of some of the root hairs can be measured. The measurements can either be left as eyepiece units (eu) or converted to millimetres if the eyepiece is calibrated. This exercise will reinforce the extent to which the root hairs are specialised for the increase of the surface area available for the uptake of water.

- This exercise introduces some of the concepts of 'How Science Works', such as observation and making single measurements.

- **Sperm cells** – Video footage of sperm cell activity is readily available. There are clips available which show fertilisation, emphasising the difference in sizes of egg cells and sperm and also the relative numbers.

- Prepared slides of rat testes could be available for students to look at, observing the different stages in sperm development. Prepare a worksheet with some drawings of different stages so that students can look for specific features and make labelled drawings of their own. This activity can link with the showing of the video.

- **How structure is related to function in animal cells** – Prepare a PowerPoint presentation of a range of different animal cells, to include blood cells, neurones, muscle cells, cells from glands, fat cells and gametes. Provide each student with a worksheet with spaces for them to fill in the names of the cells, special features and how each specialised cell differs from a generalised animal cell. Allow the students to complete the worksheets individually and then go through the cells again, discussing the important points.

- **How structure is related to function in plant cells** – This could be presented in a similar manner to the above, providing a worksheet, but using a range of plant cells, such as palisade cells, guard cells, root hair cells, lignified cells (fibres) and epidermal cells. Cells from the cortex of the stem or the root could be used as generalised plant cells.

- Students are required to be able to relate the structure of different types of cell to their functions in a tissue or an organ so these exercises, with their completed worksheets, will give them a record for future reference and revision.

ACTIVITY & EXTENSION

- **Fun with colour vision** – Students could have fun with their colour vision by staring at brightly coloured cardboard and then at white paper to perceive residual false colour images. Search the web's images for 'flags' to illustrate such after-images. In the retina, there are three types of cone: sensitive to red, green or blue. When you stare at a particular colour for too long, these receptors get 'tired' or 'fatigued'. After looking at the flag with the strange colours, your receptors that are tired do not work as well. Therefore the information from all the different colour receptors is not in balance.

- **Single-celled organisms** – Show images of single-celled organisms as a contrast to specialised cells. Good examples to find on the web are *Chlamydomonas*, *Paramecium* and *Amoeba*, and then discuss how these organisms can carry out all the functions of life.

Practical support

Root hair cells

Equipment and materials required

Cress seedlings with root hairs, forceps, cling film, blotting paper or filter paper, digital camera, binocular microscopes, Petri dishes, micrometer eyepiece if available.

Details

See 'Main'.

KEY POINTS

The students need to be able to link the structure of specialised cells to their particular functions.

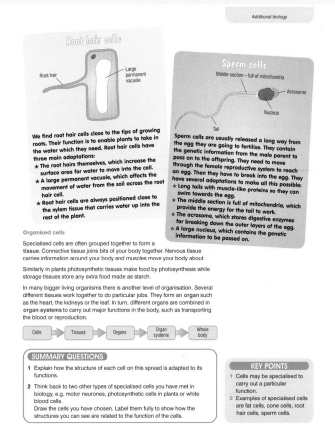

BIOLOGY   CELLS

B2 1.2 Specialised cells

LEARNING OBJECTIVES

1 What different types of cells are there?
2 How is the structure of a specialised cell related to its function?

The smallest living organisms are single cells. They can carry out all of the functions of life, from feeding and respiration to excretion and reproduction. Most organisms are bigger and are made up of lots of cells. Some of those cells become **specialised** in order to carry out particular jobs.

When a cell becomes specialised its structure is adapted to suit the particular job it does. As a result, specialised cells often look very different to our 'typical' plant or animal cell. Sometimes cells become so specialised that they only have one function within the body. Good examples of this include sperm, eggs, red blood cells and nerve cells.

PRACTICAL

Observing specialised cells

Try looking at different specialised cells under a microscope.

When you look at a specialised cell there are two useful questions you can ask yourself:

- How is this cell different in structure from a generalised cell?
- How does the difference in structure help it to carry out its function?

Fat cell

Nucleus — Fat store — Cytoplasm — Mitochondria

Fat cells are storage cells. If you eat more food than you need, your body makes fat and fills up the fat cells. They are important for helping animals, including us, to survive when food is in short supply. They have three main adaptations:

★ They have very little normal cytoplasm – this leaves plenty of room for large amounts of fat.
★ They have very few mitochondria as they use very little energy.
★ They can expand – a fat cell can end up 1000 times its original size as it fills up with fat.

Cone cell from human eye

Cone cells are in the light-sensitive layer of your eye (the retina). They make it possible for you to see in colour. They have three main adaptations:

Outer segment – containing visual pigment
Middle section – many mitochondria
Nucleus
Connections to nerve cells in optic nerve

★ The outer segment is filled with a special chemical known as a *visual pigment*. This changes chemically in coloured light. It then has to be changed back to its original form. This uses up energy.
★ The middle segment of the cell is packed full of mitochondria. They produce lots of energy. This means the visual pigment can reform and so the eye can see continually in colour.
★ The final part of the cell is a specialised nerve ending or synapse. This connects to the optic nerve which carries impulses to your brain. When coloured light makes your visual pigment change, an impulse is triggered which crosses the synapse. This is how the response of the cone cell to coloured light passes to your brain.

Root hair cells

Root hair — Large permanent vacuole

We find root hair cells close to the tips of growing roots. Their function is to enable plants to take in the water which they need. Root hair cells have three main adaptations:

★ The root hairs themselves, which increase the surface area for water to move into the cell.
★ A large permanent vacuole, which affects the movement of water from the soil across the root hair cell.
★ Root hair cells are always positioned close to the xylem tissue that carries water up into the rest of the plant.

Organised cells

Specialised cells are often grouped together to form a **tissue**. Connective tissue joins bits of your body together. Nervous tissue carries information around your body and muscles move your body about.

Similarly in plants photosynthetic tissues make food by photosynthesis while storage tissues store any extra food made as starch.

In many bigger living organisms there is another level of organisation. Several different tissues work together to do particular jobs. They form an **organ** such as the heart, the kidneys or the leaf. In turn, different organs are combined in **organ systems** to carry out major functions in the body, such as transporting the blood or reproduction.

Cells → Tissues → Organs → Organ systems → Whole body

Sperm cells

Middle section – full of mitochondria
Acrosome
Nucleus
Tail

Sperm cells are usually released a long way from the egg they are going to fertilise. They contain the genetic information from the male parent to pass on to the offspring. They need to move through the female reproductive system to reach an egg. Then they have to break into the egg. They have several adaptations to make all this possible:

★ Long tails with muscle-like proteins so they can swim towards the egg.
★ The middle section is full of mitochondria, which provide the energy for the tail to work.
★ The acrosome, which stores digestive enzymes for breaking down the outer layers of the egg. They
★ A large nucleus, which contains the genetic information to be passed on.

SUMMARY QUESTIONS

1 Explain how the structure of each cell on this spread is adapted to its functions.

2 Think back to two other types of specialised cells you have met in biology, e.g. motor neurones, photosynthetic cells in plants or white blood cells.
Draw the cells you have chosen. Label them fully to show how the structures you can see are related to the function of the cells.

KEY POINTS

1 Cells may be specialised to carry out a particular function.
2 Examples of specialised cells are fat cells, cone cells, root hair cells, sperm cells.

6   7

PLENARIES

Am I colour blind? – Search a web image bank for 'colour blind' to find tests you can use to investigate colour blindness further. (5–10 minutes)

Levels of organisation – Label some Lego bricks of one colour 'Cell' and fit them together. On the back of the block formed stick a label 'Tissue'. Make some more 'Tissue' blocks from 'Cells' of other colours. Stick these together and label it 'Organ'. Have several of these and place them in a circle on the floor or the bench labelled 'Organ system'. Get the students to identify some organ systems and work back suggesting the organs, tissues and cells involved. (10 minutes)

20 Questions? – One student goes out of the room and the others decide which type of specialised cell they are. The student comes back in and asks the rest of the class questions about their specialisation to guess what they are. Repeat several, but not too many, times. (10 minutes)

SUMMARY ANSWERS

1 **Fat cell:** not much cytoplasm so room for fat storage; ability to expand to store fat; few mitochondria as do not need much energy so do not waste space.
Cone cell from human eye: outer segment containing visual pigment; middle segment packed full of mitochondria; specialised nerve ending.
Root hair cells: no chloroplasts so no photosynthesis; root hair increases surface area for water uptake; vacuole to facilitate water movement; close to xylem tissue.
Sperm cell: tail for movement to egg; mitochondria to provide energy for movement; acrosome full of digestive enzymes to break down egg; large nucleus full of genetic material.

2 [Any two cells chosen, appropriately labelled and annotated.]

B2 1.3

How do substances get in and out of cells?

LEARNING OBJECTIVES

Students should learn:

- That substances move in and out of cells by a process called diffusion.
- The factors that affect the rate of diffusion.

LEARNING OUTCOMES

Most students should be able to:

- Define diffusion in cells.
- List factors that affect the rate of diffusion.

Some students should also be able to:

- Explain the factors that affect the rate of diffusion.
- Explain how cells may be adapted to facilitate diffusion.

Teaching suggestions

- **Special needs.** Students can assemble words or cards to make a definition of diffusion. Alternatively, it can be done as an interactive exercise using Hot Potatoes JMIX or a similar interactive web-based exercise.
- **Gifted and talented.** Investigate what is meant by surface area to volume ratio. Draw out and extrapolate a SA/V graph for cutting a 2 cm × 2 cm cube in half and then in half again and so on.
- **Learning styles**

  Kinaesthetic: Dried peas activity.

  Visual: Observing and drawing colour changes in treated gel agar.

  Auditory: Discussion of net movement.

  Interpersonal: Group work in the practicals.

  Intrapersonal: Visualisation activity.

Answers to in-text questions

a) Blood diffuses through the water.
b) The difference between the numbers of particles moving in and those moving out of cells.

SPECIFICATION LINK-UP   Unit: Biology 2.11.2

- *Dissolved substances can move into and out of cells by diffusion and osmosis.*
- *Diffusion is the spreading of the particles of a gas, or of any substance in solution, resulting in a net movement from a region where they are of a higher concentration. The greater the difference in concentration, the faster the rate of diffusion. Oxygen required for respiration passes through cell membranes by diffusion.*

Lesson structure

STARTER

Watching diffusion – Set up on each bench boiling tubes of water with a few crystals of potassium permanganate in the bottom. Draw them at the start of the lesson and then again at the end. (5 minutes)

Diffusion rates – Pour some perfume or clove oil on to cotton wool and place in the corner of the room. Students are to indicate when they can smell it. If each bench, or group of students, had a stopwatch or stopclock, they could time how long it took the smell to reach them. The distances could be measured and the rate of diffusion worked out. Discuss how the process could be speeded up or slowed down. (15 minutes)

Visualisation exercise – Ask the students to close their eyes and imagine a swimming pool. The pool and the room are empty. The water is completely still. You have a cup of tea in your hand. You walk up to the corner of the pool and gently pour the tea into the water, right in the corner. You turn around and leave the room in silence, locking the door behind you. No-one disturbs the room for a whole week. Then ask the students to open their eyes and discuss what would happen to the tea over the week and why. (5–10 minutes)

MAIN

- **Diffusion in gases** – It is possible to demonstrate and measure the rate of diffusion of ammonia along a glass tube. Litmus paper is used to show the progress of the gas along the tube. Glass tubes, 30 cm long and of diameter 20 mm should be marked using a felt tip pen at 2 cm intervals starting at 10 cm from one end. Each tube requires two corks, one ordinary one and one which has had a core of cork taken out the cavity plugged with cotton wool. Small squares of pink litmus paper are then dipped into distilled water, shaken and placed inside each tube with a piece of wire or a glass rod. The pieces of litmus paper should be pushed into position and lined up with the markings on the outside of the tube. Saturate the cotton wool in the cork at one end with a strong ammonia solution, then place it in the end of the tube, start the clock or stopwatch and time how long it takes each piece of litmus paper to turn from pink to completely blue.

- This experiment demonstrates that the ammonia diffuses along the tube from an area where it is in high concentration to a lower concentration. It is possible to work out the rate of diffusion. The overall time to diffuse 28 cm can be found and the individual times for the diffusion from one 2 cm mark to the next can be recorded. This gives several possibilities for discussion and calculation. It also introduces 'How Science Works' concepts.

- It is also possible to compare the rate of diffusion of the strong solution with that of a weaker solution by setting up an identical tube and timing the change in colour of the litmus squares.

- **Diffusion of liquids** – Cut wells into agar gel dyed with Universal Indicator or hydrogencarbonate indicator. Add acid at various concentrations into the wells, allow a set time and then measure the extent of the colour change around each well. Alkali could be used as well as acid for different colour changes.

- **Animated diffusion** – There are some good web-based animations illustrating diffusion. John Kyrk of Science Graphics has produced an excellent CD called Cella™. There is a good random molecule movement illustration of diffusion.

Practical support

The details of apparatus needed for the practicals described have been given above.

The practical opportunity mentioned in the Student Book spread requires a large room or area for students to move around.

ACTIVITY & EXTENSION IDEAS

- **More diffusion in liquids** – Give students boiling tubes containing clear gelatine up to a marked level. They can then pour a thin layer of gelatine coloured with methylene blue on to the top, allow it to set and then pour on a quantity of clear gelatine equal to the volume in the bottom of the tube. (Levels could be marked for them.) The tubes should be left for a week and then the distribution of the blue colour recorded.

- **Variations** – The experiment described above can be varied by using different concentrations of methylene blue and comparing the results. It is also interesting to compare the rates of diffusion of the methylene blue with that of the ammonia. What does this tell you about diffusion in air and in liquids?

- **Two-way diffusion** – Pour some gelatine into a boiling tube and colour it with 10 drops of cresol red (it will go yellow). Mix thoroughly and allow to set. Pour a further layer of clear gelatine on top of the coloured layer. Allow this layer to set. Finally add about 5 cm³ of ammonia solution to the top of the tube and insert a bung. Leave the tube for about 4 days. The cresol red will diffuse into the clear gelatine and the ammonia will diffuse into the gelatine. This can be shown by the cresol red turning from yellow to red.

KEY POINTS

It is important to know that diffusion is a passive process: it does not require energy. It is also important to emphasise that it is the *net* movement of particles: particles move randomly all the time.

BIOLOGY | CELLS

B2 1.3

How do substances get in and out of cells?

LEARNING OBJECTIVES

1 What is diffusion?
2 What affects the rate of diffusion?

Your cells need to take in substances such as oxygen and glucose. They also need to get rid of waste products and chemicals that are needed elsewhere in your body. Dissolved substances move into and out of your cells across the cell membrane. They can do this in three different ways – by **diffusion**, by **osmosis** and by **active transport**.

Diffusion

Sharks can smell their prey from a long way away – the smell reaches them by **diffusion**. Diffusion happens when the particles of a gas, or any substance in solution, spread out.

It is the net movement of particles from an area of high concentration to an area of lower concentration. It takes place because of the random movement of the particles of a gas or of a substance in solution in water. All the particles are moving and bumping into each other and this moves them all around.

Figure 1 Everyone knows that bleeding in the sea when there are sharks around is a bad idea. Sharks are sensitive to just a few particles of blood in the water. Blood from an injury spreads quickly through the sea by diffusion – and brings the sharks to investigate!

a) Why do sharks find an injured fish – or person – so easily?

Imagine a room containing a group of boys and a group of girls. If everyone closes their eyes and moves around briskly but randomly, people will bump into each other. They will scatter until the room contains a mixture of boys and girls. This gives you a good working model of diffusion.

Figure 2 The random movement of particles results in substances spreading out or diffusing from an area of higher concentration to an area of lower concentration

At the moment, when the blue particles are added to the red particles they are not mixed at all | As the particles move randomly, the blue ones begin to mix with the red ones | As the particles move and spread out, they bump into each other. This helps them to keep spreading randomly | Eventually, the particles are completely mixed and diffusion is complete

SCIENCE @ WORK

Cell biologists and biochemists work hard to discover the secrets of transport systems in your cells. They can use their findings both to understand human diseases at a cellular level and to change the nature of some organisms using genetic engineering. A salt-tolerant tomato plant which can actively move salt out of its cytoplasm into its vacuoles is just one example. This enables the plant to grow on salty ground.

Rates of diffusion

If there is a big difference in concentration between two areas, diffusion will take place quickly. However when a substance is moving from a higher concentration to one which is just a bit lower, the movement toward the less concentrated area will appear to be quite slow. This is because although some particles move into the area of lower concentration by random movement, at the same time other identical particles are leaving that area by random movement.

The overall or **net** movement = particles moving in − particles moving out

In general the bigger the difference in concentration, the faster the rate of diffusion will be. This difference between two areas of concentration is called the **concentration gradient**. The bigger the difference, the steeper the gradient will be.

b) What is meant by the net movement of particles?

Both types of particles can pass through this membrane – it is freely permeable

Steep concentration gradient

Beginning of experiment | Random movement means three blue particles have moved from left to right by diffusion

Shallow concentration gradient

Beginning of experiment | Four blue particles have moved as a result of random movement from left to right – but two have moved from right to left. There is a **net** movement of **two** particles to the right by diffusion

Figure 3 This diagram shows us how the overall movement of particles in a particular direction is more effective (a steep concentration gradient) between the two areas. This is why so many body systems are adapted to maintain steep concentration gradients.

Concentration isn't the only thing that affects the rate of diffusion. An increase in temperature means the particles in a gas or a solution move more quickly. This in turn means diffusion will take place more rapidly as the random movement of the particles speeds up.

Diffusion in living organisms

Many important substances can move across your cell membranes by diffusion. Water is one. Simple sugars, such as glucose and amino acids from the breakdown of proteins in your gut, can also pass through cell membranes by diffusion. The oxygen you need for respiration passes from the air into your lungs and into your cells by diffusion.

Individual cells may be adapted to make diffusion easier and more rapid. The most common adaptation is to increase the surface area of the cell membrane over which diffusion occurs. Increasing the surface area means there is more room for diffusion to take place. By folding up the membrane of a cell, or the tissue lining an organ, the area over which diffusion can take place is greatly increased. So the amount of substance moved by diffusion is also greatly increased.

GET IT RIGHT!

Diffusion is **passive** – it takes place along a concentration gradient from high to low concentration and uses up no energy.

Infoldings of the cell membrane form microvilli, which increase the surface area of the cell

Figure 4 An increase in the surface area of a cell membrane means more diffusion can take place

SUMMARY QUESTIONS

Copy and complete using the words below:

Diffusion   gas   high   low   random   solute

1 ...... is the net movement of particles of a ...... or a ...... from an area of ...... concentration to an area of ...... concentration as a result of the ...... movement of the particles.

2 Explain why a cut in water looks much worse than a cut on land in terms of diffusion and the movement of particles.

3 a) Explain why diffusion takes place faster as the temperature increases.
   b) Explain in terms of diffusion why so many cells have folded membranes along at least one surface.

KEY POINTS

1 Dissolved substances move in and out of cells by diffusion, osmosis and active transport.
2 Diffusion is the net movement of particles from an area where they are at a high concentration to an area where they are at a lower concentration.

PLENARIES

Watching diffusion – Draw the tubes set up at the beginning of the lesson. (5 minutes)

Team game – Carry out a team game with students putting dried peas into a dish. One person has one pair of blunt forceps to pick up the peas and put them in to the dish, the other person has two pairs of blunt forceps to take them out using both hands. Count the peas in the dish at the start and then run the game for a minute, stop and recount the peas. Discuss the results and relate to the net movement of particles. (5–10 minutes)

Surface area to volume – Get students to fold up a sheet of A4 paper as small as they can get it without tearing. Measure the dimensions and try to fit it into a matchbox. (5–10 minutes)

SUMMARY ANSWERS

1 Diffusion, gas (solute), solute (gas), high, low, random.

2 In water the blood diffuses through the water. Its particles spread out through the water particles making the volume of blood released seem greater than the same volume of blood released on land.

3 a) Increase in temperature means an increase in rate of movement of particles – so random movement and collisions increase which increases the rate of diffusion.

   b) Diffusion important to get substances like oxygen into or out of cells. The more surface area of membrane available, the more diffusion can take place.

B2 1.4   Osmosis

SPECIFICATION LINK-UP   Unit: Biology 2.11.2

- *Water often moves across boundaries by osmosis. Osmosis is the diffusion of water from a dilute to a more concentrated solution through a partially permeable membrane that allows the passage of water molecules but not solute molecules.*
- *Differences in the concentrations of the solutions inside and outside a cell cause water to move into or out of the cell by osmosis.*

LEARNING OBJECTIVES

Students should learn:

- That water often moves across boundaries by osmosis.
- That osmosis is the diffusion of water through a partially permeable membrane from a dilute to a more concentrated solution.
- Differences in concentrations of solutes inside and outside cells cause water to move by osmosis.

LEARNING OUTCOMES

Most students should be able to:

- Define osmosis.
- Distinguish between diffusion and osmosis.
- Carry out an experiment to find out about the process of osmosis.

Some students should also be able to:

- Explain the importance of osmosis in plants and animals.
- Explain the results of experiments in terms of osmotic movement of water.

Teaching suggestions

- **Special needs.** Carry out a stop motion of a plant wilting and being re-hydrated using Intel play microscopes (the kit pot plastic ones). Explain using a football and a pump.
- **Gifted and talented.** Investigate the effect of partial drowning. What effect would it have on the water balance? Would people who have nearly drowned and had their lungs full of water for some time face any problems? If so, what might they be and how may they be overcome?
- **Learning styles**
  Kinaesthetic: Practical work on osmosis.
  Visual: Draw a warning poster for snails not to run while carrying the salt pot!
  Auditory: Participating in the 'Lower/ higher' concentration activity with the juice and water.
  Interpersonal: Collecting and collating results from experiments.
  Intrapersonal: Considering what would happen if our osmotic barriers were removed.
- **Homework.** Students could use homework time to complete the writing up of the experiments or to make clear diagrams explaining diffusion and osmosis.

Lesson structure

STARTER

What happens to the chips – Show the students a bag of chips. Ask who is going to the chip shop tonight. At what time? Explain that there is always a rush on or about six o'clock, so the owners prepare the chips in advance and keep them in water. What effect does the water have on the chips? Draw out some ideas and ways of testing these ideas. A demonstration could be set up or this could lead into the experiments described in the Main section. (10 minutes)

Bouncy Castle – Show a picture of a Bouncy Castle. Has anyone got younger brothers or sisters who love these? How do they stay upright? Why don't they burst? What would happen if they were made out of flexible rubber like a thicker version of balloons? Draw out the idea of a balance of air going in, air coming out and pressure on a non-flexible skin providing support. Link with osmosis in plants providing support for plant tissues. (10 minutes)

MAIN

- **Modelling osmosis in cells** – Visking, or dialysis, tubing can be used to make model cells. Lengths of tubing, about 10 cm long, should be wetted thoroughly and one end of each tied firmly with string. Fill the tubing bags with a concentrated sugar solution (molar sucrose) and tie the open ends firmly with string. These Visking tubing bags represent cells and can be immersed in beakers of water, less concentrated and more concentrated sugar solutions.
- The results from the model cells, set up as described above, can be used to illustrate the principles of osmosis. Students can be asked to interpret each one in terms of the diffusion of water and sucrose molecules and the effect of the partially permeable membrane. Students may find it easier to understand osmosis if it is explained in terms of the diffusion of water molecules from where they are in high concentration (i.e. in a dilute solution) to where there is a lower concentration (i.e. a more concentrated solution). Diagrams help.
- **Osmosis in potato tissue** – Chips or discs of potato tissue can be immersed in different concentrations of salt or sugar solutions, left for a period of time and then their change in mass or dimensions measured. Such experiments offer opportunities for the introduction of 'How Science Works' concepts and can be used as whole investigations. The change in mass or length can be plotted against the concentration of the solution and the solution which results in the least change is considered to be equivalent to the concentration of the cell sap of the potato.
- There are variations on the above which can be tried. Some students could measure changes in dimensions (i.e. length or volume) and others could measure changes in mass. Are the results similar? Which do they consider to be the most accurate?
- **Setting up an osmometer** – A simple osmometer can be made using a length of Visking tubing, tied securely at one end, filled with a concentrated sugar solution (for quick results use syrup or treacle only slightly diluted) and then a capillary tube tied securely in the top. The whole apparatus is held in place by a clamp and stand and lowered into a beaker of water. The level of sucrose in the capillary tube is measured at the start and then again at regular intervals (5 minutes). A graph can be plotted of the distance moved by the sucrose against time.

PLENARIES

Followed up to What happens to the chips? – If the demonstrations were set up at the beginning of the experiment, they can looked at. What has happened to the chips? They can be measured, their texture assessed and the results discussed. (10 minutes)

Practical support

For the Visking tubing experiments, you will need:
- Lengths of dialysis (Visking) tubing for each group of students
- Molar sucrose solution which can be diluted according to the concentrations required
- Beakers
- String
- Small measuring cylinders or pipettes to fill the tubes.

For the potato experiments, you will need:
- Fairly large potatoes
- Cork borers to make cylinders of tissue
- Knives and tiles to cut chips
- Molar sucrose
- Boiling tubes and racks
- Rulers and balances
- Tissues or paper towels to dry potato discs or slices.

- **Osmosis in animals** – Experiments on blood cells cannot be carried out, but use video footage or the diagrams in the Student Book to explain what happens to red blood cells if they are placed in solutions of different concentrations. This emphasises the importance of the correct concentration of the body fluids.

- **Wilting** – Show video footage of marathon runners (especially keeping up their fluids at drinks stations) and plants wilting and being revived.

BIOLOGY   CELLS

B2 1.4 Osmosis

LEARNING OBJECTIVES
1. What is osmosis?
2. How is osmosis different from diffusion?
3. Why is osmosis so important?

Diffusion takes place where particles can spread freely from one place to another. However the solutions inside cells are separated from those outside by the cell membrane which does not let all types of particles through. Because it only lets some types of particles through, it is known as **partially permeable**.

Osmosis

Partially permeable cell membranes will allow water to move across them. It is important to remember that a dilute solution of, for example sugar, contains a **high** concentration of water (the **solvent**) and a **low** concentration of sugar (the **solute**). A concentrated sugar solution contains a relatively **low** concentration of water and a **high** concentration of sugar.

A cell is basically some chemicals dissolved in water inside a partially permeable cell membrane. The cell contains a fairly concentrated solution of salts and sugars. Water will move from a high concentration of water particles (in a dilute solution) to a less concentrated solution of water particles (in a concentrated solution) across the membrane of the cell.

This special type of diffusion, where only water moves across a partially permeable membrane, is known as **osmosis**.

a) What is the difference between diffusion and osmosis?

PRACTICAL

Investigating osmosis

You can make model cells using bags made of partially permeable membrane. Figure 1 shows you some of these model cells. You can see what happens to them if the concentrations of the solutions inside or outside of the cell change.

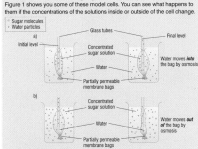

Figure 1 Using bags of partially permeable membrane to make model cells, we can clearly see the effect of osmosis as water moves across the membrane from a dilute to a concentrated solution

The internal concentration of your cells needs to stay the same all the time for the reactions of life to take place. Yet animal and plant cells are bathed in liquid which can be at very different concentrations to the inside of the cells. This can make water move into or out of the cells by osmosis.

Osmosis in animals

If a cell uses up water in its chemical reactions, the cytoplasm becomes more concentrated and more water will immediately move in by osmosis. Similarly if the cytoplasm becomes too dilute because water is produced during chemical reactions, water will leave the cell by osmosis, restoring the balance.

However osmosis can also cause some very serious problems in animal cells. (See Figure 2.) If the solution outside the cell is more dilute than the cell contents, then water will move into the cell by osmosis. The cell will swell and may burst.

On the other hand, if the solution outside the cell is more concentrated than the cell contents, then water will move out of the cell by osmosis. The cytoplasm will become too concentrated and the cell will shrivel up. Once you understand the effect osmosis can have on cells, the importance of homeostasis and maintaining constant internal conditions becomes very clear!

b) How does osmosis help maintain the body cells at the same concentration?

Osmosis in plants

Plants rely on well-regulated osmosis to support their stems and leaves. Water moves into plant cells by osmosis, making the cytoplasm swell and press against the plant cell walls. The pressure builds up until no more water can physically enter the cell. This makes the cell hard and rigid.

This swollen state keeps the leaves and stems of the plant rigid and firm. So for plants it is important that the fluid surrounding the cells always has a higher concentration of water (it is a more dilute solution of chemicals) than the cytoplasm of the cells. This keeps osmosis working in the right direction.

But sometimes plant and animal cells need to move substances such as glucose against a concentration gradient. For this there is another method of transport known as **active transport** which uses energy from respiration.

SUMMARY QUESTIONS

1. Define the following words: **diffusion**; **osmosis**; **partially permeable membrane**

2. Explain using a diagram what would happen:
   a) if you set up an experiment with a partially permeable bag containing strong sugar solution in a beaker full of pure water.
   b) if you set up an experiment using a partially permeable bag containing pure water in a beaker containing strong sugar solution.

3. Animals that live in fresh water have a constant problem with their water balance. The single-celled organism called *Amoeba* has a special vacuole in its cell. It fills with water and then moves to the outside of the cell and bursts. A new vacuole starts forming straight away. Explain in terms of osmosis why the *Amoeba* needs one of these vacuoles.

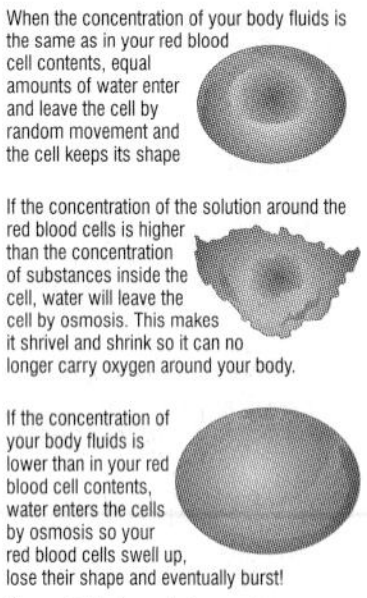

When the concentration of your body fluids is the same as in your red blood cell contents, equal amounts of water enter and leave the cell by random movement and the cell keeps its shape

If the concentration of the solution around the red blood cells is higher than the concentration of substances inside the cell, water will leave the cell by osmosis. This makes it shrivel and shrink so it can no longer carry oxygen around your body.

If the concentration of your body fluids is lower than in your red blood cell contents, water enters the cells by osmosis so your red blood cells swell up, lose their shape and eventually burst!

Figure 2 The impact of osmosis on your red blood cells can be devastating – so keeping your body fluids at the right concentration is vital

GET IT RIGHT!

Take care with your definition of osmosis. Make it clear that it is only water which is moving across the membrane, and get your concentrations right!

KEY POINTS

1. Osmosis is a special case of diffusion.
2. Osmosis is the diffusion/movement of water from a high water concentration (dilute solution) to a low water concentration (concentrated solution) through a partially permeable membrane.

SUMMARY ANSWERS

1. Diffusion – the net movement of dissolved substances or gases from an area of high concentration to an area of low concentration.
   Osmosis – the net movement of water from a high water concentration (dilute solution) to a low water concentration (concentrated solution) through a partially permeable membrane.
   Partially permeable membrane – a membrane which lets some particles through but not others.

2. **a)** See top part of Figure 1 in Student Book (page 10).
      Water moves into the bag by osmosis. The bag becomes full and solution rises up the tube.
   b) See bottom part of Figure 1 in Student Book (page 10).
      Water moves out of the bag by osmosis. The bag shrinks and the level of the solution in the glass tube falls.

3. The cytoplasm of *Amoeba* contains a solution of salts and sugars so it contains a lower concentration of water particles than the water in which the organism lives. The cell membrane is partially permeable, so water constantly moves into *Amoeba* from its surroundings by osmosis. If this continued without stopping, the organism would burst. Water could be moved into the vacuole by active transport, and then the vacuole moved to the outside of the cell using energy as well. This could prevent the organism from exploding.

Answers to in-text questions

a) Osmosis is a special type of diffusion in which only water particles move across a partially permeable membrane.

b) Water moves back and forth across cell membranes to adjust concentrations.

KEY POINTS

A good definition of osmosis is essential and worth memorising by the students. It is also important to refer to *concentrations* of solutions rather than 'stronger' or 'weaker'.

B2 1.5 Cell issues

SPECIFICATION LINK-UP

Unit: Biology 2.11.1 and 11.2

This spread gives the opportunity to revisit substantive content covered in this chapter:

- *Cells may be specialised to carry out a particular function.*

- *Dissolved substances can move into and out of cells by diffusion and osmosis.*

Teaching suggestions

- **Discovering cells** – Search the web for images of microscopes to show the class (try www.wikipedia.org). Start with Leeuwenhoek's and Hooke's microscopes and include some information about dates and what they observed through them. It would then be useful to include some different forms of light microscope, distinguishing between: simple, consisting of one lens; or compound, where there are separate objective and eyepiece lenses or lens systems. It is worth considering the magnification possible with these microscopes. It could be appropriate to show the same specimen viewed at the different magnifications (a simple slide of an insect leg or some plant tissue would be suitable). Other types of light microscope, such as binocular or stereoscopic, could be included as well, particularly if there are some available for the students to use.

- You might like to progress to electron microscopes, describing the differences between the transmission electron microscope (which requires smears or thin sections of material) and the scanning electron microscope (which does not involve the use of sections). There are good pictures of these available and some good images to illustrate what can be seen when specimens are viewed. Again, some idea of magnification can be given.

- If the school, or any students, have connections with a research or university department that has an electron microscope, then it could be worth trying to arrange a visit to see one being used. Many establishments are quite willing to demonstrate the preparation and viewing of specimens to small groups of interested students.

Discovering cells

Anton van Leeuwenhoek (1632–1723)

Over the past three centuries our ideas about cells have developed as our ability to see them has improved. In 1665, the English scientist Robert Hooke designed the first working microscope and saw cells in cork.

At around the same time a Dutchman, Anton van Leeuwenhoek, also produced a microscope. It enabled him to see bacteria, microscopic animals and blood cells for the first time ever.

Almost two centuries later, by the 1840s, scientists had accepted that cells are the basic units of all living things. From then on, as optical microscopes improved, more details of the secret life inside a cell were revealed as cells were magnified up to 1000 times.

With the invention of the electron microscope in the 1930s it became possible to magnify things much more. We can now look at cells magnified up 500 000 times!

Cork cells drawn by Robert Hooke

Human cheek cells (magnified 3500 times)

ACTIVITY

Produce a timeline to show how microscopes have developed since they were first invented. Annotate your timeline to show how important our discoveries about cells have been.

A human white blood cell at high magnification

The ability to see cells and the secret worlds inside them has developed in an amazing way since the days of the early microscopes

12

- **Beating osmosis** – The animals depicted in the Student Book spread live in different habitats and it could be helpful to students to start with the characteristics and osmotic problems associated with each habitat before considering the animals present. This can be done using a PowerPoint® presentation and providing students with work sheets for them to fill in. The suggested habitats could be freshwater, marine and terrestrial initially, but discussion could enable these to be subdivided. For example, do still freshwater habitats (ponds and lakes) differ from moving freshwater habitats (streams and rivers)? Some students might be interested in what happens in a tidal area.

- Write up a list of animals, to include invertebrates as well as vertebrates, for each major habitat. Discuss how each type of animal copes in that habitat. For example, a freshwater habitat species list could include protozoa, cnidarians, leeches, worms, insect larvae and crustaceans as well as fish and frogs. Draw up a list of different strategies for coping with osmosis.

- Students could be given the lists and sent away to do their own research using reference books or the Internet.

- **The special case of the salmon and the eels** – Salmon and eels spend part of their lives in freshwater and part of their lives in the sea, so they need to cope with the changing osmotic conditions. Students could research the life cycles and how these fish adapt.

Beating osmosis

The cells of all living organisms contain sodium chloride and other chemicals in solution. This means they can always be prone to water moving into them by osmosis. If they are immersed in a solution with a lower concentration of salts than the body cells they will tend to gain water. If in a more concentrated solution, water is lost. Either way can spell disaster. Here are just a few of the different ways in which living things attempt – largely successfully – to beat osmosis!

ACTIVITY

You have to produce some GCSE revision sheets on the exchange of materials in living organisms. Use the examples given here to help you make the sheets as lively and interesting as possible. Use any tricks which help *you* to remember things – and save the sheets to help you when exams are approaching!

No contest!

For many marine invertebrates like this jellyfish, osmosis causes no problems because the concentration of solutes in the cells of their bodies is exactly the same as the sea water. So there is no net movement of water in or out of the cells.

Copy cats!

Living on land causes all sorts of problems for the cells, particularly if water is lost and the body fluids get concentrated. Then water will leave the body cells by osmosis fast. Many insects have taken a leaf out of the plant's book – they have a tough, waterproof outer layer which prevents water loss from the body surface. They even have breathing holes known as *spiracles*. These can be closed up when they aren't needed – very like the stomata on the leaves of plants.

Flooding in

Fish that live in fresh water have a real problem. They need a constant flow of water over their gills to get the oxygen they need for respiration. But water moves into their gill cells and blood by osmosis at the same time. Like all vertebrates, fish have kidneys which play a big part in using osmosis to regulate their internal environment. So freshwater fish produce huge amounts of very dilute urine, which gets rid of the excess water that gets into their bodies. They also have special salt-absorbing glands. These use active transport to move salt against the concentration gradient from the water into the fish – rather like the situation in plant root cells.

The big ones

Marine vertebrates like this whale are constantly drinking salty water. The salt loading would cause water to move out of their body cells and kill them if they couldn't deal with it. Fortunately whales have extremely efficient kidneys. When a whale drinks 1000 cm³ of sea water, it produces 670 cm³ of very concentrated urine – and gains 330 cm³ of pure water.

13

ACTIVITY & EXTENSION IDEAS

- **Discovering cells** – The activity suggested above can be started by using photographs or drawings of different types of microscope stuck to cards. On the reverse side, write the dates (approx.) when the microscopes were first invented. Ask the students to try to sequence these cards (without looking at the back, of course). It is a bit difficult to pinpoint exact dates for some, but reference to a textbook on microscopy or a suitable web site should provide the answers. Once the sequence is established, then the timeline can be established and the annotations can be discussed. Students could make individual annotated timelines, choosing their own important discoveries. Alternatively, this could be a feature of the laboratory and the class could discuss what they thought were the important discoveries to be attached to the timeline.

- It might be relevant here to remind students that Pasteur was able to show the presence of microorganisms in his broth that went bad. Without a microscope this would have been difficult. Although this is not a discovery about cells, it is an example of how microscopes can make an important contribution to research.

- **The exchange of materials in living organisms** – There is plenty of material for the suggested GCSE revision sheets activity and students could make their own or work in groups to produce a set for each major habitat. Working in groups can help to cover many different organisms and the results pooled to make a class revision resource. Before embarking on the format of the sheets, students could decide what type of approach would make the information interesting and help them to remember the facts. This activity could make use of ICT in order to find out more information and also in the production of the revision resource.

- **Individual case histories** – It could be useful to make sheets for individual species such as salmon, frogs or camels, or for groups such as marine fish, mammals and desert plants. Students should be reminded of the general nature of the activity and that it is not just about osmosis but other materials as well.

- **Don't forget the plants!** – The suggested activity refers to 'living organisms' so the introduction of some plants into the lists for each major habitat could be of benefit. Some species of thick seaweeds such as bladderwrack or *Laminaria* (broad, strap-shaped structures) could be shown to those students not familiar with seaweeds.

Special needs

Students could be given simplified lists of animals for each major habitat and asked to say whether water would go into the cells of their bodies or whether they would lose water from their cells.

Gifted and talented

Imagine a leap in resolving power, as great as that of the microscope happening, today and a large amount of new detail about the Universe becoming visible. Ask: 'What would the reactions be?' Students could write an e-mail to a friend telling them all about this fantastic new discovery. Ask: 'Will there be a finite limit to the resolving power of electron microscopes? If so, why? Could anything theoretically take their place to give even higher resolutions?'

SUMMARY ANSWERS

1 Based on labelled diagram of *Chlamydomonas*:

   a) Nucleus, chloroplast, starch, cytoplasm.

   b) Flagellum/flagella for moving around; eye spot for sensing light.

   c) [Any sensible answer using scientific explanations.]

2 Based on a sensory nerve cell, a white blood cell and a cell with rough ER (endoplasmic reticulum) with mitochondria and ribosomes.

   a) [Marks for correct labels.]

   b) Sensory nerve cell: carrying nerve impulses.
   White blood cell: defending the body against pathogens; part of the immune system; destroying/engulfing pathogens.
   Active/secretory cell: making proteins/enzymes to be used in the body.

   c) Sensory nerve cell: sensory receptor to respond to changes; long axon to carry impulses long distances around body; synapse to pass impulse; to other nerve cells; transmitter substance in the synapse to transmit impulse across gap.
   White blood cell: makes antibodies on the surface; can flow and engulf bacteria etc.
   Secretory cell: lots of ribosomes for protein synthesis; lots of mitochondria to provide energy.

Summary teaching suggestions

Most of the answers required are based on the diagrams or passage provided, and require facts so there is little scope for differentiating between lower and higher level answers. Higher attaining students should give full answers to question 1c), perhaps not coming to a definite conclusion but giving both animal and plant features.

- **Special needs** – Question 2 could be modified, by providing students with the unlabelled diagrams and the labels and functions on stickers that could then be attached in the right places.

- **When to use the questions?**
  - These are useful revision questions. Question 2 could be particularly useful in revising the specialisation of cells. Students could find it helpful to have a diagram of the cell and then to add annotations to the labels, thus linking structure to function.
  - Question 1 revises the differences between plant and animal cells.

CELLS: B2 1.1 – B2 1.5

SUMMARY QUESTIONS

1

Chlamydomonas is a single-celled organism which lives under water. It can move itself to the light to photosynthesise, and stores excess food as starch.

a) What features does it have in common with most plant cells?

b) What features are not like plant cells and what are they used for?

c) Would you class *Chlamydomonas* as a plant cell or an animal cell? Explain why.

2

Each of these cells is specialised for a particular function in your body.

a) Copy each of these diagrams and label the cells carefully. Carry out some research if necessary.

b) Describe what you think is the function of each of these cells.

c) Explain how the structure of the cell is related to its function.

EXAM-STYLE QUESTIONS

1 The diagram is of a cell from the leaf of a plant.

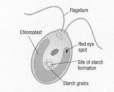

(a) Name the structures **D**, **E** and **F**.   (3)

(b) (i) What is the name of structure **A**?   (1)
    (ii) What material is structure **A** made of?   (1)

(c) (i) What is the name of structure **C**?   (1)
    (ii) What is the liquid it contains called?   (1)

(d) Structure **B** is a chloroplast. What is its function? (2)

(e) Name two different structures that are found within the material labelled **F**.   (2)

(f) (i) A different type of plant cell is a root hair cell. What is the function of this type of cell?   (1)
    (ii) State one way in which a root hair cell differs from the leaf cell shown in the diagram.   (1)

2 Copy the table below. Look at the structures listed in the first column. Fill in the empty columns by putting a tick (✓) if you think it is present and a cross (✗) if you think it is absent.   (6)

Structure	Animal cell	Plant cell
Nucleus		
Cytoplasm		
Cell wall		
Cell membrane		
Chloroplast		
Permanent vacuole		

3 A student noticed that different trees give different amounts of shade on a sunny day. She decided to investigate three species of tree – oak, sycamore and ash. She thought that the more shading, the better the tree was at gathering light for photosynthesis. She would use a light meter to record the light levels. The student had many things to consider when deciding on a method.

(a) Should she take readings in direct sunlight as well as under the trees? Explain your answer.   (2)

EXAM-STYLE ANSWERS

1 a) **D** Cell membrane
   E Nucleus
   F Cytoplasm   *(1 mark each)*

   b) i) Cell wall   *(1 mark)*   ii) Cellulose   *(1 mark)*

   c) i) Vacuole   *(1 mark)*   ii) Cell sap   *(1 mark)*

   d) *Either* Absorbs light energy   *(1 mark)*
              to make/manufacture food/sugars   *(1 mark)*
      Or   (Carries out) photosynthesis   *(2 marks)*

   The idea of light absorption and making food is needed for both marks. Either point separately earns one mark. Photosynthesis embraces both ideas and warrants both marks.

   e) Ribosomes   *(1 mark)*   Mitochondria   *(1 mark)*

   f) i) To absorb water/minerals (from the soil into the plant)
                                                    (1 mark)

      ii) • A root hair cell has a much larger surface area (to volume ratio)/a large hair-like projection.
          • A root hair cell has no chloroplasts.
                                    (1 mark for either point)

   Where the leaf cell, rather than the root hair cell, is quoted the converse points are allowed. Where 'it' is used, always assume the root hair cell unless it is very clear that this is not the case.

2

Structure	Animal cell	Plant cell
Nucleus	✓	✓
Cytoplasm	✓	✓
Cell wall	✗	✓
Cell membrane	✓	✓
Chloroplast	✗	✓
Permanent vacuole	✗	✓

(1 mark for each correct pair of symbols on any one line)

(b) Describe the weather that would be most appropriate when collecting the data. (1)

(c) Should the student collect data from one or more than one position? Explain your answer. (1)

(d) Explain why it would be necessary for the student to take as many readings as she could under the trees. (1)

(e) What type of independent variable has the student decided to use? (1)

(f) What type of dependent variable has she decided to use? (1)

(g) How should the student calculate the mean for each set of results? (1)

(h) Suggest how she should present her data. (1)

4 List **A** gives the names of different types of cells found in plants and animals. List **B** gives one special feature of each of these cells. Match each cell type with its feature by writing the relevant letter and number next to one another. (6)

List A		List B	
A	Fat cell	1	Has a long tail with muscle-like proteins
B	Root hair cell	2	Can divide and change into many different types of cell
C	Sperm cell	3	Contains chloroplasts
D	Leaf cell	4	Can expand up to 1000 times its original size
E	Stem cell	5	Contains a chemical called visual pigment
F	Cone cell (in eye)	6	Has extension to increase its surface area

HOW SCIENCE WORKS QUESTIONS

Spinning cells!

It is possible to separate the different parts of a cell using a centrifuge. Your teacher might be able to show you one of these. They really are very simple. They spin around rather like a very fast spin dryer.

They are used to separate structures that might be mixed together in a liquid. One of their uses is to separate the different parts of a cell.

The cells are first broken open so that the contents spill out into the liquid. The mixture is then put into the centrifuge. The centrifuge starts to spin slowly and a pellet forms at the bottom of the tube. This is removed. The rest is put back into the centrifuge at a higher speed and the next pellet removed and so on.

Here are some results:

Centrifuge speed (rpm)	Part of cell in pellet
3000	Nuclei
10 000	Mitochondria
12 000	Ribosomes

(rpm = revolutions per minute)

a) From these observations can you suggest a link between the speed of the centrifuge and the size of the part of the cell found in the pellet? (1)

b) What apparatus would you need to test your suggestion? (1)

c) i) What was your independent variable? (1)
   ii) Is your independent variable best described as categoric, discrete or continuous? (1)

d) What was your dependent variable? (1)

e) If your suggestion is correct, what results would you expect? (1)

f) What would be the easiest measurement to make to show the size of the mitochondria? (1)

g) Suggest how many mitochondria you might measure. (1)

h) How would you calculate the mean for the measurements you have taken? (2)

15

Exam teaching suggestions

- This test is designed primarily for foundation-level students. It tests recall and the responses needed are short with no narrative prose required. There is scope for students to pick up marks relatively easily; in question 1, part d) for example, students are asked the function of a chloroplast. The allocation of two marks for the word 'photosynthesis' might appear generous. It does however allow the not inconsiderable number of students who write 'absorbs light' to obtain one mark for a partial answer. Allowance has also been made for simple responses. In question 1, part f) for example, the words in brackets are not required for the mark, although one might expect a higher-tier candidate to include this type of detail. Part f) also illustrates the important issue of specifying in answers which of two items is being referred to when two things are compared. In this case, as the root hair cell comes first in the question (is the subject of the sentence) where a student uses 'it' they are assumed to be writing about the root hair cell. Students should, however, be discouraged from using 'it' and persuaded to use the specific name of the item and so avoid any ambiguity.

- In question 1 part a) it is very easy for students to confuse structures A (cell wall) and D (cell membrane). The need to look very carefully at what exactly the label line touches should be impressed on students.

HOW SCIENCE WORKS ANSWERS

a) The slower the centrifuge spins at the larger the cell part separated. Or reverse argument.

b) Microscope. With attachment to measure, e.g. length. Very sensitive instrument.

c) i) The independent variable is the centrifuge speed.
   ii) Continuous variable.

d) The dependent variable is the size of part of the cell (or part of cell) in pellet.

e) For the results you would expect the mean size of part of the cell in the pellet to be larger with slower centrifuge speed.

f) Measure the length – because they are 'cigar-shaped'.

g) As many as possible! But a minimum of 10.

h) Add up all the measurements and divide by how many there are.

3 a) Yes – because she would not know how much light there was shining on the tree *(1 mark)*
OR Yes – so that she could calculate the efficiency of light gathering for photosynthesis. *(2 marks)*

b) Sunny/no clouds *(1 mark)*

c) More than one position – because the shade will vary *(1 mark)*

d) To improve the reliability of the data collected *(1 mark)*

e) Categoric *(1 mark)*

f) Continuous *(1 mark)*

g) Add up all of the results from under the tree and divide by the number of results *(1 mark)*

h) Bar chart *(1 mark)*

4 A 4

B 6

C 1

D 3

E 2

F 5 *(1 mark for each correct pairing)*

How science works teaching suggestions

- **Literacy guidance**
  - Key terms that should be clearly understood: how observations can be used to make hypotheses and predictions, independent, dependent variable, sensitivity.
  - Question e) requires a longer answer, where students can practise their clarity of expression skills.

- **Higher- and lower-level answers**
  - Questions b) and e) are higher level and the answers above are also at this level.
  - The lower-level questions are a), c) and d) and answers are also at this level.

- **Gifted and talented.** Able students could suggest at what speeds other cell fragments might be found.

- **How and when to use these questions.** When wishing to encourage students to use observations to formulate hypotheses, for predictions and testing.

- **Homework.** The questions could be introduced in class and then used for homework.

- **Special needs.** Students may well need to be shown a working centrifuge – safely!

- **ICT link-up.** Students could search the Internet for photographs of cell fragments and their sizes.

B2 2.1   Photosynthesis

LEARNING OBJECTIVES

Students should learn that:

- Light energy is absorbed by the chlorophyll in the chloroplasts of green plants.
- Light energy is used by converting carbon dioxide and water into sugar.
- Oxygen is released as a by-product.

LEARNING OUTCOMES

Most students should be able to:

- Summarise the process of photosynthesis in a word equation.
- Describe where the energy comes from and how it is absorbed.
- Describe experiments that show the raw materials needed and the resulting products.

Some students should also be able to:

- Explain the build up of sugars into starch during photosynthesis.

Teaching suggestions

- **Special needs.** To illustrate the point that starch is made from sugar, use Duplo or other large building blocks. Take six or eight blocks of the same colour and label each individual block 'sugar'. Stick the blocks together and place a large sticker, labelled 'starch', over the back of all of them. Cut apart into individual blocks before using. A small number on each sugar block enables you to assemble them in the correct order.
- **Gifted and talented.** Carry out the practical exercise with photosynthetic algae encapsulated in gel, based on *Science and Plants in Schools* (SAPS) student worksheet 23: 'Photosynthesis using algae wrapped in jelly balls'. Ask the students to use chemical symbols for the photosynthesis equation and to balance it.
- **Learning styles**
  Kinaesthetic: Party poppers activity; practical work testing leaves for starch.
  Visual: Making observations on leaves and describing them.
  Auditory: Listening to the song 'Feed me' from the video clip.
  Interpersonal: Discussing Audrey from *Little Shop of Horrors*.
  Intrapersonal: Individual feedback on the lesson.

SPECIFICATION LINK-UP   Unit: Biology 2.11.3

- *Photosynthesis is summarised by the equation:*

$$carbon\ dioxide + water\ (+ light\ energy) \rightarrow glucose + oxygen$$

- *During photosynthesis:*
  - *Light energy is absorbed by a green substance called chlorophyll, which is found in chloroplasts in some plant cells.*
  - *This energy is used by converting carbon dioxide and water into sugar (glucose).*
  - *Oxygen is released as a by-product.*

Lesson structure

STARTER

Why are leaves green? – Lead a discussion based on concept cartoon-style talking head. Revise light reflection and absorbance. (5–10 minutes)

Audrey, the plant – If easily available show a video clip from the Frank Oz (1986) musical version of *Little Shop of Horrors* with Audrey, the plant, eating people. Ask: 'Was she really a plant if she eats meat?' Discuss how plants feed themselves. (10 minutes)

What will happen to my leaf? – During the growing season (or if you have plants in a greenhouse), give each student a spot label on to which they can write their initials. Allow them to choose a young leaf and stick their label on to it. They should then measure the length of the leaf and record it. Back in the laboratory, ask them to predict what will happen to the leaf and explain why. They will need to check this at a later date. (10 minutes)

MAIN

- **How leaves are adapted for photosynthesis** – In this exercise, the adaptations of leaves for the process of photosynthesis are investigated. Students should look at whole leaves and make drawings of the external appearance, labelling the features that they can see (broad lamina, green colour, veins) and annotating these labels to explain the adaptations.

- **Observing leaves** – Prepared microscope slides of transverse sections through leaves could be projected or viewed under the microscope so that students can distinguish the different tissues within the leaf. Point out the palisade tissue, the vascular tissue and the stomata. Students could draw plans of the tissues to show where photosynthesis takes place.

- **How can we show that photosynthesis has taken place?** – When carrying out experiments on photosynthesis, we can test for the products i.e. the presence of sugars or the evolution of oxygen. In most plants, the sugars are immediately converted to starch (shown by the presence of starch grains in chloroplasts). The starch test can then be used on leaves to show that photosynthesis has occurred.

- **Producing oxygen** – We can show that oxygen has been producing using water plants such as *Elodea* (Canadian pondweed) which is readily available from garden centres. The apparatus can be set up as described and kept illuminated for several hours, so that enough gas can be collected to be able to test it satisfactorily. If groups of students set up their own, it is unlikely to yield enough gas to test within a lesson.

- If students carry out the experiment, individually or in groups, several of the concepts of 'How Science Works' are introduced. They can formulate a hypothesis, make predictions, draw conclusions and evaluate the validity of experimental design.

- **Testing for starch** – To show that chlorophyll is necessary for photosynthesis, variegated plants, such as spider plant or geranium, can be used. The plants need to be kept in bright light for several hours. Keep one plant in the dark for two days to destarch it as a control. Each student can be given a leaf from an illuminated plant. A record should be made of the distribution of the green and white areas of the leaf, before testing for starch. After carrying out the test, another drawing can be made showing the areas that remain brown and those that have been stained blue/black. Comparison of the two drawings will enable a conclusion to be drawn. Testing a leaf from the control plant will show that if there is no light then no starch will be produced.

PLENARIES

Summary – Use a summary of photosynthesis with missing words. (5 minutes)

Prove it! – Write on the board, or project, a number of statements about photosynthesis. Then the students have to write out or discuss how we know each of the statements is true. (10 minutes)

ACTIVITY & EXTENSION IDEAS

- An Animation, B2 2.1 'Photosynthesis', is available on the Additional Science CD ROM.

- **Demonstration of formation of glucose molecule** – Into one hand of each of six students, put a piece of charcoal and a balloon labelled O₂. Explain that they each represent a molecule of carbon dioxide. Ask the rest of the class to form two lines facing each other with a gap of 4 or 5 metres between them – they represent a leaf. Two students are designated as guard cells and must form an arch (barn dance style) to allow the CO₂ students to enter. In advance, remove the paper streamers from six party poppers, put a hole in the top of each and attach a large loop of string to it. Attach a similar loop of string to the pull string on the base of the popper. Get the six students to stand in a circle and put their arms through the loops so that the party poppers are suspended between them. Six more students, each carrying a bottle of water, are then to come up between the rows. They swap their bottles of water for the balloons of oxygen, so that the ring represents a molecule of glucose and the students carrying the balloons exit through the stoma. This enactment can be reversed to show respiration: the oxygen comes back in, each grabs a carbon and pulls it away, breaking the bonds between the party poppers and leaving the water behind. Students could then find out the actual structure of glucose.

Practical support

Equipment and materials required

Observing leaves

Prepared slides of sections through leaves and microscopes.

Testing for starch

Variegated plants, such as a geranium, dilute iodine solution in dropping bottles (CLEAPSS Hazcard 54), water baths to kill the leaves/make them more permeable/softer, ethanol for decolourising leaves/removing chlorophyll, white tiles or dishes to put the leaves in, forceps.

Answers to in-text questions

a) carbon dioxide + water (+ light energy) →glucose + oxygen

b) The green substance that absorbs light energy in plants.

c) Provides a large surface area for the light to fall on.

B2 2.1   Photosynthesis

LEARNING OBJECTIVES

1 What is photosynthesis?
2 What are the raw materials for photosynthesis?
3 Where does the energy for photosynthesis come from and how do plants absorb it?

Like all living organisms, plants need food. It provides them with the energy for respiration, growth and reproduction. But plants aren't like us – they don't need to eat.

Plants can make their own food! They do it by **photosynthesis**. This takes place in the green parts of plants (especially the leaves) when it is light.

The process of photosynthesis

Photosynthesis can be summed up in the following equation:

carbon dioxide + water (+ light energy) →glucose + oxygen

The cells in the leaves of a plant are full of small green parts called **chloroplasts**. They contain a green substance called **chlorophyll**.

During photosynthesis, light energy is absorbed by the chlorophyll in the chloroplasts. This energy is then used to convert carbon dioxide from the air plus water from the soil into a simple sugar called **glucose**. The chemical reaction also produces oxygen gas. This is released into the air.

a) What is the word equation for photosynthesis?

Some of the glucose produced during photosynthesis is used immediately by the cells of the plant. However, a lot of the glucose made is converted into starch for storage.

Iodine solution is a yellow-brown liquid which turns dark blue when it reacts with starch. You can use this *iodine test for starch* to show that photosynthesis has taken place in a plant.

PRACTICAL

Producing oxygen

You can show a plant is photosynthesising by collecting the oxygen given off as a by-product. It is very difficult to see oxygen, a colourless gas, being given off by land plants. But if you use water plants you can collect the gas which they give off when they are photosynthesising. It will relight a glowing splint, showing that it is oxygen gas.

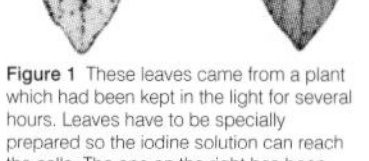

PRACTICAL

Testing for starch

Chlorophyll is vital for photosynthesis to take place. It absorbs the light which provides the energy for the plant to make glucose and convert it into starch.

Take a leaf from a variegated plant (partly green and partly white). After treating the leaves, you use iodine solution to show how important chlorophyll is. (See Figure 1.)

- What happens in the test? Explain your observations

b) What is chlorophyll?

The leaves of plants are perfectly adapted because:

- most leaves are broad, they have a big surface area for light to fall on,
- they contain chlorophyll in the chloroplasts to absorb the light energy,
- they have air spaces which allow carbon dioxide to get to the cells, and oxygen to leave them,
- they have veins, which bring plenty of water to the cells of the leaves.

Figure 1 These leaves came from a plant which had been kept in the light for several hours. Leaves have to be specially prepared so the iodine solution can reach the cells. The one on the right has been tested for starch, using iodine solution. Only the green parts of the leaf made their own starch which turns the iodine solution blue-black.

All of these adaptations mean the plant can carry out as much photosynthesis as possible whenever there is light available.

c) How does the broad shape of leaves help photosynthesis to take place?

PRACTICAL

Observing leaves

Look at a whole plant leaf and then a section of a leaf under a microscope. You can see how well adapted it is.

- Compare what you can see with Figure 2 below.
- What magnification did you use?

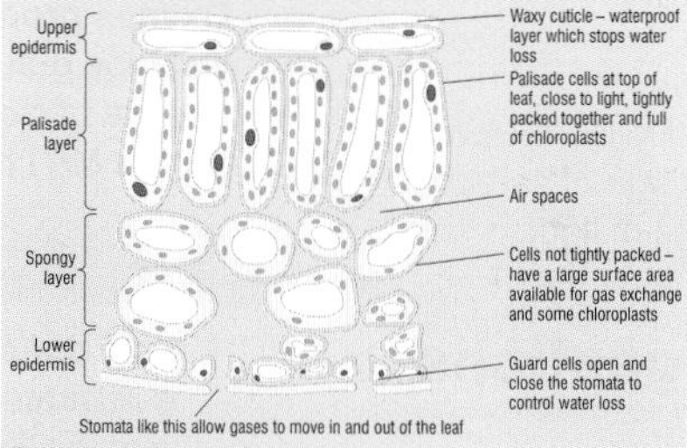

Upper epidermis
Palisade layer
Spongy layer
Lower epidermis

Waxy cuticle – waterproof layer which stops water loss
Palisade cells at top of leaf, close to light, tightly packed together and full of chloroplasts
Air spaces
Cells not tightly packed – have a large surface area available for gas exchange and some chloroplasts
Guard cells open and close the stomata to control water loss

Stomata like this allow gases to move in and out of the leaf
Figure 2 A section through a leaf

SUMMARY QUESTIONS

1 Copy and complete using the words below:

**carbon dioxide   chlorophyll   energy   gas   glucose
light   Oxygen   water**

During photosynthesis ...... energy is absorbed by ......, a substance found in the chloroplasts. This ...... is then used to convert .... from the air and ...... from the soil into a simple sugar called .... is also produced and released as a ......

2 a) Where does a plant get the carbon dioxide, water and light that it needs for photosynthesis?
b) Work out the path taken by a carbon atom as it moves from being part of the carbon dioxide in the air to being part of a starch molecule in a plant.

3 Design experiments to show that plants need a) carbon dioxide and b) light for photosynthesis to take place. For each experiment explain what your control would be and how you would show that photosynthesis has taken place.

GET IT RIGHT!

Learn the equation for photosynthesis.
Be able to explain the results of experiments on photosynthesis.

NEXT TIME YOU...

... breathe in, remember that the oxygen in the air you are breathing was produced as a by-product of photosynthesis by plants. Luckily for us, the world's plants produce about 368 000 000 000 tonnes of oxygen every year!

KEY POINTS

1 Photosynthesis can be summed up by the equation:

carbon dioxide + water [+ light energy] → glucose + oxygen

2 During photosynthesis light energy is absorbed by the chlorophyll in the chloroplasts. It is used to convert carbon dioxide and water into sugar (glucose). Oxygen is released as a by-product.

3 Leaves are well adapted to allow the maximum photosynthesis to take place.

SUMMARY ANSWERS

1 Light, chlorophyll, energy, carbon dioxide, water, glucose, oxygen, gas.

2 a) CO₂ comes from the air; water from the soil; light energy from sunlight/electric light.
b) Diffuse from the air into the air spaces in the leaf; into plant cells; into chloroplasts; joined with water to make glucose; converted to starch for storage.

3 [In both cases, give credit for sensible suggestions, awareness of difficulties, controls (fair test).]

KEY POINTS

- It is important to be able to write out the summary equation for the process of photosynthesis.
- It is also important to be able to explain the results of experiments and to be able to describe how leaves are adapted to carry out photosynthesis.
- These key points would make good revision cards, although some of the adaptations of the leaves could be added to the last point.

B2 2.2

Limiting factors

LEARNING OBJECTIVES

Students should learn that:

- The rate of photosynthesis may be limited by low temperature and the shortage of carbon dioxide or light.

- These factors interact.

- If any of these factors are in short supply, the rate of photosynthesis is limited.

LEARNING OUTCOMES

Most students should be able to:

- List the factors that limit the rate of photosynthesis.

- Describe how the factors interact.

- Describe how the environment in which plants grow can be artificially manipulated to grow more food.

Some students should also be able to:

- Interpret data showing how the factors affect the rate of photosynthesis.

- Explain why the rate of photosynthesis is limited by low temperature, shortage of carbon dioxide or shortage of light.

Teaching suggestions

- **Special needs**
  - Students could benefit from the demonstration using the hydrogencarbonate indicator solution if it was explained that the deeper the purple colour the more photosynthesis had occurred.
  - Draw analogies with football teams. One team is held back in the league by not having enough good strikers; another may be weak in the mid-field or defence. (The students will give lots of examples!)

- **Gifted and talented.** Draw out predicted graphs for light intensity, CO_2 level and temperature during a typical day during a named month of the growing season. Explain the shapes of these graphs bearing in mind respiration. Contrast with an early spring or late autumn day.

- **Learning styles**

  Kinaesthetic: Counter activity in starter; practical work.

  Visual: Observing bubbling, colour changes etc. in practicals.

SPECIFICATION LINK-UP   Unit: Biology 2.11.3

- *The rate of photosynthesis may be limited by:*
  - *low temperature*
  - *shortage of carbon dioxide*
  - *shortage of light.*

- *Light, temperature and the availability of carbon dioxide interact and, in practice, any one of them may be the factor that limits photosynthesis.*

Lesson structure

STARTER

The limiting factors game – Have three sorts of counters (or small cards): one set labelled 'L' for suitable light level, another 'T' for suitable temperature and the third 'CO_2'. For each group of students, you will need a bag into which you place some of each set of counters (or cards), so that they get a mixture of 'L', 'T' and 'CO_2'. The students are to take out a counter one at a time, placing them on a base line on paper or on the desk. The aim is to make sets of three counters side by side, at which point they can start on the next layer as they have grown. If they draw out a counter which they have already got in that layer, they put it back. The objective is to grow the 'plant' to as many levels as possible during a set time. Adjust each bag's contents so that some groups run out of 'L' counters first, some of 'T' counters and some of 'CO_2' ones. Discuss the results. (10–15 minutes)

Tree rings – Examine some cross sections of tree branches using hand lenses or binocular microscopes. Ask: 'Why are there rings present?' Draw out the links between growth rate and temperature and light intensity as limiting factors. (5–10 minutes)

Oxygen production and light intensity – Show students the pondweed under the test tube practical from the previous lesson. Ask them to draw a thumbnail graph of how the rate of oxygen production would vary with light intensity. Draw on to individual ('Show Me') boards. (5 minutes)

MAIN

- **How does the intensity of light affect the rate of photosynthesis?** – This experiment is illustrated in the student book and is easy to set up. Students can work in groups and vary the light intensity by altering the distance of the lamp from the plant.

- This is a good experiment for developing 'How Science Works' concepts. A hypothesis can be formulated, predictions made, variables such as temperature controlled, measurements taken, results expressed as graphs and conclusions drawn. Results can be plotted as number of bubbles evolved, in a set time, against distance of the lamp from the plant. A more accurate way of plotting the results is to use light intensity, given by $1/d^2$ where d is the distance of the lamp from the plant.

- **Alternative ways of investigating variations in light intensity:**
  - Consider using a mercury vapour lamp light bank of the type recommended by *Science and Plants in Schools* (SAPS) for use with their 'Rapid cycling brassicas' kit. This could be an investigation into the effects of light intensity on growth rates. (Details from SAPS, Homerton College, Cambridge CB2 2PH.) Use various filters and light sensors.

Auditory: Listening to the explanations given.

Intrapersonal: Analysing graph-tabulated data on limiting factors.

Interpersonal: Discussing ideas.

- **Homework**
- Writing up the reports of experiments could be set as a homework task.

- Alternatively, the summary questions (particularly questions 2 and 3) could be set as homework and will test understanding of the limiting factors.

PLENARIES

Finish off the graph – Give the students some semi-completed graphs showing limiting factors to finish off and label. (5–10 minutes)

Question loop – Students to ask and then answer questions on factors limiting photosynthesis. (5 minutes)

ACTIVITY & EXTENSION

- Try to arrange a visit to a commercial glasshouse or encourage students to find out how conditions are controlled.
- Use a computer simulation where conditions for plant growth are varied, such as the one suggested above.
- Carry out a data-logging exercise, recording the temperature and light levels as they fluctuate throughout the day.

Practical support

Equipment and materials required

How does the intensity of light affect the rate of photosynthesis?

Sprigs of *Elodea,* boiling tubes and
test tube racks, bench lamps, rulers, beakers, funnels, stopwatches or stop clocks, graph paper (see centre of Figure 1 on page 18 in Student Book).

BIOLOGY — HOW PLANTS PRODUCE FOOD

B2 2.2 Limiting factors

LEARNING OBJECTIVES

1 What factors limit the rate of photosynthesis in plants?
2 How can we use what we know about limiting factors to grow more food?

You may have noticed that plants grow quickly in the summer, and hardly at all in the winter. Plants need certain things like light, warmth and carbon dioxide if they are going to photosynthesise as fast as they can.

If any of these things are in short supply they may limit the amount of photosynthesis a plant can manage. This is why they are known as **limiting factors**.

a) Why do you think plants grow faster in the summer than in the winter?

Light

The most obvious factor affecting the rate of photosynthesis is light. If there is plenty of light, lots of photosynthesis can take place. If there is very little or no light, photosynthesis will stop regardless of the other conditions around the plant. For most plants, the brighter the light, the faster the rate of photosynthesis.

PRACTICAL

How does the intensity of light affect the rate of photosynthesis?

We can look at this experimentally. (See Figure 1.) At the start, the rate of photosynthesis goes up as the light intensity increases. This tells us that light intensity is a limiting factor.

However, we reach a point when no matter how bright the light, the rate of photosynthesis stays the same. At this point, light is no longer limiting the rate of photosynthesis. Something else has become the limiting factor.

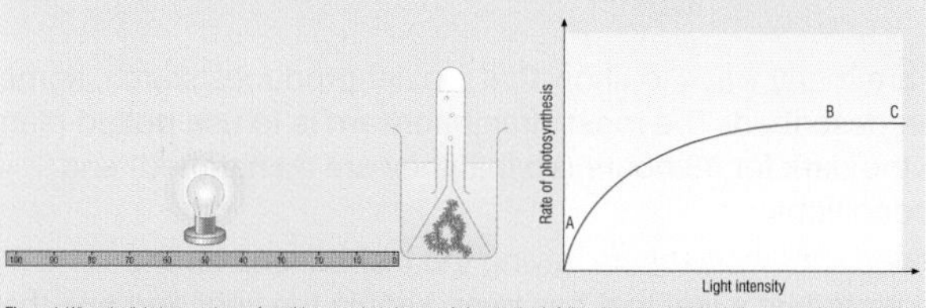

Figure 1 When the light is moved away from this water plant, the rate of photosynthesis falls – shown by a slowing in the stream of oxygen bubbles being produced. If the light is moved closer (keeping the water temperature constant) the stream of bubbles becomes faster, showing an increased rate of photosynthesis. The results can be plotted on a graph like this which shows the effect of light intensity on the rate of photosynthesis.

- Why is light a limiting factor for photosynthesis?
- Name the independent and the dependent variables in this investigation. (See page 276.)

18

Additional biology

Temperature

Temperature affects all chemical reactions, including photosynthesis. As the temperature rises, the rate of photosynthesis will increase as the reaction speeds up. However, because photosynthesis takes place in living organisms it is controlled by enzymes. Enzymes are destroyed once the temperature rises to around 40 to 50°C. This means that if the temperature gets too high, the rate of photosynthesis will fall as the enzymes controlling it are denatured.

b) Why does temperature affect photosynthesis?

Figure 2 The rate of photosynthesis increases steadily with a rise in temperature up to a certain point. After this the enzymes are destroyed and the reaction stops completely.

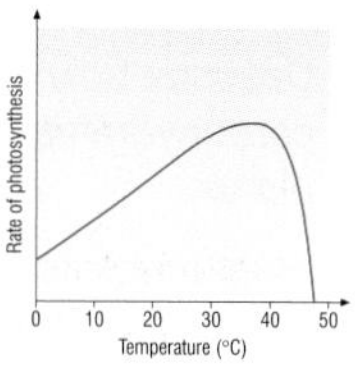

Carbon dioxide levels

Plants need carbon dioxide to make glucose. The atmosphere only contains about 0.04% carbon dioxide, so carbon dioxide levels often limit the amount of photosynthesis which can take place. Increasing the carbon dioxide levels will increase the rate of photosynthesis.

For the plants you see around you on a sunny day, carbon dioxide levels are the most common limiting factor. The carbon dioxide levels around a plant tend to rise in the night as it respires but doesn't photosynthesise. Then as the light and temperature levels increase in the morning, the carbon dioxide all gets used up.

However, in a laboratory or in a greenhouse the levels of carbon dioxide can be increased artificially. This means they are no longer limiting, and the rate of photosynthesis increases with the rise in carbon dioxide.

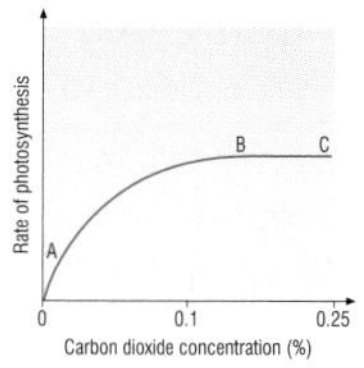

Figure 3 This graph shows the effect of increasing carbon dioxide levels on the rate of photosynthesis at a particular light level and temperature. Eventually one of the other factors becomes limiting.

DID YOU KNOW?

There are a few plants that live in very shady areas which have evolved to photosynthesise at their maximum at relatively low levels of light. For them, too much light causes the rate of photosynthesis to drop!

GET IT RIGHT!

Make sure you can explain limiting factors.
Learn to interpret graphs which show the effect of limiting factors on photosynthesis.

SUMMARY QUESTIONS

1 a) What is photosynthesis?
   b) What are the three main limiting factors that affect the rate of photosynthesis in a plant?
2 Which factors do you think would be limiting photosynthesis in the following situations? In each case, explain why the rate of photosynthesis is limited.
   a) Plants growing on a woodland floor in winter.
   b) Plants growing on a woodland floor in summer.
   c) A field of barley first thing in the morning.
   d) The same field later on in the day.
3 Look at the graph in Figure 1.
   a) Explain what is happening between points A and B on the graph.
   b) Explain what is happening between points B and C on the graph.
   c) Look at Figure 2. Explain why it is a different shape to the other two graphs on this spread.

KEY POINTS

1 There are three main factors that limit the rate of photosynthesis – light, temperature and carbon dioxide levels.
2 We can artificially change the environment in which we grow plants. We can use this to observe the effect of different factors on the rate of photosynthesis. We can also use it to control their rate of photosynthesis.

19

SUMMARY ANSWERS

1 **a)** The process by which plants use light energy trapped by chlorophyll to convert carbon dioxide and water into glucose (sugar).
  b) Carbon dioxide, light and temperature.

2 **a)** Light and temperature.
  b) Light and carbon dioxide.
  c) Temperature and light.
  d) Carbon dioxide.

3 **a)** As light intensity increases so does the rate of photosynthesis. This tells us that light intensity is a limiting factor.
  b) An increase in light intensity has no effect on the rate of photosynthesis, so it is no longer a limiting factor; something else probably is.
  c) Temperature acts as a normal limiting factor to begin with; increase in temperature increases the rate of photosynthesis. But after a certain level, the enzymes in the cells are destroyed and so no photosynthesis can take place.

Answers to in-text questions

a) It is warmer in summer and there is more light, so photosynthesis takes place more quickly making more food so plants grow.

b) Photosynthesis is a chemical reaction; temperature affects all chemical reactions. An increase in temperature speeds up the reactions as reacting particles collide more frequently and with more energy.

KEY POINTS

The key points are reinforced by the 'Get it right!' comments. Students could benefit from discussing the interaction of the factors and thinking about how the factors can be altered to control the rate of photosynthesis. Some examples of how factors are controlled in the production of glasshouse crops would be useful. For example, light, temperature and carbon dioxide levels can be controlled in order to maintain production of salad crops all year round.

B2 2.3

How plants use glucose

Students should learn that:

- Glucose is converted into starch for storage.

- Some of the glucose produced is used for respiration in the plant.

Most students should be able to:

- Describe how and where carbohydrates are stored in plants.

- State that some of the carbohydrate produced is used in respiration.

Some students should also be able to:

- Explain that the energy released by plants in respiration is used to build up smaller molecules into larger molecules.

- Explain why starch is such a good storage molecule.

Teaching suggestions

- **Special needs.** Give the students samples of glucose and corn starch. Tell them to stir the powders into two beakers of water. They should observe what happens and make comments on their solubility in a simple fashion. Then ask them to filter the contents of both beakers and isolate and dry the corn starch.

- **Gifted and talented.** Students could research other ways in which plants store food. Link with question 2 of 'Summary questions'.

- **Learning styles**

  Kinaesthetic: Testing leaves and plant parts for starch.

  Visual: Making observations using microscopes.

  Auditory: Explaining the storage process to other students.

  Intrapersonal: Writing about what happens to glucose.

  Interpersonal: Discussing the results of the investigations.

- **Homework.** Students could finish off the poster suggested in a plenary or write a plant's eye view of what it does with the glucose it produces.

SPECIFICATION LINK-UP   Unit: Biology 2.11.3

- *The glucose produced in photosynthesis may be converted into insoluble starch for storage. Plant cells use some of the glucose produced during photosynthesis for respiration.*

Lesson structure

STARTER

How much energy in a jelly baby? – Heat a couple of centimetres depth of sodium chlorate in a test tube until it melts. In a fume cupboard, and with great care, drop a jelly baby into the tube. A very vigorous exothermic reaction occurs issuing lots of smoke and flame and noise. Carry out a risk assessment and practise first. Use a metal-jawed clamp. (CLEAPSS Hazcard 77) (5 minutes)

Make a starch molecule – Give the students blank drawings of a chain of joined hexagons. Ask them to write 'glucose' inside each hexagon and then to turn the paper over and write 'starch' across the whole of the back. They can then stick the chains into their books as a fold-out. (5 minutes)

Showing that respiration has occurred – Issue all the students with drinking straws, and then give half of them boiling tubes containing a little fresh lime water in the bottom and the other half boiling tubes with a little hydrogencarbonate indicator solution in the bottom. Wearing safety glasses, ask them to blow gently through the drinking straws into the solutions. They should note and compare colour changes, suggesting explanations. (10 minutes)

MAIN

- **Making starch** – There are many ways to show that a plant produces starch, some of which have already been described. The most straightforward is to use potted plants: some should be kept in the dark for 48 hours (so that they are destarched) and others kept in daylight conditions.

- Students could be provided with worksheets, giving the instructions for the procedure, and then asked to test a leaf that has been kept in the light and one that has been kept in the dark.

- Leaves on plants can be half-covered with foil or initials cut out of thin card, kept in bright light for several hours and then tested for starch.

- **Where is the starch stored?** – The presence of large numbers of starch grains in potato tuber cells can be demonstrated by cutting thin slices of the tissue. Place the thin slices of tissues on microscope slides, cover with a drop of water and then with a cover slip. A drop of dilute iodine solution can be drawn through using filter paper. The starch grains will stain blue-black. In order to see the grains more clearly, it is advisable to draw some water through the slide to remove the iodine solution.

- The technique described above can be used on a variety of plant parts. Very thin sections of tissue from fruits, seeds, nuts and other plant organs can then be tested for the presence of starch grains.

- Roughly compare the starch content of fruits, such as apples, with potato tubers and some seeds.

PLENARIES

From the air to a chip – In small groups, the students could produce a series of bullet points of the stages from carbon dioxide in the air to the starch in the chips on their plates. (10 minutes)

Matching exercise – Write up a list of definitions and key words about photosynthesis and ask students to match them up. (5–10 minutes)

Formation, use and storage of glucose – Ask students to produce a poster showing how glucose is produced, what it is used for and how it is stored in the plant. They can finish this for homework. (10–15 minutes)

ACTIVITY & EXTENSION IDEAS

- Carry out the party popper demonstration reversing the process described for photosynthesis in order to demonstrate respiration. (See Activity and Extension box on page 17 in this Teacher Book.)
- Use microscopes to examine prepared slides of sections of stems, roots and leaves to show the distribution of the vascular (transporting) tissue.
- To demonstrate that plants respire, keep some *Elodea* in a boiling tube of hydrogencarbonate indicator. The boiling tube will need to have foil around it or be kept in the dark, so that photosynthesis does not occur. The cherry-red colour should turn yellow as it becomes more acid due to the evolution of carbon dioxide. Compare with the starter activity that shows respiration has occurred.

Practical support

Equipment and materials required

Making starch

Destarched and illuminated plants, water baths for killing leaves/making them permeable, ethanol to decolourise the leaves/remove chlorophyll, dilute iodine solution in dropping bottles (CLEAPSS Hazcard 54), white tiles, forceps for handling leaves, eye protection.

Where is the starch stored?

Microscopes, slides, cover slips, a variety of plant parts (potato tubers, fruits, seeds, nuts, etc.), dilute iodine solution in dropping bottles (CLEAPSS Hazcard 54), eye protection.

BIOLOGY — HOW PLANTS PRODUCE FOOD

B2 2.3 How plants use glucose

LEARNING OBJECTIVES

1 What do plants do with the glucose they make?
2 How do plants store food?

Plants make glucose when they photosynthesise. This glucose is vital for their survival. Some of the glucose produced during photosynthesis is used immediately by the cells of the plant. They use it for respiration and to provide energy for cell functions, growth and reproduction.

Respiration

Plants cells, like any other living cells, respire all the time. They break down glucose using oxygen to provide energy for their cells. Carbon dioxide and water are the waste products of the reaction.

The energy released in respiration is then used to build up smaller molecules into bigger molecules. Some of the glucose is converted into starch for storage (see below). Plants also build up sugars into more complex carbohydrates like cellulose. They use this to make new plant cell walls.

Plants use some of the energy from respiration to combine sugars with other nutrients (mineral ions) from the soil to make amino acids. These amino acids are then built up into proteins to be used in the cells. Energy from respiration is also used to build up fats and oils to make a food store in the seeds.

a) Why do plants respire?

NEXT TIME YOU...

. . . tuck into a plate of chips or a pile of mashed potato, remember that you are eating the winter food store of a potato plant! The starch you are enjoying was formed from glucose made in the leaves of the potato plant by photosynthesis. It was transported down from the leaves to the roots to form a tasty tuber!

Transport and storage

Plants make food by photosynthesis in their leaves and other green parts. However, the food is needed all over the plant. It is moved around the plant in a special transport system.

There are two separate transport systems in plants. The **phloem** is made up of living tissue. It transports sugars made by photosynthesis from the leaves to the rest of the plant. They are carried to all the areas of the plant. These include the growing regions where the sugars are needed for making new plant material, and the storage organs where they are needed to provide a store of food for the winter.

The **xylem** is the other transport tissue. It carries water and mineral ions from the soil around the plant.

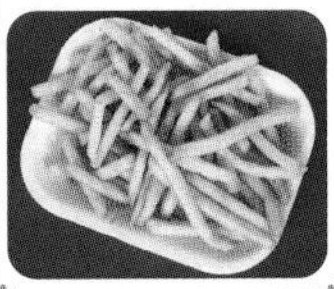

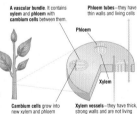

A vascular bundle. It contains **xylem** and **phloem** with **cambium cells** between them.
Phloem tubes – they have thin walls and living cells
Phloem
Xylem
Cambium cells grow into new xylem and phloem
Xylem vessels – they have thick, strong walls and are not living

Figure 1 A look at a section of a plant stem shows you how the transport system of a plant is arranged

GET IT RIGHT!

Remember:

- Plants respire 24 hours a day to release energy.
- Glucose is soluble in water, but starch is insoluble.

20

Additional biology

Plants convert some of the glucose produced in photosynthesis into starch to be stored. Glucose is **soluble** (it dissolves in water). If it was stored in plant cells it could affect the way water moves into and out of the cells. Large amounts of glucose stored in the plant cells could affect the water balance of the whole plant. Starch is **insoluble** (it doesn't dissolve in water). This means that plants can store large amounts of starch in their cells without it having any effect on the water balance of the plant.

So the main energy store in plants is starch and it is found all over a plant. It is stored in the leaves to provide an energy store for when it is dark or when light levels are low.

PRACTICAL

Making starch

You can use the presence of starch in a leaf as evidence that photosynthesis has been taking place. It is no good just adding iodine to a leaf – the waterproof cuticle and the green chlorophyll will prevent it reacting clearly with the starch. But once you have treated the leaf, adding iodine will show you clearly if the leaf has been photosynthesising or not. Look at Figure 2.

Figure 2 We use the iodine test for the presence of starch to show us that photosynthesis has taken place. The leaf on the right has been kept in the dark. It has made no glucose to turn into starch, and has used up any starch stores it had for respiration. The leaf on the left has been in the light and been able to photosynthesise. The glucose has been converted to starch which is clearly visible when it reacts with iodine and turns blue-black. The colour is removed from the leaves before testing by boiling them in ethanol.

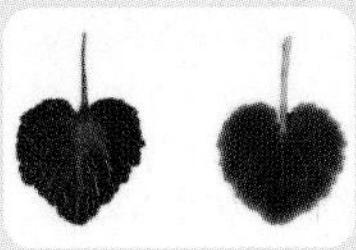

Starch is also stored in special storage areas of a plant. Many plants produce tubers and bulbs to help them survive through the winter. These are full of stored starch. We often take advantage of these starch stores and eat them ourselves. Potatoes, carrots and onions are all full of starch to keep a plant going until spring comes again!

b) What is the main storage substance in plants?

SUMMARY QUESTIONS

1 Copy and complete using the words below:

energy glucose growth photosynthesise respiration reproduction starch storage twenty-four

Plants make ...... when they .... Some of the glucose produced is used by the cells of the plant for ...... which goes on .... hours a day. It provides ...... for cell functions, ... and .... Some is converted to ...... for ....

2 List as many ways as possible in which a plant uses the glucose produced by photosynthesis.

3 a) Why is the glucose made by photosynthesis converted to starch to be stored in the plant?
b) Where might you find starch in a plant?
c) How could you show that a potato is a store of starch?

FOUL FACTS

Deer may look cute and cuddly – but they often kill trees. The transport tissue of a tree is found in the bark which deer love to nibble. If they nibble away a complete ring of bark, it is a disaster. Food made by photosynthesis in the leaves and water taken up by the roots cannot reach the rest of the plant – and it dies!

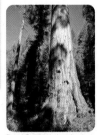

Figure 3 Trees like this giant redwood can be up to 30 metres tall – and then the roots spread out in all directions underground. Plants need a very effective transport system to move the food they make in their leaves distances like these.

KEY POINTS

1 Plant cells use some of the glucose they make during photosynthesis for respiration.
2 Some of the soluble glucose produced during photosynthesis is converted into insoluble starch for storage.

21

SUMMARY ANSWERS

1 Glucose, photosynthesise, respiration, 24, energy, growth, reproduction, starch, storage.

2 Respiration; energy for cell functions; growth; reproduction; building up smaller molecules into bigger molecules; converted into starch for storage; making cellulose; making amino acids; building up fats and oils for a food store in seeds.

3 a) Glucose is soluble and would affect the movement of water into and out of the plant cells. Starch is insoluble and so does not disturb the water balance of the plant.
b) Leaves, stems, roots and storage organs.
c) [Any sensible suggestions involving a slice of potato and dilute iodine solution.]

Answers to in-text questions

a) To provide chemical energy for their cells.

b) Starch.

KEY POINTS

The key points can be incorporated into the Plenaries 'From the air to a chip' and into the suggested poster activity.

B2 2.4

Why do plants need minerals?

LEARNING OBJECTIVES

Students should learn that:

- Plant roots absorb mineral ions (salts) needed for healthy growth.
- Nitrate is needed for protein formation and magnesium is needed for chlorophyll.
- Plants show deficiency symptoms if mineral ions are lacking.

LEARNING OUTCOMES

Most students should be able to:

- State that plants need magnesium ions to make chlorophyll and nitrate ions to make proteins.
- Describe the deficiency symptoms if nitrate and magnesium are lacking.

Teaching suggestions

- **Special needs.** Growing plants is always helpful for SEN students. Carry out on a long timescale, growing tomato plants (or sunflowers) in the early summer, with and without nitrogenous fertiliser. Each week (or more frequently if growing very quickly) hold a strip of 2–3 cm wide coloured paper next to the plant and cut the paper off at the same height as the plant. Stick the strips on to a bar chart frame, using a different colour each time. The students can predict the next and subsequent heights.
- **Gifted and talented.** Look at the structure of typical amino acids [without the structure of the R groups – this is AS level] and relate to the structure of nitrates and the need of the plant for nitrogen. They could also find out about the need for some of the other mineral ions. They could think about the differences between an etiolated plant (one grown completely in the dark) and a plant grown in a magnesium-deficient medium. Ask: 'Is there a connection?'
- **Learning styles**
  Kinaesthetic: Practical using plants.
  Visual: Checking leaves for symptoms.
  Auditory: Taking part in the Greenfingers/Blackfingers game.
  Interpersonal: Evaluation of evidence from growth experiments.
  Intrapersonal: Writing a report of findings from comparing plants.
- **ICT link-up.** Look up 'Plant mineral deficiencies' on the Internet. Reddy, T.Y. and Reddi, G.H.S. produced a good identification chart for deficiency symptoms (1997). Some good pictures of mineral-deficient tomato plants are also available.

SPECIFICATION LINK-UP   Unit: Biology 2.11.3

- *Plant roots absorb mineral salts including nitrate needed for healthy growth. For healthy growth, plants need mineral ions including:*
  - *nitrate – for producing amino acids that are then used to form proteins.*
  - *magnesium – which is needed for chlorophyll production.*
- *The symptoms shown by plants growing in conditions where mineral ions are deficient include:*
  - *stunted growth if nitrate ions are deficient.*
  - *yellow leaves if magnesium ions are deficient.*

Lesson structure

STARTER

Why do we need these? – Show images of a tractor and fertiliser spreader, together with some packets of lawn fertiliser and Baby Bio or similar. (Search the web for 'fertiliser spreader' or 'lawn fertiliser'.) Ask the students to attempt to explain why these products are used. (5–10 minutes)

What is the connection? – Burn some magnesium tape (risk assess – wear eye protection and protect eyes from glare – CLEAPSS Hazcard 59). Open a bag of crisps (to release the nitrogen they are filled with to prevent oxidation). Show students a large houseplant, as big and as gaudy as possible. Ask for the connection between the three things. (10 minutes)

MAIN

- **Investigating the effect of minerals** – Provide three specimens of tomato plants per group: one plant in good condition having had all the nutrients it needs, one short of nitrogen (grown in peat rather than potting compost; add a pinch of magnesium sulphate to the water at intervals so that it does not show symptoms of magnesium deficiency) and one grown in magnesium-deficient conditions.
- If providing the plants is a problem, large coloured photographs (laminated for future use) could be provided.
- Ask students to examine and tabulate the differences. Apart from the obvious deficiency symptoms, they could measure leaves, height etc. Lead a discussion and ask the students to draw conclusions.
- **Hydroponics** – Students could then set up their own sets of plants using water culture (hydroponics). Broad bean or cereal seedlings could be used and grown in small flasks or bottles (root development can also be observed in this way). The seedlings should all be at the same stage of growth, as the plants need to grow. This is a good experiment for introducing the concepts of 'How Science Works'. Hypotheses can be formulated, predictions made, variables considered and controlled, and measurements taken. The cultures need to be aerated at intervals and the containers covered to prevent the growth of photosynthetic algae. It is possible to use duckweed in a water culture experiment. It has the advantage of growing more quickly and the growth can be assessed by the number of leaves produced. It will also show the deficiency symptoms.
- **Where does the nitrate come from?** – Draw out the sequence of events from nitrogen in the air (remind the students of the percentage) to the protein in plants. You can start with the nitrates in the soil as the centre of a spider diagram or flow chart. This can be accompanied by a modelling activity of 'Pass the N'.

PLENARIES

PowerPoint® – Show the main learning points of the lesson with blanks to complete. (5 minutes)

Greenfingers club and Blackfingers club – Give out coloured hands – in pairs, one student (Greenfingers) to give instructions as to how to get the plant to grow really well including nutrient reference, with reasons. The other (Blackfingers) is to give instructions as to how to get the plant to wither horribly and develop ghastly symptoms, with reasons including nutrient reference. (10 minutes)

- **Root nodules of legumes** – Dig up some leguminous plants (peas, beans, clover) and wash the roots carefully. The root nodules should be obvious. Allow students to examine these and then discuss the relationship between the nitrogen-fixing bacteria and the crop. Link to the nitrogen cycle and crop rotation.
- **Other mineral ions** – Water culture experiments could include plants grown in solutions deficient in other mineral ions such as iron, phosfate etc. There are water culture tablets available to make up the appropriate solutions.
- **Do plants recover?** – Try giving some fertiliser, such as Baby Bio, to plants that have been grown in mineral-deficient conditions. Students can find out if they lose their symptoms and grow to become healthy plants. (They could try this activity at home.)
- **What is in the fertilisers?** – Students to investigate the components of the lawn fertiliser and Baby Bio and any other fertilisers, by looking at the boxes or containers. This will introduce the idea of commercial fertilisers not just containing one mineral ion, especially if the need for other mineral ions is demonstrated in the water culture experiments.

Practical support

Equipment and materials required

Investigating the effect of minerals

Tomato plants in pots, culture solutions lacking magnesium and nitrate.

Hydroponics

Small flasks or bottles, culture solutions lacking magnesium and nitrate, an aquarium aerator, kitchen foil to cover flasks or bottles.

Answers to in-text questions

a) Carbohydrates/glucose/sugars/starch.

b) To make proteins.

c) To make chlorophyll.

B2 2.4   Why do plants need minerals?

LEARNING OBJECTIVES

1 What happens if plants don't get enough nitrates?

2 Why do fertilisers make your vegetables grow so well?

Figure 1 The plants on the left of this picture have been grown in a mixture containing all the minerals they need. The experimental plants on the right have been grown without nitrates. The difference in their rate of growth is clear to see.

If you put a plant in a pot of water, and give it plenty of light and carbon dioxide, it won't survive for very long! Although plants can make their own food by photosynthesis, they cannot survive long on photosynthesis alone.

Just as you need minerals and vitamins for healthy growth, so plants need more than simply carbon dioxide, water and light to thrive. They need mineral salts from the soil to make the chemicals needed in their cells.

Why do plants need nitrates?

The problem with the products of photosynthesis is that they are all carbohydrates. Carbohydrates are very important. Plants use them for energy, for storage and even for structural features like cell walls. However, a plant can't function without proteins as well. It needs proteins to act as enzymes and to make up a large part of the cytoplasm and the membranes.

a) What are the products of photosynthesis?

Glucose and starch are made up of carbon, hydrogen and oxygen. Proteins are made up of amino acids which contain carbon, hydrogen, oxygen and **nitrogen**. Plants need **nitrates** from the soil to make proteins.

These nitrates, dissolved in water, are taken up from the soil by the plant roots. If a plant is deficient in nitrates (doesn't have enough) it doesn't grow properly. It is small and stunted. So nitrates are necessary for healthy growth.

When plants die and decay the nitrates and other minerals are returned to the soil to be used by other plants.

b) Why do plants need nitrates?

Why do plants need magnesium?

It isn't only nitrates that plants need to grow well. There is a whole range of *mineral ions* they need. For example, plants need **magnesium** to make chlorophyll.

Chlorophyll is vital to plants. It is chlorophyll which absorbs the energy from light which makes it possible for plants to photosynthesise. So if the plant can't make chlorophyll, it can't make food and it will die. This is why magnesium ions are so important for plants – they make up part of the chlorophyll molecule.

Plants only need a tiny amount of magnesium. However, if they don't get enough, they have pale, yellowish areas on their leaves where they cannot make chlorophyll.

c) Why do plants need magnesium ions?

If any of the mineral salts that a plant needs are missing it will begin to look very sickly. This is true in the garden and for houseplants just as much as for crops in a farmer's field.

PRACTICAL

Investigating the effect of minerals

You can grow young plants in water containing different combinations of minerals and see the effect on their growth.

- Why are some plants grown in water with no minerals added and some with all the minerals they need?

Figure 2 The leaf on the right came from a plant that had received all the minerals it needed. The plant on the left was grown without magnesium. It is easy to see which is which – just look for the yellow patches!

If there are not enough mineral ions in the soil, your plants cannot grow properly. They will show the symptoms of mineral deficiencies. If you can pick up the symptoms soon enough and give them the mineral ions that they need, all will be well. If not, your plants will die!

Mineral ion	Why needed?	Deficiency symptoms
nitrate	making protein	stunted growth
magnesium	making chlorophyll	pale, yellow leaves

The most recent development in growing crops is **hydroponics**. You don't plant your crops in soil. Instead you plant them in water to which you add the minerals your plants need to grow as well as possible.

Hydroponic crops are usually grown in massive greenhouses where all the other factors can be controlled as well. Everything is monitored and controlled by computers 24 hours a day. The crops are very clean – no mud on the roots! And you can grow crops very quickly, and even out of their usual season.

All this means you get a good price for them. The downside is that it is an expensive way to farm, and it uses a lot of resources.

SUMMARY QUESTIONS

1 a) Why do plants need mineral ions?
   b) Where do they get mineral ions from?
   c) Which mineral ion is needed by plants to form proteins?

2 a) Look at the plants in Figure 1. Describe how the plants grown without nitrates differ from the plants grown with all the mineral ions they need. Why are they so different?
   b) Look at the plants in Figure 2. Describe how the plants grown without magnesium differ from the plants grown with all the mineral ions they need. Why are they so different?

3 Explain the following in terms of the mineral ions needed by plants and how they are used in the cells:
   a) Farmers spread animal manure on their fields.
   b) Gardeners recommend giving houseplants a regular mineral feed containing nitrates and magnesium ions.
   c) If the same type of crop is grown in the same place every year it will gradually grow less well and becomes stunted, with pale, patchy leaves.

GET IT RIGHT!

Make sure you know the roles of nitrate and magnesium ions – and the deficiency symptoms of each of them.

Figure 3 If you are a farmer you harvest the crops that you grow and sell them. They are not left to die and decay naturally, returning minerals to the soil. So farmers add fertiliser to the soil to replace the minerals lost, ready for the next crop. The fertiliser may be a natural one like manure or an artificial mixture of the minerals that plants need to grow

KEY POINTS

1 Plant roots absorb mineral salts including nitrate needed for healthy growth.

2 Nitrates and magnesium are two important mineral ions needed for healthy plant growth.

3 If mineral ions are deficient, a plant develops symptoms because it cannot grow properly.

SUMMARY ANSWERS

1 a) To make the chemicals in their cells, such as proteins and chlorophyll.
  b) The water in the soil.
  c) Nitrate.

2 a) They are smaller and more stunted than the plants with everything. Nitrates are needed to make the amino acids that form proteins for enzymes and cell structure. Without nitrates they cannot make proteins properly so they cannot grow properly either.
  b) Their leaves have pale, yellowy patches compared to healthy plants. Magnesium is needed to make the green chemical chlorophyll. Without magnesium it cannot make enough chlorophyll so the leaves are not completely green.

3 a) Farmers harvest crops. They are not left to die and decay naturally, returning minerals to the soil. So farmers add fertiliser to the soil to replace the minerals lost, ready for the next crop.
  b) Houseplants are usually in pots with limited soil and so have a limited supply of minerals. Regular feeding makes sure they do not use up all the minerals they need e.g. nitrates for amino acid/protein production and magnesium as part of chlorophyll molecule.
  c) The same type of plant always takes up the same minerals so growing in the same soil each year, the minerals will become depleted. Plants show signs of mineral deficiencies, such as lack of nitrogen (stunted) and lack of magnesium (pale leaves).

KEY POINTS

Students must make sure they know why plants need nitrates and magnesium, and what the plants look like if they do not get enough of these minerals. Growing the plants or looking at good pictures of plants showing symptoms of the deficiencies will help students to remember the facts.

B2 2.5

Plant problems?

BIOLOGY   HOW PLANTS PRODUCE FOOD

B2 2.5   Plant problems?

SPECIFICATION LINK-UP

Unit: Biology 2.11.3

Students should use their skills, knowledge and understanding of 'How Science Works':

- *To interpret data showing how factors affect the rate of photosynthesis and evaluate the benefits of artificially manipulating the environment in which plants are grown.*

Teaching suggestions

The following suggestions are based on the material in the spread and ways in which it can be linked with the topics in the chapter. Much of this would be valuable background to gaining an understanding of present-day agriculture and could help students in carrying out the suggested activity.

- **Small-holder** – Using the material provided in the student book as a start, students could investigate the nature of small farms. Historically, many farms were worked in a similar manner with animals being raised and a variety of crops grown. In many parts of the world, farming is still carried out in this way. The methods that were, and still are, practised have a scientific foundation, but it is obvious from the passage that this type of farming does not make enough profit. Using knowledge from the chapter and by doing some research, students could find answers to the following questions:
  - What were the benefits of growing different crops every year?
  - Why were crops rotated?
  - What were the benefits of allowing the land to be rested between crops?
  - What are the pros and cons of using manure from the animals?
  - What are the disadvantages of small-holdings in the modern world?

  Hold a brainstorming session and list as many reasons as you can think of why such methods of farming are no longer economical.

- **The great organic debate** – One way in which farmers can make small farms pay is to become an 'organic' farm. Students could find out what it takes to become an organic farmer and what the advantages and disadvantages are. For information about organic farming and crop rotation go to www.soilassociation.org or www.rhs.org.uk.

- **Arable farming** – The modern trend in farming is for monoculture: farms on which one or possibly two crops are

Smallholder

'In days gone by most farms were small. Farmers fed their own families and hoped to make enough profit to survive. Different crops had to be grown each year (crop rotation) and the land was rested between crops. Fields lay fallow (no crops were grown) every few years to let the land recover. Manure from their own animals was the main fertiliser.'

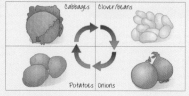

'We're trying to stick to the old ways on our little small-holding. We rotate our crops – you can see from my field plan how I do it. It helps to make sure that the minerals in the soil don't all get used up. It helps keep diseases at bay too.'

'We feed our family well, and sell our extra produce to the village shop. Of course, I earn most of my money through my computer business.'

Arable farmer

'We farm a pretty big area. I grow wheat and oil seed rape. After we have harvested, I plough the stubble back into the soil. We used to burn it off but that's not allowed now. I think it's better to plough the stuff in anyway – puts something back!'

'My farm is a big business – I can't afford to have land doing nothing. So we add fertiliser to keep the mineral levels right. We need to get the best crop we can every time! Modern fertilisers mean I can plant one crop straight after the other, and I avoid fallow years altogether.'

'I have to get the balance right – if I spend too much on fertiliser, I don't make enough profit. But if I don't put enough fertiliser on the fields, I don't grow enough crops! I manage to support the family pretty well with the farm, and we employ one local man as well.'

grown. These large farms have often arisen by the amalgamation of smaller farms. Students could consider the following consequences of monoculture:

- the destruction of hedgerows
- the effect of the use of artificial fertilisers on soil structure
- the leaching of the fertilisers through the soil and into waterways
- the problems of disease and the use of pesticides.

- **Hydroponics grower** – This system of growing plants has its advantages and its disadvantages, and raises many questions. In order to appreciate what such systems involve, students could investigate and discuss the following issues:
  - Is the system appropriate for growing all crops? They could draw up a list of crops for which this system seems suited and another list of crops which could be difficult to grow in this way.
  - Why would carbon dioxide levels need to be changed during the day?
  - What are the advantages of being able to control the temperature and light levels?
  - Why is it necessary to alter the mineral content of the water as the plants grow?

- Hydroponics systems are expensive to set up. Ask students to compile a list of ways in which such systems save money and balance it with a list of items that the grower has to budget for (apart from the initial cost of setting up the system).

Hydroponics grower

'In the laboratory you can isolate different factors and see how they limit the rate of photosynthesis. However, for most plants a mixture of these factors affects them. Early in the morning, light levels and temperature probably limit the rate of photosynthesis. Then as the level of light and the temperature rise, the carbon dioxide becomes limiting. On a bright, cold winter day, temperature probably limits the rate of the process. There is a constant interaction between the different factors.

'In commercial greenhouses we can take advantage of this knowledge of limiting factors and leave nothing to chance. We can control the temperature and the levels of light and carbon dioxide to get the fastest possible rates of photosynthesis. This makes sure our plants grow as quickly as possible. We even grow our plants in a nutritionally balanced solution rather than soil to make sure nothing limits their rate of photosynthesis and growth.'

By controlling the temperature, light and carbon dioxide levels in a greenhouse like this we can produce the biggest possible crops – fast!

'We invested in all the computer software and control systems about two years ago. It cost us a lot of money – but we are really reaping the benefits. We can change the carbon dioxide levels in the greenhouses during the day. We control the temperature and the light levels very carefully. What's more we can change the mineral content of the water as the plants grow and get bigger.

'We sell all our stuff to one of the big supermarket chains. Our lettuces are always clean, big and crisp – and we have a really fast turnover. No more ploughing fields for us!

'Of course we don't need as many staff now. We just have lots of alarm systems in our house. Then if anything goes wrong in one of the greenhouses, day or night, we know about it straight away. The monitoring systems and computers are vital to our way of growing. As far as our plants are concerned, limiting factors are a thing of the past!'

ACTIVITY

The National Farmers Union (NFU) wants to produce a resource for schools to show how arable (crop) farming has changed over the years. Your job is to design *either* one large poster *or* a series of smaller posters that they can send out free to science departments in schools around the country.
You need to explain how plants grow, and how farmers give them what they need to grow as well as possible. Use the information on this spread and in the rest of the chapter to help you.

25

- If possible, arrange a visit to a hydroponics system or investigate the ways in which small hydroponics systems can be set up in glasshouses.

- Discuss the advantages of hydroponics systems being set up where it would be difficult to grow crops conventionally.

Special needs

Students can be given, or encouraged to collect, pictures of farm machinery from different times and make a poster, showing how cultivation of the land has changed.

ACTIVITY & EXTENSION

- The poster activity under 'Special needs' is open-ended and offers scope for a number of different approaches:
  - The cultivation of one particular crop could be charted. For example, wheat was grown in the Middle East many centuries ago and the development of the bread wheats we have today can be traced. The formation of large fields from smaller ones and the increasing mechanisation, using larger and larger tractors, could be depicted.

Wheat was part of a crop rotation at one time, but development of artificial fertilisers meant that the same crop could be grown year after year. Some of the latest developments involve the breeding of shorter-stemmed varieties that are easier to harvest and produce less straw.

- The approach could be more general and show how crop growing has changed from medieval times (strip farming and the use of manure as fertiliser) to the present day (vast fields and artificial fertilisers).

- The emphasis could be on the types of crop grown. Ask the students: 'Have they changed over the years? Are we growing different crops from our ancestors?' They need to think about when the potato arrived in Britain. Much land is now producing crops such as oil seed rape and not the traditional root crops that were produced before. Ask: 'Why is this?'

- **Growing crops in outer space** – Is hydroponics the answer to growing crops on the Moon or on spaceships? Students might like to debate this and consider whether or not it is feasible. Ask: 'What sorts of things could be grown? Would it work?'

- **The effects of climate change** – There has been much speculation about the effects of climate change on the nature of crops that can be grown in different parts of the world. Students to consider: 'If the climate in Britain becomes warmer, what different crops might be grown? Would it be possible to grow more than one crop of tomatoes a year?'

- **How the field patterns have changed** – It may be possible to obtain aerial or other photographs of your local area that show how the fields have changed. Good sources of such information are local history museums and the archives of local newspapers.

- **Use simulation** – If not used previously in the chapter, use the Simulation, B2 2.2 'Limiting Factors of Photosynthesis' available on the Additional Science CD ROM.

SUMMARY ANSWERS

1 a) A4; B3; C2; D5; E1.

b) carbon dioxide + water (+ light energy) → glucose + oxygen

c) Starch.

2 a) [Credit accurately drawn graphs, correctly plotted points and correctly labelled axes, etc.]

b) Plants growing in the higher light intensity photosynthesise more and faster, so produce food and grow well. Light will not be a limiting factor, but carbon dioxide or temperature might. Light is a limiting factor in those plants grown at the lower light intensities.

3 a) Leaves.

b) Roots.

c) Xylem.

d) Phloem.

e) Xylem.

Summary teaching suggestions

- **Lower and higher level answers**

  There are different styles of question that test higher attaining students.

  - For example, the graph plotting exercise in question 2 and its explanation is a good discriminator. The higher attaining students should be able to include all the points given. Some students might use the figures, or some manipulation of them, to back up their answers.

- **Special needs**

  - Students could be given the words and descriptions for question 1 on sheets of paper and asked to match them up.
  - In question 2, if the graph was already plotted for them, they could answer the question verbally.
  - Question 3a) to e) could also be used if the one word answers were on cards for them to select and hold up.

- **Homework** – Question 2 would be a good homework exercise as a follow-up to the spread on limiting factors.

- **When to use the questions?** – Questions requiring short answers are useful to reinforce the content of a lesson, e.g. question 1 on photosynthesis and question 3.

SUMMARY QUESTIONS

1 a) Match each word related to photosynthesis to its description:

A	Carbon dioxide gas	1	...... is produced and released into the air
B	Water	2	......provides energy
C	Sunlight	3	...... from the roots moves up to the leaf through the stem
D	Glucose	4	...... is absorbed from the air
E	Oxygen	5	...... is made in the leaf and provides the plant with food

b) Write a word equation for photosynthesis.

c) Much of the glucose made in photosynthesis is turned into an insoluble storage compound. What is this compound?

2

Year	Mean height of seedlings grown in 85% full sunlight (cm)	Mean height of seedlings grown in 35% full sunlight (cm)
2000	12	10
2001	16	12.5
2002	18	14
2003	23	17
2004	28	20
2005	35	21
2006	36	23

The figures in the table show the mean growth of two sets of oak seedlings. One set was grown in 85% full sunlight, the other set in only 35% full sunlight.

a) Plot a graph to show the growth of both sets of oak seedlings.

b) Using what you know about photosynthesis and limiting factors, explain the difference in the growth of the two sets of seedlings.

3 Plants make food in one organ and take up water from the soil in another organ. But both the food and the water are needed all over the plant.

a) Where do plants make their food?

b) Where do plants take in water?

c) There are two transport tissues in a plant. One is the phloem. What is the other one?

d) Which transport tissue carries food around the plant?

e) Which transport tissue carries water around the plant?

EXAM-STYLE QUESTIONS

1 Jenny carried out an investigation to show the rate of photosynthesis in two species of plant at different light intensities.

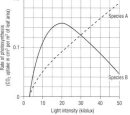

This investigation had two independent variables.

(a) Name the categoric independent variable. (1)

(b) Name the continuous independent variable. (1)

(c) Describe the pattern shown by species B. (3)
The results for species B were as follows:

Light intensity (kilolux)	CO₂ uptake (cm³/m²)
5	0.04
10	0.11
20	0.15
30	0.125
40	0.09
50	0.04

(d) Jenny was not sure where the peak of the graph should be drawn. Which extra measurements should she take to be sure of this? (1)

(e) At what light intensity do both species photosynthesise at the same rate? (1)

(f) If species A has a total leaf area of 100 m², how many cm³ of carbon dioxide will it take up at a light intensity of 10 kilolux? Show your working. (2)

(g) Which species shows the best adaptation to shade conditions? Using the information in the graph give reasons for your answer. (2)

EXAM-STYLE ANSWERS

1 a) Types of species *(1 mark)*

b) Light intensity *(1 mark)*

c) Rapid increase in rate of photosynthesis *(1 mark)*
up to a light intensity of 20 kilolux *(1 mark)*
slower decrease in rate (up to 50 kilolux) *(1 mark)*

d) Any reasonable spread around 20 kilolux *(1 mark)*

e) 30 kilolux *(1 mark)*
Both the figure and the units are required. It is important that students always give units when expressing values.

f) Reading from the graph, at 10 kilolux, there are 0.05 cm³ of carbon dioxide absorbed per m² leaf area.
i.e. 1 m² of leaf takes up 0.05 cm³ of carbon dioxide.
Therefore 100 m² of leaf will take up 0.05 × 100 cm³ of carbon dioxide.
i.e. 5 cm³.
2 marks for correct answer and accurate working.
1 mark for correct answer but no working shown, or so little working shown that it is impossible to see how the answer was arrived at.
1 mark for the wrong answer but correct working, e.g. student misreads the value from the graph but answer is consistent with a correct calculation.

g) Species B shows the best adaptation to shade conditions because:
Either In the shade the light intensity is lower than out of the shade/in the sun *(1 mark)*
and the rate of photosynthesis in species B is greater than that of species A at lower light intensities. *(1 mark)*
Or The light intensity is less in the shade than out of it/in the sun *(1 mark)*
and the maximum rate of photosynthesis of species B occurs at 20 kilolux – a much lower light intensity than the 50 kilolux that produces the maximum rate of photosynthesis for species A. *(1 mark)*

(h) What is the name of the sugar produced during photosynthesis? (1)

(i) What is the name of the process by which this sugar is broken down to provide energy for the plant? (1)

2   The diagram below represents a section through a plant leaf showing the arrangement of cells as seen under a microscope.

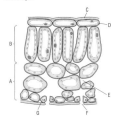

(a) Name the parts labelled **E**, **F** and **G**. (3)

(b) Give one function of the parts labelled
  (i) **C**
  (ii) **G** (2)

(c) List the four letters that indicate structures that contain chloroplasts. (4)

(d) The diagram shows only a small section through a leaf. State **FOUR** ways in which the **whole leaf** is adapted to carry out photosynthesis. In each case show how this feature helps the plant to carry out photosynthesis. (8)

3   Plants need to obtain mineral salts in order to survive.

(a) Name two mineral salts that are essential to plants and in each case give a reason why they are needed. (4)

(b) How do plants obtain the minerals they need? (2)

(c) If crops are grown for long periods on the same piece of land, they may use up some of the minerals in the soil. State two ways in which farmers can avoid these crops dying due to lack of minerals. (2)

HOW SCIENCE WORKS QUESTIONS

Water gardens – or rather hydroponics!

Ed had seen some entrepreneurs make a fortune by growing lettuce in the middle of winter. He wanted some of the action! He knew that he would have to provide heat and light as well as the nutrients and the correct pH. He knew that the plants required water and oxygen to their roots.

None of the books told him how often he should water the lettuce. Water them too often and they would not get enough oxygen. Leave them too long without watering and they would dry out. He decided on an investigation.

Ed set up five different trays and buckets. He set the timer differently for each tray. The lettuce would now be watered for a different number of times each day. He could therefore work out which was the best for his lettuce.

a) Suggest some time intervals for Ed to water his lettuce. (1)
b) Suggest a dependent variable he could measure. (1)
c) Explain why you have chosen this variable. (1)
d) Describe how Ed might measure this dependent variable. (1)
e) Suggest three control variables he should use. (3)
f) Explain why it would be sensible for Ed to repeat his results. (2)

Ed's first set of results showed very little difference. It did not seem to matter how often he watered them.

g) Suggest a problem he had with the design of his investigation. (1)
h) Why was it important that Ed did his own research and not ask advice from those already growing the lettuce? (2)

27

---

3   a) Nitrate *(1 mark)*
      to produce amino acids/proteins *(1 mark)*
      Magnesium *(1 mark)*
      to make chlorophyll *(1 mark)*

   b) Minerals are found in the soil solution/dissolved in water in the soil and are absorbed by the roots of the plant *(1 mark)*
      by diffusion/active transport. *(1 mark)*

   c) By crop rotation/growing a different crop on the land each year. *(1 mark)*
      Adding fertiliser/spreading manure/muck on the land. *(1 mark)*

Exam teaching suggestions

- Reading values from graphs (question 1 part f) is a common, and relatively straightforward, exercise in examinations. One potential pitfall however is the omission of the relevant units when writing the answer. This could cost marks. If students need convincing of the need to provide units, ask them to imagine they asked someone how far it was to the nearest shop and received the reply 'twenty'.

HOW SCIENCE WORKS ANSWERS

a) Any reasonable time interval – from every 2 hours to every 12 hours.

b) Examples of dependent variable that could be measured include: height of lettuces, wet mass of lettuce.

c) Must refer to answer in b) and be related to marketable part of the plant.

d) Depends on variable chosen – describes how marketable part of plant is measured, e.g. ruler or electric balance.

e) Control variables that should be used are: volume of water, concentration of nutrients, light levels, type of lettuce, spacing.

f) More reliable than using just one lettuce but a larger sample size would further improve the reliability of the data collected.

g) e.g. poor range chosen.

h) Any advice might have been biased – they are his competitors.

How science works teaching suggestions

- **Literacy guidance**
  - Key terms that should be clearly understood: dependent variable, control variable, bias, interval measurements.
  - Question d) expects a longer answer, where students can practise their literacy skills.

- **Higher- and lower-level answers.** Questions b) and c) are higher level questions. The answers for these have been provided at this level. Question a) is a lower-level question and the answer provided is also lower level.

- **Gifted and talented.** Able students could consider the dependent variable in terms of marketable produce. They could be asked to consider all of the possible control variables and how those that cannot be controlled might be monitored.

- **How and when to use these questions.** When wishing to develop ideas about interval measurements and bias in reporting results. The questions could be small group discussion work.

- **Homework.** The questions could also be set for homework.

- **Special needs.** Photographs of hydroponic glasshouses should be used to explain the process.

There are no marks for simply giving the correct species. With a choice of only two there is a 50% chance of arriving at this answer by guesswork alone.
To gain both marks, the student should demonstrate that light intensity is low in the shade (or conversely that it is high in the sun).

h) Glucose *(1 mark)*

i) Respiration *(1 mark)*

2   a) **E** air space

       F stoma/stomata

       G guard cell *(1 mark each)*

   b) i) C – prevents water loss/reduces transpiration *(1 mark)*
      ii) G – controls the movement of gases into and out of the leaf/opens and closes the stomata to allow gases in and out. *(1 mark)*

       *For G (guard cell) the important thing is for candidates to convey the idea of **controlling** the gases going in and out. Responses such as 'open and close stomata' are acceptable as there is some semblance of control in this expression, but 'allows gases in and out' is inadequate as this is a function of the stomata rather than the guard cells.*

   c) A, B, D and G. *(1 mark each)*

   d)
Feature of leaf	**How it affects photosynthesis**
• Large surface area	to collect/capture as much light as possible
• Contains chloroplasts/ chlorophyll	to absorb light energy (and make sugars/glucose)
• Many air spaces	to allow CO_2 and O_2 to diffuse/move around the leaf
• Has veins	to bring water to/remove glucose from the leaf cells

1 mark for each correct feature and 1 mark for each explanation.

B2 3.1

Pyramids of biomass

LEARNING OBJECTIVES

Students should learn that:

- Solar radiation is the source of energy for all communities of living organisms.
- Green plants capture solar energy to build up energy stores in their cells.
- The biomass at each stage in a food chain is less than it was at the previous stage.

LEARNING OUTCOMES

Most students should be able to:

- Explain where biomass comes from.
- Describe what a pyramid of biomass is and how it can be constructed.
- Interpret pyramids of biomass and construct them from appropriate information.

Some students should also be able to:

- Explain that all the biomass at one stage does not get passed on to the next stage.

Teaching suggestions

- **Special needs.** Students could be provided with the components of a food chain written on cards, which they can put in the correct order. Similarly, they can build up pyramids of biomass if provided with the components.
- **Gifted and talented.** Students to consider whether or not pyramids of biomass tell the whole story. They could write a short paragraph on what the pyramid of biomass does tell us about the relationships between the organisms.
- **Learning styles**
  Kinaesthetic: Carrying out the experiments.
  Visual: Examining the animals and plants.
  Auditory: Listening to instructions about practical exercises.
  Interpersonal: Discussing food chains and pyramids.
  Intrapersonal: Interpreting the results.
- **Homework.** Both questions 2 and 3 of the 'Summary questions' would make good homework exercises.
- **ICT link-up.** Use the Simulation, B2 3.1 'Pyramids of Biomass', available on the Additional Science CD ROM.

SPECIFICATION LINK-UP   Unit: Biology 2.11.4

- *Radiation from the Sun is the source of energy for most communities of living organisms. Green plants capture a small part of the solar energy which reaches them. This energy is stored in the substances which make up the cells of the plants.*
- *The mass of living material (biomass) at each stage in a food chain is less than it was at the previous stage. The biomass at each stage can be drawn to scale and shown as a pyramid of biomass.*

Lesson structure

STARTER

What am I? – Prepare definitions of key words and phrases related to the topic, such as 'producer', 'consumer', 'herbivore', 'carnivore', 'detritivore', etc.; read out or project the key words and phrases only on to the board. Students write their definitions, and then you check through. (5–10 minutes)

Food chains in the school canteen – Check out the menu for lunch and get students to discuss the food chains related to items on the menu. (5–10 minutes)

MAIN

- **Investigation of leaf litter** – Using a known mass or volume of leaf litter, allows students to sort through it by hand and separate out the soil organisms into containers. It is unwise to mix organisms in case they eat each other! This sorting should remove the larger organisms, but it might be necessary to use a Tullgren funnel to find the smaller invertebrates.
- The organisms should be identified as far as possible, counted and all those of one species weighed. It should be possible to classify most families of invertebrates into different feeding types (herbivore, carnivore or detritivore). It is then easy to add up the total numbers and the total masses for the different feeding types.
- Both a pyramid of numbers and a pyramid of biomass can be constructed and compared. Students can construct these pyramids on squared paper, choosing suitable scales.
- **Pyramids of biomass for different communities** – Data can be obtained from different communities, such as a rocky shore, in woodland or open grassland.
- **A pond or freshwater habitat** – The method described in 'Practical support' can be modified to obtain a rough estimate of the biomass in a pond or stream. Sampling in water requires the use of a net and the technique needs to be standardised.
  - In flowing water, kick sampling is carried out over a certain area (0.5m²) and the disturbed organisms are allowed to flow into a net. The net can be emptied into sampling trays and the organisms identified, grouped and their wet mass determined.
  - In still water, a sweeping technique is used. The net is swept through the water for a fixed period of time or over a fixed distance. The organisms caught are then tipped into a sampling tray and identified as before.
- Further details of the methods can be found in *Tools, Techniques and Assessment in Biology,* Adds, Larkcom, Miller and Sutton (Nelson Advanced Modular Science series). The Field Studies Council publishes excellent identification guides for plants and animals in the Aidgap series. Follow local guidelines on 'Outside Activities'.

PLENARIES

Numbers or biomass? – Students could compare a pyramid of numbers with a pyramid of biomass. The example given in the Student Book could be used or they could discuss one that they have produced from their own investigations. Ask: 'Which shows the information more accurately? Are there advantages in using numbers?' (5–10 minutes)

Anagrams with a difference – Prepare anagrams of the key words, but leave out the vowels. Show these on to the board and ask the students to work out what they are. (5–10 minutes)

Biomass is . . . – Students to complete this sentence and then to judge each other's sentences and add refinements. This could end up with a 'class' definition. (5–10 minutes)

Practical support

Investigation of leaf litter

Equipment and materials required

Quadrats, sweep nets, pooters, sorting trays and small beakers, identification keys, Tullgren funnel (see *Tools, Techniques and Assessment in Biology* (Nelson Advanced Modular Science series for details), balance for weighing organisms.

Details

The method is essentially the same for the different habitats and the results can be expressed as biomass per m². (Cover any open wounds on hands and wash hands after the investigation).

- Select an area and place a 1 m² or 0.5 m² square quadrat carefully on to the ground.
- Collect the leaf litter within the quadrat or cut the plants at the base and place in a white tray.
- Search carefully and remove all the animals present. Smaller animals can be removed using a pooter, larger ones with forceps.
- Animals should be placed in suitable containers, such as plastic beakers.
- Weigh the plant material.
- Identify and sort the animals into groups.
- Weigh the groups of animals separately.
- Return the animals to their habitat.
- Construct a pyramid of biomass.

Additional biology

BIOLOGY ENERGY FLOWS

B2 3.1 Pyramids of biomass

LEARNING OBJECTIVES

1 Where does biomass come from?
2 What is a pyramid of biomass?

As you saw in the previous chapter, radiation from the Sun is the source of energy for all the groups of living things on Earth.

Light energy pours out continually onto the surface of the Earth. Green plants capture a small part of this light energy using chlorophyll. It is used in photosynthesis. So some of the energy from the Sun is stored in the substances which make up the cells of the plant. This new plant material adds to the biomass.

Biomass is the mass of living material in an animal or plant. Ultimately all biomass is built up using energy from the Sun. Biomass is often measured as the dry mass of biological material in grams.

DID YOU KNOW?

Only about 1% of all the Sun's energy falling on the Earth is used by plants for photosynthesis!

a) What is the source of all the energy in the living things on Earth?

The energy in the biomass made by plants is passed on through food chains or food webs into the animals which eat the plants. It then passes on into the animals which eat other animals. No matter how long the food chain or complex the food web, the original source of all the biomass involved is energy from the Sun.

When you look at a food chain, there are usually more producers than primary consumers, and more primary consumers than secondary consumers. If you count the number of organisms at each level you can compare them. You can show this using a **pyramid of numbers**. However, in many cases a pyramid of numbers does not accurately reflect what is happening.

b) What is a pyramid of numbers?

Pyramids of biomass

Figure 1 Plants produce a huge mass of biological material in just one growing season

To show what is happening in food chains more accurately we can use biomass. We can draw the total amount of biomass in the living organisms at each stage of the food chain to scale and show it as a pyramid of biomass.

Figure 2 This food chain cannot be accurately represented using a pyramid of numbers. Using biomass shows us the amount of biological material involved at each level in a way that simple numbers cannot do.

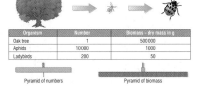

Organism	Number	Biomass – dry mass in g
Oak tree	1	500 000
Aphids	10 000	1000
Ladybirds	200	50

Pyramid of numbers   Pyramid of biomass

c) What is a pyramid of biomass?

Interpreting pyramids of biomass

The biomass found at each stage of a food chain is less than it was at the previous stage.

This is because:

- Not all organisms at one stage are eaten by the stage above.
- Some material taken in is passed out as waste.
- When a herbivore eats a plant, it turns some of the plant material into new herbivore. But much of the biomass from the plant is used by the herbivore in respiration to release energy for living. It does not get passed on to the carnivore when the herbivore is eaten.

So at each stage of a food chain the amount of energy in the biomass which is passed on gets less. A large amount of plant biomass supports a smaller amount of herbivore biomass. This in turn supports an even smaller amount of carnivore biomass.

In general, pyramids of biomass are drawn in proportion. Sometimes, when the biomass of one type of organism is much, much bigger than the others, this doesn't work and so the diagram can only give a rough idea.

Figure 3 Any food chain can be turned into a pyramid of biomass like this

GET IT RIGHT!

Make sure you can draw pyramids of biomass when you are given the data.

GET IT RIGHT!

Make sure you can work out the proportions of the different organisms by looking at a pyramid of biomass.

SUMMARY QUESTIONS

1 a) What is biomass?
   b) Why is a pyramid of biomass more useful for showing what is happening in a food chain than a pyramid of numbers?

2

Organism	Biomass, dry mass (g)
Grass	100 000
Sheep	5000
Sheep ticks	30

   a) Draw a pyramid of biomass for this grassland ecosystem.
   b) What would you expect the pyramid of numbers for this food chain to look like?
   c) Draw the pyramids of numbers and the pyramids of biomass you would expect from the following two food chains:
      i) stinging nettles → caterpillars → robin
      ii) marine plants → small fish → large fish → seals → polar bear

3 a) Explain simply why the biomass from one stage of a pyramid of biomass does not all become biomass in the next stage of the pyramid.
   b) Using the data in Figure 2, calculate the percentage biomass passed on from:
      i) the producers to the primary consumers,
      ii) the primary consumers to the secondary consumers.

KEY POINTS

1 Radiation from the Sun is the main source of energy for all living things. The Sun's energy is captured and used by plants during photosynthesis.
2 The mass of living material at each stage of a food chain is less than at the previous stage. The biomass at each stage can be drawn to scale and shown as a pyramid of biomass.

SUMMARY ANSWERS

1 a) The mass of living material in an animal or a plant.
   b) Because it shows what is happening more accurately.

2 a) [Mark for accurately drawn pyramid.]
   b) Drawn correctly it should have a large base, one sheep in the middle and more ticks at the top.
   c) [Each drawn correctly as pyramids.]

3 a) Not all organisms at one stage are eaten by the stage above them. At each stage, a lot of the biomass is used in respiration to release energy for living. It does not get passed on to the next stage.
   b) i) $1000/500\,000 \times 100 = 0.2\%$
      ii) $50/1000 \times 100 = 5\%$

Answers to in-text questions

a) The Sun.

b) The numbers of organisms at each trophic level of a food chain drawn as a pyramid.

c) The biomass of organisms at each trophic level of a food chain drawn as a pyramid.

KEY POINTS

The practical work associated with this topic supports the learning of the key points. Students should be able to draw pyramids of biomass, working out the correct proportions from data supplied.

B2 3.2

Energy losses

LEARNING OBJECTIVES

Students should learn that:

- Materials and energy are lost in an organism's waste materials.
- Energy is used in movement.
- Energy is lost as heat to the surroundings.
- Maintaining a constant body temperature results in more heat loss and more energy use.

LEARNING OUTCOMES

Most students should be able to:

- State why materials and energy are reduced at each successive stage of a food chain.

Some students should also be able to:

- Explain in detail why energy losses are particularly large in warm-blooded organisms (mammals and birds).
- Interpret Sankey diagrams.

Teaching suggestions

- **Special needs.** Visit a local petting zoo or city farm, where the students can touch the animals and talk to the keepers about how much the animals have to eat and how they use their energy.

- **Gifted and talented.** Students could look up specific heat capacity. Ask: 'How much more energy would a 10 kg animal have at 37°C as opposed to 20°C?' Assume flesh to have approximately the same specific heat capacity as water.

- **Learning styles**

  Kinaesthetic: Practical activities.

  Visual: Viewing the PowerPoint® summary and observing the practical.

  Auditory: Listening to other students' descriptions of word meanings.

  Interpersonal: Discussing the practical exercises.

  Intrapersonal: Considering the implications of energy loss over trophic levels.

- **ICT link-up.** Students could use data loggers to monitor the temperature changes in the germinating peas experiment.

SPECIFICATION LINK-UP   Unit: Biology 2.11.4

- *The amounts of material and energy contained in the biomass of organisms is reduced at each successive stage in a food chain because:*
  - *some materials and energy are always lost in the organisms' waste materials*
  - *respiration supplies all the energy needs for living processes, including movement; much of this energy is eventually lost as heat to the surroundings*
  - *these losses are especially large in mammals and birds whose bodies must be kept at a constant temperature which is usually higher than that of their surroundings.*

Lesson structure

STARTER

Sankey diagram – Show students the Sankey diagram from the Student Book available on Additional Science CD ROM (it shows flow of energy through a system; you could project one from the student book spread). Ask them to have a guess at what it is trying to show. (5 minutes)

Mammals vs reptiles – If possible bring in a mammal pet, such as a rabbit, rat or hamster, and a reptile pet, such as a snake or a tortoise (risk assessments needed). Students to take the skin temperatures of the two animals and comment on their necessary energy consumptions. Video footage of crocodiles or snakes eating enhances this (search at www.video.google.com). (10 minutes)

MAIN

- **The great burger race** – This is a large scale outside practical activity for a sunny day. The idea is to show energy loss through trophic levels. Arrange a course with five posts in a line about 10 m apart.
  - At the first post have a picture of the Sun, two buckets with holes in and two large barrels (fruit barrels or similar) full of water.
  - At the second post have a large picture of the Earth and two similar buckets with holes in them.
  - At the third post have a large picture of a wheat plant and two more buckets with holes in.
  - At the fourth post, have on one side a large picture of a burger, on the other side a picture of a cow. On the side with the burger, have a collecting vessel large enough to contain several buckets of water. On the side with the cow have another bucket with holes in.
  - At the fifth post have a picture of a burger and a collecting vessel on the cow side (nothing on the other side).

  Water represents the energy and it is lost through the holes in the buckets at each stage. Pairs of students start the race, collecting water from the 'Sun barrels' and passing it to the buckets of the next pair of students at the first post and so on up the course. The cow side has one more trophic level, so the student on that side should have less water in their bucket as measured with a dipstick when the time is up. Because this is hard to set up, it may be a good idea to video it for future reference!

- **Investigating the heat released by respiration** – Set up the demonstration of heat production by germinating peas. Record the temperatures and plot a graph of temperature against time.

- Discuss the results of this experiment in terms of cellular respiration. Ask: 'Why include the dead peas? Why is so much respiration taking place in the peas?'

PLENARIES

Pass the energy – In groups, start off with a large sheet of paper labelled 'Energy'. Give the paper to a student who is designated to play the role of the Sun. The paper is passed to another student representing the Earth, some being torn off for reflection. The paper is then passed along a 'food chain' with a bit torn off at each level. (5 minutes)

Jumbled answers – Give the students question 1 of the 'Summary questions' with the answers in the wrong places. Have a competition to see who can get the answers in the correct order the fastest. (5–10 minutes)

- **Taking things a bit further** – 'The great burger race' activity and 'Pass the energy' plenary demonstrate how energy is passed along the food chain. You could introduce students to a consideration of how much of the solar energy intercepted by the Earth is used in photosynthesis. There are figures available, but a rough estimate is that 40% is reflected by the clouds, dust in atmosphere etc., 15% absorbed by the atmosphere (ozone layer), leaving 45%. Not all the light energy is in the right range for photosynthesis. The amount of photosynthesis that occurs depends on the season. Between 20 and 50% of the chemical energy stored by the plant is used in respiration, leaving the rest that is potentially available to the next trophic level.

Practical support

Investigating the heat released by respiration

Equipment and materials required

Two Thermos flasks, thermometers or probes for data loggers, one batch of live germinating peas, one batch of boiled, dead peas (cooled and rinsed in disinfectant), cotton wool.

Details

- Into one flask, place some live germinating seeds and a thermometer. Close the mouth of the flask with cotton wool.
- Into the second flask, place the same quantity of germinating peas that have been boiled to kill them, cooled and rinsed with disinfectant to kill microorganisms.
- Insert a thermometer and close the mouth of the flask with cotton wool.
- Keep both flasks in similar conditions and monitor the temperature in both flasks at regular intervals.
- Instead of thermometers, data loggers could be used to monitor the temperatures.

Answers to in-text questions

a) Because animals do not digest everything they eat.

b) The muscles use energy to contract, and the more an animal moves about, the more energy (and biomass) it uses from its food. As the muscles contract they produce heat.

c) An animal that is able to keep its body at a constant temperature regardless of the temperature of the surroundings.

KEY POINTS

The key points are well-demonstrated by the activities and information given in the spread. They can be reinforced by testing the students with the summary questions.

B2 3.2 Energy losses

LEARNING OBJECTIVES

1 How do we lose energy to the environment?
2 What is the effect of maintaining a constant body temperature?

An animal like a zebra eats grass and other small plants. It takes in a large amount of plant biomass, and converts it into a much smaller amount of zebra biomass. This is typical of a food chain.

The amounts of biomass and energy contained in living things always gets less at each stage of a food chain from plants onwards. Only a small amount of the biomass taken in gets turned into new animal material. The question is – what happens to the rest?

Energy loss in waste

The biomass which an animal eats is a source of energy, but not all of the energy can be used. Firstly, herbivores cannot digest all of the plant material they eat. The material they can't digest is passed out of the body in the faeces.

The meat which carnivores eat is easier to digest than plants, so they tend to need feeding less often and they produce less waste. But even carnivores often cannot digest hooves, claws, bones and teeth, so some of the biomass that they eat is always lost in their faeces.

When an animal eats more protein than it needs, the excess is broken down and passed out as urea in the urine. So biomass – and energy – are lost from the body.

a) Why is biomass lost in faeces?

Figure 1 The amount of biomass in a lion is a lot less than the amount of biomass in the grass which feeds the zebra it preys on. But where does all the biomass go?

Figure 2 Animals like horses eat very large amounts of biomass every day. However they also produce very large quantities of dung made up of all the biomass they couldn't actually digest!

GET IT RIGHT!

Make sure you can explain the different ways in which energy is lost between the stages of a food chain.
Check that you know how to use energy flow (Sankey) diagrams to tell if an animal is a herbivore or a carnivore, warm-blooded or cold-blooded.

Energy loss due to movement

Part of the biomass eaten by an animal is used for respiration in its cells. This supplies all the energy needs for the living processes taking place within the body.

Movement uses a great deal of energy. The muscles use energy to contract. So the more an animal moves about the more energy (and biomass) it uses from its food. The muscles produce heat as they contract.

b) Why do animals that move around a lot use up more of the biomass they eat than animals which don't move much?

Keeping a constant body temperature

Much of the energy animals produce from their food in cellular respiration is eventually lost as heat to the surroundings. Some of this heat is produced by the muscles as the animals move.

Heat losses are particularly large in mammals and birds because they are 'warm-blooded'. This means they keep their bodies at a constant temperature regardless of the temperature of the surroundings. They use up energy all the time, to keep warm when it's cold or to cool down when it's hot. Because of this, warm-blooded animals need to eat far more food than cold-blooded animals, such as fish and reptiles, to get the same increase in biomass.

c) What do we mean by a 'warm-blooded animal'?

PRACTICAL

Investigating the heat released by respiration

Even plants produce heat by cellular respiration. You can investigate this using germinating peas in a vacuum flask.

- What would be the best way to monitor the temperature continuously?
- Plan the investigation.

Figure 3 Only between 2% and 10% of the biomass eaten by an animal such as this horse will get turned into new horse – the rest of the stored energy will be used or lost in other ways

SUMMARY QUESTIONS

1 Copy and complete using the words below:

biomass   body temperature   energy   food chain   growth   movement   producers   respiration   waste

The amounts of ...... and ...... contained in living things always gets less at each stage of a .... from ...... onwards. Biomass is lost as ...... products and used to produce energy in .... This is used for ...... and to control .... Only a small amount is used for ....

2 Explain why so much of the energy from the Sun which lands on the surface of the Earth is not turned into biomass in animals.

3 Why do warm-blooded animals need to eat more food than cold-blooded ones of the same size if they are to put on weight?

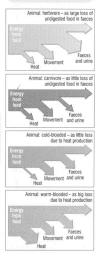

Figure 4 Sankey diagrams show how energy is transferred in a system. We can use them to look at the energy which goes in to and out of an animal and predict whether it eats plants or is a carnivore. You can even tell if it is warm-blooded or cold-blooded!

KEY POINTS

1 The amount of biomass and energy gets less at each successive stage in a food chain.

2 This is because some material is always lost in waste, and some is used for respiration to supply energy for movement and for maintaining the body temperature.

SUMMARY ANSWERS

1 Biomass, energy, food chain, producers, waste, respiration, movement, body temperature, growth.

2 Most of the Sun's energy is not captured by plants. Plant biomass eaten by animals cannot all be digested. Some is broken down by respiration to provide energy. Most energy is used for movement and control of body temperature. A small amount is used for growth to produce new biomass in animals.

3 Warm-blooded animals use up a lot of energy in keeping themselves warm or cooling themselves down to maintain a constant body temperature. They have to eat enough food to do this before they can gain new biomass. Cold-blooded animals do not lose energy in this way, so more of the food they take in becomes new biomass.

B2 3.3 Energy in food production

LEARNING OBJECTIVES

Students should learn that:

- The efficiency of food production can be improved by reducing the number of stages in a food chain.
- The efficiency can also be improved by limiting the movement and controlling the temperature of food animals.

LEARNING OUTCOMES

Most students should be able to:

- Explain why reducing the number of stages in a food chain increases the efficiency of food production.
- Describe the effects of limiting movement and controlling the temperature of food animals.

Some students should also be able to:

- Evaluate the positive and negative effects of managing food production.

Teaching suggestions

- **Special needs.** Students to make a collage of items to include in a balanced lunch that do not include any meat. They could use pictures, packets and wrappers to make it colourful.
- **Gifted and talented.** There are five types of vegetarians. Students could research these and suggest how each type gets the right type of proteins, vitamins and minerals without eating meat.
- **Learning styles**

  Kinaesthetic: Researching different diets.

  Visual: Viewing photographs of factory farming.

  Auditory: Reading out suggestions about diet.

  Interpersonal: Discussing in debates.

  Intrapersonal: Writing a speech for a debate.

- **Homework.** Students could write a short article describing the benefits of giving cows, in developing countries, hormones to increase their milk yield.

SPECIFICATION LINK-UP   Unit: Biology 2.11.4

- *At each stage in a food chain, less material and less energy are contained in the biomass of the organisms. This means that the efficiency of food production can be improved by reducing the number of stages in food chains.*
- *The efficiency of food production can also be improved by restricting energy loss from food animals by limiting their movement and by controlling the temperature of their surroundings.*

Lesson structure

STARTER

The essentials of the diet – This is a quick review of the components of a balanced diet. Ask: 'Why do we need carbohydrates, fats and proteins? Where do we get most of the protein in our diet from?' (5–10 minutes)

The great taste test – If it is allowed, and under controlled conditions (check for allergies etc.), provide small samples of burgers/sausages made with meat and meat substitutes. Ask for volunteers to feel and smell the samples (blindfold them first) to see if they can distinguish those products made from meat and those from meat substitutes. Discuss the results and look at what the substitutes are made from. (10–15 minutes)

How many food chains in my lunch? – Show the contents of three typical lunch boxes, but vary the main component. For example, one could have a cheese or egg sandwich, another a pork pie or sausage roll and the third a portion of pasta salad. Ask the students to work out the food chains. Ask: 'Which has the fewest stages?' (10 minutes)

MAIN

- **Factory farming** – Show photographs of factory farming to include reference to battery hens, intensive rearing of pigs and veal calves and fish. There are a number of web sites with down-loadable pictures and videos, but most of them are aimed at vegetarians and some have a biased view. If possible, it would be good to stick to the facts, so that students can debate the issues later. The provision of a worksheet to accompany the presentation should encourage students to keep a balanced view.

- **Factory vs free range** – Students could write a short speech in support of the intensive rearing of chickens and one against. Each speech should include scientific facts and advantages as well as disadvantages. In the lesson, hold a debate, but students to draw lots, as to which side to support, i.e. which of their speeches to read out. In this way, they appreciate that they need to have a balanced view.

- In the suggestion above, the issue of the intensive rearing of chickens has been chosen, but you may wish to broaden the topic to include intensive rearing of any animals. Students may need homework time to prepare their speeches.

- **On being a vegetarian . . .** – Invite any vegetarians in the class to give a presentation about their diet. If there are none, then invite a member of staff or the person responsible for home economics to give a presentation. This exercise is about eating more plant food rather than the ethical issues, so the emphasis is on the types of food they eat and the variety. Try to make it as scientific as possible, students identifying where their essential nutrients are coming from. If possible, suggest they bring in recipes or samples of food. This makes a good link with food and nutrition/home economics. If the laboratory is not a suitable place for trying out foods, then perhaps the use of the home economics room can be negotiated.

- Following the exercise above, some discussion on the nature of proteins from plants could be appropriate. The concept of essential amino acids and fatty acids (without necessarily naming them) could be introduced. The different types of vegetarian (vegans, ovolacto- and pesco-vegetarians) could be researched, described and the balance of their diets discussed.

- Link with reference to staple foods, which are based mainly on vegetables, in the developing countries of the world.

PLENARIES

How yellow is my yolk – or is battery best? – It is often said that the best, most nutritious eggs have the brightest yellow yolks. Students could find out if this is true. Hard-boil an egg from each of the following sources: a battery farm, a deep litter or barn system and free range. Remove the shells, slice the eggs and compare the colour of the yolks (no tasting). Ask: 'Is there a difference? If so, can you work out why?' (5–10 minutes)

Eat less meat – Students to write down five ways in which they could change their own diets to eat less meat protein without eating less protein. Choose some to read out. (5–10 minutes)

ACTIVITY & EXTENSION IDEAS

- **The use of antibiotics in factory farming** – In order to keep the animals healthy and prevent infections, antibiotics have been routinely included in the feed given to animals. Discuss this in relation to the development of antibiotic resistance in bacteria.

- **What goes into animal feed?** – Cattle and sheep have a low protein conversion efficiency (PCE), because their natural diet is high in carbohydrates that they have to digest and convert into proteins. Pigs and poultry have a higher PCE and can be fed diets containing more protein. Students to investigate the feeding of pigs and poultry in intensive systems in relation to the number of stages in the food chain.

- **Should hormones be used to increase productivity?** – Students to investigate the use of anabolic steroids in meat and milk production. Discuss their use and consider some of the other ways in which farmers try to increase yields of meat and milk.

BIOLOGY   ENERGY FLOWS

B2 3.3   Energy in food production

LEARNING OBJECTIVES

1 Why do short food chains make food production more efficient?
2 How can we manage food production to reduce energy losses?

Figure 1 Reducing the number of stages in food chains could dramatically increase the efficiency of our food production. Eating less meat would mean more food for everyone.

GET IT RIGHT!
Make sure you can use data on food production and explain both the pros and the cons.

Pyramids of biomass clearly show us that the organisms at each stage of a food chain contain less material and therefore less energy. This has some major implications for the way we human beings feed ourselves.

Food chains in food production

In the developed world much of our diet consists of meat or other animal products such as eggs, cheese and milk. The cows, goats, pigs and sheep that we use to produce our food eat plants. By the time it reaches us, much of the energy from the plant has been used up.

In some cases we even feed animals to animals. Ground up fish, for example, is often part of commercial pig and chicken feed. This means we have put another extra layer into the food chain – plant to fish, fish to pig, pig to people. What could have been biomass for us has been used as energy by other animals in the chain.

a) Name three animals which we use for food.

There is only a limited amount of the Earth's surface that we can use to grow food. The most energy-efficient way to use this food is to grow plants and eat them directly. If we only ate plants, then in theory at least, there would be more than enough food for everyone on the Earth. As much of the biomass produced by plants as possible would be used to feed people.

But every extra stage we introduce – feeding plants to animals before we eat the food ourselves – means less energy getting to us at the end of the chain. In turn this means less food to go round the human population.

b) Why would there be more food for everyone if we all ate only plants?

Artificially managed food production

As you saw on the previous page, animals don't turn all of the food they eat into new animal. Apart from the food which can't be digested and is lost as waste, energy is used in moving around and maintaining a constant body temperature.

Farmers apply these ideas to food production. People want meat, eggs and milk – but they want them as cheaply as possible. So farmers want to get the maximum possible increase in biomass from animals without feeding them any more. There are two ways of doing this:

- Limiting the movement of food animals. Then they lose a lot less energy in moving their muscles and so will have more biomass available from their food for growth.

- Controlling the temperature of their surroundings. Then the animals will not have to use too much energy keeping warm. Again this leaves more biomass spare for growth.

This means keeping the animals inside with restricted room to move, and a constant temperature. This is exactly what happens in the massive poultry rearing sheds where the majority of the chickens that we eat are produced.

Keeping chickens in these conditions means relatively large birds can be reared to eat in a matter of weeks. When animals are reared in this way they can appear more like factory products than farm animals. That's why these intensive methods are sometimes referred to as factory farming.

Intensive farming methods are used because there has been a steady increase in demand for cheap meat and animal products. This is the only way farmers can meet those demands from consumers.

On the other hand, these animals live very unnatural and restricted lives. More people are now aware of how our cheap meat and eggs are produced. So there has been a backlash against the conditions in which intensively reared animals live.

Many people now say they would be willing to eat meat less often and pay more if the animals they eat are raised more naturally.

Figure 3 Intensively reared pigs live in small stalls in a warm building with food delivered regularly for maximum growth. It makes life relatively easy for the farmer but costs money to run. Animals reared outside grow more slowly, but seem to have a much better quality of life. The farmer needs land, and has to cope with horrible weather – but it's cheaper as there is no artificial heating or lighting to pay for.

SUMMARY QUESTIONS

1 The world population is increasing and there are food shortages in many parts of the world. Explain, using pyramids of biomass to help you, why it would make better use of resources if people everywhere ate much less meat and more plant material.

2 Why are animals prevented from moving much and kept indoors in intensive farming?

3 a) What are the costs for a farmer of rearing animals intensively?
   b) What are the advantages of intensive rearing for a farmer?
   c) What are the advantages of less intensive rearing methods?
   d) What are the disadvantages of these more natural methods?

Figure 2 These chickens are provided with an ideal temperature, plenty of food and very little opportunity to move. They will produce meat and lay more eggs far faster than if they were moving about and keeping themselves warm.

FOUL FACTS

Veal crates are one of the most extreme ways of rearing animals to reduce energy losses. They are narrow, solid-sided wooden boxes used for rearing calves to produce veal. They are so narrow the calves cannot turn round. They are fed an all-liquid, iron-deficient diet to produce pale, white meat. The calves are slaughtered at 4 to 6 months old having never seen the light of day. Veal crates were banned in the UK in 1990, but they are still used in Europe. They will be banned there from 2007.

KEY POINTS

1 Biomass and energy are lost at each stage of a food chain. The efficiency of food production can be improved by reducing the number of stages in our food chains. It would be most efficient if we all just ate plants.

2 If you stop animals moving about and keep them warm, they lose a lot less energy. This makes food production much more efficient.

32   33

SUMMARY ANSWERS

1 Draw pyramids to show the bigger proportion of energy and biomass passed to people by eating plants like corn or rice than eating beef or chicken. Biomass and energy are lost at each stage of a food chain. The shorter the chain, the less resources are wasted.

2 Energy is used to move and to control body temperature. If animals do not move much and are kept warm, they waste much less energy on those things and use it to produce new biomass.

3 a) He has to heat animal houses, light animal houses, build animal houses and animals may be stressed.

   b) Work indoors, lower feed bills, animals grow faster so can be sold sooner and next lot started off.

   c) Animals reared more naturally (more contented?); animals healthier so lower vets bills; no heating/lighting bills.

   d) Have to deal with the weather; animals grow more slowly; need land.

Answers to in-text questions

a) Any sensible choices.

b) Because as little of the biomass produced by plants as possible would be wasted.

KEY POINTS

The key points can be reinforced by the lesson suggestions and the activities and extensions. Students do need to be advised to take a balanced approach, whatever their own views are.

B2 3.4   Decay

LEARNING OBJECTIVES

Students should learn that:

- Materials decay because they are broken down by micro-organisms.
- The decay process releases substances which plants need to grow.
- The materials are constantly cycled.

LEARNING OUTCOMES

Most students should be able to:

- Explain the role of micro-organisms in the process of decay.
- Explain why decay is important in the cycling of materials.

Some students should also be able to:

- Explain the factors which affect the rate of decay.

Teaching suggestions

- **Special needs.** Students could visit a food shop (with permission) and see the ways in which various foods are prevented from decaying. They could take photographs (with permission) and make a display.

- **Gifted and talented.** Students could find out about the human remains that have been found preserved in peat bogs. They could research: 'What are the conditions needed for peat formation? How can peat be used to provide us with information about what plants there were around thousands of years ago?'

- **Learning styles**
  Kinaesthetic: Practical work on decay.
  Visual: Making observations of rates of decay.
  Auditory: Listening to other students' answers.
  Interpersonal: Discussing experimental work.
  Intrapersonal: Writing own list of ways of preventing decay.

- **Homework.** Students could grow their own fungus on the windowsill at home. They could set up their own bread mould cultures, with damp bread, saucers and jam jars.

- **ICT link-up.** Use Animation, B2 3.4 'The Decay Process', from Additional Science CD ROM.

SPECIFICATION LINK-UP   Unit: Biology 2.11.4

- *Living things remove materials from the environment for growth and other processes. These materials are returned to the environment either in waste materials or when living things die and decay.*
- *Materials decay because they are broken down (digested) by microorganisms. Microorganisms digest materials faster in warm, moist conditions. Many microorganisms are also more active when there is plenty of oxygen.*
- *The decay process releases substances that plants need to grow.*
- *In a stable community, the processes which remove materials are balanced by processes which return materials. The materials are constantly cycled.*

Lesson structure

STARTER

It's gone mouldy! – Have some rotting fruit and vegetables, a piece of mouldy bread and some mushrooms, suitably covered or contained in sealed dishes. Pass these around and discuss how the organisms bringing about decay get their nutrition. (5–10 minutes)

The magic pin mould – Show the students a piece of ordinary bread and a piece which you have left exposed to the air, and then covered with a beaker or a jam jar for a couple of days (it should either have a fluffy white growth on it or a mucky brown one depending on what spores are around – keep sealed under jam jar). Show a picture of pin mould or *Rhizopus* – preferably much larger than life – with sporangia full of spores (search www.images.google.com). Ask the students to make the link and explain how the bread became mouldy. (5–10 minutes)

Where do last year's leaves go? – Have some leaf litter in trays, one for each group or bench. Provide the students with forceps and containers and see how many organisms they can find in 5 minutes. A quick check should sort out the detritivores from the rest, especially if students are provided with keys. The group with the most gets a small prize. Ask: 'What would happen in a woodland if last year's leaves did not decay?' (10–15 minutes)

MAIN

- **Investigating decay** – In the Student Book, it is suggested that students plan an investigation into the effect of temperature on the rate of decay. This can be done with cubes of bread exposed to the air and then placed in different temperatures, such as in the refrigerator, classroom, etc. All other conditions, such as moisture levels, need to be kept the same. Observations will need to be made over a period of time, or allow a set time for the investigation, e.g. a week.

- This investigation introduces concepts of 'How Science Works'. Predictions can be made, variables controlled, measurements taken and conclusions drawn. The results can be assessed in a variety of ways: use digital cameras to record the appearance, assess the area of decay, etc. A time-lapse camera could be used. The Intel 'Play' digital microscopes given away to all schools as part of Science Year have this capability.

- **Investigation into how quickly different materials decay** – This investigation could take two to three weeks. Each student, or group of students, will need a plant pot containing damp soil and a selection of objects, such as a leaf, a piece of bone, a dead earthworm, an insect and a small piece of twig. (This links to 'How Science Works' – designing investigations.)

- When setting up the experiment, the students could discuss the nature of the objects and make predictions about what will happen and why. Ask: 'Why is it important not to let the soil dry out? Why use soil?' (Again, this links to 'How Science Works' concepts.)

PLENARIES

- **Stop the rot!** – How do we stop things from decaying? Students to write down five ways in which perishable foods can be treated to prevent decay. In each case, they need to explain why the treatment prevents the decay. Choose some to read out and compile a list on the board. (10 minutes)

ACTIVITY & EXTENSION IDEAS

- **Quickest rotter game** – Provide the students with a piece of paper with six empty boxes connected in a line. Arrange pairs of boxes with 'warmth', 'air' and 'moisture' written above them. In pairs, students roll the dice: 1 and 2 lets them write in the letters 'R' and 'O' in the first two boxes; 3 and 4 lets them write in 'T' and 'T' into the middle two boxes and 5 and 6 lets them write 'E' and 'N' into the last boxes. Students race to see who gets rotten first. (5–10 minutes)

- **Treatment of sewage** – Show a (simplified) diagram of a sewage treatment or photograph of the treatment of sewage (search for images at www.images. google.com). The emphasis here is to be on the microorganisms involved in the breakdown of the waste. Students need to make notes or complete worksheets outlining the main points.

- **Visit a sewage treatment works** – If possible, arrange a visit to a treatment works.

- **A longer term experiment** – If leaf discs or leaf litter are put into nylon bags with different mesh sizes and then buried in soil, the contribution made by detritivores and decomposers can be assessed. If the mesh is small, then the detritivores will be unable to gain entry and the breakdown will be brought about by the decomposers. Mesh diameter of 6 mm allows the entry of earthworms, other detritivores and decomposers. Mesh sizes of about 0.5 mm will allow entry of other detritivores, but not earthworms. A mesh diameter of 0.003 mm will only allow decomposers through. The bags should contain a known mass of leaf material and be weighed every month. (This relates to 'How Science Works' – making measurements.)

Practical support
Investigating decay
Equipment and materials required
Cubes of bread or other suitable material, Petri dishes with lids or small glass containers with lids, thermometers to register temperatures in the different locations, access to refrigerator, incubator (do not exceed 25°C), etc. to provide about three different temperatures. Fix lids with tape but do not seal.

Answers to in-text questions

a) Plants.
b) Bacteria, fungi, maggots, worms.
c) Water is needed to prevent the microorganisms from drying out/to help them absorb their soluble food; warmth is needed for the enzymes to work efficiently; oxygen is needed for aerobic respiration.

KEY POINTS

Understanding of the key points for this spread can be tested by getting students to answer the summary questions at the end of a lesson or for homework. The summary questions are also good for revision of this topic.

B2 3.4   Decay

LEARNING OBJECTIVES

1 Why do things decay?
2 Why is decay such an important process?

GET IT RIGHT!

You need to know the type of organisms that cause decay, the conditions needed for decay and the importance of decay in recycling nutrients.

Figure 1 These tomatoes are slowly being broken down by the action of the fungi. You can see the fungi clearly, but the bacteria are too small to be seen.

FOUL FACTS

There is a forensic research site in the USA known as the Body Farm where scientists have buried or hidden human bodies in many different conditions. They are studying every stage of human decay. The information is used by police forces all over the world when a body is found. It can help to pinpoint when a person died, and show if they were the victim of a crime.

Plants take minerals from the soil all the time. These minerals are then passed on into animals through the food chains and food webs which link all living organisms. If this was a one-way process the resources of the Earth would have been exhausted long ago!

Many trees shed their leaves each year, and most animals produce droppings at least once a day. Animals and plants eventually die as well. Fortunately all these materials are recycled and returned to the environment. We can thank a group of organisms known as the decomposers for this.

a) Which group of organisms take materials out of the soil?

The decay process

The decomposers are a group of microorganisms which include bacteria and fungi. They feed on waste droppings and dead organisms.

Detritus feeders, such as maggots and some types of worm, often start the process, eating dead animals and producing waste material. The bacteria and fungi then digest everything – dead animals, plants and detritus feeders plus their waste. They use some of the nutrients to grow and reproduce. They also release waste products.

The waste products of the decomposers are carbon dioxide, water, and minerals which plants can use. When we say that things decay, they are actually being broken down and digested by microorganisms.

The recycling of materials through the process of decay makes sure that the soil remains fertile and plants can grow. It is also thanks to the decomposers that you aren't wading through the dead bodies of all the animals and plants that have ever lived!

b) Which type of organisms are the decomposers?

Conditions for decay

The speed at which things decay depends partly on the temperature. The chemical reactions in microorganisms are like those in most other living things. (See Figure 3.) They work faster in warm conditions. They slow down and even stop if conditions are too cold. Because the reactions are controlled by enzymes, they will stop altogether if the temperature gets too hot as the enzymes are denatured. You can investigate this in a simple experiment.

PRACTICAL

Investigating decay

Plan an investigation into the effect of temperature on how quickly things decay.
- Name the independent variable in this investigation. (See page 276.)

Most microorganisms also grow better in moist conditions. The moisture makes it easier to dissolve their food and also prevents them from drying out. So the decay of dead plants and animals – as well as leaves and dung – takes place far more rapidly in warm, moist conditions than it does in cold, dry ones.

Although some microbes work without oxygen, most decomposers respire like any other organism. This means they need oxygen to release energy, grow and reproduce. This is why decay takes place more rapidly when there is plenty of oxygen available.

c) Why are water, warmth and oxygen needed for the process of decay?

The importance of decay in recycling

Decomposers are vital for recycling resources in the natural world. What's more, we can take advantage of the process of decay to help us recycle our waste.

In sewage treatment plants we use microorganisms to break down the bodily waste we produce. This makes it safe to be released into rivers or the sea. These sewage works have been designed to provide the bacteria and other microorganisms with the conditions they need. That includes a good supply of oxygen.

Another place where the decomposers are useful is in the garden. Many gardeners have a compost heap. You put your grass cuttings, vegetable peelings and weeds on the compost heap. Then you leave it to let decomposing microorganisms break all the plant material down. It forms a fine, rich powdery substance known as compost. This can take up to a year.

The compost produced is full of mineral nutrients released by the decomposers. Once it is made you can dig your compost into the soil to act as a fertiliser.

Figure 2 The decomposers cannot function at low temperatures so if an organism – like this 4000 year old man – is frozen as it dies, it will be preserved with very little decay

Figure 3 Graph to show the decay rate of plant material (leaves) from two different areas of the USA. The effect of temperature can be seen clearly.

Figure 4 The decomposers are all microorganisms and so they are vulnerable to drying out. Moisture is vital for decay, along with warm temperatures and plenty of oxygen.

KEY POINTS

1 Living organisms remove materials from the environment as they grow. They return them when they die through the action of the decomposers.
2 Dead materials decay because they are broken down (digested) by microorganisms.
3 Decomposers work more quickly in warm, moist conditions. Many of them also need a good supply of oxygen.
4 The decay process releases substances which plants need to grow.
5 In a stable community the processes that remove materials (particularly plant growth) are balanced by the processes which return materials.

SUMMARY QUESTIONS

1 Copy and complete using the words below:

bacteria   carbon dioxide   dead   decomposers   digest
fungi   microorganisms   minerals   nutrients
waste droppings   water

The ...... are a group of ...... which includes ...... and .... They feed on .... and ...... organisms. They ...... them and use some of the .... They also release waste products which include ...., ... and ...... which plants can use.

2 The following methods are all ways of preserving foods to prevent them from decaying. Use your knowledge of the decomposing microorganisms to explain how each method works:

a) Food may be frozen.
b) Food may be cooked – cooked food keeps longer than fresh food.
c) Food may be stored in a vacuum pack – with all the air sucked out.
d) Food may be tinned – it is heated and sealed in an airtight container.

SUMMARY ANSWERS

1 Decomposers, microorganisms, bacteria, fungi, waste droppings, dead, digest, nutrients, carbon dioxide, water, minerals.

2 a) Microorganisms/decomposers do not work at very low temperatures, so when food is frozen decay processes do not take place and the food remains good.

b) Cooking destroys the microorganisms/decomposers; denatures their enzymes; no microorganisms then no decay.

c) Most decomposers require oxygen to respire; no air then no oxygen so microorganisms cannot grow.

d) Decomposers are killed; sealed in an airtight tin there is no oxygen so no action by decomposers; double protection against decay.

B2 3.5   The carbon cycle

LEARNING OBJECTIVES

Students should learn that:

- Carbon dioxide is removed from the atmosphere by photosynthesis in green plants and used to make carbohydrates, fats and proteins.
- Carbon dioxide is returned to the atmosphere when green plants, animals and decomposers respire.
- Detritus feeders and microorganisms break down the waste products and dead bodies of organisms, returning materials to the ecosystem.

LEARNING OUTCOMES

Most students should be able to:

- Describe the processes in the carbon cycle.
- Explain the importance of the activities of the detritus feeders and microorganisms in the cycling of nutrients.

Some students should also be able to:

- Explain the energy transfers in an ecosystem.

Teaching suggestions

- **Special needs.** Students to write the word 'carbon' using a pencil. Then they write it using a burned stick, a piece of burnt animal (a bone or a piece of burned beef jerky), a piece of coal and a charcoal briquette. These can be made into a poster for display along with a balloon of exhaled air.

- **Gifted and talented.** Students could speculate on whether there may be life on other planets that is not carbon-based. Ask: 'Do other elements have properties similar to carbon? What might non-carbon based life be like?'

- **Learning styles**
  Kinaesthetic: Role-playing the game 'Pass the carbon'.
  Visual: Observing the animation.
  Auditory: Writing and reading out a poem or song describing the carbon cycle.
  Interpersonal: Discussing the impact of climate change and what we should do about it.
  Intrapersonal: Writing down own opinions on the reasons for the freak weather.

SPECIFICATION LINK-UP   Unit: Biology 2.11.5

- *The constant cycling of carbon is called the carbon cycle. In the carbon cycle:*
  - *carbon dioxide is removed from the environment by green plants for photosynthesis; the carbon from the carbon dioxide is used to make carbohydrates, fats and proteins that make up the body of plants*
  - *some of the carbon dioxide is returned to the atmosphere when green plants respire*
  - *when green plants are eaten by animals and these animals are eaten by other animals, some of the carbon becomes part of the fats and proteins that make up their bodies*
  - *when animals respire some of this carbon becomes carbon dioxide and is released into the atmosphere*
  - *when plants and animals die, some animals and microorganisms feed on their bodies; carbon is released into the atmosphere as carbon dioxide when these organisms respire*
  - *by the time the microorganisms and detritus feeders have broken down the waste products and dead bodies of organisms in ecosystems and cycled the materials as plant nutrients, all the energy originally captured by green plants has been transferred.*

Lesson structure

STARTER

Coal into diamonds – Show a film clip from *Superman II* where he turns a piece of coal into a diamond (or set the scene by searching the web for 'Superman II watch trailer'). Lead a discussion as to where carbon comes from and whether you can destroy it. (5–10 minutes)

Carbon cycle and climate change? – Show some pictures of freak weather or video footage of a tropical storm (search the web at www.images.google.com.) Ask: 'How is this coming about?' Get each student to write down his or her ideas and then discuss or compare with a neighbour. Collect up ideas as a class. (5–10 minutes)

Fossils in coal – Have some plant fossils in coal (real ones if possible but pictures if not). Ask students to write down how the carbon got there and what would happen to it if we burned the coal. (10 minutes)

MAIN

- **Carbon cycle** – Show Animation, B2 3.5 'Carbon Cycle', from Additional Science CD ROM. It is a good idea to provide the students with a worksheet and allow time for the explanation of points.

- **Role-play game 'Pass the carbon'** – In small groups, students to be labelled as parts of the carbon cycle, such as 'The atmosphere', 'Plants', 'Animals', 'Fossil fuels', etc. Have a soft ball labelled 'Carbon', which students are to pass around going from locations to other locations via the correct processes.

- **Cartoon cycle** – Students to draw, or use, pictures to make a cartoon strip illustrating how a carbon atom goes from a lion's breath, into plants, into an impala, into a lion and out again through the lion's breath. This could be done in groups and the best displayed.

PLENARIES

The carbon cycle – Label a diagram of the carbon cycle. (5 minutes)

True or false – On the board show various statements about the carbon cycle, respiration, photosynthesis and energy transfer. Students to write on 'Show me' boards whether they are true or false. (5–10 minutes)

Get it in the right order – Prepare sets of cards with stages of the carbon cycle on them. In pairs, students have to put them in a sensible order, and then compare with another pair of students and feedback. (10–15 minutes)

ACTIVITY & EXTENSION IDEAS

- **Compost heap** – If the school has a compost heap, set up a data logger to take the temperature over a period of time. If there is no compost heap, students could investigate the possibility of setting one up in a suitable position. Investigate what types of material can be composted. Why is it best to use vegetable matter only? What kinds of organisms would you expect to find in a well-established compost heap? Why does the temperature change within the compost heap?

- **Energy in decomposers** – Set fire to some dried mushrooms to show that there is energy in decomposers (risk assessment).

- **Kyoto agreement** – Students to find out more about the Kyoto agreement and why America is not signing. They should then suggest reasons why many people think that they should. Comment on progress made at Montreal conference.

- **Carbon emissions** – There has been much discussion within the European Union and worldwide about the levels of carbon released into the atmosphere. Make a collection of newspaper and magazine articles about this topic. Find out how carbon emissions are controlled and what the targets are amongst the industrialised nations.

Answers to in-text questions

a) Fossil fuels, carbonate rocks, the atmosphere, oceans and living things.

b) It removes it from the environment.

BIOLOGY   ENERGY FLOWS

B2 3.5   The carbon cycle

LEARNING OBJECTIVES
1 What is the carbon cycle in nature?
2 Which processes remove carbon dioxide from the atmosphere – and which return it?

Figure 1 Within the natural cycle of life and death in the living world, mineral nutrients are cycled between living organisms and the physical environment

Imagine a stable community of plants and animals. The processes which remove materials from the environment are balanced by processes which return materials. Materials are constantly cycled through the environment. One of the most important of these is carbon.

All of the main molecules that make up our bodies (carbohydrates, proteins, fats and DNA) are based on carbon atoms combined with other elements.

The amount of carbon on the Earth is fixed. Some of the carbon is 'locked up' in fossil fuels like coal, oil and gas. It is only released when we burn them.

Huge amounts of carbon are combined with other elements in carbonate rocks like limestone and chalk. There is a pool of carbon in the form of carbon dioxide in the air. It is also found dissolved in the water of rivers, lakes and oceans. All the time a relatively small amount of available carbon is cycled between living things and the environment. We call this the **carbon cycle**.

a) What are the main sources of carbon on Earth?

Photosynthesis

Green plants use carbon dioxide from the atmosphere in photosynthesis. They use it to make carbohydrates which in turn make biomass. This is passed on to animals which eat the plants. The carbon goes on to become part of the carbohydrates, proteins and fats in their bodies.

This is how carbon is taken out of the environment. But how is it returned?

b) What effect does photosynthesis have on the distribution of carbon levels in the environment?

Respiration

Animals and plants respire all the time. They use oxygen to break down glucose, providing energy for their cells. Carbon dioxide is produced as a waste product and is returned to the atmosphere.

Also when plants and animals die their bodies are broken down by the decomposers. These decomposers release carbon dioxide into the atmosphere as they respire. All of the carbon dioxide released by the various types of living organisms is then available again. It is ready to be taken up by plants in photosynthesis.

Combustion

Fossil fuels contain carbon, which was locked away by photosynthesising plants millions of years ago. When we burn fossil fuels, we release some of that carbon back into our atmosphere:

Photosynthesis: carbon dioxide + water (+ light energy) → glucose + oxygen
Respiration: glucose + oxygen → carbon dioxide + water (+ energy)
Combustion: fossil fuel or wood + oxygen → carbon dioxide + water (+ energy)

DID YOU KNOW?
Every year about 166 gigatonnes of carbon are cycled through the living world. That's 16 000 000 000 tonnes – an awful lot of carbon!

The constant cycling of carbon is summarised in Figure 2.

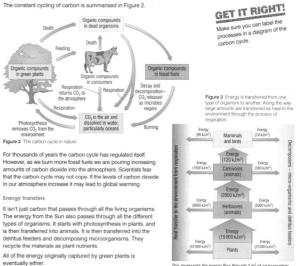

Figure 2 The carbon cycle in nature

For thousands of years the carbon cycle has regulated itself. However, as we burn more fossil fuels we are pouring increasing amounts of carbon dioxide into the atmosphere. Scientists fear that the carbon cycle may not cope. If the levels of carbon dioxide in our atmosphere increase it may lead to global warming.

Energy transfers

It isn't just carbon that passes through all the living organisms. The energy from the Sun also passes through all the different types of organisms. It starts with photosynthesis in plants, and is then transferred into animals. It is then transferred into the detritus feeders and decomposing microorganisms. They recycle the materials as plant nutrients.

All of the energy originally captured by green plants is eventually either:

- transferred into the decomposers, or
- transferred as heat into the environment by respiration.

GET IT RIGHT!
Make sure you can label the processes in a diagram of the carbon cycle.

Figure 3 Energy is transferred from one type of organism to another. Along the way large amounts are transferred as heat to the environment through the process of respiration.

This represents the energy flow through 1 m^2 of an ecosystem – the figures in brackets are those recorded for one particular area

SUMMARY QUESTIONS
1 a) What is the carbon cycle?
   b) What are the main processes involved in the carbon cycle?
   c) Why is the carbon cycle so important for life on Earth?

2 Explain carefully how a) carbon, and b) energy are transferred through an ecosystem.

KEY POINTS
1 The constant cycling of carbon in nature is known as the carbon cycle.
2 Carbon dioxide is removed from the atmosphere by photosynthesis. It is returned to the atmosphere through respiration and combustion.
3 The energy originally captured by green plants is eventually transferred into consumers, into decomposers or as heat into the environment.

SUMMARY ANSWERS

1 a) The cycling of carbon between living organisms and the environment.

   b) Photosynthesis, respiration and combustion.

   c) Because it prevents all the carbon from getting used up; returns carbon dioxide to the atmosphere to be available for photosynthesis again.

2 a) Summarise the carbon cycle – can be done by reproducing the diagram on page 37 or writing out the different stages (must cover all points in carbon cycle).

   b) Energy transfer: energy from Sun used by plants for photosynthesis, energy then transferred to animals as they eat plants, into animals which eat animals, then into detritus feeders and decomposers – all energy transferred into consumers and decomposers and eventually transferred into body mass of decomposers or transferred to heat in the environment.

KEY POINTS

A really clear diagram with all the organisms and processes labelled is essential in an understanding of the carbon cycle. It could be pointed out to that the cycle links many major activities of plants and animals, so a good understanding of the cycle provides them with a reference point for the processes of respiration and photosynthesis.

B2 3.6 Farming – intensive or free range?

SPECIFICATION LINK-UP

Unit: Biology 2.11.4

This spread can be used to revisit the substantive content covered in this chapter:

- *The efficiency of food production can also be improved by restricting energy loss from food animals by limiting their movement and by controlling the temperature of their surroundings.*

Students should use their skills, knowledge and understanding of 'How Science Works':

- *to evaluate the positive and negative effects of managing food production and distribution and to be able to recognise that practical solutions to human needs may require compromise between competing priorities.*

Teaching suggestions

The material provided on cattle and chickens may provide the stimulus for either Activity 1 or Activity 2. The following suggestions could help students to focus their ideas before attempting either of the activities.

- **Comparing intensive and free-range (extensive) farming** – There are some good videos available from Compassion in World Farming. A leaflet entitled *Intensive farming and the welfare of farm animals* is freely available. This organisation also has a visiting speaker scheme. (Visit www.ciwf.org.uk.)

- **Visits to farms** – Arrange a pair of visits, one to an intensive farm and one to an extensive farm. An organisation exists to help get schoolchildren on to farms through the Access to Farms Accreditation scheme and the Growing Schools initiative from the DfES. The Federation of City Farms may well be able to help or you could write to The Greenhouse, Hereford Street, Bristol, BS3 4NA. Your local agricultural college may also be able to help you find suitable farms or show you their systems.

- **The Soil Association** – There have been references to The Soil Association on previous spreads. These are relevant for this spread as well.

BIOLOGY   ENERGY FLOWS

B2 3.6   **Farming – intensive or free range?**

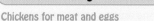

Intensive farming – costs and benefits	'Free-range' farming – costs and benefits
Chickens for meat and eggs	

Benefits:
- Lots of chickens in small space
- Little or no food wastage
- Energy wasted in movement/heat loss kept to a minimum
- Maximum weight gain/number of eggs laid
- Cheap eggs/chicken meat

Costs:
- Chickens unable to behave naturally – may be debeaked and cannot perch
- Large barns need heating and lighting
- Chickens' legs may break as bones unable to carry weight of rapidly growing bodies
- Risk of disease with many birds closely packed together

Benefits:
- Chickens live a more natural life
- No heating/lighting costs
- Less food needs supplying as they find some for themselves
- Can charge more money for free-range eggs/chickens

Costs:
- Chickens more vulnerable to weather and predators
- More land needed for each bird
- Eggs cannot be collected automatically
- Fewer eggs laid, especially in the winter when it is cold and dark for longer periods of time

ACTIVITIES

1. Choose either cattle or chickens. Produce a leaflet to be handed out in your local shopping centre either supporting intensive farming methods or supporting free-range farming methods. In each case back up your arguments with scientific reasoning.

2. You are going to take part in a debate on animal welfare and farming methods. You have been chosen to speak *either* FOR intensive farming *or* AGAINST 'free-range' farming.
   You have to think carefully about the benefits to the animals of intensive methods, and the disadvantages of free-range farming.

For Activity 3:

- **Compost heap** – Set up a compost heap in the school grounds. Liaise with the ground staff for siting and what can be composted. This could also be part of a recycling scheme for all the waste and rubbish from the school. Free or reduced cost bins can be obtained – search the Internet for 'Recycle Now'.

- **Bin search** – Empty the contents of a school bin on to a large plastic sheet. With rubber gloves, get the students to sort out the rubbish, putting it into various piles according to how easily it will decay and what sort of recycling is possible.

- **Garden waste** – Students could investigate the local authority web sites to find out their policy on dealing with garden waste. This could be extended to finding out how much recycling is going on in your area. If the local authority is about to set up a scheme, or if there is one in operation, there is bound to be some literature available. This information could be displayed around the school and could encourage more people to make use of the scheme.

Additional biology

Intensive farming – costs and benefits	'Free-range' farming – costs and benefits

Cattle for beef

Benefits:

- Uses the male calves produced by dairy cows
- Weaning takes place by about 8 weeks and then farmers know exactly how much food each calf eats
- Balance of nutrients in food changed as calf grows to maximise growth
- Kept largely indoors, energy loss through movement and heat loss is kept to a minimum – can get weight gains of 1.5 kg a day!
- Cheap meat

Costs:

- Feedstuff must be bought and can be expensive
- Cowsheds need care and cleaning
- Cowsheds have to be heated and lit

Benefits:

- Calves are weaned naturally and stay with their mothers for up to 6 months
- Feeding on grass or food grown by farmer means no contamination, such as that which led to BSE, is possible
- Cattle behave and live relatively naturally

Costs:

- Animals may take slightly longer to gain weight as they are moving more actively
- More land is needed to provide grazing, hay and silage

ACTIVITY

3 Design a poster for the school gardening club explaining how to make compost and why it is important for the soil. Use the information in this chapter to help you get your facts right!

Special needs

Students could carry out Activity 3 if they were provided with some pictures or they could use a computer to design a poster, depending on their abilities.

Homework

There is much research to be done for all these activities and ample opportunities for homework tasks. Writing a speech or doing some research in a supermarket could be done out of class time.

ICT link-up

Students can use the Internet to research their projects and these activities. ICT could also be used to design posters and leaflets.

ACTIVITY & EXTENSION

Activity 1 [?]

- In the material provided, there are references to the differences in price of the food produced, but a survey in a supermarket can reveal what the costs to the consumer are. Students could carry out a survey of prices for similar products from intensive and free-range systems. They need to calculate how much more it would cost per year to eat from free-range and/or organic sources. Draw out discussion points. Ask: 'Is this an option for people on limited incomes? Should we be eating less meat anyway?'

- Also, the statements given are about costs and benefits for the farmers and producers. A leaflet to be handed out in the local shopping centre would need to contain some information for the general public. For example, the relative costs, the availability and the quality and taste of the produce. In section 3.3, a suggestion was made that students should see if they could tell the difference between a battery egg and a free-range egg.

- One further issue worth considering is the content of processed foods. Many people nowadays buy ready-prepared dishes. Ask: 'How do we know what is used to make them? Are there any products that state that free-range produce is used in the preparation of these dishes?' A supermarket survey, or even a conversation with one of the staff, might provide some information. If that fails, one of the major producers of such dishes might be able to reveal the sources of the raw materials. Some research on the web might be necessary.

Activity 2 [?]

- In section 3.3, a debate on the intensive versus free-range rearing of chickens was suggested. The debate suggested here is a more general one, but students could expand their ideas from the previous debate and widen the arguments. This debate could include issues on animal rights, but students should be prepared to present and accept balanced opinions. As has been suggested before, students could prepare two speeches, one for and one against, and be prepared to use either one.

Activity 3

Information for Activity 3 is readily available and the students could design individual posters or work in groups. The activity does link well with recycling and can be part of a general scheme to reduce the amount of rubbish and encourage recycling.

SUMMARY ANSWERS

1 a) i) 10% **ii)** 8% **iii)** 12.5%

b) The mass of producers has to support the whole pyramid, and relatively little energy is transferred from producers to primary consumers as they are difficult to digest.

c) Relatively little energy is passed along the chain, and there is not enough by the end of the chain to support many carnivores.

d) If the animals had been birds or mammals, less energy would have been passed on between the levels. They are warm-blooded and so use a lot of energy to keep warm, which is then lost to the environment, leaving less energy to pass on along the chain.

2 a) [Marks for graph plotting, correct scale, labelled axes, axes correct way round, accurate points.]

b) Chickens use less energy maintaining their body temperature, so have more energy for growth.

c) To make sure that they move as little as possible. Energy is used up in movement: less movement means more energy for growth.

d) So that they grow as fast as possible to a weight when they can be eaten and another set of chickens started up. Economic reasons.

e) The line should be below the first line. Chickens outside use energy moving around and keeping warm or cool, so convert less biomass from their food for growth.

Summary teaching suggestions

- **Literary guidance** – There are several questions here that require answers written in continuous prose, giving students the opportunity to practise writing in complete sentences and organising their thoughts into a logical sequence.

- **Misconceptions** – Students should be very clear that they know and can explain the difference between a pyramid of numbers and a pyramid of biomass, together with the reasons for their use.

- **Special needs** – It is difficult to see how these questions can be adapted for students. The questions could be put verbally and the answers given verbally, particularly with respect to question 2. The students could be given strips of coloured paper equivalent to the mass of the chicken in question 2 and these could be stuck on a large grid in the correct order, so that the gain in mass is obvious.

- **When to use the questions?**
  - The whole set of questions could be used as an end-of-chapter test in a lesson.
  - They could also be used as a revision exercise to identify areas that need more explanation.
  - Certain questions can be linked to their topics. For example, question 1 can be linked to 3.2 'Energy losses' and would be a useful homework exercise following that lesson. Similarly, question 2 links with 3.3 'Energy in food production'.
  - Both questions 1 and 2 provide students with the opportunity to manipulate and interpret data, which is good practice in preparation for the examinations.

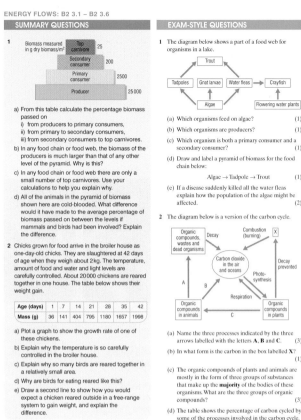

ENERGY FLOWS: B2 3.1 – B2 3.6

SUMMARY QUESTIONS

1

a) From this table calculate the percentage biomass passed on
   i) from producers to primary consumers,
   ii) from primary to secondary consumers,
   iii) from secondary consumers to top carnivores.

b) In any food chain or food web, the biomass of the producers is much larger than that of any other level of the pyramid. Why is this?

c) In any food chain or food web there are only a small number of top carnivores. Use your calculations to help you explain why.

d) All of the animals in the pyramid of biomass shown here are cold-blooded. What difference would it have made to the average percentage of biomass passed on between the levels if mammals and birds had been involved? Explain the difference.

2 Chicks grown for food arrive in the broiler house as one-day-old chicks. They are slaughtered at 42 days of age when they weigh about 2kg. The temperature, amount of food and water and light levels are carefully controlled. About 20000 chickens are reared together in one house. The table below shows their weight gain.

Age (days)	1	7	14	21	28	35	42
Mass (g)	36	141	404	795	1180	1657	1998

a) Plot a graph to show the growth rate of one of these chickens.

b) Explain why the temperature is so carefully controlled in the broiler house.

c) Explain why so many birds are reared together in a relatively small area.

d) Why are birds for eating reared like this?

e) Draw a second line to show how you would expect a chicken reared outside in a free-range system to gain weight, and explain the difference.

EXAM-STYLE QUESTIONS

1 The diagram below shows a part of a food web for organisms in a lake.

(a) Which organisms feed on algae? (1)

(b) Which organisms are producers? (1)

(c) Which organism is both a primary consumer and a secondary consumer? (1)

(d) Draw and label a pyramid of biomass for the food chain below:

    Algae → Tadpole → Trout (1)

(e) If a disease suddenly killed all the water fleas explain how the population of the algae might be affected. (2)

2 The diagram below is a version of the carbon cycle.

(a) Name the three processes indicated by the three arrows labelled with the letters **A**, **B** and **C**. (3)

(b) In what form is the carbon in the box labelled **X**? (1)

(c) The organic compounds of plants and animals are mostly in the form of three groups of substances that make up the **majority** of the bodies of these organisms. What are the three groups of organic compounds? (3)

(d) The table shows the percentage of carbon cycled by some of the processes involved in the carbon cycle.

40

EXAM-STYLE ANSWERS

1 a) Tadpoles, gnat larvae and water fleas *(1 mark)*
Any one omitted/any wrong/more than three organisms = no marks

b) Algae and flowering water plants *(1 mark)*
Either omitted/either wrong/more than 2 listed = no marks

c) Crayfish *(1 mark)*

d)

Trout
Tadpole
Algae

(Accurately drawn and labelled = 1 mark)
In the absence of other information on the relative numbers of these organisms, the exact proportions are not important provided that there is a clear reduction in size as one moves up the chain.

e) The algae population would increase *(1 mark)*
because there is one less organism consuming/eating it *(1 mark)*

2 a) A Excretion/death

   B Respiration

   C Eating/feeding *(1 mark each)*

b) Fossil fuels *(1 mark)*
Allow any correct example of a fossil fuel, e.g. coal/oil/gas

c) Carbohydrates
Fats
Proteins *(1 mark each)*
DNA/vitamins or other organic compounds that make up a small proportion of the body should not be given credit as the question says 'make up the majority of the bodies'. Equally, specific examples such as glucose should not gain marks as the question states 'groups of substances'.

d) i) *Five sectors accurately plotted and labelled.* *(3 marks)*
Four sectors accurately plotted and labelled. *(2 marks)*
Three sectors accurately plotted and labelled. *(1 mark)*
Five sectors accurately plotted but no labels/wrongly labelled. *(1 mark)*

Process	Percentage of total carbon cycled
Photosynthesis	50
Respiration by animals	20
Respiration by plants	20
Respiration by microorganisms	5
Combustion/absorbed by oceans	5

(i) Draw a pie chart of these proportions. (3)

(ii) If the total amount of carbon that is cycled in one year across the Earth is 165 gigatonnes, calculate how much carbon is cycled by the respiration of plants. Show your working. (2)

(e) Respiration is an important process in recycling carbon. The word equation for respiration is shown below, with most words replaced by the letters **A**, **B**, **C** and **D**. Give the names of **A**, **B**, **C** and **D**. (4)

$$A + B \rightarrow C + D + \text{energy}$$

(f) The concentration of carbon dioxide in the atmosphere has increased over the past 200 years. Suggest one human activity that might have contributed to this increase. (1)

3 A factory which packaged shrimps produced tonnes of waste shrimp heads. It cost money to dump these in the local tip. The managers decided to investigate the decay of shrimp heads to see if they might be used as fertiliser. They used 80 shrimp heads in 4 sealed jars. Each jar had a different amount of water. They measured the length of the shrimp heads, left them for 60 days and then measured them again:

Amount of water (cm³)	% loss in length
40	68
50	61
60	59
70	56

(a) Explain why they decided to measure the length of shrimp heads. (1)

(b) How many shrimp heads would they have put into each jar? (1)

(c) They predicted that the more water they added the greater the breakdown of the shrimp heads. Is their prediction supported? Explain your answer. (1)

Can this be true?

A scientist claims to have bred a featherless chicken.

The scientist says that it was the result of natural selective breeding and not genetic engineering. He claims that it will be ideal for warmer climates where the intensive breeding of chickens requires expensive air conditioning to keep the chickens at around 25°C. It will therefore be cheaper for farmers to rear these featherless chickens.

They will also be cheaper to feed as they will not need to use energy to grow feathers. Also they will cut down on the pollution caused by having to dump feathers before they are prepared for market.

'I looked to see if the date was April 1st when I read about this story,' said a journalist.

A biologist said, 'The birds would probably find it difficult to breed without feathers.' Others claimed that it was 'ugly science' and should not be allowed.

a) Why do you think the scientist is so keen to promote his research? (1)

b) Do you think that the scientist was wrong to do his research? (1)

c) Which groups are likely to oppose such research? (1)

d) Who should make the final decision whether farmers should breed these featherless chickens or not? (1)

e) Do we know if the chickens are suffering? How could we find out? (1)

HOW SCIENCE WORKS ANSWERS

a) He wishes to make money from his research. He can sell the chickens for breeding.

b) This question is open for debate!

For: because he can make money; others can make more money; more people can buy cheaper chickens; less energy and food used; less pollution.

Against: birds might be in physical pain; find it difficult to breed; gives science a poor name.

c) Animal welfare groups are likely to oppose such research.

d) Society in general, the government in particular. There are some questions that science should not answer.

e) Some will argue that if they grow, then they must not be suffering. Others will argue that there is a need to understand how birds suffer and it is very difficult to produce a satisfactory dependent variable with which to judge suffering in birds. There are some questions that at the moment science cannot answer.

How science works teaching suggestions

- **Literacy guidance**
  - Key terms that should be clearly understood: the limitations of present-day science.
  - The questions expecting a longer answer, where students can practise their literacy skills are: b) and e).
- **Higher- and lower-level answers.** Questions b) and e) are higher-level questions. The answers for these have been provided at this level. Questions a) and c) are lower level and the answers provided are lower level.
- **Gifted and talented.** Able students could develop questions b) and e) into a debate on animal welfare.
- **How and when to use these questions.** When wishing to develop ideas as to the limitations of science. The questions are best discussed as a class or small, very able group. There could be links here with the English department.
- **Homework.** For homework, students could tackle another animal welfare issue using the same questions.
- **Special needs.** These students will need talking through the questions in small groups and questions rephrased.
- **ICT link-up.** To research other similar issues. Students should be made aware that Internet groups with an interest are not always factually correct in their science and they might illustrate considerable bias in support of their cause.

---

ii) Total carbon cycled = 165 gigatonnes

Plant respiration cycles 20% of the total carbon

i.e. $\dfrac{165 \times 20}{100} = 33$ gigatonnes

Correct working and answer *(2 marks)*

Correct working + wrong answer (provided the answer is consequential on the error) *(1 mark)*

Correct answer but no working shown *(1 mark)*

e) **A** *or* **B** = glucose or oxygen

C *or* **D** = carbon dioxide or water *(1 mark each)*

f) Burning of fossil fuels/coal/oil/gas *(1 mark)*

3 a) To measure the rate of decay *(1 mark)*

b) 20 *(1 mark)*

c) No, the more water they added the less the loss of length of the shrimp heads. *(1 mark)*

Exam teaching suggestions

- All questions are relatively straightforward and require short answers. The test is pitched at foundation level with most questions predominately testing recall of knowledge. All questions could be effectively used to test learning at the end of teaching sessions on energy flow, either in class or as a homework. Question 3 is based on 'How Science Works'.

- When asked for a specific number of responses, as in question 2 part c), it is important to impress upon students the need to give only the requisite number. Some will try to hedge their bets and give extra responses in the hope that if they include the correct ones all will be well. Examiners will deduct marks for each incorrect response. The guiding principle followed in examinations is 'right + wrong = wrong'.

B2 4.1

Enzyme structure

LEARNING OBJECTIVES

Students should learn that:

- Enzymes are biological catalysts.
- Enzymes are proteins consisting of long chains of amino acids folded into a special shape.
- The special shape of an enzyme enables it to catalyse reactions.

LEARNING OUTCOMES

Most students should be able to:

- Describe how long chains of amino acids are folded and coiled into special shapes to form enzymes.
- State that enzymes speed up the rate of chemical reactions in the body.

Some students should also be able to:

- Explain the concepts of activation energy and the active site of the enzyme.

Teaching suggestions

- **Special needs.** Make blocks of Lego to represent large molecules, such as starch, proteins and fats. Label each one on one side with the name of the substrate ('starch', 'protein') and the individual bricks labelled with the name of the products ('sugars', 'amino acids'). Use plastic knives with the word 'Enzyme' on to cut up the blocks of Lego. Use a different colour-matched knife for each one. To show denaturing, dip the plastic knife in boiling water (care).

- **Gifted and talented.** Students could research the structure of proteins and use a length of Bunsen tubing to demonstrate the differences between the primary, secondary and tertiary structure. Different sequences of amino acids can be marked with a pen and the tubing can be coiled and twisted into a C shape to illustrate the active site. Record the demo on a video.

- Learning styles

  Kinaesthetic: Practical work on catalase.

  Visual: Viewing the video clips.

  Auditory: Listening to the views of others in discussions on enzyme activity.

  Interpersonal: Discussing the practicals and collaboration with peers.

  Intrapersonal: Evaluating the reliability of data obtained in practical work.

SPECIFICATION LINK-UP   Unit: Biology 2.11.6

- *Catalysts increase the rate of chemical reactions. Biological catalysts are called 'enzymes'.*
- *Enzymes are protein molecules made up of long chains of amino acids. These long chains are folded to produce a special shape which enables other molecules to fit into the enzymes. This shape is vital for the enzyme's function.*

Lesson structure

STARTER

Biological stains – Bring in a cheap, clean white T-shirt and allow students to smear it with selected food and drink (tomato ketchup, mustard, egg). Show the students a box of biological washing powder (Care: if it is handed around – some people can have sensitised skin). Discuss how the stains can be removed. (5–10 minutes)

Catalysis: a rapid reaction – Demonstrate a fast-catalysed reaction, such as the breakdown of hydrogen peroxide by manganese dioxide (all should wear eye protection). Collect some of the gas produced and test it. Ask: 'How does this breakdown occur?' (5–10 minutes)

The fly – Show a clip from the film *The Fly* (David Cronenberg, 1986) where the scientist, who has been in a direct matter transfer device with a fly, starts vomiting on his food before eating it. Alternatively, show photographs of a fly's mouthparts and talk through how they function, or how a spider sucks the juice out of its victims. (For a taster, search the web for 'The Fly watch trailer'). (10 minutes)

MAIN

Enzymes in action

- **Breaking down hydrogen peroxide** – This experiment shows the action of manganese(IV) oxide, an inorganic catalyst, and a piece of liver, which contains the enzyme catalase, on hydrogen peroxide. A test tube containing hydrogen peroxide is included as a control. An additional control using a piece of boiled and cooled liver would show that the enzyme from the living tissue can be denatured.

- **Catalase in living tissue** – Catalase is present in living tissue. The more active the tissue, the greater the catalase activity. Small cubes of different tissues, such as liver, muscle, apple and potato, can be dropped into test tubes containing hydrogen peroxide ($10 \, cm^3$ to $15 \, cm^3$ depending on the size of the tubes).

- The reactions can be described or they can be measured. (This links to: 'How Science Works' – making observations and measurements.) If the experiment is to be a qualitative one, i.e. just a simple comparison of the activity by observation, then written descriptions or comparative statements can be made.

- It is possible to make this experiment more quantitative by using the same quantities of each tissue, and then measuring the activity when placed in the same volume of hydrogen peroxide. Simple heights of froth up the tube in a given time can be measured. A more accurate measurement is given by collecting the gas evolved in a given time. (This demonstrates many of the 'How Science Works' concepts.)

- There are many variations of the catalase experiments:

  i) The students could investigate the volume of gas released when different quantities of fresh liver are used in the same volume of hydrogen peroxide, i.e. varying the amount of enzyme with a fixed quantity of substrate.

  ii) The converse of this is to use the same quantity of liver and vary the volumes of hydrogen peroxide used, i.e. varying the quantity of the substrate with a fixed quantity of enzyme.

- An Animation, B2 4.1 'How do enzymes work', is available on the Additional Science CD ROM.

PLENARIES

Word-matching exercise – On Hot Potatoes (www.halfbakedsoftware.com), or a similar Java program, students to drag and drop words from the lesson next to the correct definitions. (5 minutes)

Find the substrate for the enzyme – Using thin card, make sets of 'enzymes' of different shapes and with differently shaped 'active sites', and a corresponding set of 'substrates' that fit into the enzymes 'active sites'. (You could adapt very simple jigsaw pieces.) Students need to find the enzyme and substrate that fit together. (5–10 minutes)

Practical support

Breaking down hydrogen peroxide

Equipment and materials required

Fresh liver, potato tuber tissue, apple etc., tiles and knives for cutting, test tubes, hydrogen peroxide solution, eye protection, some method of measuring the gas given off (syringes/inverted test tubes or manometers; rulers if height of froth to be measured), stopwatches or stop clocks, water bath if liver is to be boiled and denatured.

Safety: CLEAPSS Hazcard 33. Do not dispose of organic waste down sink.

Answers to in-text questions

a) The minimum energy needed for particles to react.

b) A substance that changes the rate of a chemical reaction (usually speeds it up).

ACTIVITY & EXTENSION

- **Catalase activity in plant tissues** – The different parts of a plant can be tested for catalase activity. Take equal quantities of leaf, stem and root tissue and test with hydrogen peroxide.

- Use equal quantities of germinating and non-germinating seeds to show that the more active the tissue, the greater the catalase activity.

- **Starch-digesting enzymes in maize** – This is a demonstration. Soak the maize grains for 2 days to initiate germination, and then keep them moist for a further 24 hours. Cut the maize grains in half and place cut-side down on starch/agar in Petri dishes. Place lids over the top, fixing with tape – but do not seal – and leave for 24 hours. Flood with iodine solution (CLEAPSS Hazcard 54) and the starch will stain blue-black, but there will be clear areas around the starch grains. Discuss what has happened.

BIOLOGY   ENZYMES

B2 4.1   Enzyme structure

LEARNING OBJECTIVES

1 What is an enzyme?
2 How do enzymes speed up reactions?

DID YOU KNOW?

The lack of just one enzyme in your body can have disastrous results. If you don't make the enzyme phenylalanine hydroxylase you can't break down the amino acid phenylalanine. It builds up in your blood and causes serious brain damage. All UK babies are tested for this condition soon after birth. If they are given a special phenylalanine-free diet right from the start, the risk of brain damage can be avoided.

The cells of your body are like tiny chemical factories. Hundreds of different chemical reactions are taking place all the time. These reactions have to happen fast – you need energy for your heart to beat and to hold your body upright *now*! They also need to be very controlled. The last thing you need is for your cells to start exploding!

Chemical reactions can only take place when different particles collide. The reacting particles don't just have to bump into each other. They need to collide with enough energy to react.

The minimum amount of energy particles must have to be able to react is known as the **activation energy**. So you will make the reaction more likely to happen if you can make it:

- more likely that reacting particles bump into each other,
- increase the energy of these collisions, or
- reduce the activation energy needed.

a) What is the activation energy of a reaction?

Controlling the rate of reactions

In everyday life we control the rates of chemical reactions all the time. When you cook food, you increase the temperature to speed up the chemical reactions. You lower the temperature to slow reactions down in your fridge or freezer. And sometimes we use special chemicals known as **catalysts** to speed up reactions for us.

A catalyst changes the rate of a chemical reaction, usually speeding it up. Catalysts are not used up in the reaction so you can use them over and over again. Different types of reactions need different catalysts. Catalysts work by bringing reacting particles together and lowering the activation energy needed for them to react.

b) What is a catalyst?

Enzymes – the biological catalysts

In your body chemical reaction rates are controlled by **enzymes**. These are special *biological catalysts* which speed up reactions.

Enzymes do not change the overall reaction in any way except to make it happen faster. Each one catalyses a specific type of reaction.

GET IT RIGHT!

Remember that the way an enzyme works depends on the shape of the active site which allows it to bind with the substrate.

Enzymes are involved in:

- building large molecules from lots of smaller ones,
- changing one molecule into another, and
- breaking down large molecules into smaller ones.

Inorganic catalysts and enzymes both lower the activation energy needed for a reaction to take place.

42

PRACTICAL

Breaking down hydrogen peroxide

Investigate the effect of i) manganese(IV) oxide, and ii) raw liver on the breakdown of hydrogen peroxide solution.

- Describe your observations and interpret the graph below.

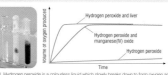

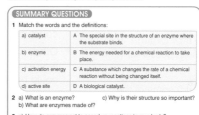

Figure 1 Hydrogen peroxide is a colourless liquid which slowly breaks down to form oxygen and water. The decomposition reaction goes much faster using manganese(IV) oxide as a catalyst. Raw liver contains an enzyme (catalase) which also speeds up the breakdown of hydrogen peroxide.

Your enzymes are large protein molecules. They are made up of long chains of amino acids, folded and coiled to give a molecule with a very special shape. The enzyme molecule usually has a hole or indentation in it. This special shape allows other molecules to fit into the enzyme. We call this the **active site**. The shape of an enzyme is vital for the way it works.

How do enzymes work?

The substrate (reactant) of the reaction fits into the shape of the enzyme. You can think of it like a lock and key. Once it is in place the enzyme and the substrate bind together. This is called the **enzyme–substrate complex**.

Then the reaction takes place rapidly and the products are released from the surface of the enzyme. (See Figure 3.) Remember that enzymes can join together small molecules as well as breaking up large ones.

Enzymes usually work best under very specific conditions of temperature and pH. This is because anything which affects the shape of the active site also affects the ability of the enzyme to speed up a reaction.

SUMMARY QUESTIONS

1 Match the words and the definitions:

a) catalyst	A The special site in the structure of an enzyme where the substrate binds.
b) enzyme	B The energy needed for a chemical reaction to take place.
c) activation energy	C A substance which changes the rate of a chemical reaction without being changed itself.
d) active site	D A biological catalyst.

2 a) What is an enzyme?
   b) What are enzymes made of?
   c) Why is their structure so important?

3 a) How do enzymes act to speed up reactions in your body?
   b) Why are enzymes so important in your body?

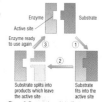

Figure 2 Enzymes have a very complex structure made up of chains of amino acids folded and coiled together. This computer-generated image shows just how complicated the structure really is!

Figure 3 Enzymes have their effect as catalysts using the 'lock-and-key' mechanism shown here. You can see that anything which changes the shape of the protein molecule might change the shape of the active site and stop the enzyme from working.

KEY POINTS

1 Catalysts increase the rate of chemical reactions. Enzymes are biological catalysts
2 Enzymes are protein molecules made up of long chains of amino acids. The chains are folded to form the active site. This is where the substrate of the reaction binds with the enzyme.

43

SUMMARY ANSWERS

1 a) C   b) D   c) B   d) A

2 a) A biological catalyst.

   b) Protein/amino acid chains.

   c) The way in which the amino acid chains are folded gives them a structure that includes a special area or indentation. This is the active site where the enzyme binds.

3 a) Substrate molecule/s arrive at the active site. They fit perfectly together, like a lock and key. The activation energy is reduced once the substrate is in place. The substrate molecules react and change shape. The products leave the active site. The enzyme is left unchanged and ready to catalyse the next reaction.

   b) Enzymes control reactions in cells, making them happen at the right speed. They stop reactions getting mixed up.

KEY POINTS

It is important for students to know what a catalyst is and to understand the structure of enzymes. The concept of the active site and the binding of the substrate molecules can be summarised in a series of diagrams, which students could keep for revision.

B2 4.2

Factors affecting enzyme action

LEARNING OBJECTIVES

- Enzymes are vital to all living cells.
- Changes in temperature affect the rate at which enzymes work.
- Different enzymes work best at different pH values.

LEARNING OUTCOMES

Most students should be able to:

- Describe experiments that show the effect of changes in temperature and pH on the rate of enzyme-controlled reactions.
- Describe how changes in temperature and pH affect enzyme action.

Some students should also be able to:

- Explain how changes in temperature and pH affect the active site of an enzyme.

Teaching suggestions

- **Special needs.** Students can be told that bits of milk need to be joined together by enzymes to make yoghurt. Make some yoghurt in a vacuum flask, a water bath or preferably a commercial yoghurt maker. Set up controls in the refrigerator and at room temperature. Prepare a work sheet with a results table for time taken for it to run through a funnel. Adjust the bore so that some yoghurt will very slowly flow through. Try it with boiled yoghurt (risk assessment).

- **Gifted and talented**
  - Students could research some of the organisms that live in hot springs, very cold conditions and conditions of extreme pH.
  - They could look at the role of DNA polymerase from thermophilic organisms in the Polymerase Chain Reaction for amplifying DNA.

- **Learning styles**

  Kinaesthetic: Practical work on enzymes.

  Visual: Making a diagram to show what happens when protein becomes denatured.

  Auditory: Listening to instructions about practical work.

  Interpersonal: Discussing the range and interval of values chosen for the independent variable (temperature).

  Intrapersonal: Writing a report of their investigative work.

SPECIFICATION LINK-UP   Unit: Biology 2.11.6

- *Enzymes are protein molecules made up of long chain amino acids. These long chains are folded to produce a special shape that enables other molecules to fit into the enzyme. This shape is vital for the enzyme's function. High temperatures destroy this special shape. Different enzymes work best at different pH values.*

- *Enzymes inside living cells catalyse processes such as respiration, protein synthesis and photosynthesis.*

Lesson structure

STARTER

Denaturing eggs – Crack raw eggs (or get students to do this) into three beakers: one beaker at room temperature, one at a temperature where visible changes to the egg white just occur, and one at boiling point. Students to describe and explain the changes that are happening to the protein. (5–10 minutes)

What happens to milk when it goes off? – Show the students fresh and sour milk. If possible, have one that is really solid but careful risk assessment is necessary. Discuss what has happened to the milk and why putting milk in the refrigerator stops it going off. (5–10 minutes)

What happens if I get too hot? – Show a picture of a soldier or a sailor in a dry suit. Describe the sad circumstances in which a recruit died while carrying out severe exercise in a dry suit. Ask: 'Why might have he died?' Link to fever, ask: 'who has been ill with a fever?' Take some class temperatures with forehead thermometers. Ask: 'Why do your parents worry when you get very hot?' Link to denaturing enzymes. (5–10 minutes)

MAIN

Investigating the effect of temperature

- **Action of amylase on starch** – Students can use their own saliva to carry out this experiment. (See 'Practical support'.)
- A graph can be plotted of the rate of disappearance of starch (1/time taken in seconds) against the temperature.
- Many concepts of 'How Science Works' can be developed in the investigative work, e.g. hypotheses are formulated, predictions are made, variables are controlled and conclusions drawn.
- **Other enzymes** – These could be used for investigations into the effect of temperature. If the use of the students' saliva is not possible, commercial amylase could be used, but it is usually derived from fungi and can give odd results.
- If pepsin or trypsin (protein digesting enzymes) are used, the substrate to use is the white of hard-boiled eggs or an egg-white suspension made by adding 5 g of egg white to 500 cm³ of very hot water and whisking briskly. The rate at which the egg white suspension clears can be timed at the different temperatures. More 'How Science Works' concepts are introduced here, too. The effects of varying pH can also be investigated.

PLENARIES

Effect of body temperature on digestion – Show a picture or footage of a reptile, such as a snake or a crocodile, eating a large lump of meat and show a picture of lions feeding. Ask: 'What consequences will their different body temperatures have on the rate at which they digest their meals? How often do they feed the reptiles in the Zoo?' Students to make a list and compare. (10 minutes)

The pH in the gut – Show a diagram of the human gut on to the board and write in the pH of the various regions (mouth, stomach etc.). Alongside the diagram, write a list of the major enzymes and the pH at which they work best. Students to match the enzyme with the region of the gut. (5–10 minutes)

- **Luciferase** – Search www.images.google.com and show pictures of flashlight fish, luminous jellyfish, fungi, glow worms that all have this enzyme, which catalyses a reaction and releases energy as light. Some plants have the enzyme and glow green. Tell the true story of a pilot lost at sea from an aircraft carrier at night who navigated his way back and landed successfully after following the faint trail of light from phosphorescent algae, which glowed in the wake of the ship following its passage. Break a lightstick of the kind used by the armed forces, campers and at discos. Demonstrate the reaction of luciferase by mixing the appropriate chemicals in vitro. Students could do Internet search on luciferase to see what else they can find out about this unique enzyme.

- **Extended experiments** – With the pH experiments, the introduction of a wider range of pH values could make the experiment more reliable. The quantities of alkali and acid could be varied and the pH ascertained by testing with pH papers. Alternatively, make up solutions of known pH for use.

- **Effect of varying pH on catalase** – Potato discs can be added to hydrogen peroxide and buffer solutions and the quantity of oxygen evolved in a set time can be measured at each pH. A graph can be plotted of volume of oxygen evolved against pH and the optimum pH for catalase determined.

Practical support

Investigating the effect of temperature

Equipment and materials required

Test tubes and racks, water baths for different temperatures, 2% starch solution, boiled saliva, iodine solution (CLEAPSS Hazcard 54), white tiles, glass rods, eye protection.

Details

Each student will need at least 2 cm depth of saliva in a test tube. Test tubes should be set up containing equal volumes of saliva and starch solution, shaken and then placed into water baths at different temperatures. Drops of the mixtures are then tested at 30 second intervals for the presence or absence of starch by dipping a glass rod into the mixture and then into a drop of iodine solution on a white tile. Note the colour each time and record how long it takes for the starch to disappear at each temperature. A control could be set up using boiled saliva.

BIOLOGY   ENZYMES

B2 4.2   Factors affecting enzyme action

LEARNING OBJECTIVES

1 How does increasing the temperature affect your enzymes?
2 What effect does a change in pH have on your enzymes?

Optimum temperature – this is when the reaction works as fast as possible

The rate of the reaction increases with the increase in temperature

The enzyme is denatured and stops working

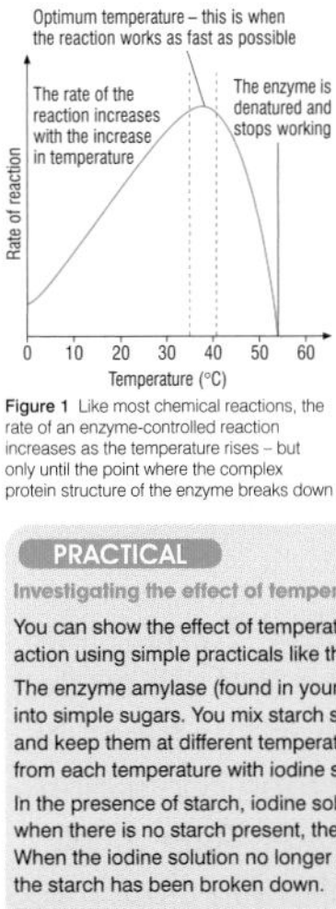

Figure 1 Like most chemical reactions, the rate of an enzyme-controlled reaction increases as the temperature rises – but only until the point where the complex protein structure of the enzyme breaks down

Leave a bottle of milk at the back of your fridge for a week or two and you'll find it is pretty disgusting. The milk will have gone off as enzymes in bacteria break down the protein structure.

Leave your milk in the Sun for a day and the same thing will happen – but much faster. Temperature affects the rate at which chemical reactions take place even when they are controlled by biological catalysts.

Biological reactions are affected by the same factors as any other chemical reactions – concentration, temperature and particle size all affect them. But in living organisms an increase in temperature only works up to a certain point.

a) Why does milk left in the Sun go off quickly?

The effect of temperature on enzyme action

The chemical reactions which take place in living cells happen at relatively low temperatures. Like most other chemical reactions, the rate of enzyme-controlled reactions increases with an increase in temperature. The enzyme and substrate particles move faster as the temperature increases, so this makes them more likely to collide with enough energy to react.

However this is only true up to temperatures of about 40°C. After this the protein structure of the enzyme is affected by the temperature. The long amino acid chains begin to unravel. As a result the shape of the active site changes. We say the enzyme has been denatured. It can no longer act as a catalyst, so the rate of the reaction drops dramatically. Most human enzymes work best at 37°C.

b) What does it mean if an enzyme is denatured?

PRACTICAL

Investigating the effect of temperature

You can show the effect of temperature on the rate of enzyme action using simple practicals like the one shown opposite.

The enzyme amylase (found in your saliva) breaks down starch into simple sugars. You mix starch solution and amylase together and keep them at different temperatures. Then you test samples from each temperature with iodine solution at regular intervals.

In the presence of starch, iodine solution turns blue-black. But when there is no starch present, the iodine stays yellow-brown. When the iodine solution no longer changes colour you know all the starch has been broken down.

This gives you some clear evidence of the effect of temperature on the rate of enzyme controlled reactions.

- How does iodine solution show you if starch is present?
- Why do we test starch solution without amylase added?
- What conclusion can you draw from the results?

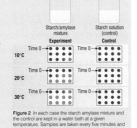

Starch/amylase mixture
Experiment

Starch solution (control)
Control

	Time 0	Time 0
10°C		
20°C		
30°C		

Figure 2 In each case the starch amylase mixture and the control are kept in a water bath at a given temperature. Samples are taken every five minutes and tested with iodine solution on a spotting tile.

Additional biology

Effect of pH on enzyme action

Enzymes have their effect by binding the reactants to a specially shaped active site in the protein molecule. Anything which changes the shape of this active site stops the enzyme from working. Temperature is obviously one thing which changes the shape of the protein molecule. The surrounding pH is another.

The shape of enzymes is the result of forces between the different parts of the protein molecule which hold the folded chains in place. A change in the pH affects these forces and changes the shape of the molecule. As a result, the active site is lost, so the enzyme can no longer act as a catalyst.

Different enzymes have different pH levels at which they work at their best – and a change in the pH can stop them working completely.

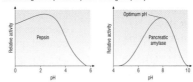

Pepsin

Optimum pH

Pancreatic amylase

Figure 3 These two enzymes are found in quite different parts of the human gut, and they need very different conditions of pH to work at their maximum rate. Pepsin is found in the stomach, along with hydrochloric acid, while pancreatic amylase is in the small intestine along with alkaline bile.

The role of enzymes

Enzymes are vital to all living cells. They catalyse a huge range of reactions. Without them respiration, photosynthesis and protein synthesis would be impossible. This also applies to all the other reactions which take place in your cells. For the enzymes to work properly the temperature and pH must be just right. This is why it is so dangerous if your temperature goes very high when you are ill and run a fever. Once your body temperature reaches about 41°C, your enzymes start to be denatured and you will soon die.

SUMMARY QUESTIONS

1 Copy and complete using the words below:

| active site | cells | denatured | enzyme | increases |
| protein | reactions | shape | temperatures | 40°C |

The chemical ...... which take place in living ...... happen at relatively low .... The rate of these ...... controlled reactions ...... with an increase in temperature. However this is only true up to temperatures of about .... After this the ...... structure of the enzyme is affected and the ...... of the .... is changed. The enzyme has been ....

2 Look at Figure 3.
   a) At which pH does pepsin work best?
   b) At which pH does amylase work best?
   c) What happens to the activity of the enzymes as the pH increases?
   d) Explain why this change in activity happens.

DID YOU KNOW?

Not all enzymes work best at around 40°C! Bacteria living in hot springs work at temperatures of over 80°C and higher. On the other hand, some bacteria which live in the very cold deep sea have enzymes working effectively at 0°C and below!

GET IT RIGHT!

The rate of enzyme-controlled reactions increases as the temperature goes up to about 40°C because the particles are moving faster. So substrate molecules collide with enzymes more often. Once the temperature goes much over 40°C most enzymes are denatured and no longer work as catalysts.
Enzymes aren't killed (they are molecules, not living things themselves) – use the term denatured.

Figure 4 The magical light display of a firefly is caused by the action of a very special enzyme called luciferase

KEY POINTS

1 Enzyme activity is affected by temperature and pH.
2 High temperatures and the wrong pH can affect the shape of the active site of an enzyme and stop it working.
3 Enzymes catalyse processes such as respiration, photosynthesis and protein synthesis in living cells.

44   45

SUMMARY ANSWERS

1 Reactions, cells, temperatures, enzyme, increase, 40°C, protein, shape, active site, denatured.

2 **a)** About pH 2.
   b) About pH 8.
   c) The activity levels fall fast.
   d) The increase in pH affects the shape of the active site of the enzyme so it no longer bonds to the substrate. It is denatured and no longer catalyses the reaction.

Answers to in-text questions

a) The reactions in the bacteria that make the milk go sour/bad happen faster as it is warmer.

b) The shape of the active site is lost so it does not work properly any more.

KEY POINTS

It is important to stress that each enzyme has an optimum temperature and an optimum pH at which it works. Variations in temperature and pH affect the rate at which each enzyme works. Extremes of pH and high temperature cause the enzyme to be denatured (not killed) because the shape of the enzyme is altered and the substrate no longer fits into the active site.

B2 4.3

Aerobic respiration

LEARNING OBJECTIVES

Students should learn that:

- During aerobic respiration, glucose and oxygen are used to release energy.

- Carbon dioxide and water are released as waste products.

- Most of the reactions in aerobic respiration occur inside mitochondria.

LEARNING OUTCOMES

Most students should be able to:

- Describe the raw materials and products of the process of respiration.

- Describe where the reactions take place in cells.

Some students should also be able to:

- Explain why more active cells, such as muscle cells, have greater numbers of mitochondria than less active cells.

- Design experiments to show that oxygen is taken up and carbon dioxide is released during aerobic respiration.

Teaching suggestions

- **Special needs.** Make model mitochondria from date boxes, washing liquid capsule boxes or similar, with corrugated cardboard. Fill with used batteries to indicate their role as energy carriers and display on a large poster.

- **Gifted and talented.** Give the students a sheet on the theories of Alan Templeton and Rebecca Cann with regard to 'Mitochondrial Eve' and the origins of the human species. Ask students to summarise points for and against each theory.

- **Learning styles**

  Kinaesthetic: Folding paper exercise, making a model mitochondrion.

  Visual: Observing electron microscope images of mitochondria.

  Auditory: Discussing the reasons for respiration.

  Interpersonal: Testing each other on the respiration equation.

  Intrapersonal: Appreciating the importance of the organelle.

SPECIFICATION LINK-UP   Unit: Biology 2.11.6

- *During aerobic respiration (respiration which uses oxygen) chemical reactions occur which:*
  - *use glucose (a sugar) and oxygen*
  - *release energy.*

- *Most of the reactions in aerobic respiration take place inside mitochondria.*

- *Aerobic respiration is summarised by the equation:*

$$glucose + oxygen \rightarrow carbon\ dioxide + water\ (+ energy)$$

- *The energy that is released during respiration is used:*
  - *to build up larger molecules using smaller ones*
  - *in animals, to enable muscles to contract*
  - *in mammals and birds, to maintain a steady body temperature in colder surroundings*
  - *in plants, to build up sugars, nitrates and other nutrients into amino acids which are then built into proteins.*

Lesson structure

STARTER

Instant energy – Show glucose drink bottles and energy drinks. Read or show labels from various foods and read as a class (search an image bank for 'energy drink label'). Students to list the energy contents from the labels and order them in terms of sugar content and energy. (10 minutes)

Turning lime water cloudy – Draw crosses on the bottoms of test tubes with a Chinagraph pencil. Half-fill each tube with lime water. Give each student a drinking straw (use bendy straws) and a tube of lime water and tell them to blow gently through the straw into the lime water until they can no longer see the cross on the bottom from the top. Eye protection must be worn. Ask: 'How long does it take? What is happening?' Go over the reaction and introduce respiration. (10 minutes)

MAIN

Composition of inhaled and exhaled air – As a follow-up to the starter 'Turning lime water cloudy', a more refined piece of apparatus can be used to show that the air that is breathed in contains less carbon dioxide than air breathed out. Arrange two tubes of lime water, tubing and clips, so that air can be drawn in through one tube containing lime water and breathed out through another tube containing lime water. After a few breaths, it can clearly be seen that the lime water in the two tubes differs in cloudiness.

Investigating respiration

- **Using a small mammal** – A small mammal can be placed under a bell jar on a glass plate sealed with Vaseline. Air is drawn through the apparatus, first passing through a U-tube of soda lime (to remove carbon dioxide) and then through a tube of lime water (to show that carbon dioxide has been removed) before entering the bell jar. After leaving the bell jar, the air is drawn through another tube of lime water to show that carbon dioxide is given off. The small mammal does not need to be there for very long – any small mammal is usually quite active and a result is achieved fairly quickly.

- **Alternatively** – Other small animals, such as earthworms, woodlice or maggots can be used in such a demonstration/investigation.

- **Using a plant** – It is possible to substitute a potted plant for the small mammal and to show that carbon dioxide is given off during respiration in plants. The pot and soil of the plant need to be enclosed in a polythene bag and the bell jar needs to be covered in black paper to exclude light. The apparatus should be left running for a couple of days. Ask: 'Why is the plant pot covered up? Why is light excluded?'

- **Controls** – All these experiments need controls, which should be discussed with the students (this relates to 'How Science Works'– validity of experimental design). In most cases, with the bell jar experiments, the removal of the living organism should be considered as a control.

PLENARIES

How small can you get it? – Have a competition to see who can fold an A4 sheet of paper into the smallest volume. Ask: 'What is the best method?' Relate to surface area and cristae in mitochondria. (5–10 minutes)

Sort it out – Give groups of students the statements in question 1 of the summary questions on separate slips of paper. See which group can sort them out correctly in the shortest time. (10 minutes)

SUMMARY ANSWERS

1 a) D b) E c) A d) C e) B

2 a) Mitochondria are the site of energy production in the cell. They have very folded membranes inside, giving a large surface area for the enzymes that control the reactions of aerobic respiration.

b) Muscle cells are very active and need a lot of energy; therefore they need large numbers of mitochondria to supply the energy. Fat cells use very little energy so need very few mitochondria.

3 The main uses of energy in the body are for movement, for building new molecules and for heat generation. The symptoms of starvation are that people become very thin. Stored energy is used up and growth stops. New proteins are not made and there is not enough energy or raw materials. People do not want to move; they lack energy, as there is a lack of fuel for the mitochondria. People feel cold, as there is not enough fuel for the mitochondria to produce heat energy.

4 See practical box 'Investigating respiration' on page 46 in Student Book.

Practical support

Composition of inhaled and exhaled air

Equipment and materials required

Test tubes half-full of lime water in racks, test tubes with 2-hole bungs, delivery tubes (one long, one short), rubber tubing, sterile mouth pieces, Chinagraph pencil, drinking straws (bendy ones if possible) or tubing and clips, eye protection.

Investigating respiration

For these demonstrations/investigations

Lime water (to show carbon dioxide produced), soda lime in U-tube (to absorb carbon dioxide for the experiments with the small mammal and the potted plant), small mammal such as a hamster in a bell jar (for the small mammal demo.), potted plant (for the potted plant demo.), earthworms, maggots or woodlice, black paper, tubing, eye protection.

ACTIVITY & EXTENSION

- **Mitochondria** – View Internet sites on electron tomography for good pictures of mitochondria. A particularly useful site is the National Center for Microscopy and Imaging Research. (www.ncmir.ucsd.edu).

- **Aerobic exercise** – Try out some aerobics, an activity for the class in the gym to calculate energy released. Several videos will give exercises and the amount of energy used. Ask: 'Why is it called aerobic exercise?'

BIOLOGY   ENZYMES

B2 4.3   Aerobic respiration

LEARNING OBJECTIVES

1 What is aerobic respiration?
2 Where in your cells does respiration take place?

DID YOU KNOW?

The average energy needs of a teenage boy is 11 510 kJ of energy every day – but teenage girls only need 8830 kJ a day. This is partly because on average girls are smaller than boys but also because boys have more muscle cells, which means more mitochondria demanding fuel for aerobic respiration.

One of the most important enzyme-controlled processes in living things is **aerobic respiration**.

Your digestive system, lungs and circulation all work to provide your cells with what they need for respiration to take place.

During aerobic respiration glucose (a sugar produced as a result of digestion) reacts with oxygen. This reaction releases energy which your cells can use. This energy is vital for everything else that goes on in your body.

Carbon dioxide and water are produced as waste products of the reaction.

We call the process aerobic because it uses oxygen from the air.

Aerobic respiration can be summed up by the equation:

glucose + oxygen → carbon dioxide + water (+ energy)

a) Why is aerobic respiration so important?

PRACTICAL

Investigating respiration

Animals and plants – even bacteria – all respire. To show that cellular respiration is taking place, you can either deprive a living organism of the things it needs to respire, or show that waste products are produced from the reaction.

Depriving a living thing of food and/or oxygen would kill it – so this would be an unethical investigation. So we concentrate on the waste products of respiration. Carbon dioxide and energy in the form of heat are the easiest to identify.

Lime water goes cloudy when carbon dioxide bubbles through it. The higher the concentration of carbon dioxide, the quicker the lime water goes cloudy. This gives us an easy way of demonstrating that carbon dioxide has been produced. We can also look for a rise in temperature to show that energy is being produced during respiration.

- Plan an ethical investigation into aerobic respiration in living organisms.

Outer membrane

A mitochondrion

Folded inner membrane gives a large surface area where the enzymes which control cellular respiration are found

Figure 1 Mitochondria are the powerhouses which provide energy for all the functions of your cells

Mitochondria – the site of respiration

Aerobic respiration involves lots of chemical reactions, each one controlled by a different enzyme. Most of these reactions take place in the **mitochondria** of your cells.

Mitochondria are tiny rod-shaped bodies (**organelles**) which are found in all plant and animal cells. They have a folded inner membrane which provides a large surface area for the enzymes involved in aerobic respiration.

Cells which need a lot of energy – like muscle cells and sperm – have lots of mitochondria. Cells which use very little energy – like fat cells – have very few mitochondria.

b) Why do mitochondria have folded inner membranes?

Reasons for respiration

- Respiration releases energy from the food we eat so that the cells of the body can use it.

- Both plant and animal cells need energy to carry out the basic functions of life. They build up large molecules from smaller ones to make new cell material. Much of the energy released in respiration is used for these 'building' activities (synthesis reactions). For example in plants, the sugars, nitrates and other nutrients are built up into amino acids which are then built up into proteins.

- Another important use of the energy from respiration in animals is in making muscles contract. Muscles are working all the time in our body, whether we are aware of them or not. Even when you sleep your heart beats, you breathe and your gut churns – and these muscular activities use energy.

- Finally, mammals and birds are 'warm-blooded'. This means that our bodies are the same temperature inside almost regardless of the temperature around us. On cold days we use energy to keep our body warm, while on hot days we use energy to sweat and keep our body cool.

SUMMARY QUESTIONS

1 Copy and complete these sentences, matching the pairs.

a) Energy is released from glucose	A ...... energy is released.
b) During respiration chemical reactions take place	B ...... because it uses oxygen from the air.
c) When glucose reacts with oxygen	C ...... are formed as waste products.
d) Carbon dioxide and water	D ...... by a process known as respiration.
e) The process is known as aerobic respiration	E ...... inside the mitochondria in the cells of your body.

2 Why are mitochondria so important and how is their structure adapted for the job that they do?

3 You need a regular supply of food to provide energy for your cells. If you don't get enough to eat you become thin and stop growing. You don't want to move around and you start to feel cold. There are three main uses of the energy released in your body during aerobic respiration. What are they and how does this explain the symptoms of starvation described above?

4 Suggest an experiment to show that a) oxygen is taken up, and b) carbon dioxide is released, during aerobic respiration.

GET IT RIGHT!

Make sure you know the equation for respiration. Remember that aerobic respiration takes place in the mitochondria.

Figure 2 Warm-blooded animals like this bird use up some of the energy they produce by aerobic respiration just to keep a steady body temperature. When the weather is cold, they use a lot more energy to keep warm. Giving them extra food supplies can mean the difference between life and death.

KEY POINTS

1 Aerobic respiration involves chemical reactions which use oxygen and sugar and release energy. The reaction is summed up as:

glucose + oxygen → carbon dioxide + water (+ energy).

2 Most of the reactions in aerobic respiration take place inside the mitochondria.

 46

 47

Answers to in-text questions

a) It provides energy for all the functions of the cells.

b) The folded inner membranes provide a large surface for all the enzymes needed to control the reactions of respiration.

KEY POINTS

Students should learn the respiration equation. Higher attaining students could put in the chemical symbols and balance the equation. They can then test each other on the respiration equation. The site of respiration in the mitochondria is important and students should be aware that muscle tissue is more active than fatty tissue.

B2 4.4   Enzymes in digestion

LEARNING OBJECTIVES

Students should learn that:

- During digestion, the breakdown of large molecules into smaller molecules is catalysed by enzymes.
- These enzymes, which are produced by specialised cells in glands, pass out into the gut.
- The enzymes include amylases that catalyse the breakdown of starch, proteases that catalyse the breakdown of proteins and lipases that catalyse the breakdown of lipids.

LEARNING OUTCOMES

Most students should be able to:

- Explain how enzymes are involved in the digestion of our food.
- Describe the location and action of the enzymes which catalyse the breakdown of carbohydrates (starch), proteins and lipids.

Some students should also be able to:

- Explain digestion in terms of the molecules involved.

Teaching suggestions

- **Special needs.** Use flip cards with foods on one side and their components on the other. Some students might need a clue, such as starting letters or vowels. Alternatively, use an Internet version for whiteboards, or individual computers such as those created through 'Quia' (use this as a search term).
- **Gifted and talented.** Research the role of ribosomes through an interactive CD-ROM, such as the protein synthesis section of www.dnai.org.
- **Learning styles**
  Kinaesthetic: Playing floor dominoes. Carrying out practical work on model gut.
  Visual: Observing Simulation B2 4.4 'Enzymes in Digestion' from the Additional Science CD ROM.
  Auditory: Listening to instructions about the Visking tubing experiments.
  Interpersonal: Discussing the ethics of experimenting with the contents of another person's stomach.
  Intrapersonal: Evaluating the strength of evidence from the digestion experiments and suggesting improvements.
- **Homework.** Write the clues for the cryptic word search.

SPECIFICATION LINK-UP   Unit: Biology 2.11.6

- *Some enzymes work outside the body cells. The digestive enzymes are produced by specialised cells in glands and in the lining of the gut. The enzymes pass out of the cells into the gut where they come into contact with the food molecules. They catalyse the breakdown of large molecules into smaller molecules:*
  - *the enzyme amylase is produced in the salivary glands, the pancreas and the small intestine. This enzyme catalyses the breakdown of starch into sugars in the mouth and small intestine*
  - *protease enzymes are produced by the stomach, the pancreas and the small intestine. These enzymes catalyse the breakdown of proteins into amino acids in the stomach and the small intestine*
  - *lipase enzymes are produced by the pancreas and small intestine. These enzymes catalyse the breakdown of lipids (fats and oils) into fatty acids and glycerol in the small intestine.*

Lesson structure

STARTER

Model gut – Liquidise a dinner, or similar food leaving some big bits, and spoon it into the leg cut from a pair of tights. Squeeze it so that some of the goo goes through but not the big bits. Describe how this models the situation in the intestines. Discuss limitations of this model. (5 minutes)

What we know about enzymes so far, a quick quiz – Ask ten questions on enzyme structure and the factors affecting their action. Students to swap and mark each others. (5–10 minutes)

MAIN

- **Making a model gut** – Each group of students will need two 15 cm lengths of dialysis (Visking) tubing to model the gut. (See 'Practical support'.)
- If desired, the experiments can be left for 24 hours at room temperature before testing.
- **A simplified version of the model gut** – If there is not time for the students to carry out their own experiments, then a length of dialysis tubing can be filled with a mixture of 30% glucose solution and 3% starch solutions and placed in a test tube of distilled water. If this is left for about 15 minutes, the water can be tested for starch and glucose.
- Some glucose should have diffused through the tubing into the water, but the starch should not. Tests for starch and glucose will confirm this. Note: This only demonstrates that glucose will pass through the tubing but starch will not; it does not show that the enzyme catalyses the breakdown of the starch.
- **Investigating digestion** – The model gut can be used to show the effect of changes in temperature and pH on the activity of saliva or amylase on starch. The tubing should be placed in boiling tubes, and samples of the water surrounding the tubing can be tested for starch and sugars at intervals to determine whether or not digestion has taken place.
- To investigate changes in temperature, the boiling tubes containing the enzyme-substrate mixtures in the tubing should be incubated in a range of temperatures from about 5°C to 60°C using water baths.
- To investigate the range of pH values, buffer solutions should be used, providing another opportunity to develop the investigative aspects of 'How Science Works'.

PLENARIES

Floor dominoes – Make up large 'domino' cards of food types, their components and the enzymes. Play in groups. (5–10 minutes)

Enzyme spider – Draw out a spider diagram to summarise the role of enzymes in digestion, with contributions from the class. (10 minutes)

Cryptic word search – Students to begin a word search, deciding on the words to include. Write cryptic definitions of the words as clues for homework. (10 minutes)

Practical support

Investigating digestion

Equipment and materials required

Visking or dialysis tubing, dropping pipettes, elastic bands, starch and enzyme solutions (the strengths of these solutions may need to be adjusted to give results in a lesson session), water baths, beakers, test tubes and racks, iodine solution (CLEAPSS Hazcard 54), Benedict's solution (Harmful – CLEAPSS Hazcards 27 and 95), eye protection.

Details

- Each group of students will need two 15 cm lengths of dialysis (Visking) tubing, which has been soaked in water. Each piece should be knotted securely at one end. Using a dropping pipette, fill one length of the tubing with 3% starch solution and place it in a test tube. Fold the top of the tubing over the rim of the test tube and secure with an elastic band. Remove all traces of the starch solution from the outside of the tubing by filling the test tube with water and emptying it several times. Finally, fill the test tube with water and place it in a rack.

- Repeat the procedure with the second length of tubing but add 5 cm³ saliva (safety as B2 4.2 with saliva) or amylase solution to the starch solution, and shake before filling the dialysis tubing. The test tubes should be labelled A and B and placed in a water bath at 35°C for 30 minutes. The water in the test tubes should then be tested for: starch, using iodine solution; sugars, using Benedict's solution.

SUMMARY ANSWERS

1 Food, insoluble, broken down, soluble, absorbed, cells, digestive enzymes.

2 Suitable table.

3 Large molecules cannot pass through gut membrane into blood, cannot be taken into cells or used.
glucose – absorbed, carried in blood, taken into cells, broken down by respiratory enzymes to provide energy
amino acids – absorbed, carried in blood, taken into cells and used in protein synthesis to build new proteins
fatty acids/glycerol – absorbed, carried in blood, taken into cells and used as a source of energy for respiration and for building new fats and oils.

ACTIVITY & EXTENSION IDEAS

- Search image bank for 'Alexis St Martin'. Enlarge on the story, as the students love to hear about the lumps of meat dangled inside him. Have some cubes of meat tied to pieces of string to emphasise the point.

Answers to in-text questions

a) They work outside the cells of your body.

b) Amylase.

c) Proteases.

d) Lipases.

KEY POINTS

These key points are general and students could add details of specific enzymes, their substrates and products, in order to expand their information. The production of a chart or flow diagram showing where and how food is digested in the gut could also be useful.

BIOLOGY ENZYMES

B2 4.4 Enzymes in digestion

LEARNING OBJECTIVES

1 How are enzymes involved in the digestion of your food?
2 What happens to the digested food?

GET IT RIGHT!

Learn the different types of digestive enzymes and the end products of the breakdown of your food. Make sure you know where the different digestive enzymes are made.

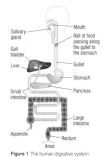

Salivary gland
Mouth
Ball of food passing along the gullet to the stomach
Gall bladder
Liver
Gullet
Stomach
Pancreas
Small intestine
Large intestine
Appendix
Rectum
Anus

Figure 1 The human digestive system

The food you eat is made up of large insoluble molecules which your body cannot absorb. They need to be broken down or *digested* to form smaller, soluble molecules. These can then be absorbed and used by your cells. This chemical breakdown is controlled by your digestive enzymes.

Most of your enzymes work **inside** the cells of your body. Your digestive enzymes are different – they work **outside** of your cells. They are produced by specialised cells which are found in glands (like your salivary glands and your pancreas), and in the lining of your gut.

The enzymes then pass out of these cells into the gut itself. It is here that they get mixed up with your food molecules and break them down.

Your gut is a hollow muscular tube which squeezes your food. The gut:
- helps to break up your food into small pieces with a large surface area for your enzymes to work on,
- mixes your food with your digestive juices so that the enzymes come into contact with as much of the food as possible, and
- uses its muscles to move your food along its length from one area to the next.

a) How do your digestive enzymes differ from most of your other enzymes?

Digesting carbohydrates

Enzymes which break down carbohydrates are known as **carbohydrases**. Starch is one of the most common carbohydrates that you eat. It is broken down into **sugars** like glucose. This reaction is catalysed by the carbohydrase called *amylase*.

Amylase is produced in your salivary glands, so the digestion of starch starts in your mouth. Amylase is also made in your pancreas and your small intestine. No digestion takes place in the pancreas. All the enzymes made there flow into your small intestine, which is where most of the starch you eat is digested.

b) What is the name of the enzyme which breaks down starch in your gut?

Digesting proteins

The breakdown of protein food like meat, fish and cheese into amino acids is catalysed by **protease** enzymes. Proteases are produced by your stomach, your pancreas and your small intestine. The breakdown of proteins into **amino acids** takes place in your stomach and small intestine.

c) Which enzymes breaks down protein in your gut?

Digesting fats

The **lipids** (fats and oils) that you eat are broken down into **fatty acids** and **glycerol** in your small intestine. The reaction is catalysed by *lipase* enzymes which are made in your pancreas and your small intestine. Yet again the enzymes made in the pancreas are passed into the small intestine.

Once your food molecules have been completely digested into soluble glucose, amino acids, fatty acids and glycerol, they leave your small intestine. They pass into your blood supply to be carried around the body to the cells which need them.

d) Which enzymes break down fats in your gut?

PRACTICAL

Investigating digestion

You can make a model gut using a bag of special membrane containing starch and amylase enzymes. When the enzyme has catalysed the breakdown of the starch, you can detect the presence of sugar on the outside of the 'gut'!

- How can you test for sugars?

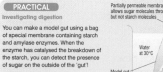

Partially permeable membrane which allows sugar molecules through, but not starch molecules
Water at 30°C
Model gut
Mixture of starch solution and amylase

Figure 2 This apparatus provides you with a model of the gut. You can use it to investigate how the gut works and the effects of factors like temperature and pH on how the gut enzymes work

Using the digested food

- The glucose produced by the action of amylase and other carbohydrases is used by the cells of your body in respiration.
- Fatty acids and glycerol may be used as a source of energy or to build cell membranes, make hormones and as fat stores.
- The amino acids produced when you digest protein are not used as fuel. Once inside your cells, amino acids are built up into all the proteins you need. These synthesis reactions are catalysed by enzymes. In other words, your enzymes make new enzymes as well as all the other proteins you need in your cells. This **protein synthesis** takes place in the **ribosomes**.

Chain of amino acids forming
Ribosome
Endoplasmic reticulum

Figure 3 Ribosomes are very small. They can only be seen using the most powerful microscopes. However their role in protein synthesis means they are vital to the working of your cells and your whole body!

SUMMARY QUESTIONS

1 Copy and complete using the words below:

absorbed broken down cells digestive enzymes food insoluble soluble

The ...... you eat is made up of large ...... molecules which need to be .... to form smaller, ... molecules. These can be ...... by your body and used by your .... This chemical breakdown is controlled by your ....

2 Make a table which shows where amylase, protease and lipase are made. For each enzyme show where it is made, which reaction it catalyses and where it works in the gut.

3 Why is digestion of your food so important? Explain in terms of the molecules involved.

FOUL FACTS

When Alexis St Martin suffered a terrible gunshot wound in 1822, Dr William Beaumont managed to save his life. However Alexis was left with a hole (or fistula) from his stomach to the outside world. Dr Beaumont then used this hole to find out what happened in Alexis's stomach as he digested food!

KEY POINTS

1 Enzymes catalyse the breakdown of large food molecules into smaller molecules during digestion.
2 Digestive enzymes are produced inside cells but they work outside of cells in the gut.
3 Enzymes in the ribosomes catalyse the build up of proteins from amino acids.

B2 4.5   Speeding up digestion

LEARNING OBJECTIVES

Students should learn that:

- The enzymes in the stomach work most effectively in the acid conditions resulting from the production of hydrochloric acid by the stomach.

- Bile produced by the liver provides the alkaline conditions needed for the enzymes in the small intestine to work most effectively.

- Bile also emulsifies the fats increasing the surface area for the enzymes to act upon.

LEARNING OUTCOMES

Most students should be able to:

- Describe how pH affects the enzymes in the different parts of the gut.

- State that bile emulsifies fats.

Some students should also be able to:

- Explain how the emulsification of fats increases the rate of their digestion.

Teaching suggestions

- **Special needs.** Show the students a Mars bar or something similar. Ask: 'If you stuck it into your mouth whole, which bits could the saliva touch?' Get a student to chop the bar in half. Ask: 'Which bits could the saliva touch now that it could not before?' Chop again repeatedly and draw out the idea of surface area being important in digestion.

- **Gifted and talented.** Present the students with a table of results of surface area against rate of reaction. Students could draw a graph and calculate the gradient of the graph at a number of points and describe how it changes, with reasons.

- **Learning styles**

  Kinaesthetic: Carrying out practical work.

  Visual: Observing demonstrations of emulsification.

  Auditory: Discussing the activities of the lesson.

  Interpersonal: Working in groups during the practicals.

  Intrapersonal: Considering the reasons for the changes in rates of reaction or writing a letter to the doctor about gall stones.

SPECIFICATION LINK-UP   Unit: Biology 2.11.6

- *Some enzymes work outside the body cells. The digestive enzymes are produced by specialised cells in glands and in the lining of the gut. The enzymes pass out of the cells into the gut where they come into contact with the food molecules. They catalyse the breakdown of large molecules into smaller molecules:*
  - *protease enzymes are produced by the stomach, the pancreas and the small intestine. These enzymes catalyse the breakdown of proteins into amino acids in the stomach and the small intestine*
  - *the stomach also produces hydrochloric acid. The enzymes in the stomach work most effectively in these acid conditions*
  - *the liver produces bile that is stored in the gall bladder before being released into the small intestine. Bile neutralises the acid that was added to the food in the stomach. This provides alkaline conditions in which enzymes in the small intestine work most effectively.*

Lesson structure

STARTER

Vomit! – Show a video clip, or still, from *Little Britain* of the woman who does the projectile vomiting over people (or discuss the sketches with the students). Search the web for 'Little Britain'. Ask: 'If we scooped up some of the sick with a spoon and tested its pH, what would it be? What does vomit taste like?' Discuss what it is and then link with bulimia and the effect of repeated vomiting on the enamel of the teeth. (10 minutes)

Emulsions – Bring in a can of emulsion paint. Ask the students what the word means (you could paint it on to a large sheet of paper). Bring in a salad, some vinegar and some olive oil. Get a student to pour some oil on top of the vinegar in a gas jar or similar vessel, shake vigorously and produce an emulsion. Students can do this themselves on a small scale in a boiling tube. Observe the globules formed and link to surface area, then to speeding up digestion. (10 minutes)

The bacon experiment – Get a volunteer to write their initials in Vaseline on a piece of bacon and immerse the bacon in protease enzyme. Students can predict what will happen and check if they're right at the end of the lesson. (5–10 minutes)

MAIN

- **Breaking down protein** – The practical described in the Student Book is easy to set up. Each group of students will require three test tubes and can set up their own experiment. An additional control tube could be added using boiled and cooled pepsin.

- **Modification to the experiment** – The experiment can be made more quantitative, and therefore extend the opportunity to teach concepts from 'How Science Works', by getting the students to formulate an hypothesis, make predictions, use stated volumes of enzyme and acid and weigh the pieces of meat used at the beginning and end of the experiment. In this case, it would be advisable to leave the experiment running for 24 hours. The pieces of meat should then be removed from the tubes, rinsed and dried on filter paper before reweighing. A bar chart can be drawn showing the percentage change in mass.

- **Comparing the action of pepsin with the action of trypsin** – Pepsin and trypsin work in different parts of the gut in different pH conditions. The experiment described in section 4.2: 'Effect of pH on enzyme action' could be used here to show that pepsin works best in acid conditions and trypsin in alkaline conditions. If specific pH values are required, then the use of buffer solutions is recommended.

- **The effect of bile salts** – The experiment described in lesson 4.4: 'Digesting fats', involves the use of bile salts and it would be appropriate to include it here.

- **Dissection of bird or mammal gut to show different regions** – Depending on the school policy and LEA regulations, a game bird or rabbit could be dissected to show the position of the liver, the gall bladder and other organs associated with the gut. If this is not allowed or advisable, then there are videos available or still pictures that can be projected. Students can be given the opportunity to see it: not for the squeamish. (Search for images on the web, looking for 'dissection gut'.) Students who object should not be forced to take part!

PLENARIES

Is the bacon done? – Check the bacon set up at the start of the lesson. If required use a web cam to display the results via a projector. (5 minutes)

Gall stones – Show some gall stones or photographs of gall stones. Discuss why gall stones occur and what might be the consequences. Get the students to write a letter to their doctor stating what problems they fear and asking advice. (10 minutes)

Colouring exercise – Give the students unlabelled diagrams of the digestive system and ask them to label them and colour in the different regions according to the different pH conditions that exist in the gut. (10 minutes)

ACTIVITY & EXTENSION

- **Increasing the surface area** – Discuss the effect of the teeth and mastication on the break up of large masses of food in the mouth. Ask: 'What is the effect on digestion in the mouth? Does chewing affect the digestion in the stomach?'

- **Design an experiment** – Students could be asked to design an experiment to find the optimum pH at which the enzyme amylase works. They need to think about where amylase is produced and then to use an appropriate range of pH values, suggest which variables need to be controlled and how to judge and evaluate the results (this is another excellent learning opportunity for 'How Science Works').

BIOLOGY   ENZYMES

B2 4.5   Speeding up digestion

LEARNING OBJECTIVES

1 Why does your stomach contain hydrochloric acid?
2 What is bile and why is it so important in digestion?

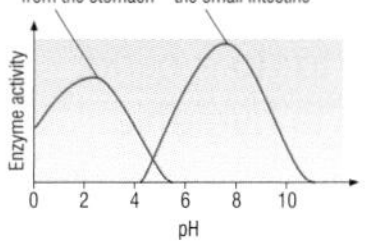

Pepsin – protease from the stomach   Trypsin – protease from the small intestine

Figure 1 Both of these enzymes catalyse the breakdown of proteins. But as these graphs show, the enzyme found in the stomach works best at a very different pH to the one made in the pancreas and used in the small intestine.

Your digestive system produces many enzymes which speed up the breakdown of the food you eat. However enzymes aren't the only important chemicals in your gut. As you saw on pages 44 and 45, enzymes are very sensitive to temperature and pH. As your body is kept at a fairly steady 37°C, your enzymes have an ideal temperature which allows them to work as fast as possible.

Keeping the pH in your gut at ideal levels isn't quite so easy. That's because different enzymes work best at different pH levels. The protease enzyme found in your stomach works best in acidic conditions.

On the other hand, the proteases made in your pancreas need alkaline conditions. Then they can catalyse protein breakdown as fast as they can. Look at the graph in Figure 1.

So your body makes a variety of different chemicals which help to give your enzymes ideal conditions all the way through your gut.

a) Why do your enzymes almost always have the right temperature to work at their best?

Changing pH in the gut

You have around 35 million glands in the lining of your stomach secreting protease enzymes to digest the protein you eat. These enzymes work best in an acid pH. So your stomach also produces a concentrated solution of hydrochloric acid from the same glands. In fact your stomach produces around 3 litres of acid a day!

This acid allows your stomach protease enzymes to work very effectively. It also kills most of the bacteria which you take in with your food.

Finally, your stomach also produces a thick layer of mucus which coats your stomach walls and protects them from being digested by the acid and the enzymes!

b) How does your stomach avoid digesting itself?

PRACTICAL

Breaking down protein

You can see the effect of acid on pepsin, the protease found in the stomach, quite simply. Set up three test tubes, one containing pepsin only, one containing only hydrochloric acid and one containing a mixture of the two. Keep them at body temperature in a water bath. Add a similar sized chunk of meat to all three of them. Set up a web cam and watch for a few hours to see what happens!

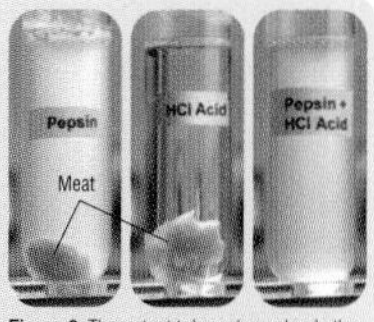

Figure 2 These test tubes show clearly the importance of protein-digesting enzymes *and* hydrochloric acid in your stomach. Meat was added to each tube at the same time.

- What conclusions can you make?

FOUL FACTS

Pigments from your bile are largely responsible for the brown colour of your faeces. If you have a disease which stops bile getting into your gut, your faeces will be white or silvery grey!

After a few hours – depending on the size and type of the meal you have eaten – your food leaves your stomach and moves on into your small intestine. Some of the enzymes which catalyse digestion in your small intestine are made in your pancreas. Some are also made in the small intestine itself. They all work best in an alkaline environment.

The acidic liquid coming from your stomach needs to become an alkaline mix in your small intestine! So how does it happen?

Your liver carries out many important jobs in your body and one of them is producing bile. Bile is a greenish-yellow alkaline liquid which is stored in your gall bladder until it is needed.

As food comes into the small intestine from the stomach, bile is squirted onto it. The bile neutralises the acid from the stomach and then makes the semi-digested food alkaline. This provides the ideal conditions for the enzymes in the small intestine.

c) Why does the food coming into your small intestine need neutralising?

Altering the surface area

It is very important for the enzymes of the gut to have the largest possible surface area of food to work on. This is not a problem with carbohydrates and proteins. However, the fats that you eat do not mix with all the watery liquids in your gut. They stay as large globules – think of oil in water – which makes it difficult for the lipase enzymes to act.

This is the second important function of the bile. It emulsifies the fats in your food. This means it physically breaks up large drops of fat into smaller droplets. This provides a much bigger surface area for the lipase enzymes to act on. The larger surface area helps them chemically break down the fats more quickly into fatty acids and glycerol.

SUMMARY QUESTIONS

1 Copy and complete using the words below:

alkaline	emulsifies	gall bladder	liver	neutralises

small intestine

Bile is an...... liquid produced by your .... It is stored in the .... and released onto food as it comes into the .... It ...... the acid food from the stomach and makes it alkaline. It also ...... fats.

2 Look at Figure 1.

a) At what pH does the protease from the stomach work best?
b) How does your body create the right pH in the stomach for this enzyme?
c) At what pH does the protease from the intestine work best?
d) How does your body create the right pH in the small intestine for this enzyme?

3 Draw a diagram to explain how bile produces a big surface area for lipase to work on and explain why this is important.

DID YOU KNOW?

Sometimes the gall bladder and bile duct get blocked by gall stones which can range in diameter from a few millimetres to several centimetres.

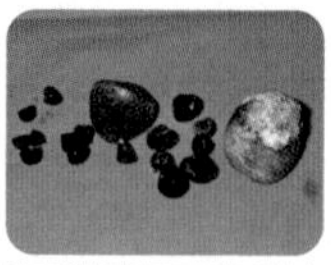

Figure 3 If gall stones like these block your bile duct, they not only affect your digestion, they cause absolute agony!

GET IT RIGHT!

Remember food is not digested in the liver or the pancreas.
Bile is **not** an enzyme and it does **not** break down fat molecules.
Bile emulsifies fat droplets to increase the surface area, which in turn increases the rate of fat digestion by lipase.

KEY POINTS

1 The enzymes of the stomach work best in acid conditions.
2 The enzymes made in the pancreas and the small intestine work best in alkaline conditions.
3 Bile produced by the liver neutralises acid and emulsifies fats.

50 | 51

SUMMARY ANSWERS

1 Alkaline, liver, gall bladder, small intestine, neutralises, emulsifies.

2 **a)** pH 2.1

b) Hydrochloric acid is made in glands in the stomach.

c) pH 7.4

d) The liver produces bile that is stored in the gall bladder and released when food comes into the small intestine.

3 [Marks for a good diagram showing a large fat droplet coated in bile splitting into many small fat droplets.] This produces a larger surface area so enzymes can get to many more fat molecules and so break them down more quickly.

Answers to in-text questions

a) The body temperature is usually maintained around 37°C.

b) The stomach glands produce a thick layer of mucus.

c) The food entering the small intestine from the stomach is acidic. The enzymes of the small intestine work best in alkaline conditions.

Practical support

 Breaking down protein

Equipment and materials required

For each group:

At least three test tubes and a rack, small cubes of meat, 2% pepsin solution, 0.1 M solution of hydrochloric acid, water bath at 35°C, balance, labels, filter papers, eye protection.

KEY POINTS

Students should be aware of the changes in pH through the gut and which enzymes work best in the different conditions. It is also important to make sure students understand that food is only digested in the gut and not by the liver or the pancreas. It could be helpful to refer to these organs as associated with the gut, or as accessory organs.

B2 4.6

Making use of enzymes

LEARNING OBJECTIVES

Students should learn that:

- Enzymes from microorganisms have many uses in the home and in industry.
- Proteases and lipases are used in the manufacture of biological detergents.
- Proteases, carbohydrases and isomerase are used in food manufacture.

LEARNING OUTCOMES

Most students should be able to:

- Explain how biological detergents work.
- Describe some of the ways in which enzymes are used in the food industry.

Some students should also be able to:

- Evaluate the advantages and disadvantages of using enzymes in home and in industry.

Teaching suggestions

- **Special needs.** Use name boards with a fold-over end. Write 'carbohydrate' on one and use the hinged fold-over to convert it into 'carbohydrase'. Have examples of all the enzymes required in the specification.
- **Gifted and talented.** Ask students to find out the differences in the structural formulae of glucose and fructose. They can try to work out why these sugars have different effects on the taste buds.
- **Learning styles**
  Kinaesthetic: Carrying out practical work; using structural models (like molymodels) to show interchange between glucose and fructose.
  Visual: Creating a poster.
  Auditory: Explaining to other students how temperature affects enzyme activity.
  Interpersonal: Conducting a survey of who has dishwashers in their homes and what they think of them.
  Intrapersonal: Thinking about whether or not they would eat their parent's vomit if it meant staying alive.
- **Homework.** There are some opportunities here for research at home. Students could find out how many people use biological detergents in dishwashers and washing machines, and whether or not there are differences between them. Some preparatory work for the next spread could be set as homework tasks here.

SPECIFICATION LINK-UP   Unit: Biology 2.11.6

- *Some microorganisms produce enzymes that pass out of the cells. These enzymes have many uses in the home and in industry.*
- *In the home, biological detergents may contain protein-digesting and fat-digesting enzymes (proteases and lipases).*
- *In industry:*
  - *proteases are used to 'pre-digest' the protein in some baby foods*
  - *carbohydrases are used to convert starch into sugar syrup*
  - *Isomerase is used to convert glucose syrup into fructose syrup, which is much sweeter and therefore can be used in smaller quantities in slimming foods.*

Lesson structure

STARTER

Taste tests – Fructose (fruit sugar) is now available in many supermarkets. It could be interesting to make up separate solutions of fructose, sucrose and glucose of the same strength (e.g. 2 teaspoons in a beaker of water) and get the students to do a blind tasting scoring them for sweetness on a 5 point scale. (Must be done in hygienic conditions following risk assessment.) (10–15 minutes)

Baby food for lunch? – Show the students some samples of baby food. Have disposable plastic spoons and be prepared for joking. Some pelican bibs will help to create the atmosphere. Ask: 'How does this food differ from adult food? What did parents do (and some still do) before the commercially prepared baby foods were available?' (10 minutes)

MAIN

- **Investigating biological washing powder** – Using agar plates containing starch, milk and mayonnaise (or salad cream or egg yolk), the activity of enzymes in biological detergents can be demonstrated. (See 'Practical support'.)

- This demonstration can be used to:
  - Compare different biological washing powders or liquids (the advantage of liquids is that volumes can be measured and dilutions made more easily).
  - Compare dishwasher detergents with clothes washing detergents.
  - Discover whether the age of the detergent has any effect on its efficiency.
  - Discuss experimental design.

- These investigations can be used to introduce many 'How Science Works' concepts. Predictions can be made, measurements made and recorded, variables controlled and conclusions drawn. It also gives students some scope for designing their own investigations.

- **What temperature should I use?** – The experiment above can be modified to demonstrate that the proteases in a biological detergent can work at higher temperatures than trypsin from an animal source. Samples of both can be heated to temperatures of 30°C, 40°C etc. and then placed in holes in milk agar plates. Use a separate plate for each enzyme or detergent tested and the number of holes should correspond to the number of different temperatures tested. The plates should then be treated as above and the clear areas measured and recorded. A graph can then be plotted of temperature against area of clear zone.

- **Egg chunks in detergent** – Cubes of egg white immersed in a solution of biological detergent will be digested. A solution of a biological washing powder is made by dissolving 3 g of powder in 30 cm³ of water. A cube of egg white is weighed and placed in this solution for 20 minutes, after which time it is removed, rinsed and dried. The effect of the washing powder can be assessed by reweighing.

- This investigation can be expanded to consider different variables. Comparisons can be made using different biological detergents. The strength of the detergent needed can be investigated and the optimum temperature found. Again, this fulfils many of the requirements in 'How Science Works'.

Practical support

Investigating biological washing powder

Equipment and materials required
Some biological detergent (either in powder or liquid form in order to make up different concentrations if needed – avoid contact with skin), egg white in chunks/cubes (or agar plates containing starch, milk, mayonnaise, salad cream or egg yolk), test tubes and racks, tissues for drying, iodine solution (CLEAPSS Hazcard 54) balance for weighing, eye protection, protective gloves.

Details
A cork borer is used to remove cylinders of agar from the prepared plates. The number of cylinders removed depends on the number of detergents being tested. Into the holes, solutions of the detergents can be placed and the plates incubated at 25°C for about 24 hours.

Iodine solution is poured over the starch-agar plate and left for 5 minutes before being poured away. The diameter of clear areas around the holes can be measured and recorded. It should be possible to measure clear areas around the holes on the milk-agar plates and the mayonnaise-agar plates.

PLENARY

Baby food II – Ask your students to close their eyes and envisage a situation where their parent or guardian asks them if they are hungry. They say they are starving, so the adult is sick into a bucket and gives them a spoon, saying 'OK, eat that!' If easily available, show video footage of adult seabirds regurgitating food for their young. Talk over the changes in food that make it an advantage for very young creatures to eat regurgitated food. Also discuss reasons why it is not a good idea to drink sick! (10 minutes)

BIOLOGY   ENZYMES

B2 4.6   Making use of enzymes

LEARNING OBJECTIVES
1. How do biological detergents work?
2. How are enzymes used in the food industry?

Enzymes were first isolated from living cells in the 19th century, and ever since we have found more and more ways of using them in industry. Some microorganisms produce enzymes which pass out of the cells and are easy for us to use. In other cases we use the whole microorganism.

Enzymes in the home

In the past, people boiled and scrubbed their clothes to get them clean – and did it all by hand. Now we not only have washing machines to do the washing for us, we also have enzymes ready and waiting to digest the stains.

Many people use biological detergents to remove stains from their clothes from substances such as grass, sweat, food and blood. Biological washing powders contain proteases and lipases which break down the proteins and fats in the stains. They help provide us with a cleaner wash. We also use them at the lower temperatures that enzymes need to work best, so we use less electricity too.

a) What is a biological washing powder?

PRACTICAL
Investigating biological washing powder
Weigh a chunk of cooked egg white and leave it in a strong solution of biological washing powder.
- What do you think will happen to the egg white?
- How can you measure just how effective the protease enzymes are?
- How could you investigate the effect of surface area in enzyme action?

Figure 1 More and more homes now have a dishwasher – and dishwasher powders often contain enzymes. They digest the cooked-on proteins like eggs which are often hard to remove even in a dishwasher.

Enzymes in industry
Pure enzymes have many uses in industry.

Proteases are used in the manufacture of baby foods. They 'pre-digest' some of the protein in the food. When babies first begin to eat solid foods they are not very good at it. Treating the food with protease enzymes makes it easier for a baby's digestive system to cope with. It is easier for them to get the amino acids they need from their food.

Carbohydrases (carbohydrate digesting enzymes) are used to convert starch into sugar (glucose) syrup. We use huge quantities of sugar syrup in food production – just have a look at the ingredients labels on all sorts of foods.

Starch is made by plants like corn, and it is very cheap. Using enzymes to convert this plant starch into sweet sugar provides a cheap source of sweetness for food manufacturers.

It is also important for the process of making fuel (ethanol) from plants.

Figure 2 Learning to eat solid food isn't easy. Having some of it pre-digested by protease enzymes can make it easier to get the goodness you need to grow!

b) Why does the starch need to be converted to sugar before it is used to make ethanol?

Sometimes the glucose syrup made from starch is passed into another process which uses a different set of enzymes. Isomerase enzyme is used to convert glucose syrup into fructose syrup by rearranging the atoms in the glucose molecule.

Glucose and fructose contain exactly the same amount of energy (1700 kJ or 400 kcal per 100 g) but fructose is much sweeter than glucose. This means much smaller amounts of it are needed to make food taste sweet. So fructose is widely used in 'slimming' foods. The food tastes sweet but contains fewer calories.

Figure 3 The market for slimming foods is enormous and growing all the time. Enzyme technology is being used to convert more and more glucose syrup into fructose syrup to make so-called 'slimming' foods.

The advantages and disadvantages of using enzymes

In an industrial process, many of the reactions need high temperatures and pressures to make them fast enough to produce the products needed. Supplying heat and building chemical plants which can stand high pressures costs a lot of money.

However, enzymes can provide the perfect answer to industrial problems like these. They catalyse reactions at relatively low temperatures and normal pressures. Enzyme-based processes are therefore often fairly cheap to run.

The main problem with enzymes is that they are very sensitive to their surroundings. For enzymes to function properly the temperature must be kept down (usually below 45°C). The pH also needs to be kept within carefully monitored limits which suit the enzyme. It costs money to control these conditions.

Whole microbes are relatively cheap, but need to be supplied with food and oxygen and their waste products removed. What's more, they use some of the substrate to grow more microbes. Pure enzymes use the substrate more efficiently, but they are also more expensive to produce.

SUMMARY QUESTIONS
1. List three enzymes and the ways in which we use them in the food industry.
2. Biological washing powders contain enzymes in tiny capsules. Explain why:
   a) they are more effective than non-biological powders at lower temperatures,
   b) they are not more effective at high temperatures.
3. Make a table to show the advantages and disadvantages of using enzymes in industry.

GET IT RIGHT!
Remember that most enzyme names end in -ase. Some enzymes used in industry work at quite high temperatures – so don't be put off if a graph shows an optimum temperature well above 45°C!

KEY POINTS
1. Some microorganisms produce enzymes which pass out of the cells and can be used in different ways.
2. Biological detergents may contain proteases and lipases.
3. Proteases, carbohydrases and isomerase are all used in the food industry.

52

53

SUMMARY ANSWERS

1. Proteases: pre-digested baby food.
   Carbohydrases: convert starch to glucose syrup.
   Isomerase: converts glucose syrup to fructose syrup.

2. **a)** The protease and lipase enzymes digest proteins and fats on the clothes, so the clothes get cleaner than detergent alone.

   b) At temperatures above about 45°C, the enzymes may be denatured and so have no effect on cleaning.

3.

Advantages	Disadvantages
Work at relatively low temperatures.	Denatured by high temperatures.
Work at relatively low pressures.	Sensitive to pH changes.
Efficient catalysts.	If whole organisms, need food, oxygen and waste products removed.

Answers to in-text questions

a) A powder that contains enzymes, usually proteases and lipases.

b) Enzymes in yeast turn sugar (glucose) into ethanol.

KEY POINTS

Students should be made aware of the use of several different enzyme groups in the manufacture of products found in the home. As these enzymes have been derived from microorganisms with optimum temperatures different from those of mammals, i.e. around 37°C, products such as washing powders may work best at higher temperatures.

Unit: Biology 2.11.6

SPECIFICATION LINK-UP

Students should use their skills, knowledge and understanding of 'How Science Works':

- *to evaluate the advantages and disadvantages of using enzymes in the home and in industry.*

Teaching suggestions

- **The washing powder debate: a question of allergies** – Show digital pictures of skin with dermatitis. Discuss the problems; ask: 'Does anyone in the class have a skin allergy or reaction to washing powders?' Show a PowerPoint® presentation on allergic skin reactions. Include information on the 'packaging' of the enzymes and also some of the instructions on the packets. Ask: 'Are the warnings clear enough?'

- **A question of temperature** – Discuss the advantages of the biological washing powders and detergents with respect to the lower temperatures needed in washing machines. Ask: 'Is this always a good thing?' Some cycles will operate at temperatures as low as 30°C, but there may be some drawbacks. Draw up a balance sheet with advantages and disadvantages of the lower operating temperatures. Ask: 'Do the advantages outweigh the disadvantages? Would you wash your baby's nappies in a low temperature wash?'

- **Dishwashers and washing machines** – Ask: 'Are the biological detergents for dishwashers and washing machines the same?' Some research into the components of biological detergents for dishwashers and those for washing clothes could be interesting. Ask: 'Are the enzymes the same?' This could be tested in one of the experiments described in the previous spread.

- **Enzymes and medicine: a simple demonstration** – Clinistix and albustix can be used to test for the presence of glucose and protein in urine. Carry out a 'Tinkle test' experiment with fake urine doctored with glucose, protein, both and neither. Discuss the benefits of such tests compared with the standard tests used in the lab (Benedict's etc.). Also discuss the value of the tests in making quick diagnoses and how they can help people with diabetes to control their condition.

- **'Sammi's story'** – Show the video *Sammi's story* (Channel 4 Television, 1995 V15.012 or animated version by Philippa

The washing powder debate

I've got three children and they are all messy eaters! Their clothes get lots of mud and grass stains as well. I always use biological detergents because they get my washing really clean.

I've got very sensitive skin. When my mum changed to a biological detergent I got dermatitis so we never use biological detergents now.

When we first started manufacturing our biological detergent we found a lot of our factory staff developed allergies. We realised they were reacting to enzyme dust in the air – proteins often trigger allergies. But once we put the enzymes in tiny capsules all the allergy problems stopped. Unfortunately it got some bad publicity and lots of people still seem to think biological detergents cause allergies.

I try to be as green as possible in my lifestyle but I'm not sure about biological detergents. Enzymes are natural, after all – but I've heard they can cause allergies. On the other hand, biological powders use a lot less electricity because they clean at lower temperatures. That's good for the environment and cheaper for me!

ACTIVITY

You are part of a team producing an article for a lifestyle magazine about biological washing powders. Create a double-page article – make it lively, interesting to look at, scientifically accurate and informative!

Allergies aren't really a problem with biological detergents. However, if the clothes aren't rinsed really thoroughly, protein-digesting enzymes can get left in the fabric. Then the enzymes may digest some of the protein in your skin and set up dermatitis. But if the detergent is used properly, there shouldn't be a problem.

54

Manning, 1994, from Health Improvement Information and Resource Centre – 02071508345) available from the cystic fibrosis charity. This goes through the necessity of taking enzymes with food due to a blocked pancreatic duct. Ask students to summarise aspects of the content of the video and explain to the rest of the class. (See www.cftrust.org.uk.)

- **Other uses** – Use the Internet to research other uses of enzymes in medicine (e.g. www.enzymestuff.com). Some of the examples given in the Student Book can be expanded as well as other examples found.

- **The raw food craze** – This is a very open-ended activity, but the two pointers given at the end can give students a starting point. Again, class discussion of the topic could be beneficial. A brainstorming session about the different aspects could draw out some themes, which could be grouped together. For example, ask: 'What does cooking do to food? How is the vitamin content affected?'

- Students could be provided with some raw food of all types (fruit, vegetables and meat). Give students the choice; ask: 'Would you eat it or not? If not, why not?' Build up a list on the board of things that most students would eat raw and things they would not. You could run a Bush Tucker challenge on some vegetables that are normally eaten cooked, such as beetroot, courgettes etc. and see how many would be eaten raw.

Enzymes and medicine

Here are just some of the ways in which enzymes are used in medicine:

To diagnose disease

If your liver is damaged or diseased, some of your liver enzymes may leak out into your blood. If your symptoms suggest your liver isn't working properly, doctors can test your blood for these enzymes to find out if your liver really is damaged.

To diagnose and control disease

People who have diabetes often have too much sugar in their blood. As a result, they also get sugar in their urine. One common test for sugar in the urine relies on a colour change on a test strip.

The test strip contains a chemical indicator and an enzyme. It is placed in a urine sample. The enzyme catalyses the breakdown of any glucose found in the urine. The products of the reaction then make the indicator change colour if glucose is present.

To cure disease

- If your pancreas is damaged or diseased it cannot make enzymes. So you have to take extra enzymes – particularly lipase – to allow you to digest your food. The enzymes are in special capsules to stop them being digested in your stomach!
- If you have a heart attack, an enzyme called streptokinase will be injected into your blood as soon as possible. It dissolves clots in the arteries of the heart wall and reduces the amount of damage done to your heart muscle.
- An enzyme from certain bacteria is being used to treat a type of leukaemia in children. The cancer cells cannot make one particular amino acid, so they need to take it from your body fluids. The enzyme catalyses the breakdown of this amino acid, so the cancer cells cannot get any and they die. Your normal cells can make the amino acid so they are not affected. Doctors hope something similar may work against other types of cancer.

ACTIVITY

Make a poster with the title 'Enzymes in medicine' which could be used on the walls of the science department to inform pupils in KS3 and KS4. Use this material as a starting point. Also do some more research about the way enzymes can be used to help you make your poster as interesting as possible.

Health special

IN THE RAW!

WILL YOU TRY THE NEW DIET SENSATION?

The latest food craze to sweep the US is to eat your food – completely raw. And now it's coming to the UK!

It has been reported that there are lots of health benefits to this new way of eating. It is claimed that raw food contains live enzymes which will help to give you more energy. Apparently when food is cooked these enzymes die.

One of the owners of a new raw food restaurant has been quoted as saying,

'It is an amazingly interesting way of preparing food, it is good to have live enzymes in your system and, most importantly, it is yummy.'

Dodgy science

ACTIVITY

Dodgy science is everywhere in the media. It is often used to make people think something is a really good – or really bad – idea. The way the new craze for eating raw food has been reported is a good example. Read the extract from a magazine article given here. You now have quite a lot of biological knowledge gained from this part of the course and what you have learnt earlier about things like the spread of disease. Use your knowledge to:

a) explain what is wrong with the science in this report and why it is so inaccurate,

b) explain what problems linked to eating raw meat have been ignored in this report.

55

Special needs

Carry out a washing test using biological and non-biological detergents on some white T-shirts that have been stained with grass, egg, blackcurrant juice etc. If possible make a video of the experiment as a spoof advert.

Gifted and talented

Students could do more research on the problems of eating raw food, especially with respect to the toxic substances present in some plants that are removed by cooking (oxalates in rhubarb, red kidney beans etc.). They could produce a guide leaflet to the problems.

ICT link-up

- There are numerous opportunities for the use of ICT in the production of posters, pamphlets and leaflets.

- There are also opportunities for researching on the Internet. When doing so, students should search for 'enzymes in medicine' and 'raw food diets'.

Learning styles

Kinaesthetic: Carrying out washing test or tests with Clinistix.

Visual: Displaying information on a poster.

Auditory: Discussing the pros and cons of using biological washing powders.

Interpersonal: Collaborating in the practical activities.

Intrapersonal: Reviewing knowledge gained from other spreads in completing one of the activities.

- **The biological washing powder activity** – The suggested activity provides scope for some imaginative work. Students could work in groups and provide material about different issues. The 'talking heads' in the students' book spread have most of the issues covered and there is plenty there for informative articles. Students could include some pictures of allergic reactions, a simplified diagram of the encapsulation of the enzymes in the manufacturing process, some facts and figures about energy-saving and something about the stains that can be removed. It would be sensible to include some information about the problems; any good magazine would try to give a balanced view!

- **The poster activity: enzymes and medicine** – It will be difficult to get all the information on one poster, depending on the amount of detail to be included. Students could decide to make a series of posters. Some discussion about the impact of a poster with masses of information or a poster about one condition clearly explained should help students to decide what they would like to do. The use of ICT could be encouraged here: images can be scanned in and used to create an interesting poster.

- **The raw food craze** – Once students have got the science sorted out, they need to decide how they are going to present their explanations. This 'dodgy' science was purported to be from a magazine article. Ask: 'Is the best reply to it a letter to the magazine or a counterbalancing article from 'Our Science Correspondent' or an article from someone who has tried it – and suffered?' It could be a case for reinforcing the '5-a-day' recommendation for the consumption of fruit and vegetables.

SUMMARY ANSWERS

1 a) i) 6 **ii)** 4 **iii)** 2 **iv)** 1 **v)** 3 **vi)** 5

b) Enzymes work by bringing reacting particles together and lowering the activation energy needed for them to react. Enzymes are large protein molecules with a hole or indentation known as the 'active site'. The substrate of the reaction fits into the active site of the enzyme like a lock and key. Once it is in place, the enzyme and substrate bind together. This is called the 'enzyme-substrate complex'. Then the reaction takes place rapidly and the products are released from the surface of the enzyme. Anything that affects the shape of the active site affects the ability of the enzyme to speed up a reaction. [The use of diagrams would make this explanation very clear.]

2 a) It catalyses the breakdown of starch to glucose.

b) An increase in temperature increases the rate of the enzyme-controlled reaction.

c) One tube is kept at each temperature without any enzyme to act as a control/to show what would happen if there were no enzyme present.

d) It could be improved by having an additional control of just starch solution kept at body temperature.

e) The rate of the enzyme activity would fall because it is working well in a neutral pH. Lowering the pH/making it more acid will affect the active site and reduce its effectiveness.

3 a) [Marks awarded for a good graph plot with suitable scale chosen, axes right way round, axes labelled correctly and accurately-plotted points.]

b) Alkaline.

c) This enzyme could be found in the small intestine, because it works in alkaline conditions. Other protein-digesting enzymes work in the stomach, but the conditions there are acidic.

Summary teaching suggestions

- **Literacy guidance** – The explanation required in the answer to question 1b) provides an opportunity for the students to write answers in continuous prose and practise their literary skills. Look for good grammar, clear expression and the correct spelling of biological terms.

- **Special needs**
  - Students may be able to cope with question 1a), if provided with the pre-prepared information to match up, and with question 3a) if given a prepared grid.
  - Some of the questions about the experiments (question 2) could be given verbally.

- **When to use the questions?**
  - Question 1b) is a summary of enzyme action and, together with a clear diagram, would make an excellent revision card.
  - Question 2 could be used as a stimulus to help students write up their accounts of the experiment if they carried it out. These are the kinds of questions they could be asked about any experiment on a test paper.
  - Graph plotting (question 3) is good practice for showing results. The interpretation of the curve is a more demanding skill. This could be set for homework.

ENZYMES: B2 4.1 – B2 4.7

SUMMARY QUESTIONS

1 a) Copy and complete the following sentences, matching the parts of the sentences.

i)	A catalyst will speed up or slow down a reaction	1	...... could not occur without enzymes.
ii)	Living organisms make very efficient catalysts	2	...... made of protein.
iii)	All enzymes are	3	...... binds to the active site.
iv)	The reactions which keep you alive	4	...... known as enzymes.
v)	The substrate of an enzyme	5	...... a specific type of molecule.
vi)	Each type of enzyme affects	6	...... but is not changed itself.

b) Explain how an enzyme catalyses a reaction. Use diagrams if they make your explanation clearer.

2 Use Figure 2 on page 44 to help you answer this question.
- a) What effect does the enzyme amylase have on starch?
- b) What do these results tell you about the effect of temperature on the action of the amylase?
- c) Why is one tube of starch solution kept at each temperature without the addition of the enzyme?
- d) How could you improve this investigation?
- e) What do you predict would happen to the activity of the enzyme if acid from the stomach were added to the mixture?

3 The table gives some data about the relative activity levels of an enzyme at different pH levels.

pH	Relative activity
4	0
6	3
8	10
10	1

- a) Plot a graph of this data.
- b) Does this enzyme work best in an acid or an alkaline environment?
- c) This is a protein-digesting enzyme. Where in the gut do you think it might be found? Explain your answer.

EXAM-STYLE QUESTIONS

1 (a) In the summary of aerobic respiration shown below, choose a word from each of the boxes that best completes the equation. (2)

Glucose + BOX A ➡ carbon dioxide + BOX B (+ energy)
BOX A: water / oxygen / nitrogen
BOX B: water / oxygen / nitrogen

(b) (i) State two ways in which the energy released during respiration is used in **all** animals. (2)

(ii) How else might the energy released be used in mammals and birds only? (1)

(iii) Give a further use of the energy released that applies to plants rather than animals. (1)

2 A, B, C, D and E are the names of enzymes or groups of enzymes. The numbers 1, 2, 3, 4 and 5 refer to the functions or uses of each of these enzymes. Match each letter with the appropriate number. (5)

A	Lipase	1	Used in the manufacture of baby foods
B	Amylase	2	Group of enzymes that act on carbohydrates
C	Proteases	3	Its substrate is starch
D	Isomerase	4	Used in the production of slimming foods
E	Carbohydrases	5	The products of its catalytic action are glycerol and fatty acids

3 Amylase is an enzyme that catalyses the conversion of starch into sugar.

(a) To which of the following groups of food does starch belong? (1)

carbohydrates   fats   protein   vitamins

(b) Give the names of the **three** organs in the human body that secrete the enzyme amylase. (3)

The graph on the next page shows the effect of temperature on the activity of amylase.

(c) (i) At what temperature did the amylase work fastest? (1)

(ii) Why did the amylase not work above 56°C? (1)

(iii) State one other factor apart from temperature that will affect the rate of reaction of amylase. (1)

EXAM-STYLE ANSWERS

1 a) Box A = oxygen *(1 mark)*
Box B = water *(1 mark)*

b) i) To build up larger molecules from smaller ones. *(1 mark)*
To enable muscles to contract. *(1 mark)*

ii) To maintain a steady/constant body temperature. *(1 mark)*

iii) Used to build up sugars, nitrates and other nutrients into amino acids and then proteins. *(1 mark)*

2 A 5
B 3
C 1
D 4
E 2 *(1 mark each)*

3 a) Carbohydrates *(1 mark)*

b) Salivary glands
Pancreas
Small intestine *(1 mark each)*

c) i) 45°C *(1 mark)*
ii) It had become denatured. *(1 mark)*
iii) pH *(1 mark)*

4 a)

Temperature (°C)	Time to clot for A (mins)	Time to clot for B (mins)

able to be used, with suitable format *(1 mark)*
labelled *(1 mark)*
labelled with units *(1 mark)*

b) Range of 10 to 60°C *(1 mark)*

c) At least 5 interval measurements *(1 mark)*

d) e.g. shake to see if it is 'solid' *(1 mark)*

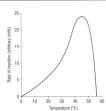

HOW SCIENCE WORKS QUESTIONS

Najma had carried out a 'rates of reaction' investigation in chemistry. Her results are in Table 1 below.

Table 1 Chemistry investigation

Temperature (°C)	Time taken (secs)
20	106
30	51
40	26
50	12
60	5

When asked in biology to do a 'rates of reaction' investigation she expected to get the same results. She reasoned that in both cases she was collecting the oxygen produced from hydrogen peroxide. The only difference was that she used manganese(IV) oxide in chemistry and she was using mashed up plant cells in biology! Her results from biology are in Table 2.

Table 2 Biology investigation

Temperature (°C)	Time taken (secs)
20	114
30	96
40	80
50	120
60	No reaction

a) What was Najma's prediction for the biology investigation? (1)

b) Was her prediction supported, refuted or should she rethink the prediction? (2)

c) Najma checked her results against some results in a textbook. Why was this a good idea? (1)

d) Najma was feeling happier now that she had been supported by other scientists' results. She had also learned that enzymes had a temperature at which they worked best. How could she change her investigation so that she could find the best temperature for this enzyme? (1)

e) Najma also learned that this enzyme was called catalase and that it occurs in nearly all organisms, even those living in hot water springs. How could she change her investigation to find the best temperature for catalase in hot water spring organisms? (2)

---

4 In the making of cheese, a commercially prepared form of an enzyme called rennin is used to make the protein in milk more solid. Rennin is an enzyme that is produced naturally in the stomachs of young mammals. The owner of a cheese making factory wanted to use a different source of rennin. She needed to find out the best temperature to use for the new rennin. She planned to set up 20 test tubes. All would have 20 cm³ of milk in them: half with the rennin added (A) and half to be left without rennin (B). One tube of each type would be left in a water bath until one of them clotted. When this happened, the time taken would be recorded.

(a) Construct a table that could be used by the owner. (3)

(b) Fill in the table to show the range of temperatures she might use. (1)

(c) Fill in the table to show the interval for the independent variable. (1)

(d) Suggest how the owner might know when the milk is clotted. (1)

(e) Would you suggest that she repeats her results? Explain your answer. (1)

(f) Why do you think she used tubes A and B at each temperature? (1)

5 Bile is a greenish liquid that plays an important role in the digestion of food.

(a) In which organ is bile produced? (1)

(b) Where is bile stored in the body? (1)

(c) Into which region of the digestive system is bile released? (1)

(d) Describe how bile is involved in the digestion of fats. (3)

(e) What is the name of the enzyme that digests fats? (1)

(f) Name two places where this enzyme is produced in the body. (2)

HOW SCIENCE WORKS ANSWERS

a) Najma's prediction was that, as the temperature was increased, the time taken for the oxygen to be collected would decrease.

b) Her prediction was supported up to about 40°C. After that, the time taken decreased until there was no reaction at all.

c) Yes, because it would check the reliability and accuracy of her results.

d) Increase the interval measurements around 40°C.

e) She would have to check the temperature of hot water springs and adjust her temperatures to match them. Collect some organisms from the spring to use instead of the plant cells she used before.

How science works teaching suggestions

- **Literacy guidance**
  - Key terms that should be clearly understood: prediction, accuracy, interval measurements.
  - The question expecting a longer answer, where students can practise their literacy skills is e).

- **Higher- and lower-level answers.** Questions b) and e) are higher-level questions. The answers for these have been provided at this level. Question c) is a lower-level question and the answer provided is also at this level.

- **Gifted and talented.** Able students could be asked to design an investigation for question e) as homework. This would be difficult if they were to use hydrogen peroxide at very high temperatures.

- **How and when to use these questions.** When wishing to develop ideas of the fallibility of predictions and the use of interval measurements. The questions are best tackled in small discussion groups.

- **Special needs.** A demonstration of the decomposition of hydrogen peroxide would bring more accessibility for some students.

---

e) Yes, because being precise about the time of clotting is very difficult. *(1 mark)*

f) B acted as a control
OR to test whether the rennin was causing the clotting. *(1 mark)*

5 a) The liver *(1 mark)*

b) The gall bladder *(1 mark)*

c) The small intestine *(1 mark)*

d) • Neutralises the acid (added to the food in the stomach).
• Provides neutral/alkaline conditions for enzymes to function/optimum pH for enzymes.
• Emulsifies fats/breaks up fats into small droplets.
• Increases the surface area of fats (so that enzymes can work on them more effectively). *Allow any accurate description of emulsification.*
(1 mark for each point to a maximum of 3 marks)

e) Lipase *(1 mark)*

f) Pancreas *(1 mark)*
Small intestine *(1 mark)*

Exam teaching suggestions

- The first three questions and the last one (question 5) are subdivided into small bite-sized pieces, making them easy to follow and requiring short answers testing largely recall of knowledge. As such, they make suitable practice examination exercises for foundation-tier students while still providing straightforward revision tests for those at higher-tier level.

- Students need to be made aware of the significance of the preamble that accompanies certain questions. All too often they dismiss it as extraneous packaging that can be disregarded. The information is always there for a purpose. It often does more than merely set the scene; it may contain clues, even vital information, that is needed to answer the question effectively.

B2 5.1

Controlling internal conditions

LEARNING OBJECTIVES

Students should learn that:

- Waste products, carbon dioxide and urea, have to be removed from the body.

- Carbon dioxide is removed via the lungs when we breathe out and the kidneys are involved in the removal of urea.

- Internal conditions, such as the water and ion content of the body, need to be controlled.

LEARNING OUTCOMES

Most students should be able to:

- Explain why carbon dioxide and urea need to be removed from the body.

- Describe how carbon dioxide is removed from the body via the lungs.

- Describe the role of the kidneys in removing urea and controlling the water and ion content of the body.

Some students should also be able to:

- Demonstrate that they understand the complexity of homeostatis.

Teaching suggestions

- **Special needs.** Give the students a blank diagram with a body outline on it in the centre and four arrows coming from appropriate places. The students are given the labels 'Urine', 'Faeces', 'Sweat' and 'CO$_2$ in breath' and asked to put them in the correct places. [Beware of additions to the body drawing!]

- **Gifted and talented.** Ask students to hold their breath for 30 seconds (risk assessment for individuals). They can feel the desire to breathe building, due to the CO$_2$ building up. Talk about drowning experiences. Ask: 'Does the feeling go when you breathe in? Why is this? Where might the sensors be that tell you that you have too much CO$_2$ in you? How can you tell?' Link to the starter: 'Can you turn the indicator yellow?'

SPECIFICATION LINK-UP   Unit: Biology 2.11.7

- *Waste products which have to be removed from the body include:*
  - *carbon dioxide produced by respiration – most of this leaves the body via the lungs when we breathe out*
  - *urea produced in the liver by the breakdown of excess amino acids – this is removed by the kidneys in the urine, which is temporarily stored in the bladder.*

- *Internal conditions which are controlled include the water content of the body, the ion content of the body, temperature and blood sugar levels.*

- *If the water or ion content of the body is wrong, too much water may move into or out of the cells and damage them. Water and ions enter the body when we eat or drink.*

- *Sweating helps to cool the body. More water is lost when it is hot, and more water has to be taken as drink or in food to balance this loss.*

Lesson structure

STARTER

Keeping warm or staying cool – Show Student Book photos from the Additional Science CD ROM of obviously different climatic conditions. Ask: 'What will their core temperature be like?' Students to predict, respond and discuss. (5–10 minutes)

Can you turn the indicator yellow? – Show the students some hydrogencarbonate indicator. It should be cherry red when it is in equilibrium with the air. If a little dilute acid is added it turns yellow, if alkali is added it will go purple. Get a volunteer to blow into a tube of indicator through a straw. Ask: 'What does this show about the effect of CO$_2$ on the indicator and therefore the pH of CO$_2$ in solution?' Use this for students to speculate on the effect of the accumulation of CO$_2$ in the cells of the body. (10 minutes)

MAIN

Analysis of inspired and expired air

A sample of air is drawn into a capillary tube (called a J-tube, it consists of a syringe attached to a capillary tube bent into a square J-shape) and its volume *a* is recorded. Potassium hydroxide solution is then drawn into the tube to absorb the carbon dioxide. The volume will decrease. The new volume *b* is noted. The potassium hydroxide solution is almost all expelled. A reagent that absorbs oxygen (pyrogallol) is then drawn into the tube, causing the volume to decrease, and the new volume *c* noted. The percentage of CO$_2$ in the air is given by the expression: $a - b/a \times 100$

The percentage of O$_2$ in the air is given by the expression: $b - c/a \times 100$

- A sample of expired air can be obtained by immersing a boiling tube in a trough of water, raising it to a vertical position and then exhaling into it through a bent straw or capillary tube. The analysis of this sample of exhaled air can then be tested as above and the percentages compared.

- This is best done as a demonstration before the whole class, but you could get a volunteer to give you a sample of expired air. The samples need to be jiggled around in the J-tube so that the absorption of the gases takes place. Three samples should be measured and a mean taken. The samples need to be at room temperature before their volume is measured. (This relates to: 'How Science Works': reliability and validity of data.)

PLENARIES

Facts and figures – Produce some facts and figures from this spread (4%, 0.04%, kidneys, urea etc.) and ask students to write a sentence about the relevance of each to the current topic. Students to read some out. (10 minutes)

Spirometer – Have a spirometer for the students to look at and show how it can be used. (This relates to 'How Science Works': making measurements.) (10 minutes)

ACTIVITY & EXTENSION

- **Spirometer** – Use a volunteer student to demonstrate the use of a spirometer. Care needed and risk assessment required.
  Students should be familiar with the diagram in the Student Book and understand the principles of the use of the apparatus. They could discuss how the tracings can be used to measure lung volume and the effect of exercise on breathing.

- **pH inside cells** – Remind students of the experiment to find the optimum pH at which catalase works inside cells. If it was not done, then a demonstration emphasises the need for the elimination of carbon dioxide to keep the conditions inside cells neutral so that enzymes, such as catalase, can work most efficiently.

- **Homeostasis in the long-distance runner** – There are articles about marathon running on The Physiological Society's web site that could be read out and discussed. (See www.physoc.org.)

Teaching suggestions – continued

- **Learning styles**
  Kinaesthetic: Investigating breathing.
  Visual: Observing colour changes in indicator solutions.
  Auditory: Listening to the opinions of other students.
  Interpersonal: Collaborating with other students in kidney dissection.
  Intrapersonal: Considering the different effects of the outside environment and the maintenance of a stable internal environment.

BIOLOGY HOMEOSTASIS

B2 5.1 Controlling internal conditions

LEARNING OBJECTIVES

1 How do you keep conditions inside your body constant?
2 How do you get rid of the waste products of your cells?

Figure 1 Whatever you choose to do in life, the conditions inside your body will stay more-or-less exactly the same. When you think of the range of things you can do, it is amazing how the balance is maintained.

For your body to work properly the conditions surrounding your millions of cells must stay as constant as possible. On the other hand, almost everything you do tends to change things.

As you move you produce heat, as you respire you produce waste, when you digest food you take millions of molecules into your body. Yet you somehow keep your internal conditions constant within a very narrow range. How do you manage this?

The answer is through **homeostasis**. As you saw in topic B1a1.5, many of the functions in your body help to keep your internal environment as constant as possible. Now you are going to find out more about some of them.

a) What is homeostasis?

Removing waste products

No matter what you are doing, even sleeping, the cells of your body are constantly producing waste products as a result of the chemical reactions which are taking place. The more extreme the conditions you put yourself in, the more waste products your cells will make. There are two main poisonous waste products which would cause major problems for your body if the levels built up. These are carbon dioxide and urea.

Carbon dioxide

Carbon dioxide is produced during cellular respiration.

Every cell in your body respires, and so every cell produces carbon dioxide. It is vital that you remove this carbon dioxide. That's because if it all remained dissolved in the cytoplasm of your cells it would affect the pH. Dissolved carbon dioxide produces an acidic solution – and a lower pH would affect the working of all the enzymes in your cells!

PRACTICAL

Investigating breathing

Find out the capacity of your lungs or the effect of exercise on breathing.

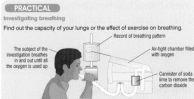

The subject of the investigation breathes in and out until all the oxygen is used up

Record of breathing pattern

Air-tight chamber filled with oxygen

Cannister of soda lime to remove the carbon dioxide

Figure 2 Because you breathe in and out of the machine all the time, you can't get rid of your waste carbon dioxide in the normal way. There has to be a special filter to remove the carbon dioxide so it doesn't poison you!

- How can we improve the reliability of investigations involving living organisms?

The carbon dioxide moves out of the cells into your blood. Your blood stream carries it back to your lungs. Almost all of the carbon dioxide you produce is removed from your body via your lungs when you breathe out. The air you breathe in contains only 0.04% carbon dioxide, but the air you breathe out contains about 4% carbon dioxide!

b) How do you remove carbon dioxide from your body?

Urea

The other main waste product of your body is urea.

Urea is produced in your liver when excess amino acids are broken down. When you eat more protein than you need, or when body tissues are worn out, the extra protein has to be broken down. Amino acids cannot be used as fuel for your body. But in your liver the amino group is removed and converted into urea. The rest of the amino acid molecule can then be used in respiration or to make other molecules. The urea passes from the liver cells into your blood.

Urea is poisonous and if the levels build up in your blood it will cause a lot of damage. Fortunately the urea is filtered out of your blood by your **kidneys**. It is then removed in your **urine**, along with any excess water and salt.

Urine is produced all the time by your kidneys. It leaves your kidneys and is stored in your **bladder** which you then empty from time to time!

c) Where is urea made?

Maintaining body balance

Water and ions enter your body when you eat or drink. The water and ion content of your body are carefully controlled to prevent damage to your cells. Water is lost through breathing, through sweating and in the urine, while ions are lost in the sweat and in the urine.

If the water or ion content of your body is wrong, too much water may move into or out of your cells. That's why control is vital.

It is also very important to control your body temperature and the levels of sugar in your blood. So homeostasis plays a very important role in your body.

FOUL FACTS

The average person produces between 1.5 and 2.5 litres of urine a day – that's up to 900 litres of urine a year!

GET IT RIGHT!

Don't confuse urea and urine. Urea is made in the liver; urine is produced by the kidney. Urine contains urea.

SUMMARY QUESTIONS

1 Copy and complete using the words below:

  blood carbon dioxide constant controlled environment
  enzymes homeostasis sugar temperature urea water

  The internal ...... of your body is kept relatively ...... by a whole range of processes which make up .... Waste products such as .... and ...... have to be removed from your ...... all the time. The ...... and ion concentration of your blood are constantly ...... and so is your blood ...... level. Your body ...... is kept the same so your ...... work effectively.

2 There are two main waste products which have to be removed from the human body – carbon dioxide and urea. For each waste product, describe:
   a) how it is formed, b) why it has to be removed, c) how it is removed from the body.

3 Explain briefly a) how a period of exercise would affect the internal conditions of your body, and b) how the conditions would be returned to normal.

KEY POINTS

1 The internal conditions of your body have to be controlled to maintain a constant internal environment.
2 Poisonous waste products are made all the time and need to be removed.
3 Carbon dioxide is produced during respiration and leaves the body via the lungs when you breathe out.
4 Urea is produced by your liver as excess amino acids are broken down, and it is removed by your kidneys in the urine.

SUMMARY ANSWERS

1 Environment, constant, homeostasis, carbon dioxide, urea, blood, water, controlled, sugar, temperature, enzymes.

2 a) **Carbon dioxide:** formed during aerobic respiration;
     glucose + oxygen → energy + carbon dioxide + water;
     Urea: excess amino acids from protein/worn out tissues;
     amino group removed from amino acids and converted to urea in the liver.
  b) Both are poisonous to the cells/damage the body.
  c) Carbon dioxide leaves cells and is carried in the blood to the lungs; from here it is breathed out in the air.
     Urea leaves the liver in the blood and is carried to the kidneys; it is filtered out of the blood by the kidneys, forms urine and is collected into the bladder.

3 a) Period of exercise – more carbon dioxide, more heat from muscles, used up blood sugar, lost salt in sweating.
  b) Breathe faster and more deeply to get rid of excess carbon dioxide, sweat and go red to cool down, release energy from store in body to replace glucose, kidneys change concentration of urine to save salt.

Answers to in-text questions

a) The maintenance of a constant internal environment.

b) From the cells in the body it is carried in the blood to the lungs and then breathed out in the air from the lungs.

c) In the liver.

KEY POINTS

The elimination of waste materials is important for the internal environment. Students should be clear on the formation of urea in the liver, its transport in the blood and removal by the kidneys. The sequence of removal of the amino group from amino acids, its conversion to urea and its eventual elimination as urine should be emphasised and learnt.

B2 5.2 Controlling body temperature

LEARNING OBJECTIVES

Students should learn that:

- The internal temperature of the body is monitored and controlled by a thermoregulatory centre in the brain.
- The thermoregulatory centre receives information from the blood as it flows through the brain and from temperature receptors in the skin.
- If the core temperature fluctuates, responses are made so that the body is kept at the temperature at which the enzymes work best. [**HT** only]

LEARNING OUTCOMES

Most students should be able to:

- Describe how the body monitors body temperature.

Some students should also be able to:

- Explain how the body temperature is monitored and controlled by the brain in coordination with other systems.
- Describe the responses made by the body if the core temperature is too high. [**HT** only]
- Describe the responses made by the body if the core temperature drops too low. [**HT** only]

Teaching suggestions

- **Special needs.** Produce a sheet with two boxes on one side with the words 'Too hot' in one and 'Too cold' in the other. Opposite these put a number of boxes with activities (e.g. put on more clothes, stamp feet and blow on hands) and physical responses (e.g. goosebumps, sweating). Students to join the boxes with lines and add illustrations to the page.
- **Gifted and talented.** Students to consider cold-blooded animals that cannot control their body temperatures. They can write out and illustrate a product-style 'User's guide for a poikilothermic body' giving warnings and suggestions.
- **Learning styles**
  Kinaesthetic: Measuring temperatures.
  Visual: Observing photographs.
  Auditory: Listening to discussions.
  Interpersonal: Working in pairs on the heat detection exercise.
  Intrapersonal: Writing 'Dear body' messages.
- **Homework.** Design and produce a 'circuit' diagram to show how thermoregulation works in the human body.

SPECIFICATION LINK-UP   Unit: Biology 2.11.7

- *Body temperature is monitored and controlled by the thermoregulatory centre in the brain. This centre has receptors sensitive to the temperature of blood flowing through the brain. Also temperature receptors in the skin send impulses to the centre giving information about skin temperature.*

- *If the core body temperature is too high:*
  - *Blood vessels supplying the skin capillaries dilate so that more blood flows through the capillaries and more heat is lost.*
  - *Sweat glands release more sweat which cools the body as it evaporates. [**HT** only]*

- *If the core body temperature is too low:*
  - *Blood vessels supplying the skin capillaries constrict to reduce the flow of blood through the capillaries.*
  - *Muscles may 'shiver' – their contraction needs respiration which releases some energy as heat. [**HT** only]*

Lesson structure

STARTER

Same temperature? – Using forehead thermometers, get the students to take their own temperatures. Collect up results and find a mean for the group. Ask: 'Why are they all about the same? How much variation is there?' (This relates to 'How Science Works': consider the reliability of data.) (5–10 minutes)

Can you tell the temperature? – Have several containers of water at different temperatures. Students are to guess the temperatures. Ask: 'How easy is it? How accurate can you be?' Give them the actual temperatures and discuss why you need to be aware of whether you are hot or cold – it could be dangerous to become too hot or too cold. (5–10 minutes)

MAIN

Differences between core and skin temperature

- Students can work in groups or this could be done as a class demonstration. Ask for volunteers (risk assessment needed) to sit with one hand in very cold water. Monitor the core temperature and skin temperature of the other hand of the volunteer using temperature sensors and data loggers. Ask: 'What happens?'

- A modification or extension of the above experiment can be done comparing heat loss from an insulated and non-insulated hand. Attach a temperature probe to each hand of a volunteer with masking tape, checking that the skin temperatures on both hands are identical. Insulate one hand fully with duvet filling, taping it and ensuring that it is of an even thickness all round. Allow time for equilibration, then record the skin temperatures of each hand and the core temperature. Change the environmental conditions (cooler temperatures, air movements) and repeat the temperature measurements.

- To cover aspects of 'How Science Works', the information gathered and the best way to present it can be discussed by the students. Ask: 'What conclusions can be drawn? Does it tell us about the thermoreceptors in the skin? Could we use this information to devise a method of measuring the heat loss from the human body?'

Comparing distributions

- Students to compare the distribution of humans with that of other mammals with respect to climatic temperatures, and include references to behavioural as well as physiological ways of controlling temperature.

Answers to in-text questions

a) If the temperature becomes too hot or too cold, it affects the action of the enzymes in the body.

b) The rate of the enzyme-controlled reactions slows down and not enough energy is made in the cells.

ACTIVITY & EXTENSION

- Use alcohol evaporating from thermometers to show the effect of evaporation on temperature. (No naked flames).
- **Does the human body temperature fluctuate much?** – Suggest to students that they monitor their own body temperature over a period of 48 hours. If the results are plotted, it can be seen that the temperature does fluctuate. Ask: 'Can it be accounted for?' If it is not possible for students to do this themselves, project a graph and get students to discuss the variations.
- **Heat detection** – In pairs, one student closes their eyes, while the other brings the palm of their hand close to the other person's cheek. The one with eyes closed says when they can feel the heat. They estimate the distance and then swap roles.
- **Animation** – Use the Animation, B2 5.2 'Controlling body temperatures', available on the Additional Science CD ROM.

Practical support

Body temperature
Equipment and materials required
Thermometers, temperature probes, masking tape, duvet filling, data loggers.

If clinical thermometers are used, it is advisable to use separate thermometers for each student and these need to be disinfected after use.

BIOLOGY   HOMEOSTASIS

B2 5.2   Controlling body temperature

LEARNING OBJECTIVES
1 How does your body monitor its temperature?
2 How does your body stop you getting too hot? [Higher]
3 How does your body keep you warm? [Higher]

Figure 1 People in different parts of the world live in conditions of extreme heat and extreme cold and still maintain a constant internal body temperature

Wherever you go and whatever you do it is vital that your body temperature is maintained at around 37°C. This is the temperature at which your enzymes work best. Your skin temperature can vary enormously without causing harm. It is the temperature deep inside your body, known as the core body temperature, which must be kept stable.

At only a few degrees above or below normal body temperature your enzymes cannot function properly. All sorts of things can affect your internal body temperature, including:

- heat produced in your muscles during exercise,
- fevers caused by disease, and
- the external temperature rising or falling.

People can control some aspects of their own temperature. We can change our clothing, light a fire, and turn on the heating or air-conditioning. But it is our internal control mechanisms which are most important in controlling our body temperature.

a) Why is control of your body temperature so important?

Control of the temperature relies on the **thermoregulatory centre** in the brain. This centre contains receptors which are sensitive to temperature changes. They monitor the temperature of the blood flowing through the brain itself.

Extra information comes from the temperature receptors in the skin. These send impulses to the thermoregulatory centre giving information about the skin temperature. The receptors are so sensitive they can detect a difference of as little as 0.5°C!

Sweating helps to cool your body down. So the loss of salt and water when you sweat can affect your water and ion balance. If you are sweating a lot you need to take in more drink or food to replace the water and ions you have lost – just watch a marathon runner!

Cooling the body down [HIGHER]

If you get too hot, your enzymes denature and can no longer catalyse the reactions in your cells. When your core body temperature begins to rise, impulses are sent from the thermoregulatory centre to the body so more heat is lost:

- The blood vessels, which supply your skin capillaries, **dilate** (open wider). This lets more blood flow through the capillaries. Your skin flushes, so you lose more heat by radiation.
- Your rate of sweating goes up. Sweat (made up mainly of water, salt and a little protein) oozes out of your sweat glands and spreads over your skin. As the water evaporates it cools the skin, taking heat from your body. In very humid conditions, when the sweat doesn't evaporate very easily, it is very difficult to cool down.

Reducing heat loss [HIGHER]

It is just as dangerous for your core temperature to drop as it is to rise. If you get very cold, the rate of the enzyme-controlled reactions in your cells falls too low. You don't make enough energy and your cells begin to die. If your core body temperature starts to get too low, impulses are sent from your thermoregulatory centre to the body to conserve and even generate more heat.

- The blood vessels which supply your skin capillaries **constrict** (close up) to reduce the flow of blood through the capillaries. This reduces the heat lost through the surface of the skin, and makes you look pale.
- Shivering begins – your muscles contract and relax rapidly which involves lots of cellular respiration. This releases some energy as heat which you use to raise your body temperature. As you warm up, shivering stops.
- Sweat production is reduced.

b) Why is a fall in your core body temperature so dangerous?

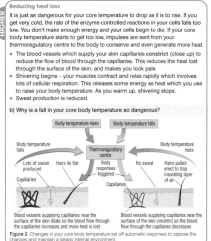

Figure 2 Changes in your core body temperature set off automatic responses to oppose the changes and maintain a steady internal environment

SUMMARY QUESTIONS

1 Here is a jumbled list of some of the events by which your body temperature is controlled when it starts to go up. Sort them out into the right order and then copy them out.
   A Her body temperature starts to rise.
   B Sally takes a long, cool drink to replace the liquid she has lost through sweating.
   C Her temperature returns to normal.
   D Her skin goes red and her rate of sweating increases so the amount of heat lost through her skin goes up.
   E Sally exercises hard.

2 a) Why is it so important to maintain a body temperature of about 37°C?
   b) Explain the role of i) the thermoregulatory centre in the brain and ii) the temperature sensors in the skin in maintaining a constant core body temperature.

3 Explain how the body responds to both an increase and a decrease in core temperature to return its temperature to normal levels. [Higher]

DID YOU KNOW?
Birds and mammals can help reduce heat loss from their bodies by pulling the hairs or feathers on their skin upright to trap an insulating layer of air. Our bodies try to do this, but we just get goose-pimples. The tiny muscles pulling on our hairs show up more than the hairs themselves!

PRACTICAL
Body temperature
Use a temperature sensor and data logger to record your skin and core body temperature on one hand as you plunge the other into icy water.
- Explain your observations.

GET IT RIGHT!
Use the terms dilate and constrict for the changes which take place in the blood vessels supplying the capillaries near the surface of the skin. Remember sweating only cools your body when the sweat actually evaporates.

KEY POINTS
1 Your body temperature must be maintained at the level at which enzymes work best.
2 Your body temperature is monitored and controlled by the thermoregulatory centre in your brain.
3 Your body responds to cool you down if you are overheating and to warm you up if your core body temperature falls. [Higher]

60   61

SUMMARY ANSWERS

1 E, A, D, C, B.

2 a) This is the temperature at which enzymes work best.
   b) i) The thermoregulatory centre in the brain is sensitive to the temperature of the blood flowing through it. It also receives information about the skin temperature from receptors in the skin and coordinates the body responses to keep the core temperature at 37°C.
   ii) Temperature sensors in the skin send impulses to the thermoregulatory centre in the brain giving information about the temperature of the skin and the things it touches. This is important for maintaining the core temperature because if the external surroundings and the skin are cold, the body will tend to conserve heat to keep the core temperature up, and vice versa.

3 Look for: To lower body temperature – blood vessels supplying capillaries dilate – more blood in capillaries so more heat is lost. More sweat produced by sweat glands which cools the body as it evaporates. To raise body temperature – blood vessels supplying capillaries constrict – less blood in them. Shivering occurs by rapid muscle movement which needs respiration – releasing some heat energy. [**HT** only]

PLENARIES

Thermostat principles – Show the students a heater connected into a circuit with a bimetallic strip, or other thermostatic device, arranged so that when it drops to a given temperature the heater switches on. When the temperature rises, the heater switches off. Run through several cycles and ask the students to draw parallels with the human body. (10 minutes)

'Dear body ...' – Students to write 'Dear body' style text messages telling the body what to do if it is too hot or too cold. (10 minutes)

Quick quiz – Ask questions on the contents of the lesson. (5–10 minutes)

KEY POINTS

The key points can be incorporated into a summary diagram of the way in which thermoregulation in the human body occurs. Students should be aware that capillaries do not contract and dilate, but it is the blood vessels that supply the capillaries that control the quantity of blood that flows through the capillaries.

B2 5.3   Controlling blood sugar

LEARNING OBJECTIVES

Students should learn that:

- The pancreas monitors and controls the level of glucose in the blood.

- The pancreas secretes insulin when the blood glucose concentration is too high, lowering the level of glucose, but when the concentration is too low, glucagon is secreted and glucose is released into the blood.

- Diabetes is caused by a lack of insulin from the pancreas.

LEARNING OUTCOMES

Most students should be able to:

- State that the pancreas monitors and controls blood sugar concentration.

- Describe the symptoms and causes of diabetes.

- Describe how diabetes can be treated.

Some students should also be able to:

- Explain how the blood sugar concentration is monitored and controlled.

- Explain the causes of diabetes and how it is treated.

Teaching suggestions

- **Special needs.** Give students a large, clear and not too complex wordsearch for the key words. The students should be provided with the definitions to the words and then cross them off as they find them.

- **Gifted and talented.** Ask the students to produce a series of Word documents showing the feedback mechanism involving insulin and glucagon, glycogen and glucose, blood glucose levels too high, too low and normal. Link these together with hyperlinks so that they form the appropriate loops.

- **Learning styles**
  Kinaesthetic: Building up feedback diagram.
  Visual: Observing animation.
  Auditory: Listening to the information gathered on the topics researched.
  Interpersonal: Taking part in role-play exercise.
  Intrapersonal: Giving feedback on research project.

SPECIFICATION LINK-UP   Unit: Biology 2.11.7

- *The blood glucose concentration of the body is monitored and controlled by the pancreas. The pancreas produces the hormone insulin which allows glucose to move from the blood into the cells.*

- *Diabetes is a disease in which a person's glucose concentration may rise to a fatally high level, because the pancreas does not produce enough of the hormone insulin. Diabetes may be treated by careful attention to diet and by injecting insulin into the blood.*

Lesson structure

STARTER

Blood sugar levels – Discuss the sweet eating habits of younger brothers and sisters. Ask: 'Who eats the most at one go? Does eating a lot of sweets have an effect on their behaviour?' Talk about the blood sugar levels and speculate as to how the body copes. (5–10 minutes)

How is the disease diagnosed? – Discuss the symptoms of the disease and why they occur. Ask: 'What simple test could indicate that someone is suffering from diabetes? What is a glucose tolerance test and how can it be interpreted?' Students to analyse blood glucose graphs for normal people and for those with diabetes.

Coping with diabetes – Ask: 'Has anyone had a go at a rowing machine?' Project a picture and discuss how much energy it takes. Show footage or stills of Sir Steven Redgrave winning Olympic gold. Discuss his problem with diabetes and any other people, possibly relatives or peers, who have the condition. (10 minutes)

MAIN

- **Animation** – Show the Animation B2 5.3 from the Additional Science CD ROM on the control of the blood glucose levels by the pancreas. This could include diagrams/photos of pancreas tissue showing the islets of Langerhans, alpha cells and beta cells. A feedback diagram can be built up showing how the control is achieved. Give students worksheets and given time to complete these during the lesson.

- **Research the disease** – There is plenty of information about diabetes available from the doctor, from textbooks and on the Internet (e.g. www.diabetes.org.uk). Students could be given the opportunity to follow up an aspect of the condition. For example, students could investigate:
  - the causes of diabetes, including Type I and Type II
  - what happens if a diabetic has insufficient glucose in the blood, i.e. is hypoglycaemic
  - the treatment of diabetes, from the use of insulin from animals to the present-day use of genetically engineered insulin
  - the possibility of islet cell transplantation techniques
  - the research of Banting and Best and why they got the Nobel prize
  - the importance of diet for a diabetic
  - the role of the diabetic nurse in your local practice.
  For each of these suggestions, students could compile a report to be presented to the class. They could be given homework time for research and writing their reports.

- **Demonstrate Clinistix testing** – Test fake urine as suggested in section 4.7, page 54. Compare this with the way in which blood is tested now. Students could be given 'mystery' samples of fake urine to test. It could be appropriate to point out that before the invention of Clinistix, urine samples were tested with Benedict's solution. Compare a Clinistix reading with a Benedict's test on the same sample. (This relates to: 'How Science Works': aspects of sensitivity and accuracy of testing.)

PLENARIES

Why diabetes mellitus? – Discuss the origins of the word 'mellitus', with its link to honey. Tell students that many years ago doctors would taste their patient's urine to check it for sweetness. Some students may have heard of the other condition known as 'diabetes insipidus', where copious quantities of urine are produced and the patient is always thirsty. (5–10 minutes)

Spelling bee – Ask for volunteers to spell key words from this topic. Once a student has spelt a word correctly, they can choose another student to give a definition. This could reinforce the differences between 'glucose', 'glucagon' and 'glycogen', which are frequently muddled by students. (10 minutes)

ACTIVITY & EXTENSION

- **What does diabetic chocolate taste like?** – Have a range of products designed for diabetics as well as some normal ones. Ask students if they can tell the difference between a 'diabetic' one and a normal one. This can be done as a sampling exercise or as a competition to try to identify which is diabetic and which is not. (5–10 minutes)

- **Diabetic diets or get the balance right** – Students could research diabetic diets. There has been a great deal of interest in the Glycaemic Index of foods and how this can help people to lose weight and maintain a weight loss. Students could design menus suitable for people with mild forms of diabetes and research foods that are said to be for diabetics. Ask: 'What is used instead of sugar? Are these sensible recommendations for people who wish to lose weight?'

- **What can you do?** – Carry out a role-play exercise of finding someone collapsed and discovering that they had a Medic alert bracelet indicating that they are diabetic. Ask and discuss: 'What would be the sensible thing to do? Why?' If possible, get a diabetic person to talk to the class.

Answers to in-text questions

a) Blood transports glucose to the cells where it is needed for cellular respiration.

b) Insulin and glucagon.

c) Insulin is needed to enable glucose to enter the cells. If there is no insulin, the cells are deprived of fuel and therefore do not make enough energy in cellular respiration.

d) They can manage their diet by avoiding foods that are rich in carbohydrates.

KEY POINTS

The key points can be reinforced by encouraging the students to produce their own feedback diagram with the effect of insulin on the glucose levels in the blood.

BIOLOGY HOMEOSTASIS

Additional biology

B2 5.3 Controlling blood sugar

LEARNING OBJECTIVES

1 How is your blood sugar level controlled?

2 What is diabetes and how is it treated?

It is very important that your cells have a constant supply of the glucose they need for cellular respiration. Glucose is transported around your body to all the cells by your blood. However you don't spend all of your time eating to keep your blood sugar levels high. Instead the level of sugar in your blood is controlled by hormones produced in your pancreas.

a) Why are the levels of glucose in your blood so important?

The pancreas and the control of blood sugar levels

When you digest a meal, large amounts of glucose pass into your blood. Without a control mechanism your blood glucose levels would vary wildly. After a meal they would soar to a point where glucose would be removed from the body in the urine. A few hours later the levels would plummet and cells would not have enough glucose to respire.

This internal chaos is prevented by your **pancreas**. The pancreas is a small pink organ found under your stomach. It constantly monitors your blood glucose concentration and controls it using two hormones known as **insulin** and **glucagon**.

When your blood glucose concentration rises above the ideal range after you have eaten a meal, insulin is released. Insulin causes your liver to remove any glucose which is not needed at the time from the blood. The soluble glucose is converted to an insoluble carbohydrate called **glycogen** which is stored in your liver.

When your blood glucose concentration falls below the ideal range, the pancreas secretes glucagon. Glucagon makes your liver break down glycogen, converting it back into glucose. In this way the stored sugar is released back into the blood.

By using these two hormones and the glycogen store in your liver, your pancreas keeps your blood glucose concentration fairly constant. Its normal concentration is usually about 90 mg glucose per 100 cm³ of blood.

b) Which two hormones are involved in the control of your blood sugar levels?

SCIENCE @ WORK

In 2005, research scientists produced insulin-secreting cells from stem cells which cured diabetes in mice. More research is needed but the scientists hope that before long diabetes will be a disease that we can cure instead of just treating the symptoms.

What causes diabetes?

Most of us never think about our blood sugar levels because they are perfectly controlled by our pancreas. But for some people life isn't quite this simple. Unfortunately, their pancreas does not make enough – or any – insulin.

Without insulin your blood sugar levels get higher and higher after you eat food. Eventually your kidneys produce glucose in your urine. You produce lots of urine and feel thirsty all the time.

Without insulin, glucose cannot get into the cells of your body, so you lack energy and feel tired. You break down fat and protein to use as fuel instead, so you lose weight.

Before there was any treatment for diabetes, people would waste away. Eventually they would fall into a coma and die. Fortunately there are now some very effective ways of treating diabetes!

c) Why do people with untreated diabetes feel very tired and lack energy?

Treating diabetes

If you have a mild form of diabetes, managing your diet is enough to keep you healthy. Avoiding carbohydrate-rich foods keeps the blood sugar levels relatively low. So your reduced amount of insulin can cope with small amounts of glucose.

However, other people with diabetes need replacement insulin before meals. Insulin is a protein which would be digested in your stomach. So it is usually given as an injection to get it into your blood.

This injected insulin allows glucose to be taken into your body cells and converted into glycogen in the liver. This stops the concentration of glucose in your blood from getting too high.

Then as the blood glucose levels fall, natural glucagon makes sure glycogen is converted back to glucose. As a result your blood glucose levels are kept as stable as possible. (See graphs on page 65.)

Insulin injections treat diabetes successfully but they do not cure it. Until a cure is developed, someone with diabetes has to inject insulin several times every day of their life.

d) How can people with mild diabetes control the disease?

DID YOU KNOW?

In 2005, doctors in Japan performed a successful living transplant of pancreas tissue. Cells from a mother were given to her daughter who had severe diabetes. Within three weeks the daughter no longer needed insulin injections – her new cells were controlling her blood sugar.

Figure 2 The treatment of diabetes involves regular blood sugar tests and insulin injections. These could become a thing of the past if some of the new treatments being developed work as well as scientists hope!

KEY POINTS

1 Your blood glucose concentration is monitored and controlled by your pancreas.

2 The pancreas produces the hormone insulin which allows glucose to move from the blood into the cells.

3 In diabetes, the blood glucose may rise to fatally high levels because the pancreas does not secrete enough insulin. It can be treated by injections of insulin before meals.

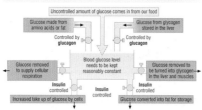

Figure 1 This model of your blood glucose control system shows the blood glucose as a tank. It has both controlled and uncontrolled inlets and outlets. In every case the control is given by the hormones insulin and glucagon.

SUMMARY QUESTIONS

1 Define the following words:
 hormone;
 insulin;
 diabetes;
 glycogen.

2 a) Explain how your pancreas keeps the blood glucose levels of your body constant.
 b) Why is it so important to control the level of glucose in your blood?

3 What is diabetes and how can it be treated?

SUMMARY ANSWERS

1 Hormone – A chemical message carried in the blood which causes a change in the body.
   Insulin   – A hormone made in the pancreas which causes glucose to pass from the blood into the cells where it is needed for energy.
   Diabetes – A condition when the pancreas cannot make enough insulin to control the blood sugar.
   Glycogen – An insoluble carbohydrate stored in the liver.

2 **a)** Blood glucose levels go up above the ideal range. This is detected by the pancreas, which then secretes insulin. Insulin causes the liver to convert glucose to glycogen and causes glucose to move out of the blood into the cells of the body, thus lowering blood glucose levels. If the blood glucose level drops below the ideal range, this is detected by the pancreas. The pancreas secretes glucagon, which causes the liver to convert glycogen into glucose that increases the blood glucose level.

   b) Glucose needed for cells of body for respiration which provides energy for everything (could add too much glucose causes problems in kidneys, etc.)

3 Diabetes is a condition where the pancreas does not make enough or any insulin. It can be treated by injections of insulin to help balance blood sugar levels. (New possibilities are pancreas cell transplants or embryonic stem cells.)

B2 5.4   Homeostasis matters!

BIOLOGY   HOMEOSTASIS

B2 5.4   Homeostasis matters!

SPECIFICATION LINK-UP

Unit: Biology 2.11.7

Students should use their skills, knowledge and understanding of 'How Science Works':

- *to evaluate the data from the experiments by Banting and Best, which led to the discovery of insulin*
- *to evaluate modern methods of treating diabetes.*

Teaching suggestions

- **Hypothermia: the silent killer** – Students can consider ways in which heat is lost from the body: radiation, conduction and evaporation. Project some thermographic camera pictures of people in hot and cold environments and discuss where the areas of greatest heat loss are. (Search an image bank for 'thermographic'). If the thermographs have indications of temperatures on them, it is possible to work out the difference between the core and skin temperatures in various parts of the body. Show students a silver plastic thermal blanket and ask them where they have seen these before. Ask: 'Why are they used? How do they work in reducing heat loss?' A PhotoPLUS on hypothermia is available from the Additional Science CD ROM.

- **Heat loss through the head** – As stated in the Student Book, up to 20% of the body heat can be lost through the head. Put a large fur hat (Russian-style with ear flaps) on a volunteer. Search for pictures of Arctic explorers, Kenny – the kid with the snorkel parka from South Park, a bald man and old photographs of people wearing hats. Discuss the benefits of hats to the young and the old. Ask: 'Why do we not wear hats so much today?'

- **The wind chill factor** – Show a PowerPoint presentation on the wind chill factor, to include a table that shows how increasing wind speed lowers the temperature on exposed skin. Students to consider the implications of this to the elderly, the very young and to people on outdoor pursuits, such as hill-walking and canoeing. Ask students to suggest why wind chill factor is made worse in wet conditions due to the evaporation of water.

- **What to take on an expedition** – Students can investigate the range of outdoor clothing available, and to

HYPOTHERMIA – THE SILENT KILLER

If your core body temperature falls too low you suffer from hypothermia. About 30 000 people die of it every year in the UK alone. Here is some more information about hypothermia:

- Hypothermia is when your body temperature drops below 35°C and the normal working of your body is affected.
- Old people, small children and people exposed in bad weather conditions are most at risk.
- Young people on outdoor expeditions are often at risk if they do not wear the right clothing. Wet weather and wind make you lose heat faster.
- The first signs of hypothermia are extreme tiredness and not wanting to move – you may not realise how cold you are.
- Up to 20% of your body heat is lost through your head.
- Warm clothing, adequate heating, regular food and warm drinks, together with exercise all help to prevent hypothermia.
- People with hypothermia have greyish-blue, puffy faces and blue lips. Their skin feels very cold to the touch. They will be drowsy, with slurred speech. As it gets worse, they will stop shivering. If the body temperature falls too low the sufferer will become unconscious and may die.
- It has been estimated that every time the temperature drops one degree Celsius below average in the winter, 8000 more elderly people will die of hypothermia.

ACTIVITY

If more people were aware of the risks of hypothermia, fewer people would die from it. Use the information to help you design **either** a poster **or** a leaflet informing people about the dangers of hypothermia and ways to avoid it.

HEAT WAVE KILLS SEVEN

The latest spell of very hot weather has led to seven deaths this week. As Britain sizzles in the latest heat-wave, with temperatures of over 33°C, people are dropping like flies.

Heat stroke and other heat-related illnesses are hitting the elderly, small babies and people with existing heart problems particularly hard.

The World Health Organisation along with the World Meteorological Organisation have suggested that a hot weather warning is added to our weather forecasts along with pollen levels, air pollution and flood warnings.

To reduce your risk of heat stroke as Britain continues to fry, stay in air-conditioned rooms where possible, drink plenty of water and take cool baths.

ACTIVITY

Climate change may well result in colder winters and hotter summers. Write an article for the lifestyle pages of a newspaper on:
- how your body copes with changes in temperature,
- the dangers to health of hot summers and cold winters, and
- the best ways to avoid any problems.

64

recommend suitable clothing to be worn or taken on an expedition to a mountainous region. Ask: 'What properties should the clothing have?' Explain why garments are chosen. Ask: 'What should the leader have in the first aid pack in case a member of the party is hurt and needs to be left while help is sought?'

- **Evaporation and heat loss** – The differences in heat lost in wet and dry conditions can be investigated by wrapping thermometers in a cloth and using volatile substances, such as ethanol. The effect of the wind chill factor could be simulated with the use of a fan.

- **Heat wave kills seven!** – Show a PowerPoint presentation on the effects of heat stress that occurs when the body can no longer cope with excessively high temperatures. The differences between heat collapse, heat exhaustion, heat cramps and heat stroke can be illustrated. Reference to the ways in which the body temperature is controlled could be discussed. Students could explain the benefits of drinking plenty of water, keeping out of direct sunlight and replacing lost salt.

- **The heat wave forecast . . .** – We already have severe weather warnings, information about the pollen count and references to the wind chill factor in our weather reports. Suggest to students that they produce and record a radio report, to be transmitted during the weather forecasts during a prolonged heat wave, advising people on what to do.

THE DIABETES DEBATE

The treatment of diabetes has changed a great deal over the years. For centuries nothing could be done. Then in the early 1920s Frederick Banting and Charles Best realised that extracts of animal pancreas could be used to keep people with diabetes alive. For many years insulin from pigs and cows was used to treat affected people. This saved millions of lives.

In recent years, bacteria have been developed using genetic engineering which produce pure human insulin. This is now injected by the majority of people affected by diabetes.

Scientists are trying to find easier ways – like nasal sprays – to get insulin into the body. Transplanting working pancreas cells from both dead and living donors has been shown to work for some people. And for the future, scientists are hoping to use embryonic stem cells to provide people affected by diabetes with new, functioning pancreas cells which can make their own insulin.

The difference these treatments have made to the lives of people with diabetes and their families is enormous. If a cure is found, it will be even better. But most of these developments have some ethical issues linked to them.

- Banting and Best did their experiments on dogs. They made some of the dogs diabetic by removing most of their pancreas, and they extracted insulin from the pancreases of other dogs. Many dogs died in the search for a successful treatment – but the scientists found a treatment to a disease which has killed millions of people over the centuries.
- Human insulin is now mass-produced using genetically engineered bacteria. The gene for human insulin is stuck into the bacterial DNA and the bacteria make pure human protein.
- There are not enough dead donors to give pancreas transplants to the people who need them. However, in living donor transplants there is a risk to the health of the donor as they have to undergo surgery.
- Stem cell research promises a possible cure – but the stem cells come from human embryos which have been specially created for the process.

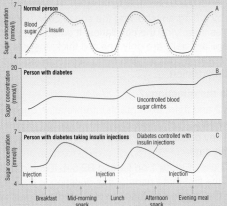

Figure 1 These graphs show the impact insulin injections have on people affected by diabetes. The injections keep the blood sugar level within safe limits. They cannot mimic the total control given by the natural production of the pancreas – but they work well enough to let people lead a full and active life.

ACTIVITY

a) You are to plan a three-minute speech for a debate. The title of the debate is:

'Ethical concerns are less important than a cure for diabetes.'

You can argue for or against the motion, but your arguments must be clear and sensible and backed up by scientific evidence.

b) Work in groups of 9 and set up a role play involving the following characters:

- Frederick Banting who first showed that animal insulin could be used to treat humans with diabetes.
- A spokesperson from a pharmaceutical company manufacturing human insulin.
- A daughter who has been cured of diabetes by receiving pancreas tissue from her mother, and her mother who donated the tissue.
- A scientist working on the development of insulin-producing cells from embryonic stem cells.
- Someone who has had diabetes since they were 10 years old.
- An animal rights activist.
- A 'pro-life' activist who is against any use of stem cells.
- A representative of a group opposed to genetic engineering.
- The chair of the discussion. Each character must explain to the chair why research into diabetes should – or should not – continue.

- **The diabetes debate** – Before preparing for the debate on diabetes, some further background research on Banting and Best's experiments could be done. The use of stem cells and pancreatic transplants should be researched, so that students know the advantages and the risks involved. (This relates to 'How Science Works': societal factors.)

Special needs

Use concept cartoons-style talking heads: in one a person is complaining about being too hot and receiving advice from a second, who has an empty speech balloon. Students can choose a response from a printed list. Similarly, another one can be given where a person is complaining about being too cold.

Learning styles

Kinaesthetic: Designing a poster or a leaflet.

Visual: Interpreting thermographic images.

Auditory: Listening to arguments being put forward in a debate.

Interpersonal: Role-playing in the diabetes activity.

Intrapersonal: Writing a speech for the debate.

ACTIVITY & EXTENSION IDEAS

- **Hypothermia: the silent killer** – The design of the poster or the leaflet requires some careful thought, as hypothermia can affect several groups of vulnerable people. Ask: 'Is it a good idea to make a general poster? Should there be one especially for older people who are most vulnerable? Where would you put the posters?' Students could discuss these possibilities and decide whether they think a poster or a leaflet would reach a greater number of people.

- **Heat wave kills seven** – The suggested article is very wide-ranging and gathers together some of the topics introduced in the preceding spreads, particularly with respect to the controlling of body temperature. Some other aspects of hot summers, such as the pollen, fumes and dangers of sunburn, could be incorporated. Problems associated with cold winters should include some mention of hypothermia and the elderly, as well as advice to everyone about the dangers of losing too much heat.

- The article for the newspaper could be a group activity, with contributions from different students covering the various aspects. It could be interesting to adapt the style of the article to the type of newspaper; ask: 'Would an article for a tabloid have a different approach from an article for a broadsheet?' Display the results for peer judgement.

- **The diabetes debate** – As with other debates, in order for students to maintain a balanced view, a speech for the motion and against the motion should be prepared. The ethical concerns in this case are quite complicated and students might benefit from some discussion before they plan their speeches. It could be beneficial to try the role-play activity in class, and suggest that students use some of the arguments put forward when preparing for the debate.

- **Role-play activity** – This will only work well if the students research their roles, so some homework time could be allocated for preparation.

SUMMARY ANSWERS

1 a) Diagram to show feedback – something goes up, receptor picks it up, chemical released to bring levels back down and the same idea if level drops. Annotations to show student understands principles of maintaining more-or-less constant levels.

b) For cells to work properly they need to be at the right temperature (so enzymes don't denature), they need to be surrounded by correct concentration so osmosis doesn't cause problems, they need glucose to provide energy and they need waste products to be removed as build up can change pH or poison systems. This is why the body systems must be controlled within fairly narrow limits.

2 a) Person: 37°C; lizard: 18°C.

b) The human core temperature becomes dangerously low at an external temperature of 10°C. Reactions slow down, hypothermia develops and the heart beat and breathing will stop.

c) It becomes dangerously high at 55°C. Once the body temperature goes over 40°C, enzymes start to denature and do not work properly.

d) Shivering produces heat; the blood supply to the skin and extremities is reduced to keep warmth in the core; goose pimples occur as the body tries to trap a layer of air next to the skin; behavioural changes such as moving about, putting on more clothes and turning up the heating take place.

e) Sweating occurs, so heat is lost by evaporation; blood vessels supplying the skin capillaries dilate, so more blood flows nearer the surface of the skin; heat is lost by radiation; behavioural changes occur, such as the removal of clothing or moving to a shady place.

3 a) The level of insulin rises after a meal because the levels of glucose in the blood rise. The pancreas releases insulin, allowing glucose to enter the cells and the liver to convert glucose to glycogen; the blood glucose concentration drops.

b) The level of glucose in the blood keeps rising because no insulin is produced. The glucose cannot enter the cells and no glycogen is made in the liver.

c) The insulin injections mean that glucose can enter the cells to provide them with energy. Glycogen stores are made in the liver and the levels of glucose in the blood do not get dangerously high. The pattern is quite similar to that of a person with a healthy pancreas.

d) The diet needs to be managed carefully. It is important for them to eat a diet that is relatively low in carbohydrates so that their blood glucose levels do not tend to go up too much and their pancreas can cope. It is particularly important to avoid sugary food, which makes the blood glucose level go up very rapidly. Starchy carbohydrates are broken down slowly and so the blood glucose level does not rise too quickly.

Summary teaching suggestions

- **Literacy guidance** – The answers requiring explanations should be clear and unambiguous. In the answers to questions 2d) and e), students need to write a passage in continuous prose, presenting their answers in a logical sequence.

- **Lower and higher level answers**

  Higher attaining students should be able to give answers using the correct scientific terminology. References to 'glucose' rather than 'sugar' are more accurate. Students should be taught to give full answers when asked for an explanation.

- **Misconceptions**
  - It is easy to detect when students are muddled about the terms they are using – in this case, the spelling of words such as 'glucose', 'glucagon' and 'glycogen'! Some students hedge their bets and provide hybrid spellings.

SUMMARY QUESTIONS

1 a) Draw and annotate a diagram explaining the basic principles of homeostasis.

b) Write a paragraph explaining why control of the conditions inside your body is so important.

2 We humans maintain our body temperature at a constant level over a wide range of environmental temperatures. Many other animals – fish, amphibians and reptiles as well as the invertebrates – cannot do this. Their body temperature is always very close to the environmental temperature.

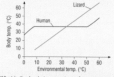

a) What is the body temperature of a person and a lizard at an atmospheric temperature of 20°C?

b) From the graph, at what external temperature does the human core temperature become dangerously low? Why is it dangerous?

c) At what external temperature does the human core temperature become dangerously high? Why is it dangerous?

d) Explain how a person maintains a constant core body temperature as the external temperature falls.

e) Explain how a person maintains a constant core body temperature as the external temperature rises. [Higher]

3 Use Figure 1 on page 65 to answer this question.

a) Look at graph A. Why does the level of insulin increase after a meal?

b) Graph B shows the blood sugar pattern of someone who has just developed diabetes and is not yet using injected insulin. What differences are there between this pattern and the one shown in A?

c) Graph C shows the effect of regular insulin injections on the blood sugar level of someone with diabetes. Why are the insulin injections so important to their health?

d) People who are mildly diabetic and those who inject insulin all have to watch the amount of carbohydrate in their diet. Explain why.

EXAM-STYLE QUESTIONS

1 Complete the passage below by choosing the correct terms from the box and matching them with the numbers in the passage.

| sweating | dilate | shivering |
| thermoregulatory | radiation | constrict |

Body temperature is controlled by the ....**1**.... centre in the brain. On a hot day it causes blood vessels in the skin to ...**2**... and so lose heat by ...**3**.... Heat may also be lost by ...**4**... . On a cold day the blood vessels ....**5**... to conserve heat. When cold, ...**6**.... may also occur to create some heat. [Higher] (6

2 The table shows the daily water loss from a typical human being.

Water lost in	Volume of water (cm³ per day)
Urine	1500
X	400
Evaporation from the skin	350
Faeces	150
Sweat	100

(a) One way in which water is lost from the body has been missed out and replaced by the letter **X**. What does **X** represent? (1

(b) These figures were taken on a cool day with the person at rest. State two ways in which the figures would be different if the person had been exercising on a hot day. (2

(c) Apart from water, what other two substances are typically found in urine? (2

(d) Where is urine stored in the body? (1

3 (a) What is the name of the hormone that causes the liver to remove glucose from the blood? (1

(b) Where in the body is this hormone produced? (1

(c) Two people drank a solution that contained 100 g of glucose. The blood sugar level of each person was measured over the next three hours. The results are shown in the table on the next page.

(i) On a piece of graph paper, draw a line graph of the data in the table opposite. (5

(ii) One of the two persons is diabetic. From the graph suggest which one and give two reasons for your answer. (2

- When writing about control of body temperature, students get muddled about the blood flow to the skin. This problem can be remedied by a diagram showing the constriction or dilation of the arterioles supplying the capillaries. It could be pointed out that the capillary walls are only one cell thick: there is no muscle present to contract and bring about constriction or to relax causing dilation.

- **When to use the questions?**
  - Questions 2 and 3 are both graph interpretation questions and could be used as homework exercises after the relevant spreads. They could also be used for revision to practise dealing with data.
  - Question 3 uses Figure 1 on spread B2 5.4. It could be useful to discuss the first three parts of this question in class as a plenary to the lesson and then to set students the last part to do at home.

EXAM-STYLE ANSWERS

1 1 Thermoregulatory **2** Dilate **3** Radiation **4** Sweating **5** Constrict **6** Shivering *(6 marks)*

2 a) Breathing/expired air *(1 mark)*

b) The figure for sweat would be higher. *(1 mark)*
The figure for urine would be lower. *(1 mark)*
Accept figures provided they show the appropriate increase/decrease.

c) Urea *(1 mark)*
Minerals/ions *(1 mark)*

d) In the bladder *(1 mark)*

3 a) Insulin *(1 mark)*

b) In the pancreas *(1 mark)*

c) i) • Time (independent variable) plotted on the *x*-axis/ abscissa and blood sugar level on the *y*-axis/ordinate.
• Scale appropriate on both axes and both axes correctly labelled (including units).

Time in minutes	Blood sugar level (mg/100 cm³ blood)	
	Person X	Person Y
0 (glucose drunk)	90	90
30	160	140
60	220	90
90	200	80
120	150	70
150	130	80
180	110	90

4 Read the following passage about diabetes.

Diabetes is a metabolic disorder in which there is an inability to control blood glucose levels due to the lack of the hormone insulin. Diabetes was a fatal disease until in 1921 Banting and Best succeeded in isolating insulin from the pancreases of pigs and cows, having first carried out experiments on dogs. Insulin is a small protein of 51 amino acids, the sequence of which was determined in the 1950s by Sanger. More recently the gene for human insulin has been isolated and the hormone can now be produced by bacteria as a result of genetic engineering. Diabetics must test their blood sugar levels regularly and inject insulin if they are to lead normal lives.

(a) Why do diabetics inject insulin rather than taking it by mouth? (2)

(b) What would happen to the blood sugar level of a diabetic who failed to inject insulin? (1)

(c) Suggest one other symptom of diabetes other than changes to blood sugar. (1)

(d) Give three advantages of using genetically engineered insulin rather than extracting the hormone from animal pancreases. (3)

(e) Injecting insulin only *treats* diabetes. In future it may be possible to replace the damaged pancreas by transplantation.
  (i) What would be the benefits to the person with diabetes of such treatment?
  (ii) State the drawbacks of this treatment. (4)

HOW SCIENCE WORKS QUESTIONS

You have probably heard the weatherman, during winter, tell you about the 'wind chill factor'. This is to give you a better idea of how cold your skin might feel if you were to go out whilst the temperature was low and it was windy. Remember that wind will cool the skin by evaporating moisture from it and therefore make it feel colder than the actual air temperature.

Until recently the wind chill factor was calculated by measuring temperatures of some water in a container in the Arctic. The tank of water was 10 metres above the ground.

a) Explain why this was a poor way to calculate the effect of wind chill on humans. (2)

Recently some investigations were carried out to get a better measure of the effect of wind chill on humans. The tests were carried out on humans dressed in protective clothing, except their cheeks were left exposed, so that their cheek skin temperature could be measured.

b) Why do you think the cheeks were chosen? (1)

c) The people were tested at different temperatures and wind speeds. What would have been a suitable sensitivity for the thermometer? (1)

d) How many people would have been chosen? (1)

e) How would these people have been chosen? (1)

f) Imagine you were carrying out these tests. Draw up a table that would let you fill in the results as you did the tests on just one person. (2)

g) Now fill in the table with some temperatures and some wind speeds that you think might be useful. (5)

d) Compared to insulin extracted from animals, genetically engineered insulin:
- is more effective (as it is an exact copy of human insulin)
- is more rapid in its action (exact copy)
- produces no immune response (exact copy)
- does not carry any risk of transmitting animal diseases
- is cheaper to produce
- does not cause patients to develop tolerance (become less sensitive) to it
- does not involve using/killing animals.
  (Each point one mark to a maximum of 3 marks)

e) i) Benefits:
  - Permanent cure
  - No need for injections
  - Cheaper in the long term (no insulin needed).
  ii) Drawbacks:
  - Insufficient donors
  - Risk to health during operation (both to live donor and recipient)
  - Some people find transplants unethical.
    (1 mark for each benefit to a maximum of 2 marks)
    (1 mark for each drawback to a maximum of 2 marks)
    Do not allow 'nasal sprays' as this is a treatment not a cure.

HOW SCIENCE WORKS ANSWERS

a) Bucket of water does not lose heat in the same way as the human body, e.g. humans have an inner source of heat and therefore remain hotter than the surroundings. Also no humans are 10 metres tall!

b) The cheeks are usually the only part of the body left exposed in very cold conditions.

c) To at least 0.1°C

d) As many as possible (actually in one study six men and six women).

e) From a wide range of ages and sexes (actually aged 22 to 42).

f) and g) There will probably be many acceptable ways to record the data. These are the actual wind speeds and temperatures used. Perhaps they should have used more temperatures and wind speeds within the range!

	Air temperature (°C)		
Wind speed (km/h)	10	0	−10
10			
20			
30			

How science works teaching suggestions

- **Literacy guidance**
  - Key terms that should be clearly understood: range; interval measurements; sensitivity.
  - Question a) expects a longer answer, where students can practise their literacy skills.
- **How and when to use these questions.** When wishing to develop good scientific method and table construction. The questions would be best used in small discussion groups.
- **Homework.** Questions f) and g) could be set as homework.
- **Special needs.** A demonstration of windchill could be done.
- **ICT link-up.** Data logging equipment could be used to demonstrate windchill on wet towelling.

- Points plotted accurately ±2 mm (scale may need to be varied depending upon the graph paper used).
- *Either* best fit curve *or* ruled point to point lines – accurately drawn.
- Two lines distinguished in some way (e.g. one solid/one broken) with key or labels. *(Allow the mark if both lines are drawn the same but distinguished by labels in close proximity to the relevant line.)*
  (1 mark for each aspect)

ii) Person X because:
- Blood sugar level of person X rises to a much higher level (200 mg/cm³ blood) than that of person Y (140 mg/cm³ blood).
- Blood sugar level of person X continues to rise until around 60 minutes after swallowing the glucose whereas that of person Y begins to fall after 40 minutes.
- Blood sugar level of person X has not even reached the starting/normal level of 90 mg/cm³ blood after 3 hours whereas that of person Y returns to the starting/normal level after just one hour.
- Any other reasonable explanation.
  (1 mark for each point to a maximum of 2 marks)
  There are no marks for simply choosing the correct person as there is a 50% chance of success using only guesswork. If the student has reversed persons X and Y on the graph – allow the marks in this part of the question provided the points made are consistent with their error on the graph.

4 a) Because it would be broken down. *(1 mark answer)*
  As insulin is a **protein**, it would be **broken down** by **enzymes** in the stomach. *(2 marks answer)*
  For both marks the key words in bold (or their equivalent) must be correctly linked.

  b) It would get higher/increase. *(1 mark)*

  c) Glucose in the urine/increased thirst/increased hunger/ urinating excessively/tiredness/weight loss/blurred vision. *(Any one for 1 mark)*

B2 6.1

Cell division and growth

Students should learn that:

- Mitosis results in the production of additional cells for growth, repair and replacement.

- Before each cell division, the genetic information on the chromosomes is copied so that the new cells have the same genes as the parent cells.

- Most animal cells differentiate at an early stage but most plant cells have the ability to differentiate throughout life.

Most students should be able to:

- Describe the process of mitosis.

- Describe how the cells produced by mitosis are genetically identical to the parent cells.

Some students should also be able to:

- Explain why plants retain the ability to grow throughout their lives whereas cell division in mature animals is involved in repair and replacement of tissues.

Teaching suggestions

- **Special needs.** Give one student two short pieces of Plasticine of one colour and two long ones of another colour. These are placed inside a ring of string representing the cell. Give the students balls of Plasticine and tell them to make copies of each and pass a set to two other students who do the same, passing on two more each until the whole class has been involved and there are many copies inside string rings on the floor. This works well in a gym.

- **Gifted and talented.** Introduce the students to the names of the stages as an introduction to AS level work.

- **Learning styles**
  Kinaesthetic: Making models with Plasticine.
  Visual: Watching animation of mitosis.
  Auditory: Discussing the properties of 'living leather'.
  Interpersonal: Compiling a small concept map for the unit and getting other students to state how the links should be labelled.
  Intrapersonal: Writing down own ideas on 'How a cell divides'.

SPECIFICATION LINK-UP   Unit: Biology 2.11.8

- *In body cells, the chromosomes are normally found in pairs. Body cells divide by mitosis to produce additional cells during growth or to produce replacement cells.*

- *Most types of animal cell differentiate at an early stage, whereas many plant cells retain the ability to differentiate throughout life. In mature animals, cell division is mainly restricted to repair and replacement.*

- *The cells of the offspring produced by asexual reproduction are produced by mitosis from parental cells. They contain the same genes as the parents.*

Lesson structure

STARTER

Matching exercise – Give each student pieces of paper with 'cell', 'nucleus', 'chromosome', 'gene' and 'DNA' on them, plus definitions all muddled up. They have to join them correctly. (5 minutes)

Growth, repair or replacement – Ask if any of the students have scabs or scars. Ask: 'Who has had their hair cut most recently or cut their fingernails?' Discuss marking children's height on the back of doors. Link with Anne Frank's father marking her height when they were in hiding. Lead in to a discussion of how our 'living leather' grows and heals. (5–10 minutes)

Multiplication – Draw one cell on the board then two cells next to it. The students have to copy this down and write beneath a short paragraph entitled 'My ideas on how cells multiply'. Read some out and discuss. (10–15 minutes)

MAIN

Observing mitosis

- This can be done using prepared longitudinal sections of root tips, or the students can make their own root tip squashes. A number of different sources will give suitable root tips, although it is a good idea to choose something that does not have a large diploid number of chromosomes. Germinating broad bean or pea seeds work well, or the tips of roots produced from hyacinth or garlic bulbs suspended in water. (See 'Practical support').

- Students may require help mounting their root tips and in using microscopes. It could be helpful to give each student a worksheet with the details of the preparation on it, and then a series of diagrams or photographs showing stages so that they can have a go at identifying stages on their own slides. If a space is left beside each stage, then the students could make a sketch of what they can see on their slides. They do not need to know the names of the stages.

Cloning a cauliflower

Students could try cloning for themselves. Using sterile techniques, it is possible to grow clones of carrot, cauliflower or potato tissue on nutrient agar. Use a 3 mm tip of an 'eye' of a potato, a mini-floret from the floret of a cauliflower or a segment of carrot tap root treated with the plant growth regulator 2,4-D. The plant tissue should be sterilised in bleach, rinsed in four washes of sterilised water and then gently pressed into agar in sterilised Petri dishes. The cultures should be sealed, wrapped loosely in cling film and kept incubated in a growth cabinet at about 25°C in the light.

- Calluses should develop over the next few weeks and tiny plantlets should develop from buds. The cultures should be examined regularly and a photographic record kept. More details are available from NCBE publications.

PLENARIES

Mitosis dominoes – In groups of four, play a dominoes-style game showing the stages of mitosis and a general description. No details, i.e. named stages, are required. (10 minutes)

Growing points – Using a small potted plant, remove all the leaves, so that the growing point (main bud) and the buds in the axils of the leaves are left. Give the students a diagram of the plant with all the leaves pulled off and get them to mark where the growing points are, and to draw in what they think the plant will look like in a couple of weeks. Keep the plant in the lab and look at it when the time is up. (10 minutes)

Practical support

Observing mitosis

Equipment and materials required

Root tips of beans, peas, onions, garlic or other suitable material, dilute acetic orsein stain and dilute hydrochloric acid, watch glasses, heater/spirit lamp/hotplate, mounted needles, microscope slides and cover slips, blotting paper, microscopes.

Details of practical

5 mm lengths of the root tips should be cut off and placed in a watch glass containing acetic orcein stain and hydrochloric acid. This should be warmed gently for 5 minutes. The tip is then placed on a microscope slide with a few drops of the stain, teased out with a pair of mounted needles and then covered with a cover slip. Cover with blotting paper and press gently to spread out the cells. The slide can then be viewed under the microscope, remembering to focus at low power first.

ACTIVITY & EXTENSION

- **Make a mitosis flick book** – Find or make some clear diagrams of the stages of mitosis. Copy on to a sheet for each student so that they can make their own 'flick book' by cutting up the pictures and assembling them in the correct order.
- **Make your own mitosis movie** – Using Plasticine to model the chromosomes and stop motion photography with a web cam, students can make their own animation of the process of mitosis.

BIOLOGY   INHERITANCE

B2 6.1   Cell division and growth

LEARNING OBJECTIVES

1. What is mitosis?
2. Why do plants grow throughout their lives while most animals stop growing once they are adults?

New cells are needed for an organism, or part of an organism, to grow. They are also needed to replace cells which become worn out and repair damaged tissue. However the new cells must have the same genetic information in them as the originals, so they can do the same job.

Each of your cells has a nucleus containing the instructions for making whole new cells and even an entire new you! These instructions are carried in the form of genes.

A gene is a small packet of information which controls a characteristic, or part of a characteristic, of your body. The genes are grouped together on chromosomes. A chromosome may carry several hundred or even thousands of genes.

You have 46 chromosomes in the nucleus of your cells (except your gametes – sperm or ova). They come in 23 pairs. One of each pair is inherited from your father, and one from your mother.

a) Why are new cells needed?

Mitosis

Body cells divide to make new cells. The cell division which takes place in the normal body cells and produces identical daughter cells is called **mitosis**. As a result of mitosis all your body cells have the same genetic information.

In asexual reproduction, the cells of the offspring are produced by mitosis from cells of their parent. This is why they contain exactly the same genes with no variety.

How does mitosis work? Before a cell divides it produces new copies of the chromosomes in the nucleus. This means that when division takes place two genetically identical **daughter cells** are formed.

In some areas of the body of an animal or plant, cell division like this carries on rapidly all of the time. Your skin is a good example – cells are constantly being lost from the surface and new cells are constantly being formed by cell division to replace them.

b) What is mitosis?

Differentiation

In the early development of animal and plant embryos the cells are very unspecialised. Each one of them (known as **stem cells**) can become any type of cell which is needed.

In many animals, the cells become specialised very early in life. By the time a human baby is born most of its cells have become specialised for a particular job, such as liver cells, skin cells and muscle cells. They have **differentiated**. Some of their genes have been switched on and others have been switched off.

Cell
Nucleus

Nucleus

Chromosomes found in pairs, one inherited from your father and one from your mother

Gene

Chromosome

Each chromosome in a pair carries genes which code for the same characteristic

Figure 1 The nucleus of your cell contains the chromosomes that carry the genes which control the characteristics of your whole body

This normal body cell has four chromosomes in two pairs.

As cell division starts, a copy of each chromosome is made

The cell divides in two to form two daughter cells. Each daughter cell has a nucleus containing four chromosomes identical to the ones in the original parent cell.

Figure 2 Identical daughter cells are formed by the simple division that takes place during mitosis. It supplies all the new cells needed in your body for growth, replacement and repair. Your cells really have 23 pairs of chromosomes – but for simplicity this cell is shown with only two pairs!

This means that when a muscle cell divides by mitosis it can only form more muscle cells. Liver cells can only produce more liver cells. So in adult animals, cell division is restricted because differentiation has occurred. Specialised cells can divide by mitosis, but this can only be used to repair damaged tissue and replace worn out cells. Each cell can only produce identical copies of itself.

In contrast, most plant cells can differentiate all through their life. Undifferentiated cells are formed at active regions of the stems and roots. In these areas mitosis takes place almost continuously.

Plants keep growing all through their lives at these 'growing points'. The plant cells produced don't differentiate until they are in their final position in the plant. What's more, the differentiation isn't permanent. If you move a plant cell from one part of a plant to another, it can re-differentiate and become a completely different type of cell. You just can't do that with animal cells – once a muscle cell, always a muscle cell!

PRACTICAL

Observing mitosis

Make a special preparation of a growing root tip to view under a microscope. Then you can see the actively dividing cells and the different stages of mitosis as it is taking place.

- Describe your observations of mitosis.

We can produce huge numbers of identical plant clones from a tiny piece of leaf tissue. Now you can see why this is possible. In the right conditions a plant cell will become unspecialised and undergo mitosis many times. In different conditions, each of these undifferentiated cells will produce more cells by mitosis. These will then differentiate to form a tiny new plant identical to the original parent.

The reason animal clones cannot be made easily is because animal cells differentiate permanently early in embryo development – and can't change back! Animal clones can only be made by cloning embryos in one way or another.

SUMMARY QUESTIONS

1. Copy and complete using the words below:

   chromosomes   genetic information   genes   growth
   mitosis   nucleus   replace

   New cells are needed for …… and to …… worn out cells. The new cells must have the same …… …… in them as the originals. Each cell has a …… containing the …… grouped together on ……. The type of cell division which produces identical cells is known as …… .

2. Division of the body cells is taking place all the time in living organisms.
   a) Why is it so important?
   b) Explain why the chromosome number must stay the same when the cells divide to make other normal body cells.

3. The process of growth and differentiation is very different in plants and animals.
   a) What is differentiation?
   b) How is differentiation in animal and plant cells so different?
   c) How does this difference affect the cloning of plants and animals?

DID YOU KNOW?

Your body cells are lost at an amazing rate – 300 million cells die every minute! No wonder mitosis takes place all the time in your body to replace them!

Figure 3 The undifferentiated cells in this onion root tip are dividing rapidly. You can see mitosis taking place, with the chromosomes in different positions as the cells divide.

GET IT RIGHT!

Cells produced by mitosis have identical genetic information.

KEY POINTS

1. In body cells, chromosomes are found in pairs.
2. Body cells divide by mitosis to produce more identical cells for growth, repair, replacement or in some cases asexual reproduction.
3. Most types of animal cells differentiate at an early stage of development. Many plant cells can differentiate throughout their life.

68   69

SUMMARY ANSWERS

1. Growth, replace, genetic information, nucleus, genes, chromosomes, mitosis.

2. a) Mitosis is important because cells die at the rate of 300 million per minute; cells are damaged; cells need to grow; in some organisms cells are needed for asexual reproduction.

   b) Cells need to be replaced with identical cells to do the same job.

3. a) Differentiation is the process by which cells become specialised.

   b) In animals, it occurs during embryo development and is permanent. In plants, it occurs throughout life and can be reversed or changed.

   c) Plants can be cloned relatively easily. Differentiation can be reversed, mitosis is induced, conditions can be changed and more mitosis induced. The cells re-differentiate into new plant tissues. In animals, differentiation cannot be reversed, so clones cannot be made easily. In order to make clones, embryos have to be made.

Answers to in-text questions

a) New cells are needed for growth, replacement and repair.

b) Mitosis is cell division that takes place in the normal body cells and produces identical daughter cells containing exactly the same genes as their parents.

KEY POINTS

The important point to stress here is that the cells produced by mitosis are genetically identical to the parent cells. This is achieved by the copying and separation of the chromosomes during mitosis. Students could write questions to test their partner on the key points.

B2 6.2 Stem cells

LEARNING OBJECTIVES

Students should learn that:

- Stem cells are unspecialised cells found in human embryos and in some adult tissues such as the bone marrow.
- Stem cells have the potential to differentiate into different types of specialised cells.

LEARNING OUTCOMES

Most students should be able to:

- Describe the structure and location of stem cells in humans.
- Describe how stem cells have the potential to treat sick people.

Some students should also be able to:

- Explain the arguments for and against using stem cells from embryos.

Teaching suggestions

- **Special needs.** Provide the students with a pre-drawn diagram of a ball of cells and some labels of cells and organs. Students can stick the labels around the stem cells to gain an understanding of these cells giving rise to all other types of cell.

- **Gifted and talented.** Students to define for themselves when life starts. They can be given a list of criteria from contrasting organisations such as the Human Fertilisation and Embryology Authority, and Pro-Life.

- **Learning styles**
  Kinaesthetic: Researching into the topic, using web sites.
  Visual: Following a sequence of therapeutic cloning diagrams.
  Auditory: Listening to the opinions of others in the discussion on pros and cons of stem cell research.
  Interpersonal: Discussing the pros and cons of research.
  Intrapersonal: Understanding the issues involved and conversation in groups.

- **ICT link-up.** There are a number of good web sites that have useful information: *New Scientist*; *Nature*; Stem Cell Information; Christopher Reeve Foundation; Stem Cell Research Foundation. (See www.nature.com; www. stemcells.nih.gov; www.christopherreeve.org; www.newscientist.com; www.stemcellresearchfoundation.org.)

SPECIFICATION LINK-UP   Unit: Biology 2.11.8

- *Most types of animal cells differentiate at an early stage whereas many plant cells retain the ability to differentiate throughout life. In mature animals, cell division is mainly restricted to repair and replacement. Cells from human embryos and adult bone marrow, called stem cells, can be made to differentiate into many different types of cells e.g. nerve cells. Treatment with these cells may help conditions such as paralysis.*

Lesson structure

STARTER

What are stem cells? – Write up the words 'stem cells' on the board. Students to write down, on an individual white board, a two-word phrase that it brings to mind. For lower ability students, just use the word 'stem' and put it into a sentence. Analyse some of the contributions. (5–10 minutes)

Growing new tissue could save lives – Search the web for some pictures of Christopher Reeve and a clip from one of his 'Superman' films. (Search also for Superman trailer!) Tie this in with a discussion of what happened to him and how growing new tissue, if it was possible, could have helped him. (10 minutes)

Losing limbs – Show photographs of amputees. Ask for a volunteer to wear a reverse sling for the lesson (not on their writing hand!). This can then stimulate a discussion of what it is like to lose a limb. If the class is musically orientated, play *The band played Waltzing Matilda,* by Eric Bogle – a poignant song about losing your legs. (10–15 minutes)

MAIN

- **Regenerating parts** – Some animals are able to re-grow parts of their bodies. Show photographs from search engines of lizards re-growing their tails and starfish re-growing limbs. Lead into a discussion of injuries and how they heal. Allow students to discuss injuries that they have had and what happens to them (time limit will be needed!).

- **Therapeutic cloning** – Find photographs about therapeutic cloning. There are a number of good web sites with lots of information on the use of stem cells. Students could be provided with a worksheet to be filled in. The important thing is to be aware of what is actually being done and what is hoped can be done in the future.

- **Sources of stem cells** – Show photographs of different sources of stem cells. Search the web for 'cell division blastocyst video' to show what happens after fertilisation. Otherwise find a photograph of a ball of stem cells. After four divisions, the cells become increasingly specialised. Discuss what would happen to the cells if they were allowed to continue development. Other sources include umbilical cord blood (rich in blood stem cells), fetal germ cells (extracted from terminated pregnancies of 5–9 weeks), frozen embryos and adult stem cells from bone marrow.

- **Pros and cons of the use of stem cells** – Both arguments need to be put forward. The cons of stem cell research could be put to the students by a visiting speaker who will argue the case. Some Catholic web sites provide a concise version of the sanctity of life (see www.justthefacts.org for some good pre-birth information). The pros can be summarised from web sites. Some useful ones are given in the 'ICT Link-up'.

- Use a summary sheet to state the main information and hold a snowball discussion where pairs of students brainstorm the concepts, then double up as fours and continue the process. The fours then gather into groups of eight in order to compare ideas and agree on a course of action (to endorse stem cell research or not). A spokesperson from each group of eight feeds back to the whole group.

Additional biology

ACTIVITY & EXTENSION

- If computers are available, set up a scavenger hunt style trail of Internet sites to pull out the main bits of the pro and con arguments and details of the research carried out.

- Ask students to find out about the original research and write a report of what was discovered. (See www.stemcellresearchfoundation.org.)

- Ask students to investigate what the words 'totipotent', 'pluripotent' and 'multipotent' mean when applied to stem cells. ['Totipotent' cells are found in very early embryos (for the first three or four divisions) and can differentiate into all types of cell. 'Pluripotent' stem cells are present in later embryos and can differentiate into any cell type. 'Multipotent' stem cells are found in adults as well as embryos and will only differentiate into certain cell types.] The Stem Cell Research Foundation has illustrations on its web site.

Answers to in-text questions

a) Unspecialised cells that can differentiate to form many different types of specialised body cell.

b) Culturing human embryonic stem cells.

c) Some people think it is wrong to use a potential human being as a source of cells to help other people.

BIOLOGY   INHERITANCE

B2 6.2   Stem cells

LEARNING OBJECTIVES

1 What is special about stem cells?
2 How can we use stem cells to cure people?

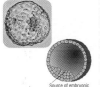

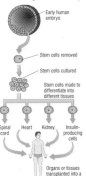

Figure 1 This ball of cells is an early human embryo. In the right conditions these few cells can form all the organs of the human body.

Early human embryo

Stem cells removed

Stem cells cultured

Stem cells made to differentiate into different tissues

Spinal cord   Heart   Kidney   Insulin-producing cells

Organs or tissues transplanted into a patient to cure them

Most of the cells in your body are differentiated. They are specialised and carry out particular jobs. But some of your most important cells are the completely unspecialised **stem cells**. They can differentiate (divide and change) into many different types of cell when they are needed. Human stem cells are found in human embryos and in some adult tissue including bone marrow.

The function of stem cells

Stem cells divide and form the specialised cells of your body which make up your various tissues and organs. When an egg and sperm fuse to form an embryo, they form a single new cell. That cell divides and the embryo is soon a hollow ball of cells. The inner cells of this ball are the stem cells which will eventually give rise to every type of cell in your body.

Even when you are an adult some of your more specialised stem cells remain. Your bone marrow is a good source of stem cells. What's more, scientists now think there may be a tiny number of stem cells in most of the different tissues in your body. This includes your blood, brain, muscle and liver.

The stem cells can stay there for many years until your tissues are injured or affected by disease. Then they start dividing to replace the different types of damaged cells.

a) What are stem cells?

Using stem cells

Many people suffer and even die because various parts of their body stop working properly. For example, spinal injuries can cause paralysis. That's because the spinal nerves do not repair themselves. Millions of people would benefit if we could replace damaged body parts.

In 1998, there was a breakthrough. Two American scientists managed to culture human embryonic stem cells that were capable of forming other types of cells.

Scientists hope that these embryonic stem cells can be encouraged to grow into almost any different type of cell needed in the body. For example, we may be able to grow new nerve cells. If new nerves grown from stem cells could be used to reconnect the spinal nerves, people who have been paralysed could walk again.

With stem cells we might also be able to grow whole new organs which could be used in transplant surgery. These new organs would not be rejected by the body. Conditions from infertility to dementia could eventually be treated using stem cells.

Unfortunately, at the moment no-one is quite sure just how the cells in an embryo are switched on or off. We don't yet know how to form particular types of tissue. Once we know how to do this, we can really start to use stem cells effectively.

b) What was the big scientific breakthrough by American scientists in 1998?

Figure 2 Some of the embryonic stem cells which scientists have produced and grown have formed into adult cells. Unfortunately no-one is quite sure how to control this process at the moment. Hopefully one day the technique shown in this diagram will be used to treat people.

Problems with stem cells

Many embryonic stem cells come from aborted embryos or from spare embryos in fertility treatment. This raises ethical problems. There are people, including many religious groups, who feel it is wrong to use a potential human being as a source of cells, even to cure others.

Some people feel that as the embryo cannot give permission, using it is a violation of its human rights. On top of this, progress with stem cells is slow. There is some concern that embryonic stem cells might cause cancer if they are used to treat sick people. This has certainly been seen in mice. Making stem cells is slow, difficult, expensive and hard to control.

c) What is the biggest ethical concern with the use of embryonic stem cells?

The future of stem cell research

We have found embryonic stem cells in the umbilical cord blood of newborn babies. These may help to overcome some of the ethical concerns.

Scientists are also finding ways of growing adult stem cells. Unfortunately the adult stem cells found so far can only develop into a limited range of cell types. However this is another possible way of avoiding the controversial use of embryonic tissue.

The area of stem cell research known as *therapeutic cloning* could be very useful – but it is proving very difficult.

Therapeutic cloning involves using cells from an adult person to produce a cloned early embryo of themselves as a source of perfectly matched embryonic stem cells. In theory these could then be used to heal the original donor and maybe many others as well.

Most people remain excited by the possibilities of embryonic stem cells in treating many diseases. Just how many of these early hopes will be fulfilled only time will tell!

SUMMARY QUESTIONS

1 Copy and complete using the words below:

   bone marrow   differentiate   embryos   hollow
   inner   stem cells

   Unspecialised cells known as .... can ...... (divide and change) into many different types of cell when they are needed. Human stem cells are found in human ...... and in adult .... The embryo forms a ...... ball of cells and the ...... cells of this ball are the stem cells.

2 a) Why was the work of the American scientists in 1998 such a breakthrough in stem cell research?
   b) How might stem cells be used to treat patients who are paralysed after a spinal injury?

3 a) What are the advantages of using stem cells to treat a wide range of diseases?
   b) What are the difficulties with stem cell research?
   c) How are scientists hoping to overcome the difficulties of using embryonic stem cells in their research?

GET IT RIGHT!

Make sure you refer to both pros and cons when you are giving information about the possible use of stem cells.

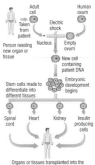

Adult cell   Human ovum

Taken from cell   Electric shock

Person needing new organ or tissue   Nucleus   Empty ovum

New cell containing patient DNA

Stem cells made to differentiate into different tissues   Embryonic development begins

Spinal cord   Heart   Kidney   Insulin producing cells

Organs or tissues transplanted into the patient with no risk of rejection

Figure 3 In 2005, a team led by Professor Woo Suk Hwang in South Korea claimed to have produced human embryos from adult cells and developed cloned stem cells from them. This seemed a huge step forward in stem cell research. But sadly, in 2006 the work was shown to be a massive scientific fraud. This was a massive blow to everyone working in stem cell research.

KEY POINT

1 Embryonic stem cells (from human embryos) and adult stem cells (from adult bone marrow) can be made to differentiate into many different types of cells.

PLENARIES

Therapeutic cloning – Draw out a sequence diagram for therapeutic cloning to illustrate how it is carried out. (10 minutes)

Poetry in motion – Give the students the key word 'stem cells'. This forms Line 1 of the poem. Line 2 consists of two words describing what the key word is. Line 3 contains three words describing what the key word does. Line 4 is four words describing what the key word means to you personally. Line 5 is one word giving an alternative to the key word. Select students to read out their efforts. (10 minutes)

Anagrams – Write up or project anagrams of the key words from the lesson. Students to write them down sequentially on individual whiteboards. (5–10 minutes)

KEY POINT

This is a statement of the facts. Students should be quite clear about the unspecialised nature of stem cells and their potential to become differentiated. This could be reinforced by a diagram of an unspecialised cell surrounded by the different types of cell.

SUMMARY ANSWERS

1 Stem cells, differentiate, embryos, bone marrow, hollow, inner.

2 a) They cultured human stem cells for the first time.

  b) They could be used to grow new nerve cells to reconnect the spinal cord.

3 a) They can be used to make any type of adult cell to repair or replace damaged tissues, with no rejection issues.

  b) There are ethical objections and concerns over possible side effects.

  c) By using stem cells from umbilical blood, adult stem cells and therapeutic cloning.

B2 6.3   Cell division in sexual reproduction

Students should learn that:

- Cells which divide to form gametes undergo meiosis. [**HT** only]

- Gametes have a single set of genetic information, whereas body cells have two sets.

- Fertilisation results in the formation of a cell with new pairs of chromosomes so sexual reproduction gives rise to variation.

Most students should be able to:

- Describe what happens to the number of chromosomes during fertilisation.

- Explain how sexual reproduction gives rise to variation.

Some students should also be able to:

- Describe what happens to the chromosomes during the process of gamete formation. [**HT** only]

Teaching suggestions

- **Special needs.** Write the word 'chromosomes' twice on the board, inside a ring to represent a cell. To model meiosis, get four students to copy the word 'chromosomes' once onto a piece of A4 and put each on the board inside a ring. To model fertilisation, cut two of these 'chromosomes' words out and stick them inside a single ring. To model mitosis, take both words, stick them onto a sheet and photocopy it repeatedly. (Bear in mind that meiosis is a concept required at Higher Tier level only).

- **Gifted and talented.** Introduce the students to some of the vocabulary associated with the AS coverage of this topic (e.g. chiasmata, centrioles, centromeres). They could also look at pictures of chromosomes during Prophase I, where chiasmata formation is occurring.

- **Learning styles**
  Kinaesthetic: Plasticine modelling; using microscopes; drawing.
  Visual: Observing animations.
  Auditory: Talking over the differences between mitosis and meiosis.
  Interpersonal: Working in groups.
  Intrapersonal: Considering what would happen if reduction in chromosome numbers did not occur.

SPECIFICATION LINK-UP   Unit: Biology 2.11.8

- *Body cells have two sets of genetic information; gametes have only one set.*

- *Cells in reproductive organs – testes and ovaries in humans – divide to form gametes.* [**HT** only]

- *This type of cell division in which a cell divides to form gametes is called meiosis.* [**HT** only]

- *When a cell divides to form gametes:*
  - *copies of the chromosomes are made*
  - *then the cell divides twice to form four gametes, each with a single set of chromosomes.* [**HT** only]

- *When gametes join at fertilisation, a single body cell with new pairs of chromosomes is formed. A new individual then develops by this cell repeatedly dividing by mitosis.*

- *Sexual reproduction gives rise to variation because when gametes fuse, one of each pair of alleles comes from each parent.*

Lesson structure

STARTER

Introducing meiosis: a mnemonic for mitosis – Contrast meiosis with mitosis. Find a picture of some ghastly toes. (Search the web for 'toes'.) Get the students to copy down and remember that 'Mitosis goes on in my toes' and toes are not sexy. Also introduce meiosis as the 'reduction' division, as it reduces the number of chromosomes. (5 minutes)

Naming the sex cells – Give the students an empty grid to stick in their books. They are to complete this with the names of the sex cells from animals and plants. Have prompts ready if needed. For the higher attaining students, you could introduce the correct spellings i.e. 'spermatozoa' etc. (5–10 minutes)

Internet – Show an Internet-based flash animation summary of mitosis if easily available. (5 minutes)

MAIN

- **Simulation** – Use the Simulation B2 6.3 'Meiosis' available from the Additional Science CD ROM to introduce the topic.

- A flow diagram of the events of meiosis can be built up, showing that there are similarities in that the chromosomes are copied, but that there are two divisions rather than one. It is probably best to concentrate on the formation of sperm to begin with (because four observable cells result from the division) and follow up with slides of testis showing stages in sperm development.

- **Microscopic examination of testis slides** – The best prepared slides are of rat or grasshopper testis squashes. Provide the students with a sheet showing stages in the development of sperm that they are likely to be able to see on their slides, and a flow diagram to show the different stages of division. They may need help with their microscopes, as they will need to use high power if they are to see any chromosomes.

- Alternatively, sections of testis could be projected on to the board and students could identify the different cells with reasons for their choices.

- **Microscopic examination of ovary slides** – Slides could be projected and viewed by the class, or slides could be viewed using a microscope. There will be obvious differences in size of the sperms and the eggs. For higher attaining students it would be possible to explain what happens during the meiotic divisions that produce ova, e.g. the formation of the polar bodies.

- **Modelling meiosis and the need for reduction** – Using model chromosomes, firstly without a reduction in number of the chromosomes, show how the number of chromosomes would go on increasing. Follow this with the reduction part of the division, so that gametes have half the number and the correct number is restored on fertilisation.

- **Introducing variation** – Using Plasticine of different colours, it is possible to show how variation can occur during the process of meiosis. Students, in groups, could make models showing how the chromosomes separate, perhaps showing some exchange of genes, and then matching one set of gametes with another set, to represent the sperm and the ovum at fertilisation.

PLENARIES

True or false? – Present students with statements about mitosis and meiosis. They are to write 'True' or 'False' on 'Show me' boards, e.g.

'Mitosis is necessary for growth, repair and replacement of tissues.' [True]

'In meiosis, the number of chromosomes stays the same.' [False]

'Meiosis takes place in the testes.' [True]

'Mitosis involves two divisions of the chromosomes.' [False]

'Mitosis results in genetically identical cells.' [True] (5–10 minutes)

Use summary questions – Give students 5 minutes to read and answer the summary questions given in the Student Book . Check answers verbally to test the students' understanding of the topic. (10 minutes)

ACTIVITY & EXTENSION IDEAS

- **Differences between mitosis and meiosis** – Students to make a leaflet or poster summarising the differences between mitosis and meiosis. They should make it memorable, perhaps using the 'non-sexy toes' statement.

- **Meiosis in plants** – Preparations of squashes of immature anthers from developing buds of lily show the stages of meiosis and chromosomes very clearly.

B2 6.3 Cell division in sexual reproduction

LEARNING OBJECTIVES

1 What happens to your chromosomes when your gametes are formed? [Higher]
2 How does sexual reproduction give rise to variation?

Mitosis is taking place all the time, in tissues all over your body. But mitosis is not the only type of cell division. There is another type which takes place only in the reproductive organs of animals and plants. **Meiosis** results in sex cells with only half the original number of chromosomes.

Meiosis

The reproductive organs in people, like most animals, are the **ovaries** and the **testes**. This is where the sex cells (the gametes) are made. The female gametes or **ova** are made in the ovaries. The male gametes or **sperm** are made in the testes.

The gametes are formed by meiosis, which is a special form of cell division where the chromosome number is reduced by half. When a cell divides to form gametes, the first stage is very similar to normal body cell division. The chromosomes are copied so there are four sets of chromosomes. The cell then divides twice in quick succession to form four gametes, each with a single set of chromosomes.

Why is meiosis so important?

Your normal body cells have 46 chromosomes in two matching sets – 23 come from your mother and 23 from your father. If two 'normal' body cells joined together in sexual reproduction, the new cell would have 92 chromosomes, which simply wouldn't work!

Fortunately, as a result of meiosis, your sex cells contain only one set of chromosomes, exactly half of the full chromosome number. So when the gametes join together at fertilisation, the new cell formed contains the right number of 46 chromosomes.

a) What are the names of the male and female gametes and how do they differ from normal body cells?

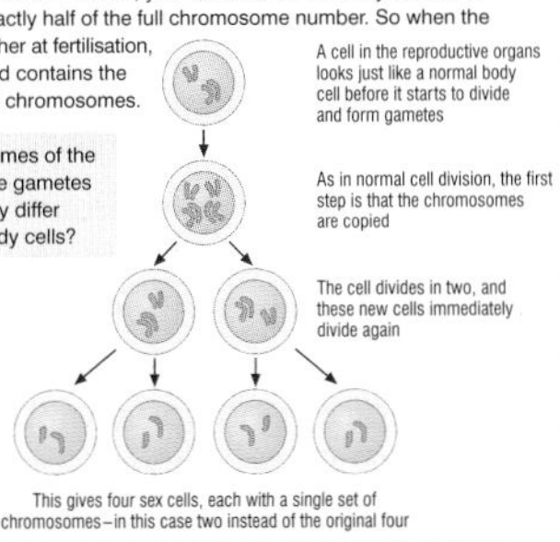

A cell in the reproductive organs looks just like a normal body cell before it starts to divide and form gametes

As in normal cell division, the first step is that the chromosomes are copied

The cell divides in two, and these new cells immediately divide again

This gives four sex cells, each with a single set of chromosomes–in this case two instead of the original four

Figure 1 The formation of sex cells in the ovaries and testes involves a special kind of cell division to halve the chromosome number. The original cell is shown with only two pairs of chromosomes to make it easier to follow what is happening.

DID YOU KNOW?

About 80% of fertilised eggs never make it to become a live baby – in fact about 50% never even implant into the lining of the womb.

GET IT RIGHT!

Be careful with the spelling of mitosis and meiosis. Make sure you know the two differences between the two processes.

DID YOU KNOW?

One testis can produce over 200 million sperm each day. As most boys and men have two working testes, that gives a total of 400 million sperm produced by meiosis every 24 hours! Only one sperm is needed to fertilise an egg. However as each tiny sperm needs to travel 100 000 times its own length to reach the ovum, less than one in a million ever completes the journey – so it's a good thing that plenty are made!

In girls, the first stage of meiosis is completed before they are even born. The tiny ovaries of a baby girl contain all the ova she will ever have.

In boys, meiosis doesn't start until puberty when the testes start to produce sperm. It then carries on for the rest of their lives.

Each gamete you produce is slightly different from all the others. The combination of chromosomes will be different. What's more, there is some exchange of genes between the chromosomes during the process of meiosis. This means that no two eggs or sperm are the same. This introduces lots of variety into the genetic mix of the offspring.

b) What type of cell division is needed to produce the gametes?

Fertilisation

More variety is added when fertilisation takes place. Each sex cell has a single set of chromosomes. When two sex cells join during fertilisation the new cell formed has a full set of chromosomes. In humans, the egg cell has 23 chromosomes and so does the sperm. When they join together they produce a new normal cell with the full human complement of 46 chromosomes.

The combination of genes on the chromosomes of every newly fertilised ovum is completely unique. Once fertilisation is complete, the unique new cell begins to divide by mitosis. This will continue long after the fetus is fully developed and the baby is born.

Variation

The differences between asexual and sexual reproduction are a reflection of the different types of cell division involved in the two processes.

In asexual reproduction the offspring are produced as a result of mitosis from the parent cells. (See the start of this chapter.) So they contain exactly the same chromosomes and the same genes as their parents. There is no variation in the genetic material.

In sexual reproduction the gametes are produced by meiosis in the sex organs of the parents. This introduces variety as each gamete is different. Then when the gametes fuse, one of each pair of chromosomes, and so one of each pair of genes, comes from each parent.

The combination of genes in the new pair will contain **alleles** (different forms of the gene) from each parent. This also helps to produce different characteristics in the offspring.

SUMMARY QUESTIONS

1 a) How many pairs of chromosomes are there in a normal human body cell?
   b) How many chromosomes are there in a human egg cell?
   c) How many chromosomes are there in a fertilised human egg cell?

2 Sexual reproduction results in variety. Explain how.

3 a) What is the name of the special type of cell division which produces gametes from ordinary body cells? Describe what happens to the chromosomes in this process.
   b) Where in your body would this type of cell division take place?
   c) Why is this type of cell division so important in sexual reproduction? [Higher]

Sperm

Ovum (egg)

Figure 2 Once meiosis has taken place, the male and female gametes develop very differently – they are adapted for very different jobs

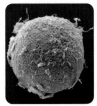

Figure 3 At the moment of fertilisation the chromosomes in the two gametes are combined and the new cell has a complete set, like any other body cell. This cell will then grow and reproduce by mitosis to form a new individual.

KEY POINTS

1 Cells in the reproductive organs divide to form the gametes (sex cells).
2 Body cells have two sets of chromosomes; gametes have only one set.
3 Gametes are formed from body cells by meiosis. [Higher]
4 Sexual reproduction gives rise to variety because genetic information from two parents is combined.

SUMMARY ANSWERS

1 **a)** 23 pairs **b)** 23 **c)** 46

2 As the gametes are formed, each gamete has a different combination of chromosomes and there is some exchange of genes. This introduces variation, as each gamete is different. In sexual reproduction, two unique gametes from two different people join together, so the combination of chromosomes and the mix of alleles on the chromosomes will be unique.

3 **a)** Meiosis. After the chromosomes are copied, the cell divides twice quickly resulting in sex cells each with half the number of chromosomes.

   b) In the reproductive organs/in the ovary or the testes.

   c) Sexual reproduction involves the joining of gametes from mother and father. The chromosome number of the body cells needs to be halved to make the gametes, otherwise the number of chromosomes in the cell would just get bigger and bigger when gametes joined at fertilisation. Meiosis halves the chromosome number. [**HT** only]

Answers to in-text questions

a) Sperm, ova, half the number of chromosomes.

b) Meiosis.

KEY POINTS

The differences between mitosis and meiosis are important and it is also important that the students spell the words correctly. They could test each other. Many of the suggested activities aim to show students how to remember the differences.

B2 6.4

From Mendel to DNA

LEARNING OBJECTIVES

Students should learn:

- About the work of Mendel and why its importance was not recognised until after his death.
- Why DNA fingerprinting is possible.
- How specific proteins are made.

LEARNING OUTCOMES

Most students should be able to:

- Describe Mendel's discoveries.
- Recognise why Mendel's ideas were not accepted in his time.
- Describe how DNA fingerprinting is used to identify individuals.

Some students should also be able to:

- Explain simply the structure of DNA.
- Explain how a gene codes for a specific protein. [**HT** only]

Teaching suggestions

- **Special needs.** Using different coloured (yellow and green) dried peas, glue and a large sheet of paper, ask the students to make a large poster showing Mendel's experiment as depicted in the Student Book.
- **Gifted and talented.** Ask students to draw up a plan for one of Mendel's experiments and calculate how long it took him to get his results. What precautions would he have to take? Did he use controls? Apply some of the criteria needed for 'How Science Works' to his experiments. Would you do it the same way as he did it? What different techniques might you use?
- **Learning styles**
  Kinaesthetic: Growing plants and counting seedlings.
  Visual: Video or PowerPoint® on Mendel.
  Auditory: Discussion of Mendel's work.
  Interpersonal: Working with partners in practical session.
  Intrapersonal: Writing a report or a letter to Mendel.
- **Homework.** Follow up the plenary interview with Mendel by writing a contemporary newspaper report about Mendel's work, along the lines of 'Mad monk sits and counts peas . . .'.
  Or Write a letter to Mendel explaining about chromosomes and how his work provided the foundation for modern genetics.

SPECIFICATION LINK-UP   Unit: Biology 2.11.8

- *Some characteristics are controlled by a single gene. Each gene may have different forms called alleles.*
- *An allele which controls the development of a characteristic when it is present on only one of the chromosomes is a dominant allele.*
- *An allele which controls the development of a characteristic only if the dominant allele is not present is a recessive allele.*
- *Chromosomes are made up of large molecules of DNA (deoxyribose nucleic acid). A gene is a small section of DNA.*
- *Each gene codes for a particular combination of amino acids which make a specific protein. [**HT** only]*
- *Each person (apart from identical twins) has unique DNA. This can be used to identify individuals in a process known as DNA fingerprinting.*

Students should use their skills, knowledge and understanding of 'How Science Works':

- *to explain why Mendel proposed the idea of separately inherited factors; and why the importance of this discovery was not recognised until after his death.*

Lesson structure

STARTER

How did Mendel start? – Give the students a collection of dried peas to sort out into groups. Include smooth and wrinkled skins, yellow and green if possible. Ask them to predict what would happen if the peas were planted. Would you get peas identical to the ones you planted? Discuss. (10 minutes)

A model of DNA – If possible have a model of DNA showing its structure with the different bases, the deoxyribose and the phosphate groups. Get the students to identify the component parts and discuss the coding on a simple level. (10 minutes)

MAIN

- **The life and work of Mendel** – Video or PowerPoint® presentation on Mendel's life and work. There is plenty of information available and scope for introducing students to the demands of research (think about all those plants he grew and seeds he counted). Consider the characteristics that he investigated, introduce some of the easier terms, such as 'pure-breeding' and some of the simple ratios. Discuss his technique. (This relates to 'How Science Works': acceptance of new ideas.) (See www.mendelweb.org. A web image bank will yield many illustrations on a search for 'Gregor Mendel'.)

- **Grow your own genetics experiment** – It is possible to obtain sets of seeds from monohybrid genetic crosses from suppliers. When the seeds grow, it is possible to observe differences between the seedlings and make predictions about the genetic constitution of the parent plants. Tobacco (colour of cotyledons, hairiness of stem, colour of stem and leaf shape), tomato (leaf shape, hairiness of stem, colour of stem) and cucumber (bitterness of leaves) are all suitable for class use. The seeds are sown in seed trays, kept in light, airy conditions and watered every two or three days. They will be ready for scoring the characteristics after about 15 to 20 days. These seeds usually come provided with instructions and an explanation of the parental cross which produced them.

- **Genetic fingerprints** – Prepare a PowerPoint® presentation on genetic fingerprinting. The technique can be fairly simply explained (see NCBE publications or web site for details) and then the implications discussed. Some examples of different uses can be given e.g. forensic evidence, paternity issues. There are some good images available on the Internet.

PLENARIES

Press conference – Select a student who is prepared to be Mendel. Other students are to interview him about his work and why he did not get recognition at the time. The student can choose other members of the class to represent workers who followed up his discoveries. (10–15 minutes)

Anagram quiz – Give the students anagrams of the key words in this topic and a small prize for the student who solves the puzzles in the fastest time. (5–10 minutes)

Be a detective! – Present the students with some genetic evidence (some DNA from a murder weapon and three sets of genetic fingerprints). Let them work out who did the crime. (5–10 minutes)

ACTIVITY & EXTENSION IDEAS

- **Did Mendel fiddle his results?** – There are several ways in which you could consider Mendel to be lucky. His choice of plants to work on, the characteristics he chose, the numbers he obtained – all these worked out well for him. Give students some of his results and let them work out the ratios. If there are any budding mathematicians in the group, ask if they can work out the probability of getting such good results. There are suggestions that he knew what he wanted to prove before he set up his experiments. Ask: 'What do you think?'

- **How to get enough DNA for a fingerprint** – Sometimes the quantity of DNA left at a crime scene is very small, but using PCR (the polymerase chain reaction) this can be increased. Find out how this works. Use a search engine and key in the words or go to the NCBE web site for more information.

BIOLOGY   INHERITANCE

B2 6.4   From Mendel to DNA

LEARNING OBJECTIVES
1 What did Mendel's experiments teach us about inheritance?
2 What are DNA fingerprints?
3 How are specific proteins made in the body? [Higher]

GET IT RIGHT!
Mendel knew nothing of chromosomes and genes. Make sure you don't confuse modern knowledge with what Mendel knew when he did his experiments.

Parents
Green peas ✕ Yellow peas

Offspring (first generation)   All green peas

But when the offspring are bred . . .   Green peas   Green peas

Offspring (second generation)
¾ Green peas   ¼ Yellow peas

Figure 1 Gregor Mendel, the father of modern genetics. When he died in 1884 he was still hoping that eventually other people would acknowledge his discoveries. In the 21st century, we know just how right he was!

For hundreds of years people had no idea about how information moved from one generation to the next. Yet now we can identify people by the genetic information in their cells!

Mendel's discoveries

Gregor Mendel was born in 1822 in Brunn, Czechoslovakia. Clever but poor, he became a monk to get an education.

He worked in the monastery gardens and became fascinated by the peas growing there. He decided to carry out some breeding experiments, using pure strains of round peas, wrinkled peas, green peas and yellow peas for his work. Mendel cross-bred the peas and counted the different offspring carefully. He found that characteristics were inherited in clear and predictable patterns.

Mendel explained his results by suggesting there were separate units of inherited material. He realised some characteristics were dominant over others and that they never mixed together. This was an amazing idea for the time.

a) Why did Gregor Mendel become a monk?

Mendel kept records of everything he did, and analysed his results. This was almost unheard of in those days! Finally in 1866, when he was 44 years old, Mendel published his findings.

He never saw chromosomes and never heard of genes. Yet he explained some of the basic laws of genetics in a way we still use today.

Sadly Mendel's genius was ahead of his time. As no-one knew about genes or chromosomes, people simply didn't understand his theories. He died twenty years later with his ideas still ignored – but convinced that he was right!

b) What was unusual about Mendel's scientific technique at the time?

Sixteen years after his death, Gregor Mendel's work was finally recognised. By 1900, people had seen chromosomes through a microscope. Three scientists, discovered Mendel's papers and repeated his experiments. When they published their results, they gave Mendel the credit for what they observed! From then on ideas about genetics developed fast. It was suggested that Mendel's units of inheritance might be carried on the chromosomes seen beneath the microscope. And so the science of genetics as we know it today was born.

DNA – the molecule of inheritance

The work of Gregor Mendel was just the start of our understanding of inheritance. Today, we know that our features are inherited on genes carried on our chromosomes. We also know what those chromosomes are made of.

Your chromosomes are made up of long molecules of a chemical known as DNA (**d**eoxyribose **n**ucleic **a**cid). Your genes are small sections of this DNA. The DNA carries the instructions to make the proteins which form most of your cell structures. These proteins also include the enzymes which control your cell chemistry.

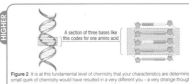
A section of three bases like this codes for one amino acid

Figure 2 It is at this fundamental level of chemistry that your characteristics are determined. A small quirk of chemistry would have resulted in a very different you – a very strange thought.

The long strands of your DNA are made up of combinations of four different chemical bases. (See Figure 2.) These are grouped into threes and each group of three codes form an amino acid.

Each gene is made up of hundreds or thousands of these bases. The order of the bases controls the order in which the amino acids are put together so that they make a particular protein for use in your body cells. Each gene codes for a particular combination of amino acids which make a specific protein.

A change or mutation in a single group of bases can be enough to change or disrupt the whole protein structure and the way it works.

DNA fingerprinting

Unless you have an identical twin, your DNA is unique to you. Other members of your family will have strong similarities in their DNA, but each individual has their own unique blueprint. Only identical twins have the same DNA. That's because they have both developed from the same original cell.

The unique patterns in your DNA can be used to identify you. A technique known as 'DNA fingerprinting' can be applied.

Certain areas of your DNA produce very variable patterns under the microscope. These patterns are more similar between people who are related than between total strangers. The patterns are known as **DNA fingerprints**. They can be produced from very tiny samples of DNA from body fluids such as blood, saliva and semen.

The likelihood of two identical samples coming from different people (apart from identical twins) is millions to one. As a result DNA fingerprinting is enormously useful in solving crimes. It is also used to show who is the biological father of a child when there is doubt.

SUMMARY QUESTIONS

1 a) How did Mendel's experiments with peas convince him that there were distinct 'units of inheritance' which were not blended together in offspring?
  b) Why didn't people accept his ideas?
  c) The development of the microscope played an important part in helping to convince people that Mendel was right. How?

2 Two men claim to be the father of the same child. Explain how DNA fingerprinting could be used to find out which one is the real father.

3 Explain the saying 'One gene, one protein'. [Higher]

DID YOU KNOW?
The first time DNA fingerprinting was used to solve a crime it not only identified Colin Pitchfork as the murderer of two teenage girls, it also cleared another innocent man of the same crimes!

Figure 3 DNA fingerprints like these can be used to identify the guilty – and the innocent – in a crime investigation

KEY POINTS
1 Gregor Mendel was the first person to suggest separately inherited factors which we now call genes.
2 Chromosomes are made up of large molecules of DNA.
3 A gene is a small section of DNA which codes for a particular combination of amino acids which make a specific protein. [Higher]
4 Everyone (except identical twins) has unique DNA which can be used to identify them using DNA fingerprinting.

74   75

SUMMARY ANSWERS

1 a) He found that characteristics were inherited in clear and predictable patterns. He realised some characteristics were dominant over others and that they never mixed together.

  b) No-one could see the units of inheritance so there was no proof of their existence. People were not used to studying careful records of results.

  c) Once people could see chromosomes, a mechanism for Mendel's ideas of inheritance became possible.

2 The DNA fingerprint of the real father would have similarities to the DNA fingerprint of the child whereas that of the other man would not.

3 A gene is made up of groups of three base pairs. Each group of three base pairs codes for a single amino acid. The order of the base pairs in the gene determines the sequence of the amino acids which are joined together to make a protein – so each gene codes for a unique protein.

Answers to in-text questions

a) Mendel became a monk because he was clever but poor and the only way to get an education if you were poor was to join the Church.

b) He kept records and analysed his results.

KEY POINTS

These key points are straightforward and can be reinforced by being made into revision cards. The higher ability students would benefit from adding their own annotations to expand the basic concepts.

B2 6.5

Inheritance in action

Teaching suggestions

- **Special needs.** Play a card game using dominant and recessive cards for lobed ears, dimples and tongue rolling. Some students might be able to cope with the sex determination game in its simplest form.

- **Gifted and talented.**
  - If the school has the facilities, students could try scoring the *Drosophila* crosses, particularly if the flies have been used for sixth-form classes.
  - Alternatively, they could research haemophilia and trace it through the offspring of Queen Victoria. They could produce a PowerPoint® report to be shown to the rest of the group.

SPECIFICATION LINK-UP   Unit: Biology 2.11.8

- *An allele that controls the development of a characteristic when it is present on only one of the chromosomes is a dominant allele.*

- *An allele that controls the development of characteristics only if the dominant allele is not present is a recessive allele.*

- *In human body cells, one of the 23 pairs of chromosomes carries the genes which determine sex. In females, the sex chromosomes are the same (XX), in males the sex chromosomes are different (XY).*

Lesson structure

STARTER

Get the words right – Put up at the front of the room word cards with the important terms from the spread on them (e.g. allele, chromosome, dominant, recessive, Mendel, inheritance etc.). Ask the students to write down sentences containing any one of these words. Select from responses, noting key ideas. (10 minutes)

Can you? – Ask some of these: 'Can you roll your tongue? Can you taste quinine? Do you have dimples? Do you have dangly ear lobes? Do you have straight thumbs or bendy thumbs?' Discuss some of these characteristics. (The invitation to poke one's tongue out at the teacher usually goes down well!) (5–10 minutes)

MAIN

- **Grow your own genetics experiment** – If students did not carry out this exercise when studying the previous spread, it could be done here as an illustration of inheritance in action.

- **The Human Genome Project** – Inherited conditions in humans are due to mutations of the DNA. The Human Genome Project has mapped all the human chromosomes. Prepare a PowerPoint® presentation on this project, including references to why it was done, how it was done and how long it took. Give the students prepared work sheets and allow time for them to make their own notes. Discuss the implications. Information is available on The Wellcome Trust web site and the Human Genome Project Information web site.

- **Sex determination game** – Prepare sets of sperm cards with either an X or a Y on the back and egg cards, all with X on the back. Working in pairs, the students are to turn one sperm card and one egg card over at a time. In a table, they note the sperm chromosome, the egg chromosome, the combination, the gender and give the baby a name. Run for about 5–7 minutes and then see who has the biggest family. Ask: 'Are there more boys than girls? What does this tell us about the ratio of the sexes?'

PLENARIES

Punnett square – Draw a Punnett square on the board with a number of different dominant and recessive alleles. Use some of the examples mentioned in the 'Can you?' starter. Get the students to fill in pre-printed frames and to describe the crosses. (10–15 minutes)

Human karyotypes – Show students some human karyotypes where the chromosomes have not been matched into pairs. Can they identify the sex chromosomes and decide where the karotype is from a male of a female? Compare with karyotypes where the chromosomes are in pairs. When is this type of information helpful? (5–10 minutes)

ACTIVITY & EXTENSION IDEAS

- **Modify the sex determination game** – Using a symbol to represent a characteristic, such as tongue rolling, which can be stuck on the cards, the inheritance of a human characteristic (not a sex-linked one) can be investigated at the same time. Just add another column to the table. It would be possible to investigate sex-linkage using this game, but it is beyond the specification.

Teaching suggestions – continued

- **Learning styles**

  Kinaesthetic: Growing plants and counting seedlings.

  Visual: Viewing PowerPoint® presentation on the Human Genome Project.

  Auditory: Discussing the Human Genome Project.

  Interpersonal: Working with partners in sex determination game.

  Intrapersonal: Completing own work sheet.

- **ICT link-up.** There are some excellent web sites with genetics games that can be played on-line, e.g. the Canadian Museum of Nature web site (nature.ca/genome).

BIOLOGY   INHERITANCE

B2 6.5   Inheritance in action

LEARNING OBJECTIVES

1 How is sex determined in humans?
2 Can you predict what features a child might inherit? [Higher]

Ideas about genetics, chromosomes and genes are everywhere in the 21st century. We read about them in the papers, see them on TV and learn about them in science lessons. The way features are passed from one generation to another follow some clear patterns. We can use these to predict what may be passed on.

How inheritance works

Scientiest have built on the work of Gregor Mendel. We now understand how genetic information is passed from parent to offspring.

Human beings have 23 pairs of chromosomes. In 22 cases, each chromosome in the pair is a similar shape and has genes carrying information about the same things. But one pair of chromosomes may be different – these are the **sex chromosomes**. Two X chromosomes mean you are female. However, one X chromosome and a much smaller one, known as the Y chromosome, give a male.

a) Twins are born. Twin A is XY and twin B is XX. What sex are the two babies?

The chromosomes we inherit carry our genetic information in the form of genes. Many of these genes have different forms, known as alleles. (See page 73.) A gene can be pictured as a position on a chromosome. An allele is the particular form of information in that position on an individual chromosome. For example, the gene for dimples may have the dimple or the no-dimple allele in place.

Figure 1 The chromosomes of the human male. The X chromosomes carries genes controlling lots of different features. The Y chromosome is much smaller than the X chromosome and carries information mainly about maleness!

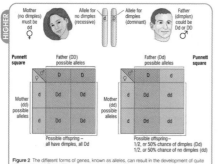

Figure 2 The different forms of genes, known as alleles, can result in the development of quite different characteristics. We can use diagrams like this Punnett square to explain what is happening or predict what the offspring might be like.

Most of your characteristics, like your eye colour and nose shape, are controlled by a number of genes. However, some characteristics, like dimples or having attached earlobes, are controlled by a single gene. Often there are only two possible alleles for a particular feature. However, sometimes you can inherit one from a number of different possibilities.

Some alleles control the development of a characteristic even when they are only present on one of your chromosomes. These alleles are **dominant**, e.g. dimples and dangly earlobes.

Some alleles only control the development of a characteristic if they are present on both alleles – in other words, no dominant allele is present. These alleles are **recessive**, e.g. no dimples and attached earlobes.

How does inheritance work?

We can use a simple model to help us understand how inheritance works. It explains how different features are passed on from one generation to another.

Imagine a bag containing marbles. If you put your hand in and – without looking – picked out two marbles at a time, what pairs might you get? If the bag contained only red marbles or only blue marbles, the pairs would all be the same. But if the bag held a mixture of red and blue marbles you could end up with three possible pairs – two blue marbles, two red marbles or one of each.

This is what happens when you inherit genes from your parents, depending on the different alleles they have. For example, if both of your parents have two alleles for dimples (like the red marbles) you will definitely inherit two dimple alleles – and you will have dimples! If both of your parents have two alleles for no dimples, you will inherit alleles for no dimples and you will be dimple free.

But if your parents both have one allele for dimples and one for no dimples, you could end up with two dimple alleles, two no dimple alleles – or one of each.

NEXT TIME YOU...

... look at a group of people, just think of the millions of genes – and the different alleles of those genes – which are controlling what they look like. Once you start counting dimples and dangly earlobes, it's difficult to stop

DID YOU KNOW?

Sex determination varies from species to species. In birds, females are XY and the males are XX. In some species of reptiles the males are XY and the females XX. In others the males are XX and the females XY. Some reptiles including alligators and tortoises don't have any sex chromosomes at all. The sex of the babies is decided by the temperature of the eggs as they incubate. And there are some species of fish and snails which change sex at different stages of their lives!

SUMMARY QUESTIONS

1 Copy and complete:

   male   sex chromosomes   23   22   X   XX   Y

   Human beings have ...... pairs of chromosomes. In ...... pairs the chromosomes are always the same. The final pair are known as .... If you inherit ...... you will be female, while an ...... and a ...... make you ....

2 a) What is meant by the term 'dominant allele'?
   b) What is meant by the term 'recessive allele'?
   c) Try and discover as many human characteristics as you can which are inherited on a single gene. Which alleles are dominant and which are recessive?

3 Use a Punnett square like the one in Figure 2 to show the possible offspring from a cross between two people who both have dimples and the genotype Dd. [Higher]

KEY POINTS

1 In human body cells the sex chromosomes determine whether you are female (XX) or male (XY).
2 Some features are controlled by a single gene.
3 Genes can have different forms called alleles.
4 Some alleles are dominant and some are recessive.
5 We can construct genetic diagrams to predict features. [Higher]

SUMMARY ANSWERS

1 23, 22, sex chromosomes, XX, X, Y, male.

2 a) Dominant allele – an allele which controls the development of a characteristic even when it is present on only one of the chromosomes.

   b) Recessive allele – an allele which only controls the development of a characteristic if it is present on both chromosomes.

   c) 2 marks for each case where students identify correctly the single gene characteristic and the dominant and recessive alleles.

3 [Marks awarded for drawing a Punnett square correctly with the appropriate gametes.] DD, Dd, dD, dd; 3 with dimples: 1 with no dimples. [**HT** only]

Answer to in-text question

a) A is male and B is female.

KEY POINTS

It is important to use the correct terms and not to muddle genes and alleles. Plenty of practice in working out crosses will help students become familiar with these terms and with the idea of characteristics having dominant and recessive alleles.

B2 6.6

Inherited conditions in humans

LEARNING OBJECTIVES

Students should learn that:

- Some human disorders are inherited.
- Some disorders are the result of the inheritance of a dominant allele (Huntington's disease), but others are the result of the inheritance of two recessive alleles (cystic fibrosis).
- Embryos can be screened for genetic disorders.

LEARNING OUTCOMES

Most students should be able to:

- State that some human disorders may be inherited.
- Describe how genetic disorders caused by a dominant allele are inherited.
- Explain how a genetic disorder caused by a recessive allele must be inherited from both parents.
- List some issues concerning embryo screening.

Some students should also be able to:

- Draw genetic diagrams to show how genetic disorders are passed on. [**HT** only]
- Make informed judgements about the economic, social and ethical issues concerning embryo screening that they have studied or from information that is presented to them.

Teaching suggestions

- **Special needs.** Students could work out genetic crosses using large printed grids and cards with the alleles on. They could work out the ratios and show them underneath.
- **Gifted and talented.** Students could do some research on the frequency of genes in populations. We are told that 1 person in 25 carries the allele for cystic fibrosis. Ask: 'How has this been calculated?' They could find out about the Hardy-Weinberg law and how it works. The law itself is fairly straightforward, students could work out how they can use it to inform people that the incidence of the alleles for certain conditions is quite high.

SPECIFICATION LINK-UP   Unit: Biology 2.11.8

- *Some disorders are inherited:*
  - *Huntington's disease – a disorder of the nervous system – is caused by a dominant allele of a gene and can therefore be passed on by only one parent who has the disorder.*
  - *Cystic fibrosis – a disorder of cell membranes – must be inherited from both parents. The parents may be carriers of the disorder without actually having the disorder themselves. It is caused by a recessive allele of a gene and can therefore be passed on by parents, neither of whom has the disorder.*
  (Attention is drawn to the potential sensitivity needed in teaching about inherited disorders.)
- *Embryos can be screened for the alleles that cause these and other genetic disorders.*

Lesson structure

STARTER

Infectious or genetic or . . . ? – Read students a list of diseases, including some infectious and some genetic. Students to respond by writing on 'Show me' boards whether a disease is infectious (writing I) or genetic (writing G). If they do not know then they should write a question mark. Draw up a list on the board in two columns. (5–10 minutes)

Interpreting a pedigree diagram – Introduce pedigree diagrams with their conventions: circles for females, squares for males, ways in which affected and carriers are shown. Illustrate with an invented 'condition' and get students to work out some of the offspring. (5–10 minutes)

MAIN

Huntington's disease

- Find and show images on Huntington's disease. The basic facts, symptoms and inheritability can be presented, together with some of the diagnostic tests. (See www.hdfoundation.org.)
- This could lead to a discussion on the disease and whether or not genetic testing is a good idea. It is a distressing condition, so it is advisable to find out whether anyone is affected before the presentation.

Cystic fibrosis

- Useful web sites can be found, including 'The Cystic Fibrosis Trust', the 'Cystic Fibrosis Foundation' (see www.cftrust.org.uk and www.cff.org), and the students could be asked to research different aspects of the disease in groups and put together a lesson on the condition.
- One group could describe the disease and its symptoms, another the genetics of how it is inherited and a further group could review the different treatments. Ask: 'According to the statistics, 1 in 25 people carries the allele, so is it worth being screened for it?'

Inherited or not?

It is difficult to know whether a particular disease or condition is inherited or not. The only way to find out is to carry out pedigree analysis and go back through the generations if possible. Suggest to students that they think of a particular family trait and see if they can draw up a pedigree within their own family. It is probably better to choose a characteristic, such as dangly ear lobes or dimples, rather than a disease unless a student has a particular interest.

PLENARIES

Play the inheritance game – The sex determination game, from the previous spread, could be modified by adding a dominant or recessive genetic disease sticker to some of the cards and to see what happens to the offspring. Allow 5 minutes for the game and then add up how many are affected offspring, how many are carriers and how many are unaffected by the disease. (10–15 minutes)

Statistics or chance? – Much emphasis is put on the ratios of incidence of the condition, but it does not necessarily follow that it works like that. Ask: 'Why are there some families where there are no boys or no girls?' Every child of a sufferer from Huntington's disease could inherit the disease. Students to try tossing a coin to see if they get equal numbers of heads and tails or if they get a run of heads. Discuss the implications if it was your family. (10 minutes)

ACTIVITY & EXTENSION

- **Other inherited conditions** – There are an estimated 6000 different conditions due to the inheritance of a single gene in humans. Students could research some of the suggested web sites (that of the Wellcome Trust is particularly useful – www.wellcome.ac.uk) for other conditions. Some suggestions could include certain forms of diabetes, phenylketonuria and sickle cell anaemia.

- **Sex-linked genetic diseases** – The best-known sex-linked genetic diseases are haemophilia and colour blindness. Discuss the inheritance of conditions with genes located on the X chromosome. Draw up Punnett squares to show how the alleles are inherited and the probability of the disease occurring. It was suggested on the last spread that gifted and talented students did some research on haemophilia. This could be a good opportunity for them to present their findings.

GET IT RIGHT!

It is sensible for students to be able to use Punnett diagrams: it makes the interpretation of any genetic cross much easier. It could be a good idea to stress to students that they are dealing with ratios and probabilities. What happens in real life is not always the same!

BIOLOGY   INHERITANCE

B2 6.6   Inherited conditions in humans

LEARNING OBJECTIVES

1 How are human genetic disorders inherited?
2 Can you predict if a child will inherit a genetic disorder? [Higher]

Not all diseases are infectious. Sometimes diseases are the result of a problem in your genes and can be passed on from parent to child. They are known as **genetic diseases** or **genetic disorders**.

We can use our knowledge of dominant and recessive alleles to work out the risk of inheriting a genetic disease.

a) How is a genetic disease different from an infectious disease?

DID YOU KNOW?

Around 7500 babies, children and young adults are affected by cystic fibrosis in the UK alone. Between 6800 and 8000 people are affected by Huntington's disease.

Figure 1 Modern medicine and determination mean that many sufferers from cystic fibrosis manage to lead full and active lives. However, the cells in their bodies are still carrying the faulty alleles and cannot function properly.

DID YOU KNOW?

Some genetic disorders cause such chaos in the cells that the fetus does not develop properly and miscarries. Yet other genetic disorders – such as colour-blindness – have little effect on people's lives!

Huntington's disease

One example of a very serious, although very rare, genetic disorder is Huntington's disease. This is a disorder of the nervous system. It is caused by a dominant allele and so it can be inherited from one parent who has the disease. If one of your parents is affected by Huntington's you have a 50% chance of inheriting the disease. That's because half of their gametes will contain the faulty allele.

The symptoms of this inherited disease usually appear when you are between 30 and 50 years old. Sadly, the condition is fatal. Because the disease does not appear until middle-age, many people have already had children and passed on the faulty allele before they realise they are affected.

b) You may inherit Huntington's disease even if only one of your parents is affected. Why?

Cystic fibrosis

Another genetic disease which has been studied in great detail is **cystic fibrosis**. This is the disease which affects many organs of the body, particularly the lungs and the pancreas.

The organs become clogged up by a very thick sticky mucus which stops them working properly. The reproductive system is affected so most people with cystic fibrosis are infertile.

Treatment for cystic fibrosis includes physiotherapy and antibiotics to help keep the lungs clear of mucus and infections. Enzymes are used to replace the ones the pancreas cannot produce and to thin the mucus.

However, although treatments are getting better all the time, there is still no cure.

Cystic fibrosis is caused by a recessive allele so it must be inherited from both parents. Children affected by cystic fibrosis are born to parents who do not suffer from the disease. They have a dominant healthy allele which means their bodies work normally but they carry the cystic fibrosis allele. Because it gives them no symptoms, they have no idea it is there.

People who have a silent disease-causing allele like this are known as **carriers**. In the UK, one person in 25 carries the cystic fibrosis allele. Most of them will never be aware of it, unless they happen to have children with a partner who also carries the allele. Then there is a 25% (one in four) chance that any child they have will be affected.

c) You will only inherit cystic fibrosis if you get the allele from both parents. Why?

The genetic lottery

When the genes from parents are combined, it is called a genetic cross. We can show this using a genetic diagram (see Figures 2 and 3). A genetic diagram shows us:

- the alleles for a characteristic carried by the parents,
- the possible gametes which can be formed from these, and
- how these could combine to form the characteristic in their offspring.

When looking at the possibility of inheriting genetic diseases, it is important to remember that every time an egg and a sperm meet it is down to chance which alleles combine. So if two parents who both carry the cystic fibrosis allele have four children, there is a 25% chance (one in four) that each child might have the disease.

But in fact all four children could have cystic fibrosis, or none of them might be affected. They might all be carriers, or none of them might inherit the faulty alleles at all. It's all down to chance!

Parent with Huntington's disease   Hh
Normal parent   hh

	H	h
h	Hh	hh
h	Hh	hh

50% chance Huntington's disease, Hh
50% chance normal, hh

Figure 2 A genetic diagram for Huntington's disease shows us how a dominant allele can affect offspring. It is important to realise that this shows that the chance of passing on the disease allele is 50%, but it cannot tell us which, if any, of the children will actually inherit the allele.

Curing genetic diseases

So far we have no way of curing genetic diseases. Scientists hope that genetic engineering will enable them to cut out faulty alleles and replace them with healthy ones. They have tried this in people affected by cystic fibrosis. But so far they have not managed to cure anyone.

There are genetic tests which can show people in affected families if they carry the faulty allele. This allows them to make choices such as whether to have a family. It is also possible to screen embryos for the alleles which cause these and other genetic disorders. These tests are very useful but raise many ethical issues. (See page 81.)

Both parents are carriers, so Cc

	C	c
C	CC	Cc
c	Cc	cc

25% normal (CC)
50% carriers (Cc)
25% affected by cystic fibrosis (cc)

3/4, or 75% chance normal
1/4, or 25% chance cystic fibrosis

Figure 3 The arrival of a child with cystic fibrosis in a family often comes as a complete shock. The faulty alleles can be covered up by normal alleles for generations until two carriers have a child and by chance both of the cystic fibrosis alleles are passed on.

GET IT RIGHT!

If one parent has a characteristic caused by a single dominant allele (e.g. Huntington's disease, dangly earlobes) you have a 50% chance of inheriting it.
If one parent has two dominant alleles (e.g. for Huntington's disease, dangly earlobes) you have 100% chance of inheriting it.
If both parents have a recessive allele for a characteristic (e.g. cystic fibrosis, attached earlobes) you have a 25% chance of inheriting that characteristic.

SUMMARY QUESTIONS

1 a) What is Huntington's disease?
  b) Why can one parent carrying the allele for Huntington's disease pass it on to their children even though the other parent is not affected?

2 At the moment, only people who have genetic diseases in their family are given genetic screening. What would be the pros and cons of screening everyone for diseases like cystic fibrosis and Huntington's disease?

3 a) Why are carriers of cystic fibrosis not affected by the disease themselves?
  b) A couple have a baby who has cystic fibrosis. Neither of the couple, nor their parents, have any signs of the disease.
     Draw genetic diagrams of the grandparents and the parents to show how this could happen. [Higher]

KEY POINTS

1 Some disorders are inherited.
2 Huntington's disease is caused by a dominant allele of a gene and can be inherited from only one parent.
3 Cystic fibrosis is caused by a recessive allele of a gene and so must be inherited from both parents.

78   79

SUMMARY ANSWERS

1 a) A genetic disease; a disorder of the nervous system which is fatal.

  b) The faulty allele is dominant so the offspring will have the disease with only one allele.

2 [Marks to be awarded for any sensible relevant points.] Can plan whether or not to have children; can choose partner without damaged allele; may worry people unnecessarily; have embryo screening if there is a risk; might not be able to get insurance if it is known that you have a genetic disease.

3 a) Carriers have a normal dominant allele, so their body works normally.

  b) Genetic diagrams based on Figure 3, page 79 in Student Book, showing how the cc arises. [**HT** only]

Teaching suggestions – continued

- **Learning styles**
  Kinaesthetic: Playing the inheritance game.
  Visual: Viewing a presentation on Huntington's disease.
  Auditory: Listening to the reports of others on their investigations.
  Interpersonal: Discussing the research on cystic fibrosis.
  Intrapersonal: Working out an individual family pedigree and researching the Human Genome Project.

- **Homework.** There is plenty of scope for homework exercises associated with this topic.

- **ICT link-up.** A great deal of research can be carried out by students, either using libraries or the Internet.

Answers to in-text questions

a) A genetic disease – inherited from parents.
   Infectious disease – caught from other people.

b) Huntington's disease is caused by a dominant allele.

c) Cystic fibrosis is caused by a recessive allele.

KEY POINTS

The key points for this spread are covered in the summary questions.

B2 6.7 Stem cells and embryos – an ethical minefield

SPECIFICATION LINK-UP

Unit: Biology 2.11.8

Students should use their skills, knowledge and understanding of 'How Science Works':

- *to make informed judgements about the social and ethical issues concerning the use of stem cells from embryos in medical research and treatments.*

- *to make informed judgements about the economic, social and ethical issues concerning embryo screening that they have studied or from information that is presented to them.*

BIOLOGY   INHERITANCE

B2 6.7   Stem cells and embryos – an ethical minefield

The stem cell dilemma

Doctors have treated people with adult stem cells for many years by giving bone marrow transplants. Now scientists are moving ever closer to treating very ill people using embryonic stem cells. This area of medicine raises many issues. Here are just a few different opinions:

> The accident happened so quickly. Now I'm stuck in this wheelchair for the rest of my life. I can't walk or even control when I go to the loo. It would be wonderful if they could develop cell stem therapy. I want them to heal my spinal cord so I can walk again!

> I think it is absolutely wrong to use human embryos in this way. Each life is precious to God. They may only be tiny balls of cells – but they could become people.

> It may become possible to take stem cells from the umbilical cord of every newborn baby. They could be frozen and stored ready for when the person might need them later in their life.

> The embryos we use would all be destroyed anyway. Now we are even making our own embryos from adult cells. We could do so much good for people that we all feel it is very important for the research to continue.

> It was terrible to see my husband suffer. By the time he died he didn't know who I was or any of the children. If these stem cells can cure Alzheimer's disease then we should do the research as fast as possible.

> We need to be careful. There are some real problems with these stem cell treatments. We don't want to solve one problem and cause another.

> I am going to volunteer to let them use some of my cells for therapeutic cloning. It is too late to help me now, but I'd like to think I could help other people.

ACTIVITY

Here is an opportunity to make your voice heard. Your class is going to produce a large wall display covered with articles both for and against stem cell research. Your display is aimed at students in Years 10 and 11, so make sure the level of content is right for your target group.

Try and carry out a survey or vote of your target group before the display is put up. Find out:

- how many people support stem cell research,
- what proportion are completely against it, and
- how many haven't made up their minds.

Record your findings

Work on your own or in a small group. Each group is to produce one piece of display material. Make sure that some of you give information in favour of stem cell research and others against. Use a variety of resources to help you – the material in this chapter is a good starting point. Make sure that your ideas are backed up with as much scientific evidence as possible.

Once the material has been displayed for a week or two, repeat your initial survey or vote. Analyse the data to see if easy access to information has changed people's views!

Teaching suggestions

- **The stem cell dilemma** – Several web sites have already been suggested as good sources of information about stem cell research, and it was suggested on a previous spread that students considered the pros and cons of the research programme and the use of stem cells. All this material should be useful when carrying out the suggested activity.

- **Can we know too much?** – Students could discuss the pros and cons of genetic screening using the material given in the Student Book and from any other information they have. This discussion could result in the need for more information so the web sites given on the previous spread could be investigated.

- If anyone knows a genetic counsellor, it might be a good opportunity to invite them in to the school to give a short talk and answer questions about the topic.

Special needs

Students can be asked simple questions, such as 'If you or someone you loved was ill, would you donate bone marrow even if it hurt?'

Learning styles

Kinaesthetic: Role play in the interviews.

Visual: Producing material for the display about stem cell research.

Auditory: Listening to the interviews.

Interpersonal: Discussing the presentation of interviews.

Intrapersonal: Writing a postcard from hospital to the person who has just donated bone marrow to you.

Can we know too much?

Today we not only understand the causes of many genetic disorders, we can also test for them. But being able to test for a genetic disorder doesn't necessarily mean we should always do it.

- People in families affected by Huntington's disease can take a genetic test which tells them if they have inherited the faulty gene. If they have, they know that they will develop the fatal disease as they get older and may pass on the gene to their children. Some people in affected families take the test and use it to help them decide whether to marry or have a family. Others prefer not to know.

- If a couple have a genetic disease in their family or already have a child with a genetic disorder, they can have a developing embryo tested during pregnancy. Cells from the embryo are checked. If it is affected, the parents have a choice. They may decide to keep the baby, knowing that it will have a genetic disorder when it is born. On the other hand, they may decide to have an abortion. This prevents the birth of a child with serious problems and allows them to try again to have a healthy baby.

- Some couples who have a genetic disease in the family or who already have a child affected by a genetic disease have their embryos screened before they are implanted in the mother. Embryos are produced by IVF (*in vitro* fertilisation). Doctors remove a single cell from each embryo and screen it for genetic diseases. Only healthy embryos free from genetic disease are implanted back into their mother. Using this method, only healthy babies are born.

ACTIVITY

Many couples who have a genetic disease in the family spend time with a genetic counsellor to help them understand what is happening and the choices they have. Plan a role-play of an interview with a genetic counsellor.

Either: Plan the role of the counsellor. Make sure you have all the information you need to talk to a couple who have already got one child with cystic fibrosis who would like to have another child. You need to be able to explain the chances of another child being affected and the choices that are open to them.

Or: Plan the role of a parent who already has one child with cystic fibrosis and who wants to have another child. Work in pairs to give the views of a couple if you like. Think carefully about the factors which will affect your decision such as: Can you cope with another sick child? Are you prepared to have an abortion? Do you have religious views on the matter? What is fairest to the unborn child – and the child you already have? Is it ethical to choose embryos to implant?

81

- **The stem cell dilemma** – Suitable material for this activity has already been discussed in previous spreads. One of the ways in which the views of the target group can be discovered is by means of a questionnaire. The questions need to be phrased correctly to elicit the information: students must not just use the three bullet points given on the Student Book spread. It might be worth asking whether people have heard of some of the arguments for and against before asking their opinion. Carefully designed questions should yield this information. The results of such a questionnaire could form part of the display.

- **Analysis of results** – The students can display the results of the original survey in a variety of different ways. They should try to be bold and innovative, making use of ICT. The subsequent survey and any changes of opinion can reveal how good their material was. Again, bold display of the data is needed. They might like to find out if their target group needed more information or whether it was pitched at the right level.

- **Bone marrow transplants** – Information about bone marrow transplants can be obtained from the Anthony Nolan Trust. It would be interesting to know whether any of the staff are members or have any interest in it.

- **Continuum** – Students place themselves, or a card with their name on, along a line from two opposing viewpoints: for and against using embryonic stem cells. They could be asked to justify their position when challenged by their peers. This could also be used to canvas opinion amongst Years 10 and 11.

- **Remember!** – There are different aspects of stem cell research: they do not all involve the use of embryos or fetal tissue.

- **Can we know too much?** – This activity is a difficult one for some students to do without carrying out research. It also requires a degree of confidence. Give students time to discuss the activities in small groups. Perhaps they could plan it like a film script or scenes for a TV documentary. The questions suggested could be expanded and some about the lives of the couple included. Ask: 'How demanding are their jobs? How have they coped with the child they already have?' If each group approached the activity from a slightly different perspective, then these role-play exercises could prove interesting to the class and give them a balanced view. For example, one interview could feature parents who would not consider an abortion, another could be with parents who are prepared to use screening and IVF.

SUMMARY ANSWERS

1 a) Mitosis is cell division that takes place in the normal body cells and produces genetically identical daughter cells.

b) [Marks awarded for correct sequence of diagrams with suitable annotations.]

c) All the divisions from the fertilised egg to the baby are mitosis. After birth, all the divisions for growth are mitosis, together with all the divisions involved in repair and replacement of damaged tissues.

2 a) Stem cells are unspecialised cells which can differentiate (divide and change) into many different types of cell when they are needed.

b) They may be used to repair damaged body parts, e.g. grow new spinal nerves to cure paralysis; grow new organs for transplants; repair brains in demented patients. [Accept any other sensible suggestions.]

c) For: They offer tremendous hope of new treatments; they remove the need for donors in transplants; they could cure paralysis, heart disease, dementia etc.; can grow tissues to order.
Against: They use tissue from human embryos; it's wrong to use embryos, as these could become people; embryos cannot give permission; stem cells could develop into cancers.
[Accept any other valid points on either side of the debate.]

3 a) Meiosis is a special form of cell division where the chromosome number is reduced by half. It takes place in the reproductive organs (the ovaries and testes).

b) [Marks awarded for correct sequence of diagrams with appropriate annotations.]

c) Meiosis is important because it halves the chromosome number of the cells so that when two gametes fuse at fertilisation, the normal chromosome number is restored. It also allows variety to be introduced as the chromosomes separate in cell divisions and when the two gametes join.
[HT only]

4 [Give credit for valid points made and the way in which the letter is written.]

5 a) Sami's alleles are **ss**. We know this because she has curved thumbs and the recessive allele is curved thumbs. She must have inherited two recessive alleles to have inherited the characteristic.

b) If the baby has curved thumbs, then Josh is **Ss**. The baby has inherited a recessive allele from each parent, so Josh must have a recessive allele. We know he also has a dominant allele as he has straight thumbs.

		Sami	
		s	s
Josh	S	Ss	Ss
	s	ss	ss

c) If the baby has straight thumbs, then Josh could be either **Ss** or **SS**. We know that the baby has inherited one recessive allele from mother, and we know that Josh has one dominant allele but we do not know if he has two dominant alleles. If he has two dominant alleles then:

		Sami	
		s	s
Josh	S	Ss	Ss
	S	Ss	Ss

[HT only]

INHERITANCE: B2 6.1 – B2 6.7

SUMMARY QUESTIONS

1 a) What is mitosis?
b) Explain, using diagrams, what takes place when a cell divides by mitosis.
c) Mitosis is very important during the development of a baby from a fertilised egg. It is also important all through life. Why?

2 a) What are stem cells?
b) It is hoped that many different medical problems may be cured using stem cells. Explain how this might work.
c) There are some ethical issues about the use of embryonic stem cells. Explain the arguments both for and against their use.

3 a) What is meiosis and where does it take place?
b) Explain, using labelled diagrams, what takes place when a cell divides by meiosis.
c) Why is meiosis so important?
[Higher]

4 Hugo de Vries is one of the scientists who made the same discoveries as Mendel several years after his death. Write a letter from Hugo to one of his friends after he has found Mendel's writings. Explain what Mendel did, why no-one took any notice of him and how the situation is so different now for you if you were doing the same sort of experiments.

5 Whether you have a straight thumb or a curved one is decided by a single gene with two alleles. The straight allele **S** is dominant to the curved allele **s**. Use this information to help you answer these questions.
Josh has straight thumbs but Sami has curved thumbs. They are expecting a baby.
a) We know exactly what Sami's thumb alleles are. What are they and how do you know?
b) If the baby has curved thumbs, what does this tell you about Josh's thumb alleles? Fill in a Punnett square to show the genetics of your explanation.
c) If the baby has straight thumbs, what does this tell us about Josh's thumb alleles? Fill in a Punnett square to show the genetics of your explanation.
[Higher]

EXAM-STYLE QUESTIONS

1 The diagram below is of stages in sexual reproduction in a mammal.

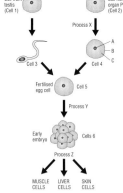

(a) What is the name of organ **P**? (1)
(b) Give the names of parts **A**, **B** and **C** in cell 4. (3)
(c) What is the name of cell 3? (1)
(d) What type of cell division takes place in processes **Y** and **Z**? (1)
(e) Which two of the cells labelled 1–6:
(i) are genetically identical to one another? (1)
(ii) are known as gametes? (1)
(f) Cells 6 will in due course change into a range of different cell types.
(i) What name is given to the type of cell labelled as cells 6? (1)
(ii) What is the process called by which these cells change into different cell types? (1)

Summary teaching suggestions

- **Lower and higher level answers** – Question 5 has been flagged as suitable for higher ability students. The answers to section b) and c) of this question should have the Punnett squares in order to qualify for full marks.

- **Homework** – All the questions here are suitable as homework exercises and many would be useful for revision of the topic.

- **When to use the questions?**
  - The questions do link to particular topics within the chapter and can be used to test students' understanding at the end of a topic if the summary questions have been used in the lesson.
  - Question 2 could be set as an exercise after holding a debate about the ethics of using stem cells. Students are then encouraged to present a balanced view of the issues involved.
  - Question 4 could be used when teaching about Mendel and the letter-writing suggestion has already been made as an activity.

- **Special needs** – Students could answer some of the questions verbally, especially parts of questions 1 and 2. In the question on the processes of mitosis, students could be given diagrams, or pictures, of the stages that they could put into the correct order and label or annotate with pre-printed labels.

EXAM-STYLE ANSWERS

1 a) Ovary *(1 mark)*

b) A Nucleus
B Cell membrane
C Cytoplasm *(1 mark each)*

c) Sperm *(1 mark)*

d) Mitosis *(1 mark)*

e) i) Cell 5 and cells 6 *(1 mark)*
ii) Cell 3 and cell 4 *(1 mark)*

f) i) Stem cells *(1 mark)*
ii) Differentiation *(1 mark)*

HOW SCIENCE WORKS QUESTIONS

2 Cystic fibrosis is a condition in which people suffer from the accumulation of thick and sticky mucus in their lungs. The chart shows part of a family tree in which some members have cystic fibrosis.

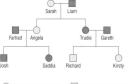

○ Female with cystic fibrosis   □ Male with cystic fibrosis
● Unaffected female   ■ Unaffected male

(a) Using two pieces of evidence from the family tree, explain why cystic fibrosis appears to be controlled by a recessive gene. (2)

(b) Trudie and Gareth want to have another child. What is the chance that this child will inherit cystic fibrosis? Explain, with the aid of a genetic diagram, how you reached your answer. (4)

(c) The letters **A**, **B** and **C** show the three different possible combinations of alleles possessed by the members of this family tree.

  A dominant and dominant
  B dominant and recessive
  C recessive and recessive

For each of the individuals below, give the letter that represents the alleles they possess.

  (i) Liam (1)
  (ii) Angela (1)
  (iii) Saddia (1)

(d) Explain how it is possible that Farhad and Angela could have a child with cystic fibrosis. (3)
  [Higher]

Amjid grew some purple flowering pea plants he had bought at the garden centre.

Here are his results.

Seeds planted	247
Purple-flowered plants	242
White-flowered plants	1
Seeds not growing	4

a) Is the white flowered plant an anomaly? (1)
b) Are the seeds that did not grow anomalies? (1)
c) What might Amjid do with the white-flowered plant? (1)

Amjid was interested in these plants, so he collected the seed from some of the purple-flowered plants and used them in the garden the following year. He made a careful note of what happened.

Here are his results:

Seeds planted	406
Purple-flowered plants	295
White-flowered plants	102
Seeds not growing	6

Amjid was slightly surprised. He did expect to find that a third of his flowers would be white.

d) Suggest how Amjid could display his results. (1)
e) Check how closely Amjid's results match his prediction. How accurate were they? (3)
f) How could Amjid have improved his method of growing the peas to make his results more valid? (1)

83

• If the father/Farhad has one dominant and one recessive allele (Ff), there is a 50% chance that a child might inherit the second recessive allele from him.

(1 mark for each point)

There are a number of different ways to explain why a child with cystic fibrosis is possible. Provided the reasoning is logical and genetically accurate, even if longwinded, full credit should be given. **[HT** only**]**

Exam teaching suggestions

- While question 1 tests recall in places, it also requires students to demonstrate an understanding of cell division and associated material.

- Question 2 is designed for higher-tier students. It involves predicting and explaining the outcome of genetic crosses between individuals with different combinations of alleles and also the construction of genetic diagrams. Both these skills are much more likely to be tested on Higher Tier papers.

- Question 2, part b). The use of letters other than F and f are acceptable – indeed C and c are much more likely to be used. While it makes sense to use the first letter of cystic fibrosis, it can also lead to marks being lost because the higher and lower case versions of the letter are the same in form and differ only in size. Unfortunately candidates often fail to distinguish the size adequately and so either get mixed up themselves or make it impossible for the examiner to follow what is happening.

HOW SCIENCE WORKS ANSWERS

a) Yes, the white flowered plant is an anomaly because it is not as expected.

b) Yes, the seeds that did not grow are also anomalies probably due to the way they were grown or some genetic problem.

c) As an anomaly, the white flowered plant should be investigated, e.g. to see if the colour was a result of a mutation or because of the particular conditions in which it was grown. He could breed from it, plant it in a different soil, etc.

d) The results are best presented in a bar graph.

e) Response should hypothesise that the parents were heterozygous and draw a Punnett square to predict a 3:1 ratio and show how accurate his actual results were by comparing with his predicted results.

f) To improve his method of growing the peas to make his results more valid Amjid could have grown them under control conditions.

How science works teaching suggestions

- **Higher- and lower-level answers.** Question e) is a higher-level question and the answers provided above are also at this level. Question f) is lower level and the answer provided is also lower level.

- **How and when to use these questions.** When wishing to develop the importance of checking on the cause of anomalies and developing ideas of scientific method.

  The questions are best done as small group work which will need some support for those struggling with the genetics.

- **Homework.** Question c) could be developed into experimental design for homework.

- **ICT link-up.** There are many programs which allow interactive work in genetics, for example, Drosophilia Genetics at www.newbyte.co.uk.

---

2 a) *Any two accurate pieces of evidence, e.g.:*
- Sarah has cystic fibrosis but her daughter Trudie does not.
- Angela has cystic fibrosis but neither of her children does.
- Neither Trudie nor Gareth has cystic fibrosis but both their children do.

(Any two points, 1 mark each)
The first two points show the condition cannot be dominant and therefore it must be recessive. The third point shows it to be recessive.

b) Trudie and Gareth already have two children with cystic fibrosis and therefore both must carry the allele for the condition.
(1 mark)

As neither Trudie nor Gareth suffer from cystic fibrosis themselves, they must both possess one dominant and one recessive allele.
(1 mark)

Let F = normal allele and f = cystic fibrosis allele
Trudie = Ff and Gareth = Ff
Sex cells (gametes) for both = F and f

Gareth

Trudie	F	f
F	FF	Ff
f	Ff	ff

(1 mark)

As cystic fibrosis is a recessive condition, only a child with both recessive alleles (ff) will be affected. Only one in four (25%) of the possible offspring have the ff alleles and therefore the chance of the next child having cystic fibrosis is one in four (25%).
(1 mark)

c) i) Liam **B** *(1 mark)*
  ii) Angela **C** *(1 mark)*
  iii) Saddia **B** *(1 mark)*

d) • To have cystic fibrosis the child would need to have two recessive alleles (ff).
  • The mother/Angela has cystic fibrosis and so is ff and must therefore pass one recessive allele to each of her children.

Answers to Questions

1 (a) *Quality of written communication*   *(1 mark)*
The mark should be given where correct scientific terms are used and the ideas are given in a sensible order. The mark can be awarded for a scientific and logical answer, even if it is inaccurate; it cannot be given if the answer is non-scientific or nonsensical.
- Microorganisms/bacteria/fungi/saprotrophs/ saprophytes/saprobionts
- digest/break down organic matter/leaves/ decompose (reference to decomposers)/decay/ rot
- use of enzymes/correctly named example
- absorption by diffusion/active transport
- respiration/combustion
- carbon dioxide can be used (by trees) in photosynthesis.
    (1 mark for any point to a maximum of 3)

(b) • warmth/suitable temperature *(heat/hot weather are not acceptable)*
- damp/water/rain/humid/moisture
- oxygen
- suitable pH.
    (1 mark for any point to a maximum of 2)

2 (a) The concentration of fructose increases   *(1 mark)*
then levels off/rate of increase slows   *(1 mark)*

(b) (i) They acted as controls.   *(1 mark)*

(ii) Exactly the same as tube A.   *(1 mark)*

(c) (i) less sugar is used/cheaper than using glucose
    (1 mark)

(ii) food is just as sweet/fructose is sweeter
    (1 mark)
there is less sugar to convert to fat/less surplus energy   *(1 mark)*

3 (a) Mouth temperature was used in both investigations for all those tested.   *(1 mark)*

(b) He carried out the largest survey.   *(1 mark)*

(c) E.g. tests carried out several times on the same people; used a digital thermometer which is less easy to misread; more recent thermometers are more likely to be more accurate.   *(1 mark)*

(d) E.g. more accurate diagnosis of disease and therefore more appropriate treatment.   *(1 mark)*

continues opposite ❯

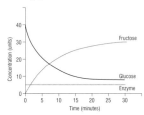

EXAMINATION-STYLE QUESTIONS

1 Each autumn, many trees lose their leaves.   *See pages 34–7*

(a) Describe how carbon compounds in the leaves can be recycled so that they can be used again by the trees.   *(4 marks)*

To gain full marks in this question you should write your ideas in good English. Put them into a sensible order and use the correct scientific words.

GET IT RIGHT
When giving a change in an environmental condition, remember to say in which direction the change takes place. Use terms such as 'higher', 'lower', 'more', 'less'.

(b) Give **two** environmental conditions that speed up the processes that you have described in part (a).   *(2 marks)*

2 In an investigation, an enzyme was added to glucose syrup in test tube A. In another test tube (B) glucose was left without the enzyme. In a third test tube (C) the enzyme was left without the glucose. The concentrations of glucose, fructose and the enzyme were measured for thirty minutes. The results for test tube A are shown in the graph.   *See pages 42–5*

(a) Describe the changes in the concentration of fructose.   *(2 marks)*

(b) (i) Explain why test tubes B and C were used.   *(1 mark)*

(ii) How should tubes B and C have been treated.   *(1 mark)*

(c) Fructose is often added to foods used by people on a slimming diet.   *See pages 52–3*

(i) Give **one** advantage of this for the company making the slimming food.   *(1 mark)*

(ii) Explain **one** advantage of this for a person on a slimming diet.   *(2 marks)*

GET IT RIGHT!

Given that even a single mark can improve a final grade, it is important to teach students the significance of being precise especially in the use of scientific terms. Another common failure to accurately distinguish related terms occurs in the use of 'breathing' and 'respiration'. A useful exercise to help students avoid these errors is to compile a list of commonly confused pairs of terms when marking students' work. These could then be used as an exercise in which students are asked to state at least one way in which the two terms in each pair can be clearly distinguished.

In question 4, part b) i), the importance of reading every word of a question is stressed. Here the key word is 'system' indicating that 'nervous system' is required rather than a specific part of that system such as the brain.

Additional biology

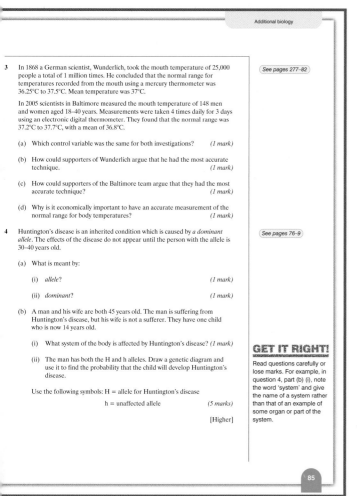

3 In 1868 a German scientist, Wunderlich, took the mouth temperature of 25,000 people a total of 1 million times. He concluded that the normal range for temperatures recorded from the mouth using a mercury thermometer was 36.25°C to 37.5°C. Mean temperature was 37°C.

See pages 277–82

In 2005 scientists in Baltimore measured the mouth temperature of 148 men and women aged 18–40 years. Measurements were taken 4 times daily for 3 days using an electronic digital thermometer. They found that the normal range was 37.2°C to 37.7°C, with a mean of 36.8°C.

(a) Which control variable was the same for both investigations? *(1 mark)*

(b) How could supporters of Wunderlich argue that he had the most accurate technique. *(1 mark)*

(c) How could supporters of the Baltimore team argue that they had the most accurate technique? *(1 mark)*

(d) Why is it economically important to have an accurate measurement of the normal range for body temperatures? *(1 mark)*

4 Huntington's disease is an inherited condition which is caused by *a dominant allele*. The effects of the disease do not appear until the person with the allele is 30–40 years old.

See pages 76–9

(a) What is meant by:

(i) *allele*? *(1 mark)*

(ii) *dominant*? *(1 mark)*

(b) A man and his wife are both 45 years old. The man is suffering from Huntington's disease, but his wife is not a sufferer. They have one child who is now 14 years old.

(i) What system of the body is affected by Huntington's disease? *(1 mark)*

(ii) The man has both the H and h alleles. Draw a genetic diagram and use it to find the probability that the child will develop Huntington's disease.

Use the following symbols: H = allele for Huntington's disease

h = unaffected allele *(5 marks)*

[Higher]

GET IT RIGHT!

Read questions carefully or lose marks. For example, in question 4, part (b) (i), note the word 'system' and give the name of a system rather than that of an example of some organ or part of the system.

85

BUMP UP THE GRADE

Some students fail to pace themselves adequately during an examination, either finishing too early or running out of time. Students usually notice how many marks are available for each portion of a question, but cannot translate this into the time they should spend on answering it. One way of overcoming the problem is to train students to divide the total mark allocation into the time available in minutes. Both pieces of information appear on the front cover of the examination paper. In general there are around 135 marks on a 2 hour 15 minute paper which translates into spending one minute for each available mark. It is not practical to time each separate mark but the total for each question or double page is usually given in the bottom corner of each page. A glance at this when turning the page can help students pace themselves through the examination and so avoid careless loss of marks as a result of rushing parts of the paper.

› *continues from previous page*

4 (a) (i) *Either* one of two (/of several) forms of a gene
Or (a variant) form of a gene *(1 mark)*

(ii) *Either* expressed even if only one copy is inherited
Or expressed/seen in heterozygote *(1 mark)*

(b) (i) nervous (*'brain' is not 'a system' and therefore not allowed*) *(1 mark)*

(ii) Man/affected = **Hh**, and wife unaffected = **hh** *(1 mark)*
correct gametes from parental genotypes *(1 mark)*
F_1 genotypes correctly derived from parental gametes *(1 mark)*
Identification of **Hh** in F_1 as having Huntington's disease *(1 mark)*
Correct probability from F_1 genotypes, e.g. $\frac{1}{2}$/0.5/50%/1 in 2/1:1/50:50 *(1 mark)*
Care should be taken not to allow '1:2' or '50/50'.
As the question specifically asks for 'a genetic diagram', a mark must be deducted if one is omitted, even though the answer itself is correct. Provided the chain of logic can be picked up from the previous statement, the following mark can be given even if the previous statement was wrong. In other words, an error should only be penalised once as long as the rest that follows is logical and genetically accurate. [**HT** only]

Key Stage 3 curriculum links

The following link to 'What you already know':

- How elements combine through chemical reactions to form compounds [for example, water, carbon dioxide, magnesium oxide, sodium chloride, most minerals] with a definite composition.

- To represent compounds by formulae and to summarise reactions by word equations.

- How mass is conserved when chemical reactions take place because the same atoms are present, although combined in different ways.

- How metals react with oxygen, water, acids and oxides of other metals, and what the products of these reactions are.

- About the displacement reactions that take place between metals and solutions of salts of other metals.

- How metals and bases, including carbonates, react with acids, and what the products of these reactions are.

- To identify patterns in chemical reactions.

QCA Scheme of work
8E Atoms and elements
8F Compounds and mixtures
9H Using chemistry

RECAP ANSWERS

1 iron + sulfur → iron sulfide
   The reaction mixture is magnetic whereas the product of the reaction (iron sulfide) is not magnetic.

2 18 g

3 calcium chloride + hydrogen

4 a) Two.   b) Three.   c) Three.

5 One.

6 A displacement reaction. Zinc displaces the copper in the solution and copper metal forms as the solid.

7 There is a visible change as a new product forms and a large amount of energy is given out.

Activity notes

- **Poster** – Students should be encouraged to make a poster explaining the recent advances in our knowledge of the atom. They could think about why most advances have been made in the last 200 years (since the advent of electricity).

- To extend students, they could research CERN on the Internet.

- To encourage group work, they could work as a class, if each student were given a different aspect of the topic to study. Then a giant (display board) sized poster could be generated.

CHEMISTRY

C2 | Additional chemistry

What you already know

Here is a quick reminder of previous work that you will find useful in this unit:

Diamond is made up only of carbon atoms

- Elements combine through chemical reactions to form compounds.
- We can represent compounds by formulae and we can summarise reactions by word equations and balanced symbol equations.
- Mass is conserved in chemical reactions because the same atoms are there before and after the reaction.
- Many, but not all, metals react with oxygen, water, acids.
- Displacement reactions can take place between metals and solutions of salts of other metals. Displacement can also occur between metals and metal oxides.
- Bases react with acids.
- We can identify patterns in chemical reactions.

Diamond

Graphite

A fullerene

Diamond, graphite and the fullerenes are all forms of the element, carbon

RECAP QUESTIONS

1 Write a word equation for the reaction between iron and sulfur.
   How can we show that a new substance is formed in this reaction?

2 When 16 g of oxygen react with 2 g of hydrogen, how much water is formed?

3 Complete the word equation:
   calcium (metal) + hydrochloric acid → ......

4 How many types of atom are there in:
   a) sodium chloride (NaCl),
   b) ethanol (C_2H_5OH),
   c) sulfuric acid (H_2SO_4)?

5 How many different types of atoms are there in a pure sample of an element?

6 When we put zinc metal into blue copper sulfate solution a pink solid forms and the solution becomes much lighter in colour.
   What is happening?

7 When magnesium burns in air it produces a white powder. The magnesium gets very hot and you see a bright white light.
   Why do these observations suggest that a chemical reaction is taking place?

Teaching suggestions

What you already know

- **Questions** – Students could know this information, but may not be able to think of when they would use it. The students could generate questions that are answered by the bullet points in this section.

SPECIFICATION LINK-UP
Unit: Chemistry 2

How do sub-atomic particles help us to understand the structure of substances?

Simple particle theory is developed in this unit to include atomic structure and bonding. The arrangement of electrons in atoms can be used to explain what happens when elements react and how atoms join together to form different types of substance.

How do structures influence the properties and uses of substances?

Substances that have simple molecular, giant ionic and giant covalent structures have very different properties. Ionic, covalent, and metallic bonds are strong. The forces between molecules are weaker, e.g. in carbon dioxide and iodine. Nanomaterials have new properties because of their very small size.

How much can we make and how much do we need to use?

The relative masses of atoms can be used to calculate how much to react and how much we can produce because no atoms are gained or lost in a chemical reaction. In industrial processes, atom economy is important for sustainable development.

How can we control the rate of chemical reactions?

Being able to speed up or slow down chemical reactions is important in everyday life and in industry. Changes in temperature, concentration of solutions, surface area of solids, and the presence of catalysts all affect the rates of reactions.

Do chemical reactions always release energy?

Chemical reactions involve energy transfers. Many chemical reactions involve the release of energy. For other chemical reactions to occur, energy must be supplied. In industrial processes, energy requirements and emissions need to be considered both for economic reasons and for sustainable development.

How can we use ions in solutions?

Ionic compounds have many uses and can provide other substances. Electrolysis is used to produce alkalis and elements such as chlorine and hydrogen. Oxidation–reduction reactions do not just involve oxygen. Soluble salts can be made from acids and insoluble salts can be made from solutions of ions.

Making connections

Developing ideas about substances

Many people think that Antoine Lavoisier was the father of modern chemistry. If this is so, then his wife, Marie-Anne may well be the mother. She was well educated, and translated documents and illustrated his scientific texts with great skill.

Antoine Lavoisier lived in France between 1743 and 1794. His experiments were some of the first proper chemical experiments involving careful measurements. For example, in chemical reactions he carefully weighed reactants and products. This was an important advance over the work of earlier chemists.

Working with his wife, Lavoisier showed that the quantity of matter is the same at the end as at the beginning of every chemical reaction. Working with other French chemists, Lavoisier invented a system of chemical names which described the structure of chemical compounds. Many of these names are still in use, including names such as sulfuric acid and sulfates.

Ernest Rutherford was born in New Zealand in 1871. After his education in New Zealand he worked and studied in England and Canada. Then in 1910 he showed that the structure of the atom consists of a tiny positively charged nucleus that makes up nearly all of the mass of the atom. The nucleus is surrounded by a vast space which contains the electrons – but most of the atom is simply empty space! Rutherford received the Nobel Prize for Chemistry in recognition of his huge contribution to our understanding of the atom.

ACTIVITY

The three scientists described here made enormous contributions to our understanding of the behaviour of matter and chemistry. Using this information, produce a poster with a timeline showing how our understanding of the behaviour of matter changed in the period from the early 18th century to the beginning of the 20th century.
You could research these ideas further using the Internet, especially at www.timelinescience.org.

Michael Faraday came from very humble beginnings, but his work on electricity and chemistry still affects our lives today. His achievements were acknowledged when his portrait was included on the £20 note in 1991.

Born in Yorkshire in 1791, Michael Faraday was one of 10 children. Apprenticed to a bookbinder, Faraday became an assistant to the great chemist Sir Humphry Davy. After hearing some of Davy's lectures in London, he sent him a bound copy of some notes he had made and was taken on.

After much work on electricity, Faraday turned his attention to electrolysis. He produced an explanation of what happens when we use an electric current to split up a chemical compound. Not only did Faraday explain what happens, he also introduced the words we still use today – *electrolysis, electrolyte* and *electrode*.

Ernest Rutherford was responsible for producing the evidence that completely changed our ideas about the structure of atoms

Chapters in this unit

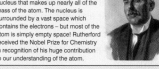

Structures and bonding | Structures and properties | How much? | Rates of reaction | Energy and reactions | Electrolysis | Acids, alkalis and salts

---

- **Word equations** – Most of the key points can be represented as word equations, e.g. bases react with acids:

copper oxide + hydrochloric acid → copper chloride + water

Encourage the student to write relevant word equations for the different points, and higher attaining students could attempt to write balanced symbol equations.

Recap questions

- **Starter** – These questions could be used as a starter for appropriate lessons, e.g. question 1 for section 1.3 'Chemical bonding'.

- **AfL (Assessment for Learning)** – Give students a set amount of time to answer the questions. Then ask the students to swap their answers with another student. They should mark each others' work, compare answers and annotate corrections.

Making connections

- **Card sort** – Make a pack of cards with the names of the scientists/philosophers and their contribution to the discovery of the structure of the atom on separate cards. Students should then match the names with their discoveries.

- For lower ability groups, pictures of the scientists and their discoveries could be used.

- An extension would be to ask the students to put the discoveries in date order.

- **Mind map** – Students often compartmentalise information and do not link things learned in different topics together. Give them the key words on separate cards, some Blu Tack, felt pens and sugar paper. Working in small groups, they stick two related key words on to their paper and join them with an arrow. The group then adds text so that the two words are the start and end of a sentence. They then add more key words (there may be lots of arrows to or from each card, or just one). This helps students to view the topic as a whole, and any missing links can be quickly identified and teachers can challenge any misconceptions.

○ Chapters in this unit

- ○ Structures and bonding
- ○ Structures and properties
- ○ How much?
- ○ Rates of reaction
- ○ Energy and reactions
- ○ Electrolysis

- ○ Acids, alkalis and salts

C2 1.1   Atomic structure

Students should learn:

- That there are particles inside an atom.
- That the number of protons equals the number of electrons in an atom.
- That the atoms are arranged on the periodic table.
- The relative charges on sub-atomic particles.

Most students should be able to:

- Label the sub-atomic particles in an atom.
- State the charge of the sub-atomic particles in an atom.
- Define atomic number (proton number).
- Describe how the elements are ordered in the periodic table.

Some students should also be able to:

- Explain why atoms are electrically neutral.

Teaching suggestions

- **Learning styles**

  Kinaesthetic: Sorting the different elements into groups.

  Visual: Labelling of an atom.

  Auditory: Listening to discussion on thought provoking questions.

  Interpersonal: Working as a group to order different elements.

  Intrapersonal: Evaluating different representations of atoms.

- **Homework.** John Dalton believed that atoms could not be split (*atomos* means 'indivisible'). Students could find out which scientist disproved this and how. [JJ Thompson, in 1897, discovered electrons.]

- **ICT link-up.** Search the web for atom diagrams, then stipulate a type of animation format e.g. applets/flash/macromedia.

SPECIFICATION LINK-UP   Unit: Chemistry 2.12.1

- *Atoms have a small central nucleus made up of protons and neutrons around which there are electrons.*
- *The relative electrical charges are as shown:*

Name of particle	Charge
Proton	+1
Neutron	0
Electron	−1

- *In an atom, the number of electrons is equal to the number of protons in the nucleus. Atoms have no overall electrical charge.*
- *All atoms of a particular element have the same number of protons. Atoms of different elements have different numbers of protons.*
- *The number of protons in an atom is called its atomic number (proton number). Atoms are arranged in the modern periodic table in order of their atomic number (proton number).*

Lesson structure

STARTER

Spot the mistake – 'When different compounds join together, atoms of the same element are made.' [Compounds do not join together, atoms join up to make compounds. Also, if all the atoms are the same in a material, then it is an element, not a compound.] (5 minutes)

Define – Ask the students to match these definitions to key words:

- Positive particle in the nucleus of an atom. [Proton]
- Negative particle that orbits the nucleus of an atom. [Electron]
- A sub-atomic particle that carries no charge and is found in the nucleus of the atom. [Neutron] (5 minutes)

MAIN

- Students will need to be able to recognise atom diagrams in a lot of different forms. Some will be two-dimensional dot and cross diagrams, others will be three-dimensional moving representations of the atom. Give each student an element from the first 20 on the periodic table. Encourage them to research their element and represent its structure in as many different ways that they can find.
- Students could compile their diagrams into a poster, with the sub-atomic particles labelled. The posters could be displayed in the classroom.
- Atoms were discovered and grouped in many different ways. Supply students with cards for the first 20 elements. On one side of the card there should be the elements name, symbol, atomic number and electronic structure.
- As an extension, on the reverse general physical and chemical properties could be listed.
- Students should then work in small teams to order the elements in different ways (alphabetically, proton number, number of electrons in the outer shell, physical properties etc.). You should tour the other groups, asking them about their grouping structure and encouraging them to find new ways to group the elements.
- Then ask the students to sort their cards into the order of Mendeleev's periodic table.
- Ask the students what they notice [that the elements are in atomic/proton number order], higher attaining students may notice the links between the group/period number and the electronic structure.
- Then ask students to summarise in one sentence how the atoms are arranged in the periodic table.

PLENARIES

Label – On the board draw a diagram of a helium atom (two protons, two neutrons in the nucleus and two electrons in the first shell). Ask the students to copy the diagram and label the particles with their name and their charge. (5 minutes)

Thinking – Ask the students the following thought-provoking questions. Students work in small groups discussing the question, then you could ask them to feedback into a class discussion:

- What mostly makes up atoms? [Space]

- What stops electrons whizzing off into space? [The electrostatic force of attraction between them and the nucleus]

- Which bit of the atom do you think does the chemistry? [Electrons – more specifically the outer shell electrons]

- Which bit of an atom do you think radioactivity comes from? [The nucleus] (10 minutes)

AfL (Assessment for Learning) – Students could look at the different ways of representing the atom, as highlighted on the different posters. They could then evaluate the different diagrams and decide which they think is the most useful way of representing the atom and explain why. (15 minutes)

ACTIVITY & EXTENSION IDEAS

- Ask students to find out who discovered each sub-atomic particle, how and when.

- Instead of organising cards with elements' details on, the elements themselves could be provided in sealed gas jars and Petri dishes. The relevant information could then be stuck onto the container with tape.

CHEMISTRY   STRUCTURES AND BONDING

C2 1.1   Atomic structure

LEARNING OBJECTIVES

1 What is inside atoms?
2 Why is the number of protons in an atom equal to the number of electrons?
3 What is the order in which atoms are arranged in the periodic table?
4 What is the charge on a proton, neutron and electron?

In the middle of an atom is a small nucleus. This contains two types of particles, which we call **protons** and **neutrons**. A third type of particle orbits the nucleus – we call these particles **electrons**. Any atom has the same number of electrons orbiting its nucleus as it has protons in its nucleus.

Protons have a positive charge while neutrons have no charge – they are neutral. So the nucleus itself has an overall positive charge.

The electrons orbiting the nucleus are negatively charged. The size of the negative charge on an electron is exactly the same as the size of the positive charge on a proton. (In other words, the relative charge on a proton is +1, while the relative charge on an electron is −1.)

Because any atom contains equal numbers of protons and electrons, the overall charge on any atom is exactly zero. For example, a carbon atom has 6 protons, so we know it also has 6 electrons.

a) What are the names of the three particles that make up an atom?
b) An oxygen atom has 8 protons – how many electrons does it have?

Figure 1 Understanding the structure of an atom gives us important clues to the way chemicals react together

Type of sub-atomic particle	Relative charge
proton	+1
neutron	0
electron	−1

To help you remember the charge on the sub-atomic particles:

Protons are **P**ositive;
Neutrons are **N**eutral;
so that means **E**lectrons must be **N**egative!

Atomic number

We call the number of protons in the nucleus of an atom its **atomic number** or **proton number**.

As all of the atoms of a particular element have the same number of protons, they also have the same atomic number. So the atomic number of hydrogen is 1 and it has one proton in the nucleus. The atomic number of carbon is 6 and it has 6 protons in the nucleus. The atomic number of sodium is 11 and it has 11 protons in the nucleus.

Each element has its own atomic number. If you are told that the atomic number of an element is 8, you can identify that element from the periodic table. In this case it is oxygen.

c) Which element has an atomic number of 14?

Elements in the periodic table are arranged in order of their atomic numbers.

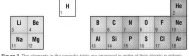

Figure 2 The elements in the periodic table are arranged in order of their atomic numbers

You read the periodic table from left to right, and from the top down – just like reading a page of writing.

Look at the atomic numbers of the elements in the last group of the periodic table:

d) What do you notice about the atomic numbers going from helium to neon to argon?

You will be able to explain this pattern when you learn more about the arrangement of electrons in atoms later in this chapter.

SUMMARY QUESTIONS

1 Copy and complete using the words below:

   atomic   electrons   negative   neutrons   protons

   In the nucleus of atoms there are …… and …… . Around the nucleus there are …… which have a …… charge. In the periodic table, atoms are arranged in order of their …… number.

2 Use the periodic table in Figure 2 to find the atomic number of the elements lithium, sulfur, magnesium, chlorine and nitrogen.

3 Atoms are always neutral. Explain why this means that an atom must always contain the same number of protons and electrons.

GET IT RIGHT!

In an atom, the number of protons is always equal to the number of electrons. You can find out the number of protons and electrons in an atom by looking up its atomic number in the periodic table.

DID YOU KNOW?

In 1808, a chemist called John Dalton published a theory of atoms, explaining how these joined together to form new substances. Not everyone liked his theory though – one person wrote 'Atoms are round bits of wood invented by Mr Dalton!'

KEY POINTS

1 Atoms are made of protons, neutrons and electrons.
2 Protons and electrons have equal and opposite electric charges. Protons are positively charged, and electrons are negatively charged.
3 Atoms are arranged in the periodic table in order of their atomic number.
4 Neutrons have no electric charge. They are neutral.

88

89

SUMMARY ANSWERS

1 Protons (neutrons), neutrons (protons), electrons, negative, atomic.

2 Li = 3, S = 16, Mg = 12, Cl = 17, N = 7.

3 Because protons and electrons have the same amount of charge but with opposite signs, the charge on a proton is exactly cancelled out by the charge on an electron.

Answers to in-text questions

a) Protons, neutrons and electrons.

b) 8 electrons.

c) Silicon.

d) They increase by 8 between each element.

DID YOU KNOW?

Atoms are very small. Ask students to guess how small this would be [about 0.000 000 000 1 m in diameter].

KEY POINTS

Students could translate the key points into text language.

C2 1.2

The arrangement of electrons in atoms

LEARNING OBJECTIVES

Students should learn:

- To represent the electronic structures of the first 20 elements.
- That the number of electrons in the highest energy level relates to the group number in the periodic table.
- That the number of electrons in the highest energy level determines chemical properties.

LEARNING OUTCOMES

Most students should be able to:

- Draw the electronic structure of the first 20 elements of the periodic table, when the atomic/proton number is given.
- State the relationship between the number of electrons in the highest energy level and the group number.

Some students should also be able to:

- Explain how the number of electrons in the highest energy level relates to the chemical properties of an element.

Teaching suggestions

- **Special needs**
  - Give the students the electronic structure of the first 20 elements and their names as a cut and stick activity.
  - Some students may find ordering 40 pieces of information too much, so these students could be given the data in packs of 10 (5 elements at a time).

- **Learning styles**

  Kinaesthetic: Sorting the information on sub-atomic particles into a table.

  Visual: Creating a table to represent the electronic structure of the first 20 elements.

  Auditory: Listening to another student's list on electrons.

  Interpersonal: Working as a class to model different types of atom.

  Intrapersonal: Detailing two facts from the lesson.

- **Homework.** Give each student a different element and ask him or her to find out a fascinating fact about it. Next lesson, encourage the students to share their facts.

SPECIFICATION LINK-UP   Unit: Chemistry 2.12.1

- *Electrons occupy particular energy levels. Each electron in an atom is at a particular energy level (in a particular shell). The electrons in an atom occupy the lowest available energy levels (innermost available shells). (Though only energy levels are referred to throughout this specification, the candidate may answer in terms of shells if they prefer.)*
- *Elements in the same group in the periodic table have the same number of electrons in the highest energy levels (outer electrons).*

Students should use their skills, knowledge and understanding of 'How Science Works':

- *to represent the electronic structure of the first twenty elements of the periodic table.*

Lesson structure

STARTER

Card sort – Give the students a pack of eight cards, each with different information on: proton, electron, neutron, nucleus, shell, +1, 0, −1. Students should also be given a table on a piece of laminated paper, consisting of three columns (labelled: sub-atomic particle, charge, position) and three rows. They then sort the cards, putting them in the appropriate positions on the table. (10 minutes)

List – Ask students to list all the information they can think of about electrons. [For example, have a charge of −1, are very small, are found in shells/energy levels of an atom, are what electricity is made of, there are the same number as protons in an atom.] Then ask students to share their ideas in pairs, then groups of four. Ask each group of four to give a piece of information that a scribe writes onto the board. You should address any misconceptions revealed in this activity. (15 minutes)

MAIN

- Students need to be able to draw diagrams of the first 20 elements, but many kinaesthetic learners find it difficult to use information from the periodic table to draw the structure. If it is possible, try to do a room swap to a hall or playground. Other materials that would be needed are a number of different coloured sports bibs, A3 paper and felt pens. The students will be electrons to act out different atoms.

- Get two volunteers to stand in the centre of the room – a student is a proton (should wear a red bib) and another is a neutron (should wear a green bib). Tell the students which atom they are going to represent, e.g. oxygen.

- Using question and answer, ask them to work out how many protons and neutrons would be in the nucleus and instruct those students to write the appropriate numbers onto paper and hold them up.

- Then ask the students how many electrons the atoms would have and in each shell. Place the students around the nucleus into shells – each shell should be made up of students with bibs of a different colour.

- Ask students to create a table to show the element name, symbol, number of electrons, electronic structure and short-hand notation for the first 20 elements. Students should be encouraged to use the periodic table to get the information to complete this activity.

- **ICT link-up.** Take a digital photograph of the students acting out the atoms. Then, when the group returns to the classroom, project the different images. Ask for volunteers to draw around the atom to show the different shells, they could also draw crosses on top of the students to display the electronic structure as detailed in the specification.

PLENARIES

Guess the atom – Create flash cards to show the electronic structure of the first 20 elements in a random order. Ask the students to look at the images and work out which atom is being displayed. Students to write their answer on an A4 whiteboard and hold up their response for you to give instant feedback. (10 minutes)

Reflection – Ask students to consider a fact that they have revised in the lesson and a new fact that they have learned in the lesson. As they leave the classroom, ask them for their facts. You should challenge any misconceptions during the reflection plenary of the following lesson. (5 minutes)

Scientists now don't believe that neutrons and protons are indivisible. Ask students to find out what makes up these sub-atomic particles. [Quarks and Leptons.]

CHEMISTRY   STRUCTURES AND BONDING

Additional chemistry

C2 1.2 The arrangement of electrons in atoms

LEARNING OBJECTIVES

1 How are the electrons arranged inside an atom?
2 How is the number of electrons in the highest energy level of an atom related to its group in the periodic table?
3 How is the number of electrons in the highest energy level of an atom related to its chemical properties?

GET IT RIGHT!

Make sure that you can draw the electronic structure of the atoms of all of the first 20 elements when you are given their atomic numbers.

One model of the atom which we use has electrons arranged around the nucleus in **shells**, rather like the layers of an onion. Each shell represents a different **energy level**. The lowest energy level is shown by the shell which is nearest to the nucleus.

With their negative charge, electrons are attracted to the positively charged nucleus. To move an electron from a shell close to the nucleus to one further away we need to put energy into the atom. The energy is needed to overcome this attractive force. This means that electrons in shells further away from the nucleus have more energy than electrons in shells closer to the nucleus.

a) Where are the electrons in an atom?
b) Which shell represents the lowest energy level in an atom?

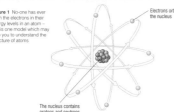

Figure 1 No-one has ever seen the electrons in their energy levels in an atom – this is one model which may help you to understand the structure of atoms.

Electrons orbit the nucleus

The nucleus contains protons and neutrons

We could not possibly draw atoms which look like this every time we wanted to show the structure of an atom. It's easier to draw atoms as in Figure 2.

An energy level can only hold a certain number of electrons. The first, and lowest, energy level holds two electrons. The second energy level is filled up by eight electrons. Once there are eight electrons in the third energy level, the fourth begins to fill up, and so on.

Elements whose atoms have a full outer energy level are very stable and unreactive. They are called the **noble gases** – helium, neon and argon are examples.

The most usual way of drawing the arrangement of electrons in an atom is shown in Figure 2. We can also write down the numbers of electrons in each energy level.

The atomic number of an element tells us how many electrons there are in its atoms. For example, for the carbon atom in Figure 2 the atomic number is 6, giving us 6 electrons. This means that we write its **electronic structure** as 2,4.

An atom with the atomic number 13 has an electronic structure 2,8,3. This represents 2 electrons in the first, and lowest, energy level, then eight in the next energy level and 3 in the highest energy level (its outermost shell).

Figure 2 A simple way of representing the electrons in a carbon atom and the energy levels where they are found. We can show this as 2,4. This is called the **electronic structure** (or electronic configuration) of the atom.

The best way to understand these arrangements is to look at some examples.

c) How many electrons can the first energy level hold?

Filling up the energy levels (shells)

We call the horizontal rows of the periodic table **periods**. As we move across a period of the table, each element has one more electron in its highest energy level (or outer shell) than the element before it. When we start a new period, a new energy level begins to fill with electrons.

The pattern is quite complicated after argon. However, the elements in the main groups all have the same number of electrons in their highest energy level. These electrons are often called the **outer electrons** because they are in the outer shell.

All the elements in Group 1 have one electron in their highest energy level and the noble gases, except for helium, have 8 electrons in their highest energy level.

1 | 2,3 | 2,6
Hydrogen H | Boron B | Oxygen O

2,8,1 | 2,8,8 | 2,8,8,2
Sodium Na | Argon Ar | Calcium Ca

Figure 3 Once you know the pattern, you should be able to draw the energy levels and electrons in any of the first 20 atoms (given their atomic number)

Li | Be | B | C | N | O | F | Ne

Figure 4 As a period builds up, the number of electrons in the outer shell of each element increases by one

We call the vertical columns of the periodic table **groups**. The chemical properties of an element depend on how many electrons it has. Most importantly, the way an element reacts is determined by the number of electrons in its highest energy level or outer shell. As we have seen, the elements in a particular group all have the same number of electrons in their highest energy levels. This means that they all share similar chemical properties.

SUMMARY QUESTIONS

1 Copy and complete using the words below:

electron   energy   energy levels   group   nucleus
period   shells

The electrons in an atom are arranged around the ...... in ...... or .... The electrons further away from the nucleus have more ...... than those close to the nucleus. As you go across a ...... of the periodic table, each element has one more ...... than the previous element. All elements in the same ...... have the same number of electrons in their outer shell.

2 Draw the arrangement of electrons in the following atoms:

a) Li   b) B   c) P   d) Ar.

3 What is special about the electronic structure of neon and argon?

KEY POINTS

1 The electrons in an atom are arranged in energy levels or shells.
2 Atoms with the same number of electrons in their outer shell belong in the same group of the periodic table.
3 The number of electrons in the outer shell of an atom determines the way that the atom behaves in chemical reactions.

90 | 91

SUMMARY ANSWERS

1 Nucleus, shells (energy levels), energy levels (shells), energy, period, electron, group.

2 a)

Li

b)
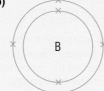
B

c)
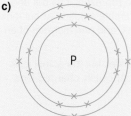
P

d)

Ar

3 They both have full outer shells or energy levels of electrons/ have very stable arrangements of electrons.

Answers to in-text questions

a) Arranged around the nucleus.

b) The energy level closest to the nucleus.

c) 2

KEY POINTS

Match the key points to which learning objective in the Student Book they best answer.

C2 1.3   Chemical bonding

LEARNING OBJECTIVES

Students should learn that:

- Elements form compounds.
- Elements in Group 1 react with elements in Group 7.

LEARNING OUTCOMES

Most students should be able to:

- State why atoms react.
- Name the two types of bonding present in compounds.
- Represent Cl^- and Na^+ using a diagram.

Some students should also be able to:

- Explain why atoms bond.
- Explain and work out the charge on an ion.
- Explain the formation of ions when a Group 1 and Group 7 element react together.

Teaching suggestions

- **Learning styles**

  Visual: Creating a poster about ionic bonding.

  Auditory: Listening to explanations of bonding.

  Interpersonal: Discussing the nature of ionic bonding.

  Intrapersonal: Reflecting on the lesson.

- **Homework.** Ask students to answer the learning objective questions at the start of the spread in the Student Book.

- **ICT link-up.** Record the demonstration using a web cam. The film can then be played back, annotated and paused on an interactive whiteboard during a discussion about the reaction.

Answers to in-text questions

a) Mixing involves a physical change (easily reversed) while reacting involves a chemical change, which is much less easily reversed.

b) Covalent.

c) Ionic.

SPECIFICATION LINK-UP   Unit: Chemistry 2.12.1

- *Compounds are substances in which atoms of two, or more, elements are not just mixed together but chemically combined.*
- *Chemical bonding involves either transferring or sharing electrons in the highest occupied energy levels (shells) of atoms.*
- *When atoms form chemical bonds by transferring electrons, they form ions. Atoms that lose electrons become positively charge ions. Atoms that gain electrons become negatively charged ions. Ions have the electronic structure of a noble gas (Group 0).*
- *The elements in Group 1 of the periodic table, the alkali metals, have similar chemical properties. They all react with non-metals to form ionic compounds in which the metal ion has a single positive charge.*
- *The elements in Group 7 of the periodic table, the halogens, have similar chemical properties. They react with the alkali metals to form ionic compounds in which the halide ions have a single negative charge.*

Students should use their skills, knowledge and understanding of 'How Science Works':

- *to represent the electronic structure of the ions in sodium chloride . . .*

Lesson structure

STARTER

Think – Ask students to think about why atoms bond. They should talk about the question in pairs and could refer to the Student Book. Then they feedback with questions and answers while you note bullet points on the board. (5 minutes)

True or false – Ask the students to decide if the following are true or false. Encourage them to use the Student Book to help them decide.

- Only compounds contain chemical bonds. [False]
- The nuclei of atoms form chemical bonds. [False]
- Atoms usually bond to get a full shell of electrons. [True]
- Covalent bonds form when pairs of electrons are shared between atoms. [True]
- A chloride ion has a positive charge. [False] (5 minutes)

MAIN

- The formation of sodium chloride from its elements is an exciting and impressive reaction. The elements can be shown to the students in sealed containers – chlorine is toxic and should be stored in a sealed gas jar; sodium is highly flammable and should be stored under oil.
- Students could describe the properties of these elements and the electronic structure could be generated in their notes.
- Then you could demonstrate the formation of sodium chloride in a fume cupboard.
- Following this, provide students with sodium chloride to note down its properties. They should be encouraged to contrast the properties of the elements with the compound and reflect on the fact that the properties of the compound can be completely different from its constituent elements.
- Students need to be able to understand ionic bonding and represent it as dot and cross diagrams. Ask students to use the Student Book to create a poster about ionic bonding. They should include at least two diagrams of ions, and one diagram of an ionic bond.
- Stress to students that ionic bonding involves electron transfer, but the actual ionic bonds arise from the electrostatic attraction between the oppositely charged ions formed as a result of electron transfer.

PLENARIES

Reflection – Ask the students to note down:

- What I have seen . . .
- What I have heard . . .
- What I have done . . .

These can be collected in from the class to be used to see what the students have remembered. (10 minutes)

Chemical equation – Ask students to write a word equation for the synthesis of sodium chloride from its elements. (Higher attaining students could write a balanced symbol equation with state symbols.) Then the students should draw the electronic structure of each element and the compound beneath the equation. (15 minutes)

ACTIVITY & EXTENSION IDEAS

- Students could look at and draw models of a salt crystal. They could label the ions.

- Sodium chloride is an important compound in our diet. Ask students to research why humans need to eat salt, and what can happen if we eat too much salt.

- Sodium (a rice grain sized piece) could be put into water (CARE!) to demonstrate that it is a highly reactive metallic element that should not be eaten, and contrast this with sodium chloride. Safety screens all around and above. Wear eye protection. (CLEAPSS Hazcard 88.)

CHEMISTRY   STRUCTURES AND BONDING

C2 1.3   Chemical bonding

LEARNING OBJECTIVES

1 How do elements form compounds?
2 Why do the elements in Group 1 react with the elements in Group 7?

You already know that we can mix two substances together without either of them changing. For example, we can mix sand and salt together and then separate them again. No change will have taken place. We can even dissolve sugar in tea and separate it out again. But in chemical reactions the situation is very different.

When the atoms of two or more elements react they make a compound. The compound formed is different to both of them and we cannot get either of the elements back again easily. We can also react compounds together to form other compounds, but the reaction of elements is easier to understand as a starting point.

a) What is the difference between mixing two substances and reacting them?

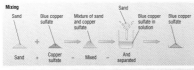

Figure 1 The difference between mixing and reacting. Separating mixtures is usually quite easy, but separating substances once they have reacted can be quite difficult.

Why do atoms react?

When an atom has a full outer shell it is stable and unreactive (like the noble gases in Group 0). However most atoms do not have a full outer shell. When atoms react they take part in changes which give them a stable arrangement of electrons. They may do this by either:

- sharing electrons, which we call **covalent bonding**, or by
- transferring electrons, which we call **ionic bonding**.

In ionic bonding the atoms involved lose or gain electrons so that they have a noble gas structure. So for example, if sodium, 2,8,1 loses one electron it is left with the stable electronic structure of neon 2,8.

However, it is also left with one more proton in the nucleus than there are electrons in orbit around the nucleus. The proton has a positive charge so the sodium atom has now become a positively charged particle. We call this a **sodium ion**. The sodium ion has a single positive charge. We write the formula of a sodium ion as Na^+. The electronic structure of the Na^+ ion is $[2,8]^+$.

b) When atoms join together by **sharing** electrons, what type of bond is this?
c) When atoms join together as a result of **gaining** or **losing** electrons, what type of bond is this?

Similarly some atoms gain electrons during reactions to achieve a stable noble gas structure. Chlorine, for example, has the electronic structure 2,8,7. By gaining a single electron, it gets the stable electronic structure of argon [2,8,8].

In this case there is now one more electron than there are positive protons in the nucleus. So the chlorine atom becomes a negatively charged particle known as a **chloride ion**. This carries a single negative charge. We write the formula of the chloride ion as Cl^-. Its electronic structure is $[2,8,8]^-$.

Representing electron transfer

When atoms react together to form ions, atoms which need to lose electrons react with elements which need to gain electrons. So when sodium reacts with chlorine, sodium loses an electron and chlorine gains that electron so they both form stable ions.

We can show this in a diagram. Look at Figure 4:

The electrons of one atom are represented by dots, and the electrons of the other atom are represented by crosses.

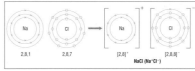

Figure 4 The formation of sodium chloride (NaCl) – an example of ion formation by transferring a single electron

Figure 2 A positive sodium ion (Na^+) is formed when a sodium atom loses an electron during ionic bonding with another element

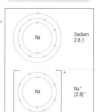

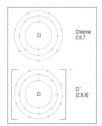

Figure 3 A negative chloride ion (Cl^-) is formed when a chlorine atom gains an electron during ion formation with another element

SUMMARY QUESTIONS

1 Copy and complete using the words below:

covalent   difficult   gaining   ionic   losing   new
noble   sharing

When two substances react together they make a ...... substance and it is ...... to separate them. Some atoms react by ...... electrons – we call this ...... bonding. Other atoms react by ...... or ...... electrons – this leads to ...... bonding. When atoms react in this way they tend to get the electronic structure of a ...... gas.

2 Draw diagrams to show the ions being formed when the following atoms transfer electrons. For each one, state whether electrons have been lost or gained and show the charge on the ions formed.

a) aluminium (Al)   b) fluorine (F)
c) potassium (K)   d) oxygen (O)

KEY POINTS

1 Elements react to form compounds by gaining or losing electrons or by sharing electrons.
2 The elements in Group 1 react with the elements in Group 7 because Group 1 elements can lose an electron to gain a full outer shell. This electron can be given to an atom from Group 7, which then also gains a full outer shell.

92   93

SUMMARY ANSWERS

1 New, difficult, sharing, covalent, losing (gaining), gaining (losing), ionic, noble.

2 a) Al^{3+} ion, electrons lost.

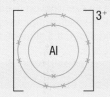

c) K^+ ion, electron lost.

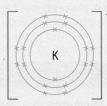

b) F^- ion, electron gained.

d) O^{2-} ion, electrons gained.

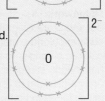

KEY POINTS

Note the points onto flash cards.

C2 1.4

Ionic bonding

Students should learn:

- How ions are held together in a giant structure.
- That elements which aren't in Groups 1 and 7 can also form ions.

Most students should be able to:

- Describe ionic bonding as electrostatic forces of attraction.
- Draw the dot and cross diagram for magnesium oxide and calcium chloride.

Some students should also be able to:

- Describe an ionic lattice.
- Apply their knowledge of ionic bonding to draw dot and cross diagrams for other ionic compounds.

Teaching suggestions

- **Special needs.** Give these students a sheet with dot and cross diagrams of a sodium ion, magnesium ion, calcium ion, oxide ion and two chloride ions. Encourage them to represent sodium chloride, magnesium oxide and calcium chloride by cutting out the ions and sticking them into the correct arrangement.

- **Gifted and talented**
  - Students could be encouraged to research and find out the charges of transition metals and to find out different examples of ionic lattices involving these elements.
  - Students could compare copper oxide produced with the two differently charged copper ions.

- **Learning styles**

  Kinaesthetic: Completing the practical to form magnesium oxide.

  Visual: Creating a flow chart to represent the formation of magnesium oxide.

  Auditory: Listening to different students' opinions on the marking of fictitious student answers.

  Interpersonal: Working in groups to generate questions for which answers are provided.

  Intrapersonal: Individually naming the ions.

SPECIFICATION LINK-UP   Unit: Chemistry 2.12.1

- *An ionic compound is a giant structure of ions. Ionic compounds are held together by strong forces of attraction between oppositely charged ions. These forces act in all directions in the lattice and this is called ionic bonding.*

Students should use their skills, knowledge and understanding of 'How Science Works':

- *to represent the electronic structure of the ions in sodium chloride, magnesium oxide and calcium chloride.*

Lesson structure

STARTER

Define – Give students the following definitions and ask them to decide which key word it is relating to:

- A charged particle formed by an atom losing or gaining electrons. [Ion]
- All the atoms are the same. [Element]
- More than one type of atom chemically bonded together. [Compound]
- A chemical bond formed as electrons are transferred. [Ionic bond]
- A section of the periodic table whose elements all form 1+ ions. [Group 1/Alkali metals] (5 minutes)

Guess the ion – Give the students a diagram of chlorine, sodium, calcium, oxygen and calcium ions. Encourage them to use the periodic table and the textbook to name each ion. (10 minutes)

MAIN

- Magnesium oxide can be made in the lab by the students in a variety of ways. Encourage students to represent the reaction in terms of a flow chart. The first stages should detail the structure of the atoms of the elements, the middle stages could show the observations of the reaction and the final stage would include a dot and cross diagram representing the resulting ionic compound.

- Often students consider ionic bonds in isolation and in two-dimensional particle diagrams or in dot and cross diagrams. Show students already made-up structures of calcium chloride and magnesium oxide.

- Students could then compare the structures to the actual substances (crystalline powders).

- Then give students molecular model kits and ask them to generate a sodium chloride crystal. Using question and answer, encourage students to understand which part of the model represents ions and bonds and what the bonds are (an electrostatic force of attraction between oppositely charged ions).

PLENARIES

Question – Split the class into four groups and give each team a different key term: 'ions', 'ionic bond', 'lattice', 'charge'. Each group should write a question which matches their answer. Students then share their questions with the rest of the class. (5 minutes)

AfL (Assessment for learning) – Give students an examination question with a fictitious student answer. Encourage the students to work in small groups to mark the work. Then ask the class to say how many marks they would award the student, and reveal the actual mark. (10 minutes)

- **Homework.** Ask students to draw the dot and cross diagrams to represent sodium chloride, magnesium oxide and calcium chloride. To extend this homework, students could research and draw a diagram to represent the ionic lattice for each compound.

Practical support

Burning magnesium

Equipment and materials required

Magnesium ribbon (flammable – CLEAPSS Hazcard 59), magnesium powder (flammable), spatula, tongs, Bunsen burner and safety equipment, eye protection, blue plastic.

Details

Safety: During both of these reactions, eye protection must be worn. Magnesium oxide powder will aspirate, so it is advisable to complete this in a well-ventilated area, or demonstrate.

Students hold a small piece (<1 cm) of magnesium ribbon in tongs. The metal should be held at the top of the blue gas cone in the Bunsen flame. As soon as it ignites, they need to remove it from the flame. This reaction produces a bright light that can blind if looked at directly, so either encourage the students to look past the reaction or through the special blue plastic.

Then ask the students to sprinkle about half a spatula of magnesium powder directly into the blue Bunsen flame and observe. As the surface area is greater, it will combust more quickly and produces a twinkling effect. Make sure that they hold the Bunsen at an angle or the magnesium powder may fall down the Bunsen chimney and fuse the collar to the chimney.

ACTIVITY & EXTENSION

- Students could be encouraged to draw more complex dot and cross diagrams, e.g. aluminium oxide.
- Students could research into elements that can have more than one charge, e.g. manganese.
- Students could evaluate dot and cross diagrams as a means of representing ionic compounds.

CHEMISTRY STRUCTURES AND BONDING

C2 1.4 Ionic bonding

LEARNING OBJECTIVES

1. How are ionic compounds held together?
2. Which elements, other than those in Groups 1 and 7, form ions?

You have seen how positive and negative ions form during some reactions. Ionic compounds are usually formed when metals react with non-metals.

The ions formed are held to each other by enormously strong forces of attraction between the oppositely charged ions. This electrostatic force of attraction, which acts in all directions, is called the **ionic bond**.

The ionic bonds between the charged particles results in an arrangement of ions that we call a **giant structure**. If we could stand among the ions they would seem to go on in all directions for ever.

The force exerted by an ion on the other ions in the lattice acts equally in all directions. This is why the ions in a giant structure are held together so strongly.

The giant structure of ionic compounds is very *regular*. This is because the ions all pack together neatly, like marbles in a tin or apples in a box.

a) What name do we give to the arrangement of ions in an ionic compound?
b) What holds the ions together in this structure?

DID YOU KNOW?

Common salt is sodium chloride. In just 58.5 g of salt there are over 600 000 000 000 000 000 000 000 ions of Na⁺ and the same number of Cl⁻ ions.

$-$ = Cl⁻
$+$ = Na⁺
Strong ionic bonds between oppositely charged ions

Figure 1 A giant ionic lattice (3D network) of sodium and chloride ions

Other ionic compounds

Sometimes the atoms reacting need to gain or lose two electrons to gain a stable noble gas structure. An example is when magnesium (2,8,2) reacts with oxygen (2,6). When these two elements react they form magnesium oxide (MgO). This is made up of magnesium ions with a double positive charge (Mg²⁺) and oxide ions with a double negative charge (O²⁻).

We can represent the atoms and ions involved in forming ions by *dot and cross diagrams*. In these diagrams we only show the electrons in the outermost shell of each atom or ion. So they are quicker to draw than the diagrams on the previous page. Look at Figure 2 on the next page:

2,8,2   2,6   [2,8]²⁺   MgO   [2,8]²⁻

Figure 2 When magnesium oxide (MgO) is formed the reacting atoms lose or gain two electrons

In some cases one of the atoms needs to gain or lose more electrons than the other has to lose or gain. In this case, two or more atoms of each element may react.

For example, think about calcium chloride. Each calcium atom needs to lose two electrons but each chlorine atom needs to gain only one electron. This means that two chlorine atoms react with every one calcium atom to form calcium chloride. So the formula of calcium chloride is CaCl₂.

DID YOU KNOW?

The structure of ionic lattices is investigated by passing X-rays through them.

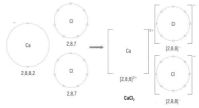

Ca   2,8,7   2,8,8,2   2,8,7   Ca   [2,8,8]⁻   [2,8,8]²⁺   CaCl₂   [2,8,8]⁻

Figure 3 The formation of calcium chloride (CaCl₂)

SUMMARY QUESTIONS

1 Copy and complete the table:

Atomic number	Atom	Electronic structure of atom	Ion	Electronic structure of ion
8	O	c)	e)	[2,8]²⁻
19	a)	2,8,8,1	K⁺	g)
17	Cl	d)	Cl⁻	h)
20	b)	2,8,8,2	f)	i)

j) Explain why potassium chloride is KCl but potassium oxide is K₂O.
k) Explain why calcium oxide is CaO but calcium chloride is CaCl₂.

2 Draw dot and cross diagrams to show how you would expect the following elements to form ions together:

a) lithium and chlorine,
b) calcium and oxygen,
c) aluminium and chlorine.

KEY POINTS

1. Ionic compounds are held together by strong forces between the oppositely charged ions. This is called ionic bonding.
2. Other elements that can form ionic compounds include those in Groups 2 and 6.

94   95

SUMMARY ANSWERS

1

Atomic number	Atom	Electronic structure of atom	Ion	Electronic structure of ion
8	O	2,6	O²⁻	[2,8]²⁻
19	K	2,8,8,1	K⁺	[2,8,8]⁺
17	Cl	2,8,7	Cl⁻	[2,8,8]⁻
20	Ca	2,8,8,2	Ca²⁺	[2,8,8]²⁺

j) K forms K⁺ and Cl forms Cl⁻. Therefore one type of each ion is needed to make the compound electrically neutral. But O forms O²⁻, so two K⁺ are needed.

k) Ca forms Ca²⁺ and O forms O²⁻. Therefore one type of each ion is needed to make the compound electrically neutral. But Cl forms Cl⁻, so two Cl⁻ are needed.

2 Dot and cross diagrams in style of those shown on page 95 in the Student Book, showing:

a) Li⁺ [2]⁺ and Cl⁻ [2,8,8]⁻   b) Ca²⁺ [2,8,8]²⁺ and O²⁻ [2,8]²⁻
c) Al³⁺ [2,8]³⁺ and 3 × Cl⁻ [2,8,8]⁻

Answers to in-text questions

a) Lattice.
b) Attractive forces between oppositely charged ions.

DID YOU KNOW?

Using X-rays, scientists have discovered that ionic lattices aren't perfect. There are sections where the ions aren't perfectly arranged, and if you tap the crystal they will break along cleavage planes.

KEY POINTS

Begin to make a spider diagram using the key points on this spread. Then at the end of each lesson during the unit, or as a homework activity, the other key points from the topic can be added. Therefore, at the end of the topic, a powerful revision tool will have been created.

Additional chemistry

C2 1.5

Covalent bonding

Students should learn:

- How a covalent bond is formed.
- The types of substances formed from covalent bonds.

Most students should be able to:

- State a simple definition for a covalent bond.
- Draw a dot and cross diagram for simple covalent bonds (hydrogen, chlorine, hydrogen chloride, water).
- Name an element that has a giant covalent structure (carbon, diamond).

Some students should also be able to:

- Explain the formation of a covalent bond.
- Draw dot and cross diagrams for more complex covalent substances (methane, ammonia and oxygen).
- Explain the bonding in a giant covalent structure and give an example e.g. silicon oxide.

Teaching suggestions

- **Special needs.** To help the students understand how to draw dot and cross diagrams, give them the electronic structures of key atoms (hydrogen, chlorine) OHTs. Then ask them to arrange the images so that each atom has a full outer shell of electrons, by overlapping one image onto another. When they have the correct arrangement of electrons they can copy the diagram into their book. This process can be demonstrated on an OHP in front of the class.

- **Learning styles**

  Kinaesthetic: Completing a card sort.

  Visual: Watching the demonstration of the exploding hydrogen balloon.

  Auditory: Listening to explanations of covalent bonding.

  Interpersonal: Working in groups to model different substances.

  Intrapersonal: Drawing dot and cross diagrams.

SPECIFICATION LINK-UP   Unit: Chemistry 2.12.1

- *When atoms share pairs of electrons, they form covalent bonds. These bonds between atoms are strong. Some covalently bonded substances consist of simple molecules such as H_2, Cl_2, O_2, HCl, H_2O and CH_4. Others have giant covalent structures (macromolecules), such as diamond and silicon dioxide.*

Students should use their skills, knowledge and understanding of 'How Science Works':

- *to represent the covalent bonds in molecules such as water, ammonia, hydrogen, hydrogen chloride, chlorine, methane and oxygen and in giant structures such as diamond and silicon dioxide.*

Lesson structure

STARTER

Demonstration – Ignite a hydrogen balloon to get the attention of the class and generate excitement. The hydrogen will explode, as it reacts with the oxygen in the air to make water (steam). Encourage the students to write a word and balanced symbol equation for this reaction. (10 minutes)

Card sort – Give the students separate cards with images (just coloured circles and dot and cross diagrams) and words on: 'compound', 'element', 'molecule', 'mixture', 'ionic bond', 'ion'. Students should then try to match the image with the key term. (10 minutes)

MAIN

- Students need to be able to draw dot and cross diagrams for certain molecules and some students should be able to explain how and why they are formed. Ask for volunteers to draw the electronic structure of hydrogen on the board.
- Then ask the students how many electrons it needs to obtain a complete outer shell [1]. Then explain how and why hydrogen atoms make diatomic molecules.
- Ask the students to draw the dot and cross diagram of a chlorine molecule and explain, in no more than two sentences, why chlorine forms a diatomic molecule.
- Demonstrate how hydrogen and chlorine atoms bond to form hydrogen chloride. Then ask students to draw the other dot and cross diagrams for the appropriate molecules in their books.
- Most substances that form covalent bonds make discrete molecules, however there are some macromolecules, e.g. carbon and silicon oxide, that the students need to be aware of.
- Give students molecular model kits and ask them to make models of different molecules. Then focus on carbon, and ask them to make a carbon molecule using only single bonds – hopefully the students will find that the structure is never-ending.
- Explain to students that this is an example of a macromolecule and that it too is made of covalent bonds.
- To extend this, students could brainstorm the properties of diamond and try to explain them in terms of the structure.

PLENARIES

Model – Split the class into teams and give each team a different covalent compound to represent. In their team, students should represent atoms and their hands and feet can make up to four bonds (e.g. C in methane). Each team should 'act out' their molecule and explain it to the class. (10 minutes)

Ionic/covalent – Give the students a piece of paper. Ask them to write in large letters 'ionic bonding' and 'covalent bonding', one on each side of the paper. Then read out the following substances, and the students should hold up which type of bonding is present:

- Methane [Covalent]
- Sodium chloride [Ionic]
- Oxygen [Covalent]
- Water [Covalent]
- Magnesium oxide [Ionic]
- Carbon [Covalent]
- Silicon oxide [Covalent]
- Ammonia [Covalent]
- Calcium chloride [Ionic]
- Hydrogen chloride [Covalent] (5 minutes)

Definitions – Ask the students to define the term 'covalent bonding' in one sentence and explain this using a labelled diagram. (5 minutes)

Practical support

Burning hydrogen

Materials and equipment required

Rubber balloon, string, hydrogen gas cylinder (pressurised gas), metre rule, splint, tape, matches.

Details

Fill a rubber balloon with hydrogen from a gas cylinder. Tie the balloon with a piece of string onto a tap or 1 kg mass, so that it is clear of any flammable materials, students and the ceiling.

Then light a splint taped to the end of a metre ruler. Hold the lighted splint onto the stretched part of the rubber.

Safety: It is advised that the demonstrator wears eye protection and should be aware that hot rubber can fly from the balloon. Hydrogen is flammable – CLEAPSS Hazcard 48. NB Soap bubbles filled with hydrogen are an alternative here.

Answers to in-text questions

a) Covalent.

b) Two electrons.

c) A giant covalent structure (macromolecule).

ACTIVITY & EXTENSION

- Students could define the term 'allotrope' and look up other allotropes of carbon [fullerenes].
- Students could draw dot and cross diagrams of other covalent compounds.

KEY POINTS

- Ask students to draw diagrams or pictures to illustrate each key point.
- Alternatively, ask them to imagine that each key point is an answer, then to write the question to match it.

CHEMISTRY   STRUCTURES AND BONDING

C2 1.5   Covalent bonding

LEARNING OBJECTIVES

1 How are covalent bonds formed?
2 What kinds of substances do covalent bonds produce?

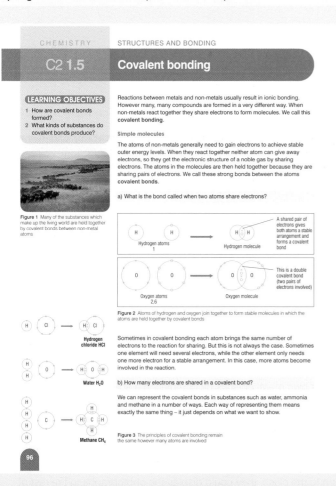

Figure 1 Many of the substances which make up the living world are held together by covalent bonds between non-metal atoms

Reactions between metals and non-metals usually result in ionic bonding. However many, many compounds are formed in a very different way. When non-metals react together they share electrons to form molecules. We call this **covalent bonding**.

Simple molecules

The atoms of non-metals generally need to gain electrons to achieve stable outer energy levels. When they react together neither atom can give away electrons, so they get the electronic structure of a noble gas by sharing electrons. The atoms in the molecules are then held together because they are sharing pairs of electrons. We call these strong bonds between the atoms **covalent bonds**.

a) What is the bond called when two atoms share electrons?

Figure 2 Atoms of hydrogen and oxygen join together to form stable molecules in which the atoms are held together by covalent bonds

Sometimes in covalent bonding each atom brings the same number of electrons to the reaction for sharing. But this is not always the case. Sometimes one element will need several electrons, while the other element only needs one more electron for a stable arrangement. In this case, more atoms become involved in the reaction.

b) How many electrons are shared in a covalent bond?

We can represent the covalent bonds in substances such as water, ammonia and methane in a number of ways. Each way of representing them means exactly the same thing – it just depends on what we want to show.

Figure 3 The principles of covalent bonding remain the same however many atoms are involved

Water
H₂O

Figure 4 We can represent a covalent compound by showing the highest energy level, the outer electrons or just the fact that there are a certain number of covalent bonds

Giant structures

Many substances containing covalent bonds consist of small molecules, for example, H_2O. However some covalently bonded substances are very different. They have giant structures where huge numbers of atoms are held together by a network of covalent bonds.

Diamonds have a giant covalent structure. In diamond, each carbon atom forms four covalent bonds with its neighbours in a rigid giant covalent lattice.

Silicon dioxide (silica) is another substance with a giant covalent structure.

c) What do we call the structure of a substance held together by a network of covalent bonds?

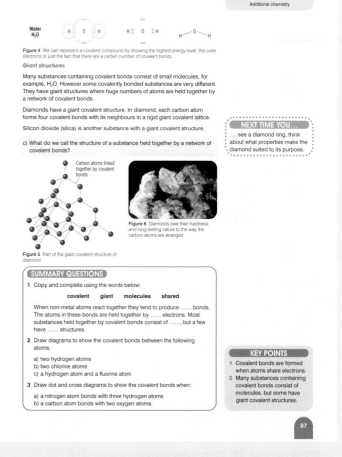

Figure 5 Part of the giant covalent structure of diamond

Figure 6 Diamonds owe their hardness and long-lasting nature to the way the carbon atoms are arranged

NEXT TIME YOU…

… see a diamond ring, think about what properties make the diamond suited to its purpose.

SUMMARY QUESTIONS

1 Copy and complete using the words below:

    covalent   giant   molecules   shared

When non-metal atoms react together they tend to produce …… bonds. The atoms in these bonds are held together by …… electrons. Most substances held together by covalent bonds consist of ……, but a few have …… structures.

2 Draw diagrams to show the covalent bonds between the following atoms.

a) two hydrogen atoms
b) two chlorine atoms
c) a hydrogen atom and a fluorine atom

3 Draw dot and cross diagrams to show the covalent bonds when:

a) a nitrogen atom bonds with three hydrogen atoms
b) a carbon atom bonds with two oxygen atoms.

KEY POINTS

1 Covalent bonds are formed when atoms share electrons.
2 Many substances containing covalent bonds consist of molecules, but some have giant covalent structures.

96

97

SUMMARY ANSWERS

1 Covalent, shared, molecules, giant.

2 a) 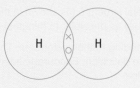   b) 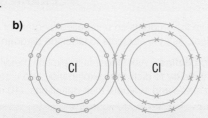   c)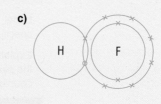

3 a)   b)

C2 1.6   Bonding in metals

Teaching suggestions

- **Learning styles**

  Kinaesthetic: Finding different examples of metal crystals.

  Visual: Labelling a metallic structure.

  Auditory: Listening to explanations of metallic bonding.

  Interpersonal: Working in groups to find different examples of metal crystals.

  Intrapersonal: Deciding which metal is the odd one out and why.

- **Homework.** Ask students to answer the following question:

  'Which metal do you think would have the strongest bonding: sodium or aluminium, and why?' [Al has more delocalised electrons]

- **ICT link-up.** Digital images taken by students or from the Internet could be used by the students to create a PowerPoint® about metal crystals and where you can find them. They could then show their presentations to their classmates.

SPECIFICATION LINK-UP   Unit: Chemistry 2.12.1

- *Metals consist of giant structures of atoms arranged in a regular pattern. The electrons in the highest occupied energy levels (outer shell) of metal atoms are delocalised and so free to move through the whole structure. This corresponds to a structure of positive ions with electrons between the ions holding them together by strong electrostatic attractions.* [**HT** only]

Students should use their skills, knowledge and understanding of 'How Science Works':

- *to represent the bonding in metals in the following form:* [**HT** only]

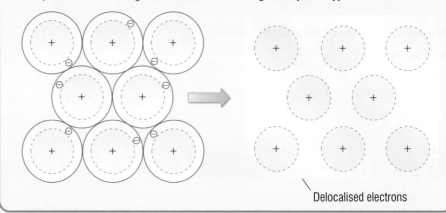

Delocalised electrons

Lesson structure

STARTER

5,4,3,2,1 – Ask students to write a list of: 5 metal symbols, 4 metal properties, 3 magnetic elements, 2 metals used in jewellery, 1 liquid metal at room temperature. Build up a class list on the board through questions and answers. (10 minutes)

Odd one out – Ask students to look at the list and decide which metal doesn't fit the pattern and why. The metals are: 'nickel, cobalt, iron and steel'. [Steel is the odd one out as it is an alloy, whereas nickel, cobalt and iron are elements.] (5 minutes)

MAIN

- Metals are made up of grains, which can be seen using very powerful microscopes. Show students images of the grains and grain boundaries. The grains order themselves in metals and form crystals.

- Students can grow their own metal crystals by completing a solution displacement reaction. Students could be encouraged to record the metal crystal in the form of a diagram in their book.

- Visible metal crystals can be found in a variety of structures in and around the school site. Students could go out and about in small teams, armed with digital cameras to find examples.

- When students return to the class, they could display the photographs to the rest of the class.

PLENARIES

Label – Give the students an unlabelled diagram of a metal structure (as shown in the specification). Ask the students to label the diagram as fully as possible. (5 minutes)

Explain and define – Ask students to explain metallic bonding to their neighbour. Then the pair should try to distil their explanation into a concise definition. Encourage a few couples to share and evaluate their definitions. (10 minutes)

Practical support

Growing silver crystals

Equipment and materials required

Boiling tube, boiling tube rack, copper wire, silver nitrate solution <0.5 M (irritant – CLEAPSS Hazcard 87), eye protection.

Details

- Wrap the copper wire into a spring shape and put into a boiling tube. Eye protection should be worn and silver nitrate solution added to the boiling tube so that it is about half full.
- Leave to allow displacement to occur: it would be best if the experiment were left until next lesson and reviewed as a starter.

Survey of metallic crystals

Equipment and materials required

Clipboards, digital camera, stationery.

Details

- Split the class into small groups. Take the students to an example of a metal crystal e.g. a galvanised dustbin on the school site.
- Give the students a time limit (10 minutes) to find further examples around the school of metal crystals. They should record, in a table, the photograph number, place and item that the metal crystal was found on.

ACTIVITY & EXTENSION IDEAS

- Students could electrolyse copper sulfate solution in order to grow copper crystals or grow lead crystals from zinc foil suspended in lead nitrate solution.
  [**Safety:** Copper sulfate is harmful (CLEAPSS Hazcard 27) and lead nitrate is toxic (CLEAPSS Hazcard 57).]
- If the school has any examples, students could be shown different metal crystals and metal structural models.
- Students could try to make a three-dimensional model of a metallic structure using art materials, e.g. polystyrene balls, string, paint and a shoe box.

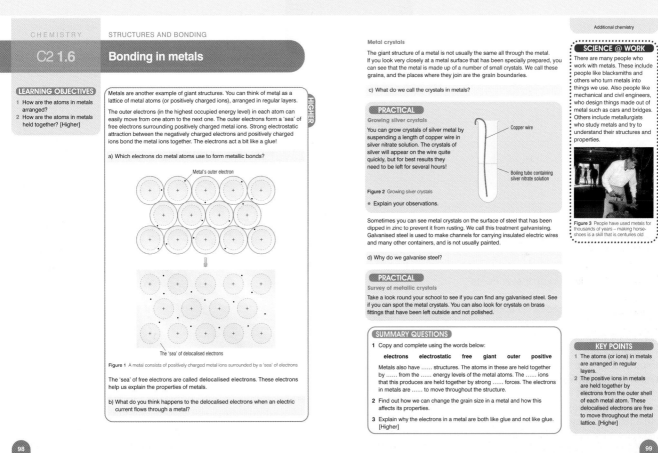

CHEMISTRY — STRUCTURES AND BONDING

C2 1.6 — Bonding in metals

LEARNING OBJECTIVES

1 How are the atoms in metals arranged?
2 How are the atoms in metals held together? [Higher]

Metals are another example of giant structures. You can think of metal as a lattice of metal atoms (or positively charged ions), arranged in regular layers.

The outer electrons (in the highest occupied energy level) in each atom can easily move from one atom to the next one. The outer electrons form a 'sea' of free electrons surrounding positively charged metal ions. Strong electrostatic attraction between the negatively charged electrons and positively charged ions bond the metal ions together. The electrons act a bit like a glue!

a) Which electrons do metal atoms use to form metallic bonds?

Metal's outer electron

The 'sea' of delocalised electrons

Figure 1 A metal consists of positively charged metal ions surrounded by a 'sea' of electrons

The 'sea' of free electrons are called **delocalised electrons**. These electrons help us explain the properties of metals.

b) What do you think happens to the delocalised electrons when an electric current flows through a metal?

Metal crystals

The giant structure of a metal is not usually the same all through the metal. If you look very closely at a metal surface that has been specially prepared, you can see that the metal is made up of a number of small crystals. We call these grains, and the places where they join are the **grain boundaries**.

c) What do we call the crystals in metals?

PRACTICAL

Growing silver crystals

You can grow crystals of silver metal by suspending a length of copper wire in silver nitrate solution. The crystals of silver will appear on the wire quite quickly, but for best results they need to be left for several hours!

Copper wire

Boiling tube containing silver nitrate solution

Figure 2 Growing silver crystals

- Explain your observations.

Sometimes you can see metal crystals on the surface of steel that has been dipped in zinc to prevent it from rusting. We call this treatment **galvanising**. Galvanised steel is used to make channels for carrying insulated electric wires and many other containers, and is not usually painted.

d) Why do we galvanise steel?

PRACTICAL

Survey of metallic crystals

Take a look round your school to see if you can find any galvanised steel. See if you can spot the metal crystals. You can also look for crystals on brass fittings that have been left outside and not polished.

SUMMARY QUESTIONS

1 Copy and complete using the words below:

electrons   electrostatic   free   giant   outer   positive

Metals also have …… structures. The atoms in these are held together by …… from the …… energy levels of the metal atoms. The …… ions that this produces are held together by strong …… forces. The electrons in metals are …… to move throughout the structure.

2 Find out how we can change the grain size in a metal and how this affects its properties.

3 Explain why the electrons in a metal are both like glue and not like glue. [Higher]

SCIENCE @ WORK

There are many people who work with metals. These include people like blacksmiths and others who turn metals into things we use. Also people like mechanical and civil engineers, who design things made out of metal such as cars and bridges. Others include metallurgists who study metals and try to understand their structures and properties.

Figure 3 People have used metals for thousands of years – making horse-shoes is a skill that is centuries old

KEY POINTS

1 The atoms (or ions) in metals are arranged in regular layers.
2 The positive ions in metals are held together by electrons from the outer shell of each metal atom. These delocalised electrons are free to move throughout the metal lattice. [Higher]

SUMMARY ANSWERS

1 Giant, electrons, outer, positive, electrostatic, free.

2 Student research – e.g. cold working, annealing.

3 Like glue – because they hold the atoms together.
Unlike glue – because atoms can still move/flow past each other when force is applied. The electrons can also move freely through the structure.
[**HT** only]

Answers to in-text questions

a) Outer electrons.

b) They drift towards the positive terminal.

c) Grains.

d) To prevent rusting.

KEY POINTS

Answer each learning objective from Student Book page 98 using a key point.

C2 1.7

The history of the atom

SPECIFICATION LINK-UP

Unit: Chemistry 2.12.1

This spread provides the opportunity to revisit the following substantive content already covered in this chapter:

- *Compounds are substances in which atoms of two, or more, elements are not just mixed together but chemically combined.*

Teaching suggestions

Activities

- **Letter writing** – Encourage the students to imagine that they are John Dalton, in the 1700s, after his discoveries about atoms. Ask the students to pick a person to whom he might have written a letter (encourage them to find out actual names of scientists who were alive at the same time, his parents' names, or publications which would have printed his letter at the time). Then ask them to write a letter conveying the excitement of his discoveries, but also in appropriate language for the audience. Students may then also like to 'age' their work, using damp tea bags to stain paper, burning the edges with a candle and could even create a seal using coloured candle wax.

- **Safety:** Be aware that candle wax can cause thermal burns. If the wax gets in contact with the skin, wash under cold water for 10 minutes and seek further medical attention. If the edges of the paper are singed, use a lighted candle on a flame-proof mat, be sure to tie back long hair and keep ties away from the flame. If the paper begins to burn, it could be blown out, or dropped onto the heat-proof mat and allowed to burn out.

John Dalton's atomic theory

John Dalton – the man who gave us atoms

John Dalton was born in 1766 in the Lake District in England. His father was a weaver who taught John at home before sending him to a Quaker school in Eaglesfield, where they lived. John was amazingly clever – by the time he was 12 he was teaching other children!

He was interested in almost everything. He made observations of the weather as well as being the first person to study colour-blindness. (John was colour-blind himself – see the photo below.)

But Dalton is best-remembered for his ideas about chemistry – and in particular his theories about atoms. As a result of a great deal of work, Dalton suggested that:

- All matter is made up of indivisible particles called atoms.
- Atoms of the same element are similar in mass and shape but differ from the atoms of other elements.
- Atoms cannot be created or destroyed.
- Atoms join together to form compound atoms (what we would now call molecules) in simple ratios.

Dalton's statements were backed up with much research, even though not all of it was accurate. For example, he insisted that one hydrogen atom combined with one oxygen atom to form water. However, most of his research reflected the same results as other scientists of the time were getting.

Dalton's atomic theory explained much of what scientists were seeing, and so his idea of atoms was accepted relatively quickly. Some scientists even made wooden models of atoms of different elements, to show their different relative sizes.

By 1850, the atomic theory of matter was almost universally accepted and virtually all opposition had disappeared. Dalton's atomic theory was the basis of much of the chemistry done in the rest of the 19th and early 20th centuries.

John Dalton's eyes (on the watch-glass) were taken out after his death as he requested. He wanted a doctor to check his theory of colour blindness. Unfortunately this theory proved incorrect.

ACTIVITY

Imagine that you are John Dalton and that you have just finished writing a book about your ideas on atoms. Write a letter to someone explaining your ideas. You can choose to write to:

- another scientist,
- a member of your family,
- a journalist who is interested in your ideas and who wants to know more about them in order to write a newspaper article for the general public.

100

- **Information cards** – Encourage the students to research the work of Dalton. Give them index cards: on one side they could summarise the experiment that Dalton did (either diagram or text), and on the reverse detail what he discovered from that particular experiment.

- **Poster** – Scientific research costs a lot of money. Encourage students to find out some sources of funding. Then, with a question and answer session, draw out from the class some positive and negative points about research. Then ask the class to vote whether they think that research should happen. Students could then design and make a poster showing points for and against academic research.

Homework (cut and stick) – Give the students a set of discoveries about the atom and who discovered them in separate boxes on paper. They should then cut out and match the discoverer with the discovery.

Extensions

- **Brainstorm** – Often when a scientist made a discovery, many people were against the new ideas as it contradicted what they already knew. Ask the class to brainstorm what type of people would be against Dalton's ideas and why. Then ask the class to imagine the answers that Dalton could have prepared to counter arguments put forward against his ideas.

Atoms and the future

Deep underneath the Swiss countryside lies a huge maze of tunnels. Inside these tunnels, scientists are working to puzzle out the structure of the atom. They are searching for the particles that make up the protons and neutrons inside each atom.

To find these tiny particles they need to use huge machines. These accelerate particles like electrons and protons up to speeds close to the speed of light. Then the particles smash into each other in a kind of 'subatomic demolition derby'!

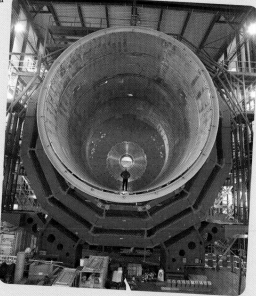

This is a particle detector under construction

It's really important that we know as much as we can about atoms. Although it doesn't seem like this knowledge is very useful at the moment, it could lead to important discoveries in the future. And besides, we should try to find out as much as we can about the world around us!

This shows a section of a particle accelerator

The money that's spent on this kind of research is enormous. We should spend money on APPLIED kinds of scientific research that may be able to help people, not on research that isn't any practical use.

ACTIVITY

Research like this costs a great deal of money. Who do you agree with?

Design a poster to show your ideas.

101

- **Time line** – There are philosophers and scientists who have contributed to our knowledge of the structure of the atom. Encourage students to use the Internet and books to create a time line ranging from 400BCE (Democritus) to modern day (quarks and leptons). Students could summarise the discoveries/theories in text or diagrams (e.g. JJ Thomson's plum pudding model is easier described in a diagram). Instead of individuals making their own time line, it could be made into a class effort. Each student, or pair of students, could be given a discovery that they must document. Then all the information could be constructed onto a giant time line spanning the top of the room. Use PhotoPLUS C2 1.7 'History of the atom'.

Learning styles

Visual: Preparing the time line for atom discovery.

Interpersonal: Working as a group to prepare resources for the class time line.

Intrapersonal: Writing a letter from Dalton.

ICT link-up

New information about the atomic structure is being discovered at CERN, Europe. Students could use the Internet to find out what CERN is and the discoveries they are making (www.cern.ch).

Special needs

Give the students the names and discoveries of Democritus, John Dalton, Ernest Rutherford, Neils Bohr and James Chadwick, as these scientists discovered parts of the atom as we know it today. They can then use this limited information to make their own time line.

SUMMARY ANSWERS

1 a) Proton, neutron, electron.

b) Proton – positive, neutron – neutral, electron – negative.

2 Diagrams to show the following electronic structures:

a) 2 **b)** 2,6 **c)** 2,8,8,1 **d)** 2,8,7 **e)** 2,8,3

3 a) A (Magnesium).

b) Group 7.

c)
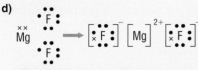

d)

Where Mg = A
and F = C

4 a) Atoms held together by sharing a pair of electrons to form a covalent bond, joining two Br atoms together.

Br —— Br

Sharing electrons
produces attractive force

b) Diagram to show a giant lattice of covalent bonds. (See Student Book page 97.)

c) Diagram to show a giant lattice of Na^+ and Cl^- ions, held together by strong electrostatic attractive forces between opposite charges. (See Student Book page 94.)

5 Diagram to show a giant lattice of positively charged sodium ions held together by delocalised ('sea') of electrons. (See Student Book page 98.)

Summary teaching suggestions

- **Special needs** – Question 2 requires students to draw their own atomic structures of certain elements. Give these students a framework with the element symbol under the correct amount of shells (circles) so that the students only need to add their crosses on to it.

- **Gifted and talented** – Question 5 is a good example of a higher-level question.

- **Misconceptions** – Often students do not use all the information given to them in an examination question. Question 3 requires candidates to choose examples from those given in the diagrams. However, some students will ignore this information and try to answer the questions immediately and will give chemically correct answers but not be awarded any marks.

- **Learning styles**
  Visual: Questions 2, 4 and 5 require students to draw diagrams, and question 3 requires students to use diagrams to answer the question.
  Interpersonal: Question 4 and 5 lend themselves to class discussion before the students attempt the questions.

- **When to use the questions?**
  - Split the class into groups of three, each member of the team should tackle a different part of question 4. You should time this (3 minutes), encouraging students to use their exercise books and textbooks to help them. Then the papers should be swapped, to the right within the group, and the next student also has time to read the previous answer and amend, then add their own thoughts. This process of passing the paper and correcting previous work continues until the papers are returned to the original owner and the group could then discuss their thoughts about all of the parts.

STRUCTURES AND BONDING: C2 1.1 – C2 1.7

SUMMARY QUESTIONS

1 a) Unscramble the following words to make the names of the three different particles in an atom:
nropto   erontun   lentroce

b) Now show the charge on each of these particles by writing one of the following words next to each name – neutral, positive, negative.

2 Draw the structure of the following atoms showing all the energy levels in each atom:
a) helium (He, atomic number 2),
b) oxygen (O, atomic number 8),
c) potassium (K, atomic number 19),
d) chlorine (Cl, atomic number 17),
e) aluminium (Al, atomic number 13).

3 The diagrams show the energy levels in three atoms:
(The letters are NOT the chemical symbols.)

A   B

C

a) Which atom belongs to group 2?
b) To which group does atom C belong?
c) Atom B bonds with four atoms of hydrogen. Draw a dot and cross diagram to show the compound that is formed.
d) Draw dot and cross diagrams to show how atom A bonds with C atoms.

4 Describe, with diagrams, how the particles are held together in the following substances:
a) a molecule of bromine (Br_2),
b) a sample of diamond (carbon),
c) a salt crystal (NaCl).

5 Explain the bonding in sodium metal. You may wish to include a diagram. (The atomic number of sodium is 11.)

EXAM-STYLE QUESTIONS

1 The diagram represents an atom of an element.

(a) Write the electronic structure of this atom as numbers and commas. (1)
(b) How many protons are in the nucleus of this atom? (1)
(c) Name the other particles that are in the nucleus. (1)
(d) In which group of the periodic table is this element? (1)
(e) Draw a similar diagram to show the ion formed by this atom in ionic compounds. Show the charge on the ion. (2)

2 Complete the missing information (a) to (f) in the table.

Atomic number	Symbol	Electronic structure of atom	Formula of ion	Electronic structure of ion
9	F	(a)	(b)	[2,8]$^-$
11	(c)	2,8,1	Na$^+$	(d)
(e)	S	2,8,6	S^{-}	(f)

(6)

3 A hydrogen atom can be represented by the diagram:

(a) Draw a similar diagram to show the electrons in the outer shell of a chlorine atom. (1)
(b) Draw a dot and cross diagram to show the bonding in a molecule of hydrogen chloride. (2)
(c) Explain why hydrogen and chlorine form a single covalent bond. (2)
(d) Explain why silicon can form giant structures. (3)

- Question 1 could be answered by the students creating a labelled diagram of atomic structure, this would create a good revision aid.
- Question 2 could be turned into a card sort, with the diagrams on separate cards to the element that they are representing.

EXAM-STYLE ANSWERS

1 a) 2,8,3 *(1 mark)*

b) 13 *(1 mark)*

c) Neutrons *(1 mark)*

d) 3 *(1 mark)*

e) Dot at centre with two concentric circles, two crosses on first circle, eight crosses on outer circle, surrounded by brackets with 3+ at top right-hand side.
(All correct – 2 marks, one error – 1 mark)

2 a) 2,7 *(1 mark)*

b) F$^-$ *(1 mark)*

c) Na *(1 mark)*

d) [2,8]$^+$ (allow 2,8) *(1 mark)*

e) 16 *(1 mark)*

f) [2,8,8]$^{2-}$ (allow 2,8,8) *(1 mark)*

3 a) Cl or dot in centre of circle with seven crosses on the circle.
(1 mark)

b) Two circles intersecting, one with H at centre and one with Cl at centre, with a dot and cross at intersection, and six more dots or crosses on circle around Cl. *(2 marks)*

c) *One mark each for:*
- Both hydrogen and chlorine need to gain one electron for a stable structure
- so they share one pair of electrons/can only form one covalent bond. *(2 marks)*

(a) Draw a dot and cross diagram to show the arrangement of electrons in a magnesium ion. Show the charge on the ion. (3)

(b) Draw a dot and cross diagram to show the arrangement of electrons in an oxide ion. (3)

(c) What is the formula of magnesium oxide? (1)

Berzelius (1779–1848) carried out experiments to discover the atomic mass of many elements. He wrote about the fact that bodies combine in definite proportions and that led him to suggest the existence of a cause.

(a) Suggest an observation that Berzelius might have made. (1)

(b) Is what Berzelius wrote a prediction or a hypothesis? Explain your answer. (1)

(c) Berzelius gave oxygen the number 100 to represent its relative atomic mass. He then set out to compare the mass of other elements with oxygen. However, he could not measure these directly because they could not be turned into gases – the temperature needed was too high and he did not have the equipment to do this.

(i) Explain, in general terms, the problem he had. (1)

(ii) Use this example to explain the relationship between technology and science. (1)

The diagram represents atoms of potassium in the solid metal.

(a) What is the electronic structure of a potassium atom? (1)

(b) Explain as fully as you can how the atoms are held together in solid potassium metal. (3)

[Higher]

HOW SCIENCE WORKS QUESTIONS

How the atomic theory was developed

2,500 years ago, Democritus believed that matter could be broken into smaller and smaller pieces until finally there would be particles that were 'indivisible' – the Greek word for this is *atomos*. He thought they looked like this:

Humphry Davy, who went to Truro Grammar School, discovered many of the elements that we are familiar with in chemistry lessons. He separated potassium, sodium and chlorine. As he couldn't break these elements down any further, he said that this must be the definition of an element.

Dalton became convinced that each element was made of a different kind of atom. He can be credited with the first scientific use of the term 'atom', although the Greeks had used the idea thousands of years before.

Dalton believed that

- the atom must be very small,
- all matter is made from atoms, and
- these atoms cannot be destroyed.

He gave hydrogen the atomic weight of 1, because he knew it to be the lightest atom.

He thought water was made of 1 hydrogen and 1 oxygen atom and therefore predicted that oxygen must have an atomic weight of 7.

Berzelius, a Swedish chemist, tested Dalton's theory experimentally. He correctly found the atomic weights of 40 elements.

a) When was the first theory of the atom put forward? (1)

b) What observation led to the definition of an element? (1)

c) What hypothesis did Dalton come up with? (1)

d) What prediction was made by Dalton? (1)

e) Check in the periodic table whether Dalton's prediction was correct. (1)

f) What was Berzelius' contribution to the atomic theory? (1)

g) Is Dalton's atomic theory completely true? Explain your answer. (1)

103

Exam teaching suggestions

- The questions could be used when the chapter has been completed in a single session. If used in this way, allow 35 minutes (total 35 marks). Alternatively, Q1, Q2 and Q4 could be used after completing spread 1.4, and Q3 after spread 1.5.

- Students should be able to represent atoms and ions in the ways described in the specification. Use of different symbols (dots or crosses) for electrons can be helpful when considering bonding, but students should know that all electrons are identical. Students will not be penalised for using only one symbol in their answers, either dots or crosses, for all electrons in atoms. When drawing diagrams to show bonding, it is usual to show only the electrons in the highest energy level or outer shell.

- Many students think of ionic compounds in terms of pairs or triplets of ions rather than giant structures. It is important in teaching ionic bonding to distinguish between ion formation, which is often described as the transfer of electrons from one atom to another, and the bonding that holds the ions together in a giant lattice.

- When writing formulae for ionic compounds, as in Q4c), students should be encouraged to balance the charges on the ions by using multiples of the ions, but should then write the empirical formula of the compound without any charges. This avoids confusion when showing multiples of ions and the need for brackets around ions and their charges.

HOW SCIENCE WORKS ANSWERS

a) 2,500 years ago.

b) That certain pure substances could not be broken down any further.

c) Dalton's hypothesis was that each element was made of a different kind of atom. That the atom must be very small, that all matter is made from atoms and that these atoms cannot be destroyed.

d) Dalton's prediction was that oxygen must have an atomic weight of 7.

e) Dalton was not correct according to the periodic table, but of course he was not to know!

f) Berzelius tested Dalton's prediction. He found Dalton to be wrong in his prediction.

g) Dalton's atomic theory is largely still correct, but of course the atom has been split!

How science works teaching suggestions

- **Literacy guidance.** Key terms that should be clearly understood: observation, prediction, theory.

- **Higher- and lower-level answers.** Question f) is a higher level question and the answer provided above is also at this level. Questions a) and b) are lower level and the answers provided are also lower level.

- **Gifted and talented.** Able students could find other examples in the history of science on how hypotheses have led to predictions that have been tested and theories amended.

- **How and when to use these questions.** When wishing to develop ideas of how observation leads to hypothesis and then to prediction and testing of that prediction. The questions are probably best used as homework and then discussed in class.

- **Misconceptions.** That a hypothesis is the same as a prediction. To address this: stress the fact that the prediction is based on the hypothesis and is used to test it. If a prediction holds true then that lends support to the hypothesis.
  Another misconception is that observations are just the outcome of investigations and not the stimulus. To address this: this is the equivalent of drawing graphs and not using them to draw conclusions when you analyse your data! Observations, especially unexpected ones, prompt questions. The observation, if repeated when checked, will stimulate an investigation and a new hypothesis is made to explain the observation and then tested.

- **Homework.** The questions are probably best used as homework and then discussed in class.

---

d) *Three from:*
- Silicon has four electrons in its outer shell/highest energy level.
- So it can share four electrons.
- It forms four covalent bonds.
- The covalent bonds between silicon atoms are strong.

(3 marks)

4 a) *One mark each for:*
- Dot or Mg at centre of two concentric circles.
- Two crosses or dots on inner circle, eight dots or crosses on outer circle.
- Surrounded by brackets with 2+ outside top right-hand side.

(3 marks)

b) *One mark each for:*
- Dot or O at centre of two concentric circles.
- Two crosses or dots on inner circle, eight dots or crosses on outer circle
- Surrounded by brackets with 2− outside top right hand side.

(3 marks)

c) MgO *(accept $Mg^{2+}O^{2-}$)* *(1 mark)*

5 a) E.g. that when compounds are broken down they always do so in the same proportions. *(1 mark)*

b) A hypothesis – it cannot be directly used to design an investigation. *(1 mark)*

c) i) The technology had not been invented to allow him to investigate the science. *(1 mark)*
   ii) The idea that science and technology feed from each other. *(1 mark)*

6 a) 2,8,8,1 *(1 mark)*

b) *Three from:*
- The outer electrons move from one atom to the next one/delocalise.
- The (delocalised) electrons form a cloud or 'sea' of electrons.
- The electrons surround positive ions.
- (Delocalised) electrons strongly attract the positive ions.

(3 marks)
[HT only]

C2 2.1

Ionic compounds

Students should learn that:

- Ionic compounds are solids at room temperature and have high melting points.
- Ionic compounds conduct electricity when they are molten or dissolved in water.

Most students should be able to:

- State that ionic compounds have high melting points and are solid at room temperature.
- Describe how ionic compounds can conduct when they are molten or dissolved in water.

Some students should also be able to:

- Explain why ionic compounds have high melting points.
- Explain why ionic compounds can conduct electricity when molten or in solution.

Teaching suggestions

- **Special needs**
  - Instead of completing the practical with two ionic compounds, focus only on sodium chloride. This is a chemical that they have everyday experience of and is safe to use.
  - Provide the results' table for the students, so they just have to fill it in.

- **Learning styles**

  Kinaesthetic: Testing the different physical properties of ionic compounds.

  Visual: Looking at images to decide how they are connected.

  Auditory: Listening to explanations of the different physical properties of ionic compounds.

  Interpersonal: Working in groups to explain a certain physical property of ionic compounds.

  Intrapersonal: Making an individual set of revision cards.

- **Homework.** Students could choose an ionic compound and explain why it is used for a specific purpose, e.g. sodium fluoride is used in drinking water. [Fluoride has been found to make teeth stronger and sodium fluoride dissolves easily into the drinking water supply.]

SPECIFICATION LINK-UP   Unit: Chemistry 2.12.2

- *Ionic compounds have regular structures (giant ionic lattices) in which there are strong electrostatic forces in all directions between oppositely charged ions. These compounds have high melting points and high boiling points.*
- *When melted or dissolved in water, ionic compounds conduct electricity because the ions are free to move and carry the current.*

Students should use their skills, knowledge and understanding of 'How Science Works':

- *to relate the properties of the substances named in this unit to their uses.*
- *to suggest the type of structure of a substance given its properties.*

Lesson structure

STARTER

Pictures – Show students different images of sodium chloride (an ionic lattice, someone putting salt onto their chips, a chemical storage bottle of sodium chloride). Ask the students to work out what all the pictures have in common. (5 minutes)

List – Ask students to make a list of as many ionic substances as they can. Through question and answer, build up a list on the board and ask the students what they all have in common, other than that they have the same bonding [all will be compounds, most examples given will probably consist of a metal bonded to a non-metal]. (10 minutes)

Anagrams – Give the students this set of anagrams on the board; they should work out the key word and then define it:

- noi [Ion – a charged particle made when an atom loses or gains electrons]
- eeontrcl [Electron – negative particle that orbits the nucleus of an atom]
- ttalcei [Lattice – a 3D arrangement of particles in a giant structure]
- conii dobn [Ionic bond – the electrostatic force of attraction between oppositely charged ions] (10 minutes)

MAIN

- There are many examples of ionic compounds in everyday life, but rarely have students considered the properties of these substances. Encourage them to investigate the properties of sodium chloride and potassium chloride.
- Students should first design a table to record information about the appearance, hardness, melting point and conductivity in different states. As it will be near impossible to melt these substances using a Bunsen burner, encourage students to use reference material to find out in which states these substances will conduct.
- Give the students four same-coloured index cards. On one side, they should write a key physical property (high melting point, soluble in water and conducts in (aq) or (l)). Then on the reverse of each card, they should explain that property using key scientific terms and at least one labelled diagram.
- The fourth card should be a title card about ionic bonding. The cards could then be hole punched in a corner, as could the front of the student's exercise book. Using a piece of string the cards could be secured to the book and removed to add other revision cards about bonding.

PLENARIES

AfL (Assessment for Learning) – Give students an examination question about the properties of ionic compounds. Time the students (about 1 minute per mark). Then ask them to swap their answers with a partner, and give out mark schemes. Encourage the students to mark the work, as it is presented, no discussions about 'what they really meant'. Then swap the papers back, and you could collect in the marks. (10 minutes)

Summary – Split the class into three groups. Ask each team to explain why ionic compounds have certain physical properties (soluble in water, high melting point, conduct electricity when (l) or (aq)). Give each group a few minutes to come up with their explanations, then ask them to read these out to the class. (10 minutes)

Practical support

Testing conductivity
Equipment and materials required
Sodium chloride, potassium chloride, hand lens, mounted needle, spatula, two boiling tubes, boiling tube rack, boiling tube holder, Bunsen burner and safety equipment, two carbon electrodes, lab pack, two crocodile clips, three wires, lamp, beaker, wash bottle with water, glass rod, eye protection.

- The bulb does not light at first but does once the salt dissolves.
- The ions are stuck in position within the giant lattice. However, as the sodium chloride dissolves in water, ions become free to move, carrying charge between the electrodes and the bulb lights up.

Details
Students to investigate the following:

Appearance – Students to look at the crystal through a hand lens and draw a diagram of the crystal.

Hardness – Students to try to scratch the surface with a mounted needle, and view the area using the hand lens.

Melting point – Students to put about half a spatula of the compound into a boiling tube and then hold it just above the blue gas cone in a roaring Bunsen flame. The tube should be at an angle, not pointing at any faces and eye protection should be worn. They should keep it in the flame until they have decided if it has a high/low melting point – the compounds are unlikely to melt. Then they place the boiling tube on a flameproof mat to cool.

Conductivity – Students to put some sodium chloride/potassium chloride crystals into a beaker (to about a depth of 1 cm). They submerge the electrodes and connect them to a lamp and power supply. Then they turn on the power and make observations. Then they add water from the wash bottle (half fill the beaker) and observe. Encourage the students to swirl the beaker to help the ionic compound dissolve. **Safety:** Please note that this electrolysis will produce a small amount of chlorine gas, therefore it should be completed in a well-ventilated area and be aware of students with respiratory problems (e.g. asthma) as the gas can aggravate it.

Solubility – Students to half fill a beaker with warm water from the tap, then add a few crystals and swirl or stir with a glass rod.

ACTIVITY & EXTENSION IDEAS

- Other sets of coloured cards could be given to the students to makes notes about covalent and metallic bonding. These could be added to the set about ionic bonds.
- Students could be encouraged to explain other physical properties of ionic compounds, e.g. crystal structure and hardness in terms of the structure of the ionic lattice.

Answers to in-text questions

a) Attractive electrostatic forces.

b) Because of the strong attractive electrostatic forces holding the oppositely charged ions together.

c) Because the ions are free to move.

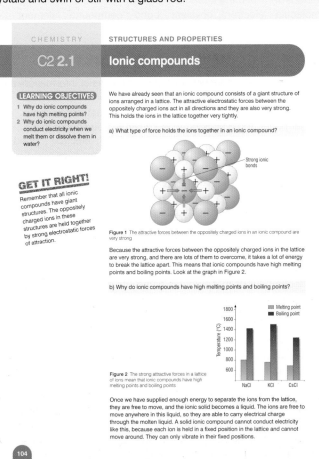

CHEMISTRY · STRUCTURES AND PROPERTIES

C2 2.1 Ionic compounds

LEARNING OBJECTIVES

1 Why do ionic compounds have high melting points?
2 Why do ionic compounds conduct electricity when we melt them or dissolve them in water?

We have already seen that an ionic compound consists of a giant structure of ions arranged in a lattice. The attractive electrostatic forces between the oppositely charged ions act in all directions and they are also very strong. This holds the ions in the lattice together very tightly.

a) What type of force holds the ions together in an ionic compound?

GET IT RIGHT!

Remember that all ionic compounds have giant structures. The oppositely charged ions in these structures are held together by strong electrostatic forces of attraction.

Figure 1 The attractive forces between the oppositely charged ions in an ionic compound are very strong

Because the attractive forces between the oppositely charged ions in the lattice are very strong, and there are lots of them to overcome, it takes a lot of energy to break the lattice apart. This means that ionic compounds have high melting points and boiling points. Look at the graph in Figure 2.

b) Why do ionic compounds have high melting points and boiling points?

Figure 2 The strong attractive forces in a lattice of ions mean that ionic compounds have high melting points and boiling points

Once we have supplied enough energy to separate the ions from the lattice, they are free to move, and the ionic solid becomes a liquid. The ions are free to move anywhere in this liquid, so they are able to carry electrical charge through the molten liquid. A solid ionic compound cannot conduct electricity like this, because each ion is held in a fixed position in the lattice and cannot move around. They can only vibrate in their fixed positions.

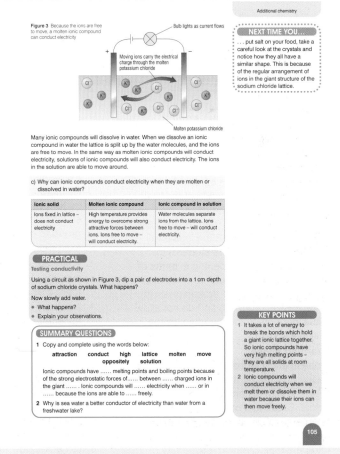

Figure 3 Because the ions are free to move, a molten ionic compound can conduct electricity

Many ionic compounds will dissolve in water. When we dissolve an ionic compound in water the lattice is split up by the water molecules, and the ions are free to move. In the same way as molten ionic compounds will conduct electricity, solutions of ionic compounds will also conduct electricity. The ions in the solution are able to move around.

c) Why can ionic compounds conduct electricity when they are molten or dissolved in water?

Ionic solid	Molten ionic compound	Ionic compound in solution
Ions fixed in lattice – does not conduct electricity	High temperature provides energy to overcome strong attractive forces between ions. Ions free to move – will conduct electricity.	Water molecules separate ions from the lattice. Ions free to move – will conduct electricity.

PRACTICAL

Testing conductivity

Using a circuit as shown in Figure 3, dip a pair of electrodes into a 1 cm depth of sodium chloride crystals. What happens?

Now slowly add water.
- What happens?
- Explain your observations.

SUMMARY QUESTIONS

1 Copy and complete using the words below:

attraction   conduct   high   lattice   molten   move
oppositely   solution

Ionic compounds have ...... melting points and boiling points because of the strong electrostatic forces of...... between ...... charged ions in the giant .... Ionic compounds will ...... electricity when ...... or in ...... because the ions are able to ...... freely.

2 Why is sea water a better conductor of electricity than water from a freshwater lake?

NEXT TIME YOU...

... put salt on your food, take a careful look at the crystals and notice how they all have a similar shape. This is because of the regular arrangement of ions in the giant structure of the sodium chloride lattice.

KEY POINTS

1 It takes a lot of energy to break the bonds which hold a giant ionic lattice together. So ionic compounds have very high melting points – they are all solids at room temperature.
2 Ionic compounds will conduct electricity when we melt them or dissolve them in water because their ions can then move freely.

SUMMARY ANSWERS

1 High, attraction, oppositely, lattice, conduct, molten, solution, move.

2 Because it contains dissolved salt (ions).

KEY POINTS

Ask the students to re-write the key points in their own words. This could be in a paragraph, question and answers or changing the bullet points so that it is not just copied.

C2 2.2   Simple molecules

LEARNING OBJECTIVES

Students should learn:

- The properties of substances made up of simple molecules.
- The reasons why simple molecular substances have low melting and boiling points. [**HT** only]
- That substances made up of simple molecules do not conduct electricity.

LEARNING OUTCOMES

Most students should be able to:

- Recognise substances made up of simple molecules.
- List examples of substances made up of simple molecules.
- State the physical properties of substances made up of simple molecules.

Some students should also be able to:

- Explain why substances made up of simple molecules have low melting and boiling points. [**HT** only]
- Explain why substances made up of simple molecules do not conduct electricity.

Teaching suggestions

- **Gifted and talented**
  - You, or the students, could put some iodine crystals into a conical flask and seal with a bung. Then heat the flask with running warm water and the iodine will sublime. Then run the flask under cold water and the iodine will solidify again. Ask the students to explain what is happening in terms of intermolecular forces.
  - **Safety:** Be aware of broken glass (if the flask is dropped) and do not allow the students to touch iodine, as the skin will stain.
- **Learning styles**
  Kinaesthetic: Choosing where to stand based on whether they agree or disagree with statements.
  Visual: Creating a mind-map.
  Interpersonal: Working as a group to make a mind-map.
  Intrapersonal: Creating a summary about the properties of simple covalent molecules.
- **Homework.** Find an example of a covalent compound, its melting and boiling point. Then relate this information to a use of it.

SPECIFICATION LINK-UP   Unit: Chemistry 2.12.2

- *Substances that consist of simple molecular gases, liquids or solids have relatively low melting points and boiling points.*
- *Substances that consist of simple molecules have only weak forces between the molecules (intermolecular forces). It is these intermolecular forces that are overcome, not the covalent bonds, when the substance melts or boils.* [**HT** only]
- *Substances that consist of simple molecules do not conduct electricity because the molecules do not have an overall electric charge.*

Students should use their skills, knowledge and understanding of 'How Science Works':

- *to relate the properties of the substances named in this unit to their uses.*
- *to suggest the type of structure of a substance given its properties.*

Lesson structure

STARTER

Models – Split the class into small groups. Ask for volunteers to draw the dot and cross diagrams of hydrogen, then instruct the groups to make a model (using a molecular model kit) of this diagram and hold it in the air so that you can easily check. Then repeat with the other simple molecules that the students should know: hydrogen chloride, water, oxygen, ammonia and methane. (15 minutes)

Crosswords – Create a crossword with the answers being key words that will be needed in the lesson: 'molecule', 'electron', 'covalent', 'bond', 'compound', 'element', 'dot and cross'. (10 minutes)

MAIN

- Students often find it difficult to make connections between pieces of information. A mind map can be a very useful tool to help them make links within a topic.
- Split the students into groups of about four, and give them a felt pen each, some Blu Tack, a piece of sugar paper and a pack of A6 word cards. You should make these cards in advance, including key words for this topic: 'atom', 'electron', 'bond', 'covalent', 'melting point', 'boiling point', 'intermolecular forces', 'insulator', 'molecule', 'solid', 'liquid', 'gas'.
- The students should stick two key words onto the page, one should be the start of the sentence the other the end. They should draw an arrow in the correct direction linking the words, then on the arrow write the middle section of the sentence. There is no limit to the number of arrows that can be drawn to and from each. You should circulate during this activity and suggest links by pointing to words and asking the group to consider how they link. Very good pieces could be highlighted as exemplars, and other groups could be encouraged to look at them for ideas.
- There are many covalent compounds that students come into contact with in everyday life, but they have probably not considered the properties of them. Give them a selection of covalently bonded compounds, e.g. water, ethanol, iodine, sulfur.
- Ask them to discuss, in groups, any similarities in appearance [dull]. Then they could experimentally determine the physical properties of this group of substances.
- If it is not possible to complete the practical, students could use data books to obtain melting point, boiling point and conductivity information.

PLENARIES

Stand by – Ask for a volunteer to stand in the centre of the classroom. They should say a statement about simple covalent molecules (for higher ability it could be their own idea, for lower ability there could be statement cards already prepared). The rest of the class decide how much they agree with this statement, the more they agree, the closer they should stand to the person who spoke. (5 minutes)

Summarise – Ask the students to summarise the physical properties of simple molecular compounds and give brief reasons for them in a bullet-point format. (10 minutes)

Practical support

Conductivity
Equipment and materials required
Beaker, water, carbon electrodes, lamp, power pack, wires, ethanol (flammable – CLEAPSS Hazcard 40), solid wax pieces.

Details
Half-fill a beaker with water and put in the carbon electrodes. Set up a simple circuit with a lamp and power pack, to see if the liquid conducts. Repeat the experiment with ethanol and solid wax pieces. (Keep ethanol away from any naked flames.)

Melting and boiling points
Equipment and materials required
Boiling tubes, boiling tube rack, boiling tube holder, Bunsen burner and safety equipment, thermometer, water, wax, eye protection.

Details
Ask students to predict whether covalent compounds have low or high melting/boiling points and why they think this. Get the students to prepare a results table.

They need to put a small piece of wax into a boiling tube and heat in a blue flame, noting the temperature that the wax begins to melt.

They then put about a 1 cm depth of water into a boiling tube and heat in a blue Bunsen flame, noting the temperature of boiling.

KEY POINTS
Students could create a limerick to remember these two key points.

- Information from data books including databases such as the CD-ROM *RSC Data Book* could be used to get melting point/boiling point/conductivity information. The data for a particular group of covalent compounds could be collected and students could represent this data in a bar chart format. (Or search for conductivity at www.wikipedia.org.)

- Gently heat sulfur in a mineral wool plugged ignition tube. The sulfur should melt. When the sulfur has melted, remove from the heat and take out the plug. In a fume cupboard, tip the sulfur into a beaker of cold water. The sulfur is now plastic and can be pulled into new shapes easily.

- Students should then endeavour to explain why changing its structure could change the properties of this element.

- **Safety:** Be careful not to burn the sulfur – as sulfur dioxide is produced, which is an irritant. Also, the liquid sulphur can cause nasty burns, even if it is run under cold water. (Sulfur is flammable – CLEAPSS Hazcard 96)

- Students could find out how the intermolecular forces between water molecules make ice less dense than liquid water.

CHEMISTRY — STRUCTURES AND PROPERTIES

C2 2.2 Simple molecules

LEARNING OBJECTIVES
1 Which type of substances have low melting points and boiling points?
2 Why are some substances gases or liquids at room temperature? [Higher]
3 Why don't these substances conduct electricity?

When the atoms of non-metal elements react to form compounds, they share electrons in their outer shells. Then each atom gets a full outer shell of electrons. The bonds formed like this are called **covalent bonds**.

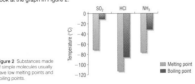

Figure 1 Covalent bonds hold the atoms found within molecules tightly together

a) How are covalent bonds formed?

Substances made up of covalently bonded molecules tend to have low melting points and boiling points.

Look at the graph in Figure 2.

Figure 2 Substances made of simple molecules usually have low melting points and boiling points

These low melting points and boiling points mean that many substances with simple molecules are liquids or gases at room temperature. Others are solids with quite low melting points, such as iodine and sulfur.

b) Do the compounds shown on the graph exist as solids, liquids or gases at room temperature of 20°C?

c) You have a sample of ammonia (NH_3) at $-120°C$. Describe the changes that you would see as the temperature of the ammonia rises to 20°C (approximately room temperature).

Covalent bonds are very strong. So the atoms within each molecule are held very tightly together. However, each molecule tends to be quite separate from its neighbouring molecules. The attraction between the individual molecules in a covalent compound tends to be small. We say that there are weak *intermolecular forces* between molecules. Overcoming these forces does not take much energy.

d) How strong are the forces between the atoms in a covalent bond?

e) How strong are the forces between molecules in a covalent compound?

The covalent bonds between the hydrogen and oxygen atoms within a water molecule are strong. However, the forces of attraction between water molecules are relatively weak.

Look at the molecules in a sample of chlorine gas:

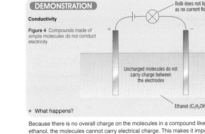

Figure 3 Covalent bonds and the weak forces between molecules in chlorine gas. It is the weak intermolecular forces that are overcome when substances made of simple molecules melt or boil. The covalent bonds are *not* broken.

GET IT RIGHT!
Although the covalent bonds in molecules are strong, the forces between molecules are weak. [Higher]

Although a substance that is made up of simple molecules may be a liquid at room temperature, it will not conduct electricity.

Look at the demonstration below.

DEMONSTRATION
Conductivity

Figure 4 Compounds made of simple molecules do not conduct electricity

- What happens?

Because there is no overall charge on the molecules in a compound like ethanol, the molecules cannot carry electrical charge. This makes it impossible for substances which are made up of simple molecules to conduct electricity.

f) Why don't molecular substances conduct electricity?

SUMMARY QUESTIONS

1 Copy and complete using the words below:

   boiling   covalent   melting   molecules   strongly

   Non-metals react to form ...... which are held together by ...... bonds. These hold the atoms together very .... The forces between molecules are relatively weak, so these substances have low ...... points and ...... points.

2 A compound called sulfur hexafluoride (SF_6) is used to stop sparks forming inside electrical switches designed to control large currents. Explain why the properties of this compound make it particularly useful in electrical switches.

3 The melting point of hydrogen chloride is $-115°C$ whereas sodium chloride melts at 801°C. Explain why. [Higher]

KEY POINTS
1 Substances made up of simple molecules have low melting points and boiling points.
2 The forces between simple molecules are weak. These weak intermolecular forces explain their low melting points and boiling points. [Higher]
3 Simple molecules have no overall charge, so they cannot carry electrical charge. Therefore substances containing simple molecules do not conduct electricity.

106 / 107

SUMMARY ANSWERS

1 Molecules, covalent, strongly, melting, boiling.

2 It is a (simple) molecular substance so it doesn't conduct electricity, it has a low boiling point so it is a gas at normal temperatures.

3 To separate the oppositely charged sodium and chloride ions requires a lot of energy to overcome the strong electrostatic forces of attraction operating in every direction. In hydrogen chloride, there are only weak forces of attraction between individual HCl molecules so they require far less energy to separate them (no covalent bonds are broken in the process of melting.) [**HT** only]

Answers to in-text questions

a) By sharing pairs of electrons.

b) Gases.

c) It would be a solid to start with but at about $-80°C$ it would melt into a liquid. Then at about $-35°C$ it would boil to form ammonia gas. At 20°C it remains a gas.

d) Very strong.

e) Weak (compared to the forces between atoms held together by a covalent bond).

f) There are no charged particles to carry the electric current.

C2 2.3

Giant covalent substances

Teaching suggestions

- **Special needs.** Supply these students with diagrams of the structure of diamond and graphite. On a separate sheet include the labels for the diagram and encourage the students to annotate their work.

- **Learning styles**

  Kinaesthetic: Handling samples of giant covalent compounds.

  Visual: Creating an A-map.

  Auditory: Listening to explanations of the key words.

  Interpersonal: Working in groups explaining key terms.

  Intrapersonal: Making a poster to contrast the properties of carbon allotropes.

- **Homework.** Students could find out a use for graphite and explain which property makes it suitable to this use.

- **ICT link-up.** Use C2 2.3 'Giant covalent' from the Additional Science CD ROM.

SPECIFICATION LINK-UP   Unit: Chemistry 2.12.2

- *Atoms that share electrons can also form giant structures or macromolecules. Diamond and graphite (forms of carbon) and silicon dioxide (silica) are examples of giant covalent structures (lattices) of atoms. All the atoms in the structure are linked to other atoms by strong covalent bonds and so they have high melting points.*

- *In diamond each carbon atom forms four covalent bonds with other carbon atoms in a rigid, giant covalent structure, so diamond is very hard.*

- *In graphite, each carbon atom bonds to three others, forming layers. The layers are free to slide over each other and so graphite is soft and slippery.*

- *In graphite, one electron from each carbon atom is delocalised. These delocalised electrons allow graphite to conduct heat and electricity. [**HT** only]*

Students should use their skills, knowledge and understanding of 'How Science Works':

- *to relate the properties of the substance named in this unit to their uses.*

- *to suggest the type of structure of a substance given its properties.*

Lesson structure

STARTER

List – Show students different images of diamonds – in the raw state, in jewellery, and on a saw. Ask the students to list different uses of diamonds, and then ask for a few suggestions. (5 minutes)

Word search – Give students a word search about covalent bonding; however do not include the words. Encourage students to think about the topic and use the double page spread in the students' book to work out which words they should be finding. (10 minutes)

MAIN

- Although graphite and diamond are both carbon, they have completely different structures. Give students some graphite to handle (this may be a bit messy!) and if it is possible samples of diamonds to study. Brainstorm the different properties of each of these materials, but explain they are the same element.

- Ask students to make a poster to contrast the properties of these two substances and explain them in terms of their structures.

- Students could use the textbook for information to create an A-map about giant covalent structures. They should select three colours. In the centre of the page, in one colour only, they should write the key phrase 'Giant covalent structures' and draw a small image that might help them to remember this. This colour is then not used again. The second colour is then used to create four long, wavy lines. Following the contour of the line, the student should write 'formation', 'graphite', 'diamond' and 'silica' on separate lines, each including an image.

- Each idea is then added to, with a third colour, again with wavy lines. Each line again should contain key words or phrases to summarise that branch of thought, and include an image to help the student remember.

- Encourage the students to complete one branch before moving to the next.

PLENARIES

Explain – Split the students into pairs, and give them a pack of cards with key terms on it: 'graphite', 'diamond', 'silica', 'delocalised electrons', 'lattice'. The cards should be face down in front of the group. Each student should take it in turns to take a card and try to explain the key term, but the guesser must draw a labelled diagram to match the key term. (10 minutes)

Models – Show the students molecular models of diamond and graphite. Ask them to list down the similarities and the differences. Ask for a volunteer to scribe onto the board. Then through questions and answers, build up bullet points onto the board. (10 minutes)

- Graphite is used in pencil leads. Encourage students to research how the different hardness (e.g. H and HB) of pencils is achieved.

- Students could research into other allotropes of carbon, e.g. Bucky balls and Bucky tubes.

Answers to in-text questions

a) Giant covalent (lattice).

b) High melting and boiling points.

c) The layers of carbon atoms can easily slide over each other.

d) These are delocalised (free) electrons.

CHEMISTRY   STRUCTURES AND PROPERTIES

C2 2.3   Giant covalent substances

LEARNING OBJECTIVES

1 How do substances with giant covalent structures behave?

2 Why is diamond hard and graphite slippery?

3 Why can graphite conduct electricity? [Higher]

While most non-metals react and form covalent bonds which join the atoms together in molecules, a few form very different structures. Instead of joining a small number of atoms together in individual molecules, the covalent bonds form large networks of covalent bonds. We call networks like this giant covalent structures. They are sometimes called macromolecules or giant molecular structures.

Substances such as diamond, graphite and silicon dioxide have giant covalent structures.

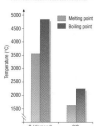

Figure 2 The large attractive forces in a giant lattice of covalently bonded atoms means that these compounds have high melting points and boiling points

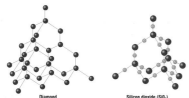

Diamond   Silicon dioxide (SiO₂)

Figure 1 The structures of diamond and silicon dioxide (sand)

All of the atoms in these giant lattices are held together by strong covalent bonds in both diamond and silicon dioxide. This gives these substances some very special properties. They are very hard, they have high melting points and boiling points and they are chemically very unreactive.

a) What do we call the structure of compounds which contain lots (millions) of atoms joined together by a network of covalent bonds?

b) What kind of physical properties do these substances have?

DID YOU KNOW?

Diamond is the hardest natural substance that we know. Artificial diamonds can be made by heating pure carbon to very high temperatures under enormous pressures. The 'industrial diamonds' made like this are used in the drill bits which oil companies use when they drill through rocks looking for oil.

Figure 3 Hard, shiny and transparent – diamonds make beautiful jewellery

We don't always find carbon as diamonds – another form is graphite (well known as the 'lead' in a pencil). In graphite, carbon atoms are arranged in giant layers. There are only weak forces between the layers so they can slide over each other quite easily.

c) Why is graphite slippery?

HIGHER

Another important property of graphite comes from the fact that there are free electrons within its structure. These free electrons allow graphite to conduct electricity, which diamond – and most other covalent compounds – simply cannot do. We call the free electrons found in graphite delocalised electrons. They behave rather like the electrons in a metallic structure.

The carbon atoms in graphite's layers are arranged in hexagons. So each carbon atom bonds to three others. (See Figure 4.) This leaves one spare outer electron on each carbon atom. It is this electron that becomes delocalised along the layers of carbon atoms.

d) Why can graphite conduct electricity?

Fullerenes

Apart from diamond and graphite, there are other different molecules that carbon can produce. In these structures the carbon atoms join together to make large cages which can have all sorts of weird shapes. Chemists have made shapes looking like balls, onions, tubes, doughnuts, corkscrews and cones!

Chemists discovered carbon's ability to behave like this in 1985. We call the large carbon molecules containing these cage structures fullerenes. They are sure to become very important in nanoscience applications. (See pages 112 and 113.)

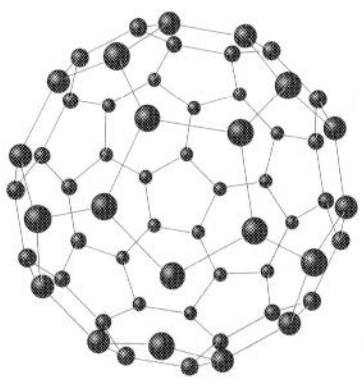

Figure 4 The giant structure of graphite. When you write with a pencil, some layers of carbon atoms slide off the 'lead' and are left on the paper.

GET IT RIGHT!

Giant covalent structures are held together by covalent bonds throughout the structure.

Figure 5 The first fullerene to be discovered contained only 60 carbon atoms, but chemists can now make *giant fullerenes* which contain many thousands of carbon atoms. Scientists can now place other molecules inside these carbon cages. This has exciting possibilities, including the delivery of drugs to specific parts of the body.

KEY POINTS

1 Some covalently bonded substances contain giant structures.

2 These substances have high melting points and boiling points.

3 The giant structure of graphite contains layers of atoms that can slide over each other which make graphite slippery. The atoms in diamond have a different structure and cannot slide like this – so diamond is a very hard substance.

4 Graphite can conduct electricity because of the delocalised electrons along its layers. [Higher]

SUMMARY QUESTIONS

1 Copy and complete using the words below:

atoms   boiling   carbon   hard   high   layers   slide   soft

Giant covalent structures contain many …… joined by covalent bonds. They have …… melting points and …… points. Diamond is a very …… substance because the …… atoms in it are held strongly to each other. However, graphite is …… because there are …… of atoms which can …… over each other.

2 Graphite is sometimes used to reduce the friction between two surfaces that are rubbing together. How does it do this?

3 Explain in detail why graphite can conduct electricity but diamond cannot. [Higher]

SUMMARY ANSWERS

1 Atoms, high, boiling, hard, carbon, soft, layers, slide.

2 The graphite is used to coat the two surfaces. As they rub together the layers of atoms in the graphite slip over each other, reducing the friction.

3 Graphite can conduct electricity because of the delocalised (free) electrons in its structure. These arise because each carbon is only bonded to 3 other carbon atoms. This leaves one electron to become delocalised. However, in diamond all 4 outer electrons on each carbon atom are involved in covalent bonding so there are no delocalised electrons. **[HT only]**

DID YOU KNOW?

Life Gem is a company that offers to cremate pets and humans in a special way, which turns them into diamonds. Encourage students to use the Internet to look up this idea.

KEY POINTS

Ask the students to copy out the key points and highlight any key words in their notes.

C2 2.4 Giant metallic structures

LEARNING OBJECTIVES

Students should learn:

- That metals conduct electricity and heat, and can be bent and shaped.
- Why metals can be bent and shaped.
- Why metals can conduct electricity and heat. [**HT** only]

LEARNING OUTCOMES

Most students should be able to:

- State the physical properties of metals.
- Match the uses of certain metals with specific properties.
- Explain in detail why metals are malleable and ductile.

Some students should also be able to:

- Explain why metals conduct electricity and heat in terms of delocalised electrons in their structures. [**HT** only]

Teaching suggestions

- **Learning styles**

  Kinaesthetic: Standing up or sitting down to show the answer to questions.

  Visual: Using magazine images to create a poster to explain metal properties.

  Auditory: Listening to explanations of the statement 'metal ions in a sea of electrons'.

  Interpersonal: Working in groups explaining the statement 'metal ions in a sea of electrons'.

  Intrapersonal: Making a poster to explain metal properties.

- **ICT link-up.** Set up flexi-cam and connect to a digital projector or a TV. Then focus in on the bubble raft experiment. Using the image you can then explain how this experiment relates to the structure of metals.

Answers to in-text questions

a) Because the layers of atoms can slide over each other when sufficient force is applied.

b) By delocalised electrons from the outer energy levels of the metal atoms.

c) Through the delocalised electrons being able to move through the metal lattice.

SPECIFICATION LINK-UP   Unit: Chemistry 2.12.2

- *Metals conduct heat and electricity because of the delocalised electrons in their structure. [**HT** only]*
- *The layers of atoms in metals are able to slide over each other and so metals can be bent into shape.*

Students should use their skills, knowledge and understanding of 'How Science Works':

- *to relate the properties of the substances named in this unit to their uses.*
- *to suggest the type of structure of a substance given its properties.*

Lesson structure

STARTER

Circle of truth – This is an interactive, self-marking exercise designed to be used on an interactive whiteboard. To create this activity, open board-specific interactive whiteboard software, or PowerPoint®. Firstly, in a text box, type in the title: 'Which are properties of metals?' Then in a small font size, and in separate text boxes, write the wrong answers e.g.: 'dull', 'brittle' and 'insulator'. Then draw a circle, you may wish to add the text 'circle of truth' and group the objects. This circle should occlude the previously written text, i.e. the wrong answers. Then, in separate text boxes write the correct answers: 'ductile', 'malleable', 'conductor', 'shiny' and 'sonorous'. To use this activity, ask the students for volunteers to come to the board and suggest an answer to the question [Which are the properties of metals?]. They should then move (by dragging) the circle to their answer. If they are correct the answer is still visible; if it is incorrect, then the circle will cover the answer. (5 minutes)

Flash boards – Give the students A4 whiteboards (or laminated paper), a washable pen and eraser. Ask the students to draw an electronic diagram of a metal of their choice, and then hold their answer up to you (these should be dot and cross diagrams). Instant praise can be given. Students can also play the game and use their textbook to help them or look at other people's answer and teacher response. Then ask the students to draw a diagram of a metal structure (as shown in the text book). You could pose other questions about metals. (5 minutes)

MAIN

- Metals are used in everyday life, but often students do not consider which properties make it useful for certain jobs. Give the students adverts or catalogues to look through.
- Ask the students to pick items that use metals and cut them out. They could then make a poster using these items, explaining which part is metal.
- Students could then explain the useful property in terms of metallic bonding. It is important that each poster contains an example of a metal conducting heat, a metal conducting electricity, a metal being ductile and a metal being malleable.
- Metal properties can be modelled in a variety of ways. Show the students any pre-made molecular models that the school may have. Soap bubbles can be used to represent metal atoms and show ductility and malleability.
- Students should then explain their results relating the model to metallic bonding.
- Show the students Animation C2 2.4 'Metals' from the Additional Science CD ROM.

ACTIVITY & EXTENSION IDEAS

- Metals atoms stack in different layers, e.g. ABAB or ABCABC. Encourage students to find out different atoms arrangements in different metals.
- Some metals are more useful for certain jobs, but substitutes are used, e.g. silver is the best metal electrical conductor, but it degrades easily; so other metals, e.g. gold, are used for satellites. Ask students to find other interesting uses and facts about metals.

Practical support
Blowing bubbles

Equipment and materials required
Petri dish, pointed end of a dropping pipette, dropping pipette, soap solution, rubber tubing to connect to gas tap.

Details
Students should, using the pipette, blow similar-sized bubbles into the Petri dish. They observe and then blow different-sized bubbles using a normal dropping pipette and observe.

KEY POINTS

Pick famous people (either in the wider world or the school community) and put their names into a bag. Ask for volunteers to come to pick out a name, they should then read the key points in character.

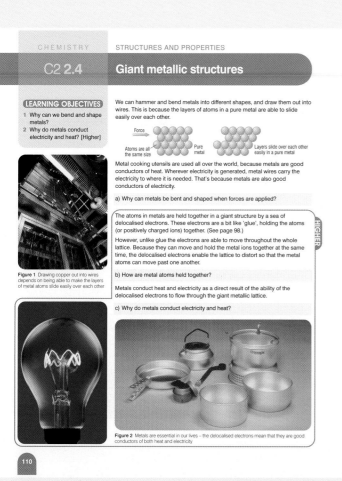

CHEMISTRY   STRUCTURES AND PROPERTIES

C2 2.4 Giant metallic structures

LEARNING OBJECTIVES
1 Why can we bend and shape metals?
2 Why do metals conduct electricity and heat? [Higher]

We can hammer and bend metals into different shapes, and draw them out into wires. This is because the layers of atoms in a pure metal are able to slide easily over each other.

Force →
Atoms are all the same size — Pure metal — Layers slide over each other easily in a pure metal

Metal cooking utensils are used all over the world, because metals are good conductors of heat. Wherever electricity is generated, metal wires carry the electricity to where it is needed. That's because metals are also good conductors of electricity.

a) Why can metals be bent and shaped when forces are applied?

The atoms in metals are held together in a giant structure by a sea of delocalised electrons. These electrons are a bit like 'glue', holding the atoms (or positively charged ions) together. (See page 98.)

However, unlike glue the electrons are able to move throughout the whole lattice. Because they can move and hold the metal ions together at the same time, the delocalised electrons enable the lattice to distort so that the metal atoms can move past one another.

b) How are metal atoms held together?

Metals conduct heat and electricity as a direct result of the ability of the delocalised electrons to flow through the giant metallic lattice.

c) Why do metals conduct electricity and heat?

Figure 1 Drawing copper out into wires depends on being able to make the layers of metal atoms slide easily over each other

Figure 2 Metals are essential in our lives – the delocalised electrons mean that they are good conductors of both heat and electricity

PRACTICAL
Making models of metals

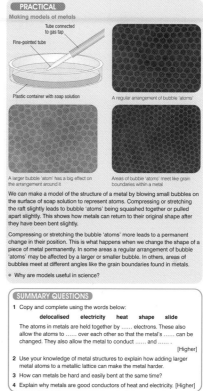

Tube connected to gas tap
Fine-pointed tube
Plastic container with soap solution
A regular arrangement of bubble 'atoms'

A larger bubble 'atom' has a big effect on the arrangement around it

Areas of bubble 'atoms' meet like grain boundaries within a metal

We can make a model of the structure of a metal by blowing small bubbles on the surface of soap solution to represent atoms. Compressing or stretching the raft slightly leads to bubble 'atoms' being squashed together or pulled apart slightly. This shows how metals can return to their original shape after they have been bent slightly.

Compressing or stretching the bubble 'atoms' more leads to a permanent change in their position. This is what happens when we change the shape of a piece of metal permanently. In some areas a regular arrangement of bubble 'atoms' may be affected by a larger or smaller bubble. In others, areas of bubbles meet at different angles like the grain boundaries found in metals.

- Why are models useful in science?

SUMMARY QUESTIONS

1 Copy and complete using the words below:

   delocalised   electricity   heat   shape   slide

   The atoms in metals are held together by ...... electrons. These also allow the atoms to ...... over each other so that the metal's ...... can be changed. They also allow the metal to conduct ...... and ....
   [Higher]

2 Use your knowledge of metal structures to explain how adding larger metal atoms to a metallic lattice can make the metal harder.

3 How can metals be hard and easily bent at the same time?

4 Explain why metals are good conductors of heat and electricity. [Higher]

NEXT TIME YOU...
... get in a car, ride your bike or use anything made of metal, think how the metal object you are using has been made from a piece of metal with a very different shape. The fact that you can use it depends on the way that the layers of metal atoms can be persuaded to slide over each other!

KEY POINTS
1 We can bend and shape metals because the layers of atoms (or ions) in a metal can slide over each other.
2 Delocalised electrons in metals allow them to conduct heat and electricity well. [Higher]

110   111

PLENARIES

Explain – Split the class into small groups to discuss a phrase. Bonding in metals can be described as 'metal ions in a sea of electrons'. Encourage the students to explain what this statement means. Choose some groups to feedback to the rest of the class. (5 minutes)

True or false – Ask the students to stand up if they think the fact is true, and remain seated if they think the fact is false.
- All metals are conductors of heat. [True]
- Metals are the best conductors of heat. [False – diamond is a better conductor at room temperature.]
- Metals are listed on the left of the periodic table. [True]
- Metals are ductile and dull. [False]
- The free electrons in metals allow the material to conduct electricity and heat. [True]
(5 minutes)

SUMMARY ANSWERS

1 Delocalised, slide, shape, heat (electricity), electricity (heat).

2 This helps to stop the layers of metal atoms sliding over each other.

3 Because the atoms are held tightly together, so the metal resists sudden changes to its shape. However, force applied carefully in the right way will change the shape of the metal as the layers of atoms slide over each other.

4 The delocalised electrons in their structures carry the charge through a metal when it conducts electricity, and the energy through it when it conducts heat. [**HT** only]

C2 2.5 Nanoscience and nanotechnology

SPECIFICATION LINK-UP
Unit: Chemistry 2.12.2

- *Nanoscience refers to structures that are 1–100 nm in size, of the order of a few hundred atoms. Nanoparticles show different properties to the same materials in bulk and have a high surface area to volume ratio which may lead to new computers, new catalysts, new coatings, highly selective sensors, and stronger and lighter construction materials.*

Students should use their skills, knowledge and understanding of 'How Science Works':

- *to evaluate developments and applications of new materials, e.g. nanomaterials, smart materials.*

CHEMISTRY   STRUCTURES AND PROPERTIES

C2 2.5 Nanoscience and nanotechnology

The science of tiny things – what can we do?

Nanoscience

Nanoscience is a new and exciting area of science. 'Nano' is a prefix like 'milli' or 'mega'. While 'milli' means 'one-thousandth', 'nano' means 'one-thousand-millionth' – so nanoscience is the science of really tiny things.

What is nanoscience?

Our increasing understanding of science through the 20th century means that we now know that materials behave very differently at a very tiny scale. When we arrange atoms and molecules very carefully at this tiny scale, their properties can be truly remarkable.

Nanoscience at work

Glass can be coated with titanium oxide nanoparticles. Sunshine triggers a chemical reaction that breaks down dirt which then lands on the window. When it rains the water spreads evenly over the surface of the glass washing off the dirt.

Socks that are made from a fabric which contains silver nanoparticles never smell!

A type of lizard called a gecko can hang upside down from a sheet of glass. That's because the hairs on its feet are so tiny they can use the forces that hold molecules together. Scientists can make sticky tape lined with tiny nano-hairs that work in the same way.

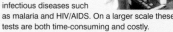

Using nanoscience, health workers may soon be able to test a single drop of blood on a tiny piece of plastic no bigger than a ten pence piece. The tiny nanolab would replace individual tests for infectious diseases such as malaria and HIV/AIDS. On a larger scale these tests are both time-consuming and costly.

Nanoscience can do some pretty amazing things – these toy eyes are being moved using a tiny current from an electric battery

But some nanoscience is pure science fiction – tiny subs that travel through your blood to zap cancer cells with a laser; self-reproducing nanobots that escape and cover the Earth in 'grey goo' – only in airport novels!

112

Teaching suggestions

Activities

- **Scientific ethics** – Write each of the headlines onto flip-chart paper and put on each wall of the classroom.

- Split the group into pairs and ask them to consider each headline in turn and discuss the issues. Then allow the teams to circulate around the papers to mark on their thoughts.

- Now split the class into quarters and give each set the flip-chart paper for the headline they are considering. Allow this large group to make a 3 minute long presentation about their issue, considering whether it is possible and if we should do it. (This relates to 'How Science Works': the questions science can and cannot answer.)

- To extend this activity, students could make a PowerPoint® presentation to illustrate their talk. They could then present their work, and at the end there should be a question section, where the audience can put points to the group about their issue.

- **Poster** – Show the students examples of the RSC poster campaign 'Not all chemist wear white coats'. Then ask students to design their own poster with nanotechnology in mind.

- **PhotoPlus** – Show students the PhotoPLUS C2 2.5 'Nanotechnology' from the Additional Science CD ROM.

Homework

- **Definitions** – Ask students to define the terms 'nanoscience', 'nanometer' and 'nanoparticles'. Their definition should include a text definition and a labelled diagram.

Extension

- **New materials** – Encourage students to research how nanotechnology could impact on new computers, catalysts, coatings, sensors and construction materials. They could use the Internet to find one example of how nanotechnology has made improvements in the aforementioned areas.
(See www.nano.org.uk or search for 'nanotechnology applications'.)

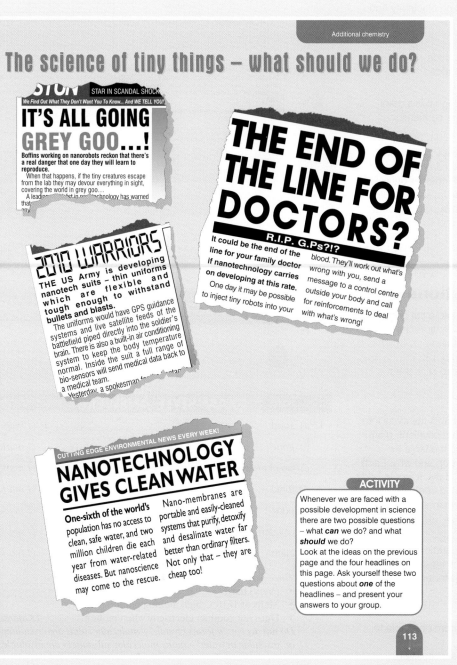

The science of tiny things – what should we do?

STUN STAR IN SCANDAL SHOCK
We Find Out What They Don't Want You To Know... And WE TELL YOU!

IT'S ALL GOING GREY GOO...!

Boffins working on nanorobots reckon that there's a real danger that one day they will learn to reproduce.

When that happens, if the tiny creatures escape from the lab they may devour everything in sight, covering the world in grey goo...

A leading scientist in nanotechnology has warned that any...

THE END OF THE LINE FOR DOCTORS?
R.I.P. G.Ps?!?

It could be the end of the line for your family doctor if nanotechnology carries on developing at this rate.

One day it may be possible to inject tiny robots into your blood. They'll work out what's wrong with you, send a message to a control centre outside your body and call for reinforcements to deal with what's wrong!

2010 WARRIORS

THE US Army is developing nanotech suits – thin uniforms which are flexible and tough enough to withstand bullets and blasts.

The uniforms would have GPS guidance systems and live satellite feeds of the battlefield piped directly into the soldier's brain. There is also a built-in air conditioning system to keep the body temperature normal. Inside the suit a full range of bio-sensors will send medical data back to a medical team.

Yesterday, a spokesman for the centre...

CUTTING EDGE ENVIRONMENTAL NEWS EVERY WEEK!

NANOTECHNOLOGY GIVES CLEAN WATER

One-sixth of the world's population has no access to clean, safe water, and two million children die each year from water-related diseases. But nanoscience may come to the rescue.

Nano-membranes are portable and easily-cleaned systems that purify, detoxify and desalinate water far better than ordinary filters. Not only that – they are cheap too!

ACTIVITY

Whenever we are faced with a possible development in science there are two possible questions – what *can* we do? and what *should* we do?

Look at the ideas on the previous page and the four headlines on this page. Ask yourself these two questions about *one* of the headlines – and present your answers to your group.

113

- The ideas could be listed on the board and at the end of the lesson, students could vote which one they think is the best development. Then ask a few students why they voted the way they did.

Learning styles

Kinaesthetic: Handling zeolites and models of zeolites.

Visual: Creating a poster about nanotechnology.

Auditory: Listening to opinions from other people.

Interpersonal: Working in a group to make a presentation.

Intrapersonal: Defining key terms.

Gifted and talented

School might have some examples of natural zeolites and structures of them. Ask students to research the role of zeolites and nanotechnology in developing new catalysts.

Special needs

The definitions and the key words could be supplied to these students; they could then match them up.

ICT link-up

Images of nanoparticles can be found by completing an image search on Google. These images could be shown or printed out for them to use in their written work.

SUMMARY ANSWERS

1 a) D **b)** A **c)** B **d)** C

2 The ionic compound is sealed in a container with two electrodes and placed in the reactor. It is connected into an electrical warning circuit. If the temperature reaches 800°C in the reactor the compound will melt, conducting electricity and activating the alarm.

3 a) Giant covalent: graphite, silicon dioxide.
   Giant ionic: aluminium oxide, sodium bromide.
   Molecular: hydrogen chloride, carbon dioxide.
   Metallic: copper, nickel.

b) Graphite – it conducts electricity even though it is a giant covalent compound, because the structure contains delocalised electrons.

4 Metals and graphite conduct electricity because both contain delocalised (free) electrons that can flow and carry an electric current. Layers of atoms in graphite are held together only weakly by these delocalised electrons, so the layers are able to slide easily over each other, making graphite soft. Although layers of atoms can slide over each other in metals, this does not happen so easily, and metals are therefore hard.

[**HT** only]

Summary teaching suggestions

- **Special needs** – Question 1 could be turned into a cut and stick activity, if you type in the sentences into Word (ensure the font is suitable, e.g. 14 point Comic Sans) and print them out. Cut the sentences in the same place as in the Student Book. The students can then physically match them up and stick them directly into their books.

- **When to use the questions?**
  - Question 3 can be used in a class exercise. Split the class into four groups and give each a specialism (giant covalent, giant ionic, molecular, metallic). Their job is to use the table to decide which substances belong to their group and why. Each group should then feedback verbally to the class. It would add something to have these substances in sealed containers so that the students could look at them if they wished.
  - These questions could be used as homework, as questions 1 and 2 match section 2.1 'Ionic compounds'.
  - These questions could be used as test preparation, where the students attempt the questions for half of the lesson. Then, in the second half, answers are given out and students mark each others' work.

- **Learning styles**
  Visual: Question 3 involves transferring data from one table to another table.
  Auditory: Question 4 could be used in a class discussion.

- **Misconceptions** – Often students are adamant that covalent bonds are weaker than ionic bonds and this is why simple molecular substances have a low melting point. It is vital that they understand that when you melt a simple molecular substance, no covalent bonds are broken; just the weak intermolecular forces of attraction between molecules. Stress to students that ionic bonds are about the same strength as covalent bonds.

STRUCTURES AND PROPERTIES: C2 2.1 – C2 2.5

SUMMARY QUESTIONS

1 Match the sentence halves together:

a) Ionic compounds have	A	...... conduct electricity when molten or in solution.
b) Ionic compounds	B	...... held together by strong electrostatic forces.
c) The oppositely charged ions in an ionic compound are	C	...... a giant lattice of ions.
d) Ionic compounds are made of	D	...... high melting points.

2 A certain ionic compound melts at exactly 800°C. Suggest how this compound could be used in a device to activate a warning light and buzzer when the temperature in a chemical reactor rises above 800°C.

3 The table contains data about some different substances.

Substance	Melting point (°C)	Boiling point (°C)	Electrical conductor
nickel	1455	2730	good
carbon dioxide	–	−78	poor
aluminium oxide	2072	2980	solid – poor liquid – good
copper	1083	2567	good
sodium bromide	747	1390	solid – poor liquid – good
silicon dioxide	1610	2230	poor
hydrogen chloride	−115	−85	poor
graphite	3652	4827	good

a) Make a table with the following headings: Giant covalent, Giant ionic, Molecular, Giant metallic. Now write the name of each substance above in the correct column.

b) One of these substances behaves in a slightly different way than its structure suggests – why?

4 'Both graphite and metals can conduct electricity – but graphite is soft while metals are not.' Use your knowledge of the different structures of graphite and metals to explain this statement.   [Higher]

EXAM-STYLE QUESTIONS

1 The table contains information about some substances. Complete the missing information (a) to (g).

Melting point (°C)	Boiling point (°C)	Electrical conductivity when solid	Electrical conductivity when molten	Solubility in water	Type of bonding	Type of structure
1660	3287	(a)	good	insoluble	metallic	giant
−101	−35	poor	(b)	soluble	covalent	(c)
712	1418	poor	good	soluble	(d)	giant
−25	144	(e)	poor	insoluble	(f)	small molecules
1410	2355	poor	poor	insoluble	covalent	(g)

(7

2 Quartz is a very hard mineral that is used as an abrasive. It is insoluble in water. It is a form of silica, SiO_2. It can form large, attractive crystals that are transparent and can be used for jewellery. It melts at 1610°C. It does not conduct electricity when solid or when molten. It is used in the form of sand in the building and glass-making industries.

(a) Give **three** pieces of evidence from the passage that tell you that quartz has a giant structure.   (3

(b) What type of bonding is in quartz? Explain your answer.   (2

3 Copper can be used to make electrical wires, water pipes, and cooking pans.

(a) Suggest **three** reasons why copper is used to make cooking pans.   (3

(b) Which **two** properties of copper depend on the ability of delocalised electrons to flow through the metal?   (2

(c) Explain what happens to the atoms in the metal when a piece of copper is pulled into a wire.   (2
[Higher]

4 Nanotechnology promises to revolutionise our world. Nanoparticles and new devices are being rapidly developed but production is still on a very small scale. The properties of nanoparticles that make them useful can cause problems if they are made in large quantities. These include explosions because of spontaneous combustion on contact with air.

114

EXAM-STYLE ANSWERS

1 a) good   *(1 mark)*

b) poor   *(1 mark)*

c) small molecules   *(1 mark)*

d) ionic   *(1 mark)*

e) poor   *(1 mark)*

f) covalent   *(1 mark)*

g) giant   *(1 mark)*

2 a) *Three from:*
- (Very) hard.
- Melts at 1610°C/high melting point.
- Does not conduct electricity when molten.   *(3 marks)*

Do not accept: 'it forms crystals' – molecular solids are crystalline or 'insoluble in water' – many molecular substances are insoluble.

b) Covalent   *(1 mark)*
One from:
- Silicon and oxygen are non-metals.
- Silicon and oxygen both need to gain electrons.   *(1 mark)*

3 a) *Three from:*
- Good conductor of heat.
- Does not corrode/is not attacked by food or water or acids.
- Can be bent/pressed into shape.
- Is not brittle/does not break/is hard.
- High melting point/does not melt at cooking temperatures.   *(3 marks)*

Do not allow 'good conductor of electricity'

b) *One mark each for:*
- Conduction of electricity.
- Conduction of heat.   *(2 marks)*

c) *Two from:*
- Layers of atoms slide over each other.
- Atoms slip into new positions.

(a) What are nanoparticles? (2)

(b) Suggest **two** reasons why nanotechnology is being developed rapidly. (2)

(c) Why are nanoparticles more likely to catch fire when exposed to air compared with normal materials? (2)

Piezoceramics are smart materials that can be made to vibrate by passing an electric current through them. They can be made small enough to work inside mobile phones.

(a) Suggest a possible economic advantage of piezoceramics. (1)

(b) Suggest an environmental advantage of piezoceramics. (1)

Some smart materials can only be seen at higher temperatures. They can be used in the manufacture of clothing.

(c) Suggest how this feature could be useful. (1)

A molecule of pentane can be represented as shown:

```
      H   H   H   H   H
      |   |   |   |   |
  H — C — C — C — C — C — H
      |   |   |   |   |
      H   H   H   H   H
```

(a) What do the letters C and H represent? (1)

(b) What do the lines between each C and H represent? (2)

(c) Explain why liquid pentane does not conduct electricity. (2)

(d) Pentane boils at 36°C. Explain what happens to the molecules of pentane when liquid pentane boils and becomes a gas. (2)

[Higher]

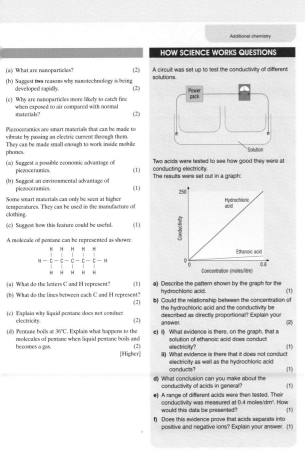

HOW SCIENCE WORKS QUESTIONS

A circuit was set up to test the conductivity of different solutions.

Two acids were tested to see how good they were at conducting electricity.
The results were set out in a graph:

a) Describe the pattern shown by the graph for the hydrochloric acid. (1)

b) Could the relationship between the concentration of the hydrochloric acid and the conductivity be described as directly proportional? Explain your answer. (2)

c) i) What evidence is there, on the graph, that a solution of ethanoic acid does conduct electricity? (1)

   ii) What evidence is there that it does not conduct electricity as well as the hydrochloric acid conducts? (1)

d) What conclusion can you make about the conductivity of acids in general? (1)

e) A range of different acids were then tested. Their conductivity was measured at 0.4 moles/dm³. How would this data be presented? (1)

f) Does this evidence prove that acids separate into positive and negative ions? Explain your answer. (1)

- Atoms stay bonded together because of delocalised electrons.
- Atoms remain in position when force removed. *(2 marks)*
  [HT only]

4 a) *One each for:*
- Particles or structures about 1 nanometre in size/between 1 and 100 nm.
- Containing a few hundred atoms. *(2 marks)*

b) *Any two points or specific examples from:*
- Have different properties to same materials in bulk.
- Can be used to make new types of devices, e.g. computers/processors/sensors.
- New catalysts/coatings/construction materials. *(2 marks)*

c) *One each for:*
- Much larger surface area (than bulk materials).
- Exposes more atoms to air/increases rate of reaction. *(2 marks)*

5 a) e.g. increased sale of mobile phones. *(1 mark)*

b) e.g. don't use up much natural resources because of small size of devices. *(1 mark)*

c) e.g. warn fire fighters if their protective clothing is getting too hot as it will change colour at a particular temperature. *(1 mark)*

6 a) Atoms (of carbon and hydrogen). *(1 mark)*

b) Covalent *(1 mark)* bonds *(1 mark)* *(2 marks)*

c) *Two from:*
- Its particles/molecules have no charges.
- It has no ions.
- It is made of molecules.
- It is covalently bonded.
- Its electrons cannot move from molecule to molecule. *(2 marks)*

d) *Any two points from:*
Molecules have enough energy to move apart/escape from the liquid/overcome intermolecular forces/but covalent bonds are not broken. *(2 marks)*
[HT only]

Exam teaching suggestions

- Q1 should not be attempted until this chapter has been completed. Q6 could be used after spread 2.2, Q2 after 2.3 and Q3 after 2.4. Allow 35 minutes for the complete set of questions with a total of 35 marks.

- Many students find it difficult to distinguish between intermolecular forces and covalent bonds. In particular many believe that covalent bonds are broken when liquids become gases. Q6d) should identify problems with these ideas.

- Q2 and Q3 require the identification of appropriate evidence in support of concepts about structures. These questions could be used as the basis for pair or small group discussions to produce exemplar answers. Note especially the 'do not accept' points in the mark scheme, which could form the basis of further discussion. The relationship between the number of marks and the number of points needed in answers can also be emphasised here.

- Q3c) requires a clear understanding of metal structures to achieve full marks. There are several ways in which this can be expressed and the mark scheme has more marking points than the marks available. Students sometimes give too much information in answers, leading to contradictions or loss of clarity. Students should be encouraged to use diagrams when explaining structures.

HOW SCIENCE WORKS ANSWERS

a) As the concentration of the hydrochloric acid increases so too does the conductivity.

b) Yes, because the graph shows a positive linear relationship in which the straight line does go through (0,0).

c) i) The graph for ethanoic acid is just above 0 and increases very slightly.
   ii) The slope is always below that of hydrochloric acid.

d) None – we only have evidence for two acids.

e) Bar chart.

f) No – we cannot go beyond the data we have.

How science works teaching suggestions

- **Literacy guidance.** Key terms that should be clearly understood: conclusions, patterns.

- **Higher- and lower-level answers.** Question b) is a higher level question and the answers provided above are also at this level. Question a) is lower level and the answer provided is also lower level.

- **Gifted and talented.** Able students could gather data on the conductance of other acids. They might consider why an acid might be a good or a poor conductor.

- **How and when to use these questions.** When wishing to develop skills associated with interpretation of data from graphs. The questions could be used for homework or in the lesson for individual work.

- **Misconceptions.** That any straight line can be described as directly proportional. To address this, state that this is only true for lines passing through (0,0). Give the students two straight line graphs, one passing through the origin, the other intercepting the y-axis above zero. Then ask the students to use the lines to see if doubling a value of x will result in a doubling of the value of y. Only the straight line through the origin will. If still in doubt, let the students try their own straight lines to test out by substitution.

- **Special needs.** Some help will be needed to understand the term conductance.

- **ICT link-up.** The Internet could be researched to gather more data to help to answer question e) e.g. search for 'conductance of acids' or 'conductivity of acids'.

C2 3.1

Mass numbers

LEARNING OBJECTIVES

Students should learn:

- The relative masses of sub-atomic particles.
- That atoms have a mass number.
- That some atoms can have isotopes.

LEARNING OUTCOMES

Most students should be able to:

- Define mass number.
- Use the periodic table to get mass numbers for any atom.
- State a definition for isotopes.

Some students should also be able to:

- Use information from the periodic table to work out the number of neutrons an atom has.
- Explain how isotopes are different.

Teaching suggestions

- **Special needs.** These students may find it difficult to find the key words to match with the definitions. Therefore, write a list of key words onto the board so they can use these throughout the lesson.
- **Gifted and talented.** Students could draw diagrams for the three hydrogen isotopes (hydrogen, deuterium, tritium).
- **Learning styles**

  Kinaesthetic: Voting by using thumb position during the true or false starter.

  Visual: Creating a spider diagram to summarise the information.

  Auditory: Listening to key terms and associating other facts.

  Interpersonal: Working in pairs, e.g. in 'association' plenary.

  Intrapersonal: Defining key terms.
- **Homework.** Students could find out an example of an isotope pair. Ask them to record the symbols, with its proton and mass number, and state the numbers of sub-atomic particles in the atoms of each isotope.

SPECIFICATION LINK-UP   Unit: Chemistry 2.12.3

- *Atoms can be represented as shown:*

  Mass number $\quad 23$
  Atomic number $\quad 11$ Na
- *The relative masses of protons, neutrons and electrons are:*

Name of particle	Mass
Proton	1
Neutron	1
Electron	Very small

- *The total number of protons and neutrons in an atom is called the mass number.*
- *Atoms of the same element can have different numbers of neutrons: these atoms are called isotopes of that element.*

Lesson structure

STARTER

Definitions – Give the students the definitions on the board. They should match each with a key word:

- A positive particle in an atom's nucleus. [Proton]
- A neutral particle with a relative mass of 1. [Neutron]
- The sub-atomic particle that is found in energy levels. [Electron]
- Atoms with the same number of protons, but different number of neutrons. [Isotope] (5 minutes)

True or false – If students agree with these statements they should show a thumbs up sign, if they disagree their thumbs should point downwards, and if they don't know their thumbs should be horizontal.

- Atoms are charged particles. [False]
- Electrons are found in energy levels or shells. [True]
- Electrons have a negative charge. [True]
- Protons are in the nucleus of an atom. [True]
- Neutrons are found in shells around the nucleus. [False] (5 minutes)

MAIN

- The structure of the atom can be summarised into a spider diagram. Encourage the students to include information about atomic mass, sub-atomic particles, isotopes and uses of isotopes.
- Students could be asked to include a key in their diagram. For example, use specific colours for key terms: red – proton, green – neutron, blue – electron, yellow – atom, purple – isotope.
- Students need to be able to use the periodic table to work out the number of each sub-atomic particle in an atom. With a question and answer session, draw out how the periodic table can be used to supply information about an atom.
- Show the students how to calculate the number of each sub-atomic particle using mass number and proton number.
- Then ask the students to design a table to record the number of each sub-atomic particle in the first 20 elements. Ask them to then complete their table.

PLENARIES

Think – On the board, write the symbol for carbon-12 and carbon-14 isotopes. Ask the students to use the periodic table and their knowledge of isotopes to list all the similarities between the atoms and all their differences. [Similarities – same number and arrangement of electrons, same number of protons in the nucleus, same chemical properties, same atomic/proton number. Differences – different number of neutrons in the nucleus, different mass numbers, different physical properties.] (10 minutes)

Association – Split the class into pairs, each student should face their partner. All students on the right should start first, saying a word or phrase about the lesson. Then the next person says another fact/key word based on the lesson. The activity swaps between partners until all the facts are exhausted. If a student hesitates or repeats previous statements then they have lost the association game. (10 minutes)

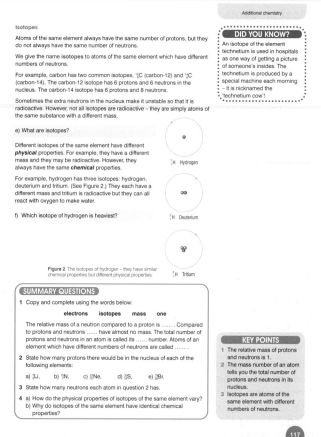

CHEMISTRY   HOW MUCH?

C2 3.1   Mass numbers

LEARNING OBJECTIVES

1 What are the relative masses of protons, neutrons and electrons?
2 What is an atom's mass number?
3 What are isotopes?

As we saw earlier on, an atom consists of a nucleus containing positively charged protons, together with neutrons which have no charge. The negatively charged electrons are arranged in energy levels (shells) around the nucleus.

Every atom has the same number of electrons orbiting its nucleus as it has protons in its nucleus. The number of protons that an atom has is its **atomic number**.

The mass of a proton and a neutron are the same. Another way of putting this is to say that the *relative mass* of a neutron compared with a proton is 1. Electrons are far, far smaller than protons and neutrons – their mass is negligible. Because of this, the mass of an atom is concentrated in its nucleus. You can ignore the tiny mass of the electrons when it comes to thinking about the mass of an atom!

Type of sub-atomic particle	Relative mass
proton	1
neutron	1
electron	negligible (very small)

a) How does the number of electrons in an atom compare to the number of protons?
b) How does the mass of a proton compare to the mass of a neutron?
c) How does the mass of an electron compare to the mass of a neutron or proton?

Mass number

Almost all of the mass of an atom is found in the nucleus, because the mass of the electrons is so tiny. We call the total number of protons and neutrons in an atom its mass number.

When we want to show the atomic number and mass number of an atom we do it like this:

Mass number $\quad {}^{12}_{6}C$ (carbon) $\quad {}^{23}_{11}Na$ (sodium)
Atomic number

We can work out the number of neutrons in the nucleus of an atom by subtracting its atomic number from its mass number. The difference is the number of neutrons:

mass number − atomic number = number of neutrons

For the two examples here, carbon has 6 protons and a mass number of 12, so the number of neutrons is (12 − 6) = 6.

Sodium, on the other hand, has an atomic number of 11 but the mass number is 23, so (23 − 11) = 12. In this sodium atom there are 11 protons and 12 neutrons.

d) How do we calculate the number of neutrons in an atom?

Figure 1 Chemists use the atomic number and the mass number of an element in many ways

- Proton   Number of protons gives atomic number
- Neutron   Number of protons plus number of neutrons gives mass number

Isotopes

Atoms of the same element always have the same number of protons, but they do not always have the same number of neutrons.

We give the name **isotopes** to atoms of the same element which have different numbers of neutrons.

For example, carbon has two common isotopes, ${}^{12}_{6}C$ (carbon-12) and ${}^{14}_{6}C$ (carbon-14). The carbon-12 isotope has 6 protons and 6 neutrons in the nucleus. The carbon-14 isotope has 6 protons and 8 neutrons.

Sometimes the extra neutrons in the nucleus make it unstable so that it is radioactive. However, not all isotopes are radioactive – they are simply atoms of the same substance with a different mass.

e) What are isotopes?

Different isotopes of the same element have different *physical* properties. For example, they have a different mass and they may be radioactive. However, they always have the same *chemical* properties.

For example, hydrogen has three isotopes: hydrogen, deuterium and tritium. (See Figure 2.) They each have a different mass and tritium is radioactive but they can all react with oxygen to make water.

f) Which isotope of hydrogen is heaviest?

${}^{1}_{1}H$ Hydrogen

${}^{2}_{1}H$ Deuterium

${}^{3}_{1}H$ Tritium

Figure 2 The isotopes of hydrogen – they have similar chemical properties but different physical properties

DID YOU KNOW?

An isotope of the element technetium is used in hospitals as one way of getting a picture of someone's insides. The technetium is produced by a special machine each morning – it is nicknamed the 'technetium cow'!

SUMMARY QUESTIONS

1 Copy and complete using the words below:

    electrons   isotopes   mass   one

The relative mass of a neutron compared to a proton is .... Compared to protons and neutrons ...... have almost no mass. The total number of protons and neutrons in an atom is called its ...... number. Atoms of an element which have different numbers of neutrons are called ....

2 State how many protons there would be in the nucleus of each of the following elements:

a) ${}^{7}_{3}Li$,   b) ${}^{14}_{7}N$,   c) ${}^{20}_{10}Ne$,   d) ${}^{32}_{16}S$,   e) ${}^{79}_{35}Br$.

3 State how many neutrons each atom in question 2 has.

4 a) How do the physical properties of isotopes of the same element vary?
   b) Why do isotopes of the same element have identical chemical properties?

KEY POINTS

1 The relative mass of protons and neutrons is 1.
2 The mass number of an atom tells you the total number of protons and neutrons in its nucleus.
3 Isotopes are atoms of the same element with different numbers of neutrons.

116

117

SUMMARY ANSWERS

1 One, electrons, mass, isotopes.

2 **a)** protons = 3
  b) protons = 7
  c) protons = 10
  d) protons = 16
  e) protons = 35

3 **a)** neutrons = 4
  b) neutrons = 8
  c) neutrons = 12
  d) neutrons = 17
  e) neutrons = 44

4 **a)** The atoms have a different mass and they may be radioactive.
  b) Because they have identical electronic structures.

Answers to in-text questions

a) Number of electrons = number of protons.

b) Mass of proton = mass of neutron.

c) Mass of electron is much less than the mass of a proton or neutron.

d) Number of neutrons = mass number minus atomic number.

e) Isotopes are atoms of the same element with different numbers of neutrons (or words to that effect).

f) Tritium, ${}^{3}_{1}H$.

KEY POINTS

Make cards containing parts of the sentences. The students could then arrange the word tiles to make up the key points. This activity can be made easier by splitting each sentence into just three parts.

C2 3.2

Masses of atoms and moles

LEARNING OBJECTIVES

Students should learn:

- That the masses of atoms can be compared by their relative atomic masses.
- That the relative formula mass of compounds can be calculated.

LEARNING OUTCOMES

Most students should be able to:

- Give a definition of relative formula mass.
- Calculate relative formula mass if its formula and the relative atomic mass are given.

Some students should also be able to:

- Give a full definition of relative atomic mass. [**HT** only]
- Explain what a mole is.

Teaching suggestions

- **Special needs.** Provide the students with a pre-cut out cube template that is also ready scored. To help further, add some information already on it, for example the titles or prose with missing words.

- **Gifted and talented.** Give these students the names of different compounds. Let them work out the formula (either by using the text book or using dot and cross diagrams). Then encourage them to use the periodic table to get the A_r before working out the M_r.

- **Learning styles**

  Kinaesthetic: Matching up cards.

  Visual: Creating revision cube on this topic.

  Auditory: Listening to other students describing key words.

  Interpersonal: Discussing how different samples relate to each other.

  Intrapersonal: Finding the key words in a word search.

SPECIFICATION LINK-UP   Unit: Chemistry 2.12.3

- *The relative atomic mass of an element (A_r) compares the mass of atoms of the element with the carbon-12 isotope. It is an average value for the isotopes of the element. [**HT** only]*
- *The relative formula mass (M_r) of a compound is the sum of the relative atomic masses of the atoms in the numbers shown in the formula.*
- *The relative formula mass of a substance, in grams, is known as one mole of that substance.*

Students should use their skills, knowledge and understanding of 'How Science Works':

- *to calculate chemical quantities involving formula mass (M_r).*

Lesson structure

STARTER

Demonstration – Have a mole of different substances pre-measured in sealed containers, e.g. 12 g of carbon, 24 g of magnesium. Allow the students to handle different samples. Explain to these students that all these examples have something in common – but what? Encourage the students to use the Student Book and discuss in small groups how these samples relate to each other. Hopefully they will realise that these are all examples of moles. Then ask students for hands up if they can tell you the mass of, e.g., 1 mole of carbon (and hold up the sample) etc. Repeat for all the samples that you have. (10 minutes)

Word search – Give the students a word search for the key words that they will be using in the lesson: 'relative', 'atomic', 'mass', 'formula', 'mole', 'atom'. (5 minutes)

MAIN

- Students need to be able to obtain A_r from the periodic table and calculate M_r. Give the students a set of cards of different elements (single atoms and molecules) and compound formulas. On separate cards, write numbers that represent A_r or M_r.

- Students should complete calculations and match the formula with its A_r and M_r. They should also decide if the number represents A_r or M_r. This could be made into a competition, by splitting the class into small teams, the first group to correctly match all the cards may get a prize.

- Students need to be able to define the key terms: 'relative atomic mass', 'relative formula mass' and 'moles'.

- Give the students a template of a cube. They should write definitions of relative atomic mass, moles and relative formula mass on three faces. On the remaining faces, they should include a worked example of calculations relating to this topic using lots of colours.

- Then they cut out the template and score the lines to create sharp folds and stick the cube together.

PLENARIES

Difference – Ask the students to explain the difference between the symbols A_r and Ar. Choose a volunteer to explain to the class. [Ar is the symbol for the element argon, A_r is the shorthand notation for relative atomic mass]. (5 minutes)

In the bag – Put the key words: 'relative atomic mass', 'relative formula mass' and 'mole' into a colourful bag. Ask for three volunteers to come to the front and remove a word in turns. After they have removed their word, they should show the class the word and explain what it means. You should interject with a question and answer session to help rectify any misconceptions. (5 minutes)

Teaching suggestions – continued

- **Homework**
  Ask students to work out the mass of a mole of the following:
  - Oxygen atoms [16 g]
  - Oxygen molecules [32 g]
  - Water molecules [18 g]
  Encourage the students to show their working.

- **ICT link-up.** Celebrate mole day, there are lots of resources on www.moleday.org

ACTIVITY & EXTENSION IDEAS

- Give students a set of timed questions to calculate relative formula masses of different substances.

- Find out how Avogadro's number was discovered.

C2 3.2   Masses of atoms and moles

LEARNING OBJECTIVES

1. How can we compare the mass of atoms? [Higher]
2. How can we calculate the mass of compounds from the elements they are made from?

Chemical equations show you how many atoms of the reactants we need to make the products. But when we actually carry out a chemical reaction we need to know what amounts to use in grams or cm³. You might think that a chemical equation would also tell you this.

For example, does the equation:

$$Mg + 2HCl \rightarrow MgCl_2 + H_2$$

mean that we need twice as many grams of hydrochloric acid as magnesium to make magnesium chloride?

Unfortunately it isn't that simple. The equation tells us that we need twice as many hydrogen and chlorine atoms as magnesium atoms – but this doesn't mean that the mass of hydrochloric acid will be twice the mass of magnesium. This is because atoms of different elements have different masses.

To turn equations into something that we can actually use in the lab or factory we need to know a bit more about the mass of atoms.

a) Why don't chemical equations tell us how much of each reactant to use in a chemical reaction?

Relative atomic masses

The mass of a single atom is so tiny that it would be impossible to use it in calculations. To make the whole thing manageable we use a much simpler way of thinking about the masses of atoms. Instead of working with the **real** masses of atoms we just focus on the **relative** masses of atoms of different elements. We call these relative atomic masses (A_r).

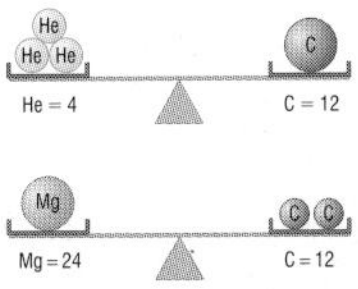

He = 4   C = 12

Mg = 24   C = 12

Figure 1 The A_r of carbon is 12. Compared with this, the A_r of helium is 4 and the A_r of magnesium is 24

Relative atomic mass		Relative ionic mass	
Na	23	Na⁺	23
O	16	O²⁻	16
Mg	24	Mg²⁺	24

We use an atom of carbon ($^{12}_6C$) as a standard atom. We give this a 'mass' of 12 units, because it has 6 protons and 6 neutrons. We then compare all of the masses of the atoms of all the other elements to this standard carbon atom.

The mass of an atom found by comparing it with the $^{12}_6C$ atom is called its relative atomic mass (A_r).

The relative atomic mass of an element is usually the same as, or very similar to, the mass number of that element. The A_r takes into account any isotopes of the element. The relative atomic mass is the average mass of the isotopes of the element in the proportions in which they are usually found (compared with the standard carbon atom).

When atoms change into ions they either lose or gain electrons. However, for all practical purposes the mass of electrons isn't worth bothering about. So the 'relative ionic mass' of an ion is exactly the same as the relative atomic mass of that element.

b) What do we call the mass of an atom compared with the mass of an atom of carbon-12?

HIGHER

Relative formula masses

We can use the A_r of the various elements to work out the relative formula mass (M_r) of chemical compounds. This is true whether the compounds are made up of molecules or collections of ions. A simple example is a substance like sodium chloride. We know that the A_r of sodium is 23 and the A_r of chlorine is 35.5. So the relative formula mass of sodium chloride (NaCl) is:

23 + 35.5 = 58.5
A_r Na A_r Cl M_r NaCl

Another example is water. Water is made up of hydrogen and oxygen. The A_r of hydrogen is 1, and the A_r of oxygen is 16. Water has the formula H_2O, containing two hydrogen atoms for every one oxygen, so the M_r is:

(1 × 2) + 16 = 18
A_r H × 2 A_r O M_r H_2O

c) What is the relative formula mass of hydrogen sulfide, H_2S?
(A_r values: H = 1, S = 32)

Moles

Saying or writing 'relative atomic mass in grams' or 'relative formula mass in grams' is rather clumsy. So chemists have a shorthand word for it – **mole**.

They say that the relative atomic mass in grams of carbon (i.e. 12 g of carbon) is a mole of carbon atoms. One mole is simply the relative atomic mass or relative formula mass of any substance expressed in grams. A mole of any substance always contains the same number of particles.

Figure 2 We know how many actual atoms or molecules a mole contains, thanks to an Italian count born in the 18th century, Amedeo Avogadro. He worked out that a mole of any element or compound contains 6.02×10^{23} atoms, ions or molecules. That's 602 000 000 000 000 000 000 000! This is called **Avogadro's number**.

SUMMARY QUESTIONS

1. Copy and complete using the words below:

   atomic   carbon-12   elements   formula   number

   We measure the masses of atoms by comparing them to the mass of one atom of .... The relative ...... mass of an element is usually almost the same as its mass .... We calculate the relative ...... mass of a compound from the relative atomic masses of the ...... in it.

2. The equation for the reaction of magnesium and fluorine is:

   $$Mg + F_2 \rightarrow MgF_2$$

   a) How many moles of fluorine molecules react with one mole of magnesium atoms?
   b) What is the relative formula mass of MgF_2? (A_r values: Mg = 24, F = 19)

3. The relative atomic mass of oxygen is 16, and that of magnesium is 24. How many times heavier is a magnesium atom than an oxygen atom?

DID YOU KNOW?
One mole of soft drinks cans would cover the surface of the Earth to a depth of 200 miles!

We can use the same approach with relatively complicated molecules like sulfuric acid, H_2SO_4. Hydrogen has a A_r of 1, the A_r of sulfur is 32 and the A_r of oxygen 16. This means that the M_r of sulfuric acid is:

(1 × 2) + 32 + (16 × 4) = 2 + 32 + 64 = 98

GET IT RIGHT!
You don't have to remember Avogadro's number! But practise calculating the mass of one mole of different substances from relative atomic masses that you are given.

KEY POINTS

1. We compare the masses of atoms by measuring them relative to atoms of carbon-12. [Higher]
2. We work out the relative formula mass of a compound from the relative atomic masses of the elements in it.
3. One mole of any substance always contains the same number of particles.

SUMMARY ANSWERS

1. Carbon-12, atomic, number, formula, elements.

2. a) 1
   b) 62

3. 1.5 times heavier.

Answers to in-text questions

a) Because the atoms of different elements have different masses.

b) Its relative atomic mass.

c) 34

DID YOU KNOW?

If you drew a line that was as long in millimetres as Avogadro's number, it would stretch from the Sun to the Earth and back 2 million times!

KEY POINTS

Students could make a poem with three verses, one to reflect each key point.

C2 3.3   Percentages and formulae

LEARNING OBJECTIVES

Students should learn:

- How to calculate the percentage mass of an element in a compound.

- How to calculate the formula of a compound from the percentage composition. [**HT** only]

LEARNING OUTCOMES

Most students should be able to:

- Calculate the percentage composition of an element in a compound.

Some students should also be able to:

- Calculate the formula of a compound if the percentage composition of the elements is given. [**HT** only]

Teaching suggestions

- **Special needs.** These students will often struggle with calculations. Provide them with a writing frame to help them.

- **Gifted and talented.** Students could be given more complex empirical formula type questions to attempt.

- **Learning styles**

  Kinaesthetic: Experimentally determining the formula of magnesium oxide.

  Visual: Interpreting concept cartoon.

  Auditory: Listening to the answers to questions.

  Interpersonal: Working in pairs to give AfL (Assessment for Learning).

  Intrapersonal: Completing calculations.

- **Homework.** Ask: 'Which of the following compounds contains the highest proportion of oxygen?' Encourage the students to calculate the percentage composition and to show their working.
  - CO [57% O]
  - C_2H_4OH [36% O]
  - CH_3COOH [53% O]

- **ICT link-up.** Download a template for a self-marking exercise where students choose their answers from menus. These templates use Excel and are found at www.chemit.co.uk.

SPECIFICATION LINK-UP   Unit: Chemistry 2.12.3

- *The percentage of an element in a compound can be calculated from the relative mass of the element in the formula and the relative formula mass of the compound.*

Students should use their skills, knowledge and understanding of 'How Science Works':
- *to calculate chemical quantities involving percentages of elements in compounds.*
- *to calculate chemical quantities involving empirical formulae. [**HT** only]*

Lesson structure

STARTER

Measurement – Show the students different mass values on balances. Ask them to note to the nearest two decimal places the values shown. Read out the answers and ask the students to put up their hands if they got them all right, one wrong, two wrong etc. Approach students that have been having difficulty and help them to see why they recorded the wrong answer. (5 minutes)

Concept cartoon – Show the students a concept cartoon to highlight the conservation of mass theory. Ask them to discuss the cartoon in small groups, and then feedback to the rest of the class. (5 minutes)

MAIN

- To complete calculations there is often a set order of steps involved. Choose an example question to calculate the percentage composition of an element and write out each step onto separate cards.
- Encourage the students to order the cards and copy out the worked example correctly. Then give the students other examples to work out themselves.
- Then the same idea can be repeated, but for generating a formula of a compound from percentage composition data instead.
- Give the students two flash cards. On one side they should write how to calculate the percentage composition of an element, and on the reverse they should make up some questions of their own.
- On the second card they should write how to generate the formula on one side, and on the reverse some questions.
- The students can then work out the answers and write them upside down on their revision card.
- Students could experimentally determine the formula of magnesium oxide. This requires them to be able to read a balance accurately to 2 decimal places.
- They should design their own results table and show all their working to generate the formula. They should calculate the mass of magnesium used (mass of initially full crucible – empty crucible). Then they should calculate the mass of oxygen in the compound (mass of crucible after heating – mass of initially full crucible).
- Once the mass of each element in the compound is known the formula can be calculated as detailed in the Student Book.

PLENARIES

On the spot – Ask for a volunteer to stand at the front of the class, and give the other students scrap paper. Read out questions to the volunteer and they should say their answer. The rest of the class then writes a number and holds it up to show whether they strongly disagree (1) or strongly agree (10) with the answer. You could reveal the true answer. (10 minutes)

Calculation – Ask the students to calculate the percentage composition of each element in ammonia. They should recall the formula of ammonia from previous work. [N = 82%; H = 18%] (5 minutes)

AfL (Assessment for Learning) – In pairs, students swap their revision cards and tackle each other's questions and check their answers. They should be encouraged to feedback any problems that they are having to their partner. (10 minutes)

Practical support

Determining the formula of magnesium oxide

Equipment and materials required

Small strips of magnesium ribbon (flammable), ceramic crucibles and lids, Bunsen burner and safety equipment, tongs, pipe clay triangle, tripod, accurate balance, eye protection.

Details

Students to note the mass of the crucible and lid, and then twist the magnesium ribbon into a coil shape and put into the crucible. Also note the new mass of the crucible, and put onto the pipe clay triangle. Heat strongly in a blue Bunsen flame, and lift the lid gently and occasionally to boost the oxygen flow. They must not lift the lid up high, as some of the product will be lost. When the lid is lifted and there is no white light, then the reaction is complete.

Then turn off the Bunsen and allow the crucible to cool, noting the mass of the crucible at the end of the reaction.

Safety: Eye protection should be worn throughout the reaction and students should be warned that the crucible will retain heat for a surprising amount of time and may crack. Magnesium is flammable – CLEAPSS Hazcard 59.

ACTIVITY & EXTENSION IDEAS

Additional chemistry

Students could try to calculate the water of crystallisation in certain formulae, e.g. $CuSO_4.5H_2O$.

C2 3.3   Percentages and formulae

LEARNING OBJECTIVES

1 How can we calculate the percentage mass of each element in a compound from its formula?

2 How can we calculate the formula of a compound from its percentage composition? [Higher]

Figure 1 A tiny difference in the amount of iron in the ore might not seem very much, but when millions of tonnes of iron ore are extracted and processed each year, it all adds up!

We can use the formula mass of a compound to calculate the percentage mass of each element in it. Calculations like these are not just done in GCSE chemistry books! In life outside the school laboratory, geologists and mining companies base their decisions about whether to exploit mineral finds on calculations like these.

Working out the amount of an element in a compound

We can use the relative atomic mass (A_r) of elements and the relative formula mass (M_r) of compounds to help us work out the percentage of an element in a compound.

> **Worked example (1)**
> What percentage mass of white magnesium oxide is actually magnesium, and how much is oxygen?
>
> **Solution**
> The first thing we need is the formula of magnesium oxide, MgO.
> The A_r of magnesium is 24, while the A_r of oxygen is 16.
>
> Adding these together gives us a M_r of 40 i.e. (24 + 16).
>
> So from 40 g of magnesium oxide, 24 g is actually magnesium:
>
> $$\frac{\text{mass of magnesium}}{\text{total mass of compound}} = \frac{24}{40}$$
>
> so the percentage of magnesium in the compound is:
>
> $$\frac{24}{40} \times 100\% = 60\%$$

To calculate the percentage of an element in a compound:

* Write down the formula of the compound.
* Using the relative atomic masses from your data sheet work out the relative formula mass of the compound. Write down the mass of each element making up the compound as you work it out.
* Write the mass of the element you are investigating as a fraction of the total M_r.
* Find the percentage by multiplying your fraction by 100.

> **Worked example (2)**
> A white powder is found at the scene of a crime. It could be strychnine, a deadly poison with the formula $C_{21}H_{22}N_2O_2$ – but is it?!
>
> When a chemist analyses the powder, 83% of its mass is carbon. What is the percentage mass of carbon in strychnine, and is this the same?
>
> **Solution**
> The formula mass (M_r) of strychnine is:
>
> $(12 \times 21) + (1 \times 22) + (14 \times 2) + (16 \times 2) = 252 + 22 + 28 + 32 = 334$
>
> The percentage mass of carbon in strychnine is therefore:
>
> $$\frac{252}{334} \times 100 = 75.4\%$$
>
> This is **not** the same as the percentage mass of carbon in the white powder – so the white powder is not strychnine.

a) What is the percentage mass of hydrogen in methane, CH_4? (A_r values: C = 12, H = 1)

HIGHER

Working out the formula of a compound from its percentage composition

We can also do this backwards! If we know the percentage composition of a compound we can work out the ratio of the numbers of atoms in the compound. We call this its **empirical formula**. It tells us the simplest whole number ratio of elements in a compound.

This is sometimes the same as the actual number of atoms in one molecule (which we call the **molecular formula**) – but not always. For example, the empirical formula of water is H_2O, which is also its molecular formula. However, hydrogen peroxide has the empirical formula HO, but its molecular formula is H_2O_2.

> **Worked example**
> If 9 g of aluminium react with 35.5 g of chlorine, what is the empirical formula of the compound formed?
>
> **Solution**
> We can work out the ratio of the number of atoms by dividing the mass of each element by its relative atomic mass:
>
> For aluminium: $\frac{9}{27}g = \frac{1}{3}$ mole of aluminium atoms
>
> For chlorine: $\frac{35.5}{35.5}g = 1$ mole of chlorine atoms
>
> So this tells us that one mole of chlorine atoms combines with $\frac{1}{3}$ mole of aluminium atoms.
>
> This means that the simplest whole number ratio is 3 (Cl) : 1 (Al). In other words 1 aluminium atom combines with 3 chlorine atoms. So the empirical formula is $AlCl_3$.

b) A compound contains 16 g of sulfur and 24 g of oxygen. What is its empirical formula? (A_r values: S = 32, O = 16)

Given the percentage composition and asked to find the empirical formula, just assume you have 100 g of the compound. Then do a calculation as shown above to find the simplest ratio of elements.

SUMMARY QUESTIONS

1 Copy and complete using the words below:

> **compound   dividing   hundred   relative formula mass**

The percentage of an element in a ...... is calculated by ...... the mass of the element in the compound by the .... of the compound and then multiplying the result by one ....

2 Ammonium nitrate (NH_4NO_3) is used as a fertiliser. What is the percentage mass of nitrogen in it? (A_r values: H = 1, N = 14, O = 16)

3 22.55% of the mass of a sample of phosphorus chloride is phosphorus. What is the formula of phosphorus chloride? (A_r values: P = 31, Cl = 35.5) [Higher]

Figure 2 Chemical analysis of substances found at the scene of a crime may help to bring a murderer to justice – or free an innocent suspect

GET IT RIGHT!

Make sure that you can do these calculations from formula to percentage mass and the other way round.

How to work out the formula from reacting masses:

* Begin with the number of grams of the elements that combine.
* Change the number of grams to the moles of atoms by dividing the number of grams by the A_r. This tells you how many moles of the different elements combine.
* Use this to tell you the simplest ratio of atoms of the different elements combined in the compound.
* This gives you the empirical formula of the compound.

KEY POINT

1 The relative atomic masses of the elements in a compound can be used to work out its percentage composition.

2 We can calculate empirical formulae given the masses or percentage composition of elements present. [Higher]

SUMMARY ANSWERS

1 Compound, dividing, relative formula mass, hundred.

2 35%

3 PCl_3 [**HT** only]

Answers to in-text questions

a) 25%

b) SO_3

KEY POINTS

Before the lesson begins, select five famous people and write their names on a piece of paper and attach them to the underside of five chairs in the class. Then ask students to check under their chairs; if they have a famous person, they should read out the key point in the style of the famous person to the rest of the class.

C2 3.4

Equations and calculations

LEARNING OBJECTIVES

Students should learn:

- That chemical equations can give information about the relative numbers of reacting particles and products formed in a reaction. [**HT** only]

- That chemical equations can be used to calculate reacting masses. [**HT** only]

LEARNING OUTCOMES

Most Higher Tier students should be able to:

- Interpret how many moles of reactants/products are shown in a balanced equation. [**HT** only]

- Balance symbol equations. [**HT** only]

- Use a balanced symbol equation to calculate the mass of reactants or products. [**HT** only]

Teaching suggestions

- **Special needs.** These students will find the calculations difficult. Give them half-finished calculations, where they need to add numbers into the working out to generate the answers. Also peer mentoring could be used, where the students are split into pairs, where the higher attaining student supports the lower attaining.

- **Learning styles**

  Kinaesthetic: Completing the card loop.

  Auditory: Listening to other students in group work.

  Interpersonal: Working in groups to give AfL (Assessment for Learning).

  Intrapersonal: Completing calculations.

- **Homework.** Ask students to go through the work and pick out the key terms (e.g. reactant, product, mass). They should then define these key terms.

SPECIFICATION LINK-UP   Unit: Chemistry 2.12.3

- *The masses of reactants and products can be calculated from balanced symbol equations.* [**HT** only]

Students should use their skills, knowledge and understanding of 'How Science Works':

- *to calculate chemical quantities involving reacting masses.* [**HT** only]

Lesson structure

STARTER

Multiple-choice – Give each student three coloured flash cards, e.g. blue, green and red. Then create a few multiple-choice questions, one per slide on PowerPoint® with three answers, each one written in a different colour to match the flash cards. This could also be achieved using Word or whiteboard software. Then show each question in turn and the students should hold up the card that represents the answer that they think is correct. (5 minutes)

Chemical equations – Ask the students to complete the following chemical equations:

1 magnesium + [oxygen] → magnesium oxide

2 methane + oxygen → [carbon dioxide] + water

3 zinc + copper sulfate → [copper] + [zinc sulfate]

4 [sodium hydroxide] + hydrochloric acid → sodium chloride + water

To extend this activity, you could ask the students to say what type of reaction each of the above represents [1 oxidation; 2 combustion/oxidation; 3 displacement; 4 neutralisation]. Then students could turn these into balanced symbol equations. (10 minutes)

MAIN

- Students need to be able to work out the masses of different substances in balanced symbol equations. Create a card loop by drawing a rectangle 10 cm by 15 cm. Draw a dotted line to make a square 10 cm by 10 cm. In the square write out questions that involve balancing equations and calculating reacting masses. Then in the rectangle 5 cm by 10 cm write an answer (not one that matches the question on the card). Ensure that the questions match with answers on other cards so that a loop is made.

- Give the question loop set to small groups of students and allow them to complete the card sort. Then encourage the students to pick two of the questions and answers to copy out into their book, but show their working out stage by stage (as demonstrated in the Student Book).

- Split the class into pairs, and on separate pieces of paper write enough calculation questions for one per group. Give out the questions and allow the students to start to answer for three minutes (timed using a stopwatch). Then ask the students to hand the paper to another group.

- Give the next group three minutes to correct the previous work and then continue with the answer.

- Repeat this a number of times until there has been enough time for the answers to be completed. Then return the paper back to the 'owners' where they should copy up the question and the full answer.

- Use the Simulation C2 3.4 'Equations' from the Additional Science CD ROM.

PLENARIES

AfL (Assessment for Learning) – Give students some calculations, but instead of tackling the questions encourage them to create the mark scheme. Ask the students to work in small groups discussing the question and devising the marking points, and include alternative answers that could still be given credit, and those that definitely should not be awarded marks. (10 minutes)

Reflection – Ask students to think about the objectives for today's lesson. Ask them to consider if they have been met, and discuss this in small groups. Ask a few groups to feed back to the rest of the class, explaining how they know that they have met the objectives. (5 minutes)

- Students could include state symbols in more complex balanced symbol equations.
- Students may attempt industrial-sized calculations (involving tonnes). This would involve them multiplying up the masses of the different components.

C2 3.4   Equations and calculations

LEARNING OBJECTIVES

1 What do chemical equations tell us about chemical reactions?

2 How do we use equations to calculate masses of reactants and products?

Chemical equations can be very useful when we want to know how much of each substance is involved in a chemical reaction. But to do this, we must be sure that the equation is balanced.

To see how we do this, think about what happens when hydrogen molecules (H_2) react with oxygen molecules (O_2), making water molecules (H_2O):

$$H_2 + O_2 \rightarrow H_2O \text{ (not balanced)}$$

This equation shows the reactants and the product – but it is not balanced. There are 2 oxygen atoms on the left-hand side and only 1 oxygen atom on the right-hand side. To balance the equation there need to be 2 water molecules on the right-hand side:

$$H_2 + O_2 \rightarrow 2H_2O \text{ (still not balanced)}$$

This balances the number of oxygen atoms on each side of the equation – but now there are 4 hydrogen atoms on the right-hand side and only 2 on the left-hand side. So there need to be 2 hydrogen molecules on the left-hand side:

$$2H_2 + O_2 \rightarrow 2H_2O \text{ (balanced!)}$$

This balanced equation tells us that '2 hydrogen molecules react with one oxygen molecule to make 2 water molecules'. But remember that 1 mole of any substance always contains the same number of particles. So our balanced equation also tells us that '2 moles of hydrogen molecules react with one mole of oxygen molecules to make two moles of water molecules'.

a) What must we do to a chemical equation before we use it to work out how much of each chemical is needed or made?

b) '$2H_2$' has two meanings – what are they?

2 hydrogen molecules	1 oxygen molecule	2 water molecules
$2H_2$	$+$ O_2	$\longrightarrow$ $2H_2O$
2 moles of hydrogen molecules	1 mole of oxygen molecules	2 moles of water molecules

This is really useful, because we can use it to work out what mass of hydrogen and oxygen we need, and how much water is made.

To do this, we need to know that the A_r for hydrogen is 1 and the A_r for oxygen is 16:

A_r of hydrogen = 1 ...... so mass of 1 mole of H_2 = 2 × 1 = 2 g
A_r of oxygen = 16 ...... so mass of 1 mole of O_2 = 2 × 16 = 32 g
M_r of water = (16 + 2) = 18 ...... so mass of 1 mole of water = 18 g

Our balanced equation tells us that 2 moles of hydrogen react with one mole of oxygen to give 2 moles of water. So turning this into masses we get:

2 moles of hydrogen = 2 × 2 g = 4 g
1 mole of oxygen   = 1 × 32 g = 32 g
2 moles of water   = 2 × 18 g = 36 g

Figure 1 When 4 g of hydrogen react with 32 g of oxygen we get 36 g of water

---

Calculations

These kind of calculations are important when we want to know how much of two chemicals to react together. For example, a chemical called sodium hydroxide reacts with chlorine gas to make bleach.

Here is the equation for the reaction:

$$2NaOH + Cl_2 \rightarrow NaOCl + NaCl + H_2O$$
sodium   chlorine   bleach   salt   water
hydroxide

This reaction happens when chlorine gas is bubbled through a solution of sodium hydroxide dissolved in water.

If we have a solution containing 100 g of sodium hydroxide, how much chlorine gas should we pass through the solution to make bleach? Too much, and some chlorine will be wasted, too little and not all of the sodium hydroxide will react.

	So mass of 1 mole of	
	NaOH	**Cl_2**
A_r of hydrogen = 1		
A_r of oxygen = 16	$= 23 + 16 + 1 = 40$	$= 35.5 \times 2 = 71$
A_r of sodium = 23		
A_r of chlorine = 35.5		

The table shows that 1 mole of sodium hydroxide has a mass of 40 g.

So 100 g of sodium hydroxide is $\frac{100}{40} = 2.5$ moles.

The chemical equation for the reaction tells us that for every two moles of sodium hydroxide we need one mole of chlorine.

So we need $\frac{2.5}{2} = 1.25$ moles of chlorine.

The table shows that 1 mole of chlorine has a mass of 71 g.

So we will need 1.25 × 71 = **88.75 g** of chlorine to react with 100 g of sodium hydroxide.

DID YOU KNOW?

Mole is the English version of the German word *Mol* which is short for *Molekulargewicht*, the 'molecular weight.'

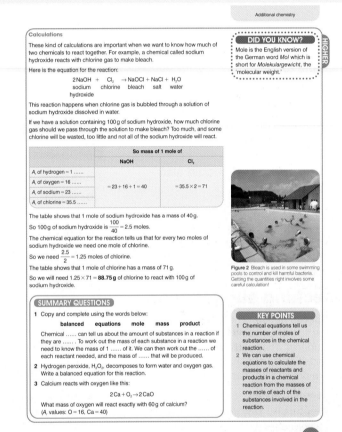

Figure 2 Bleach is used in some swimming pools to control and kill harmful bacteria. Getting the quantities right involves some careful calculation!

SUMMARY QUESTIONS

1 Copy and complete using the words below:

balanced   equations   mole   mass   product

Chemical ...... can tell us about the amount of substances in a reaction if they are .... To work out the mass of each substance in a reaction we need to know the mass of 1 ...... of it. We can then work out the ...... of each reactant needed, and the mass of ...... that will be produced.

2 Hydrogen peroxide, H_2O_2, decomposes to form water and oxygen gas. Write a balanced equation for this reaction.

3 Calcium reacts with oxygen like this:

$$2Ca + O_2 \rightarrow 2CaO$$

What mass of oxygen will react exactly with 60 g of calcium?
(A_r values: O = 16, Ca = 40)

KEY POINTS

1 Chemical equations tell us the number of moles of substances in the chemical reaction.

2 We can use chemical equations to calculate the masses of reactants and products in a chemical reaction from the masses of one mole of each of the substances involved in the reaction.

SUMMARY ANSWERS

1 Equations, balanced, mole, mass, product.

2 $2H_2O_2 \rightarrow 2H_2O + O_2$

3 24 g

Answers to in-text questions

a) Balance it.

b) '2 hydrogen molecules' and '2 moles of hydrogen molecules'.

KEY POINTS

Ask the students to copy out the key points, then encourage them to illustrate each of the key points by using a worked example of a calculation.

C2 3.5

Making as much as we want

LEARNING OBJECTIVES

Students should learn:

- That the amount of product made can be expressed as a yield.

- How to calculate percentage yield. [**HT** only]

- That different factors affect yield.

- What atom economy is and why it is important.

- How to calculate atom economy. [**HT** only]

LEARNING OUTCOMES

Most students should be able to:

- Give a definition for yield.

- List factors that affect yield.

- Explain why atom economy is important.

Some students should also be able to:

- Calculate percentage yield. [**HT** only]

- Calculate atom economy. [**HT** only]

Teaching suggestions

- **Special needs.** The different steps in the flow chart could be given to the students. They could then cut them out and stick them in the correct order into a pre-drawn flow chart outline.

- **Learning styles**

  Kinaesthetic: Moving to show the order of a calculation.

  Visual: Creating a flow chart to explain how to tackle a calculation.

  Auditory: Listening to others in group work.

  Interpersonal: Working in a group to answer a series of questions.

  Intrapersonal: Defining percentage yield and reflecting on factors affecting yield.

- **Homework.** Ask students to explain why it is important for a company to maximise its yield.

- **Science @ work.** Industry has to reduce the energy consumption and raw materials to keep costs down and make more profit. However, it also has positive effects for the environment. Often chemical plants use the heat from exothermic reactions elsewhere in manufacture of products or even to heat the offices!

SPECIFICATION LINK-UP   Unit: Chemistry 2.12.3

- *Even though no atoms are gained or lost in a chemical reaction it is not always possible to obtain the calculated amount of a product because:*
  - *the reaction may not go to completion because it is reversible*
  - *some of the product may be lost when it is separated from the reaction mixture*
  - *some of the reactants may react in ways different to expected reaction.*

- *The amount of product obtained is known as the yield. When compared with the maximum theoretical amount as a percentage, it is called the percentage yield.* [**HT** only]

- *The atom economy (atom utilisation) is a measure of the amount of starting materials that end up as useful products. It is important for sustainable development and for economic reasons to use reactions with high atom economy.*

Students should use their skills, knowledge and understanding of 'How Science Works':

- *to calculate chemical quantities involving percentage yield.* [**HT** only]

- *to calculate the atom economy for industrial processes and be able to evaluate sustainable development issues related to this economy.* [**HT** only]

Lesson structure

STARTER

Definition – Ask the students to explain what a yield and atom economy is and how it can be calculated. They could use the Student Book to help them. (5 minutes)

Mirror words – Ask the students to work out these key words that will be used in the lesson:

- stnatcaer [reactants]

- stcudorp [products]

- dleiy [yield]

- egatnecrep [percentage]

- noitaluclac [calculation] (5 minutes)

MAIN

- Split the class into teams of about five pupils. Prepare ten questions for each group – they could be written on colour-coded paper. The questions should be face-down on a front desk.

- A volunteer from each group should retrieve their first question and take it back to their table, and the team should complete the calculation. As soon as they have an answer, they take it to you to be checked.

- If they are correct, then they can get their next question, if they are incorrect they should try again, with help where needed. The team to complete all the questions correctly first could win a prize.

- Ask Higher Tier students to look carefully at the worked example for calculating the yield and atom economy. Ask them to draw two flow charts to show the steps of how to complete these calculations.

- Then give the students a number of questions that they can answer using their flow charts to help them.

- Discuss the importance of maximising percentage yield and atom economy to support sustainable development. Students can then list the advantages.

PLENARIES

Steps – On the board, write a question that involves the calculation of a yield (an example could be used from the Student Book). Put each separate number or mathematical procedure onto separate sheets of A3 paper and arrange them on the floor in the wrong order. Ask for a volunteer to stand on the starting number and move onto the next sheet physically showing the order of the calculation. The student should be encouraged to describe how they would do the calculation as they stand on the different pieces of paper. (5 minutes)

What's the question? – Give students an answer to a yield or atom economy question, including full calculations. Encourage the students to work in small groups to generate questions that match the answer given. (10 minutes)

List – In reality, no reaction ever produces the theoretical yield. Ask the students to think about why this is so, and note their ideas on a spider diagram in their books. Then ask them to contribute to an exhaustive diagram on the board – they should amend their own to ensure all the points are included and are correct. (15 minutes)

C2 3.5 Making as much as we want

LEARNING OBJECTIVES

1. What do we mean by the yield of a chemical reaction and what factors affect it?
2. How do we calculate the yield of a chemical reaction? [Higher]
3. What is atom economy and why is it important?
4. How do we calculate atom economy? [Higher]

Many of the substances that we use every day have to be made from other chemicals, using complex chemical reactions. Food colourings, flavourings and preservatives, the ink in your pen or computer printer, the artificial fibres in your clothes – all of these are made using chemical reactions.

One simple kind of reaction for making a new substance is when we make a new chemical from two others, like this:

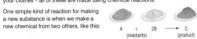

A + 2B ⟶ C
(reactants) (product)

If we need 1000 kg of C it seems quite simple for us to work out how much A and B we need to make it. As we saw earlier in this chapter, all we need to know is the relative formula masses of A, B and C.

a) How many moles of B are needed to react with each mole of A in this reaction?
b) How many moles of C will this make?

If we carry out our reaction, it is very unlikely that we will get as much of C as we think. This is because our calculations assumed that ***all*** of A and B would be turned into C. We call the amount of product that a chemical reaction produces its **yield**.

Calculating percentage yield (HIGHER)

Rather than talking about the yield of a chemical reaction in grams, kilograms or tonnes it is much more useful to talk about its **percentage yield**. This compares the amount of product that the reaction ***really*** produces with the maximum amount that it could ***possibly*** produce:

$$\text{percentage yield} = \frac{\text{amount of product produced}}{\text{maximum amount of product possible}} \times 100\%$$

Worked example

Using known masses of A and B, it was calculated that the chemical reaction above could produce 2.5 g of product, C. When the reaction is carried out, only 1.5 g of C is produced.

What is the percentage yield of this reaction?

Solution

$$\text{Percentage yield} = \frac{\text{amount of product produced}}{\text{maximum amount of product possible}} \times 100\%$$

$$= \frac{1.5}{2.5} \times 100\%$$

$$= 60\%$$

The percentage yield is **60%**.

c) How is percentage yield calculated?

Very few chemical reactions have a yield of 100% because:

- The reaction may be reversible (so as products form they react to form the reactants again).
- Some reactants may react to give unexpected products.
- Some of the product may be left behind in the apparatus.
- The reactants may not be completely pure.
- Some chemical reactions produce more than one product, and it may be difficult to separate the product that we want from the reaction mixture.

Atom economy

Chemical companies use chemical reactions to make products which they sell. So it is very important to use chemical reactions that produce as much product as possible. In other words, it is better for them to use chemical reactions with high yields.

Making as much product as possible means making less waste. It means that as much product as possible is being made from the reactants. This is good news for the company's finances, and good news for the environment too.

The amount of the starting materials that end up as useful products is called the **atom economy**. So the aim is to achieve maximum atom economy.

(HIGHER)

We can calculate percentage atom economy using this equation:

$$\text{percentage atom economy} = \frac{\text{relative formula mass of useful product}}{\text{relative formula mass of all products}} \times 100$$

Worked example

Ethanol (C_2H_5OH) can be converted into ethene (C_2H_4) which can be used to make poly(ethene).

Solution

$$C_2H_5OH \longrightarrow C_2H_4 + H_2O$$

M_r values: $(12 \times 2) + (1 \times 4) = 28$; $(1 \times 2) + (16 \times 1) = 18$

$$\text{percentage atom economy} = \frac{28}{(28 + 18)} \times 100 = 61\%$$

To conserve the Earth's resources, as well as reduce pollution and waste, industry tries to maximise both atom economy and percentage yield.

SUMMARY QUESTIONS

1. Copy and complete using the words below:

   high maximum percentage product waste yield

   The amount of ...... made in a chemical reaction is called its .... The ...... yield tells us the amount of product that is made compared to the ...... amount that could be made. Reactions with ...... yields are important because they make less ....
2. A reaction produces a product which has a relative formula mass of 80. The total of the relative formula masses of all the products is 120. What is the percentage atom economy of this reaction? [Higher]
3. A reaction that could produce 200 g of product produces only 140 g. What is its percentage yield? [Higher]
4. If the percentage yield for a reaction is 100%, 60 g of reactant A would make 80 g of product C. How much of reactant A is needed to make 80 g of product C if the percentage yield of the reaction is only 75%? [Higher]

SCIENCE @ WORK

Chemical factories (or *plants*) are designed by chemical engineers. It's the job of a chemical engineer to try to ensure that the yield of a chemical reaction means that the plant makes the product safely and economically. It should waste as little energy and raw materials as possible.

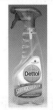

Figure 1 When you make and sell large quantities of chemicals, it's important to know the yield of the reactions you are using

KEY POINTS

1. The yield of a chemical reaction describes how much product is made.
2. The percentage yield of a chemical reaction tells us how much product is made compared with the maximum amount that could be made (100%). [Higher]
3. Factors affecting the yield of a chemical reaction include product being left behind in the apparatus and difficulty separating the products from the reaction mixture.
4. It is important to maximise atom economy to conserve resources and reduce pollution.

SUMMARY ANSWERS

1. Product, yield, percentage, maximum, high, waste.
2. 67% [**HT** only]
3. 70% [**HT** only]
4. 80 g [**HT** only]

Answers to in-text questions

a) 2

b) 1

c) (amount of product made ÷ amount of product possible) × 100%

KEY POINTS

Give the students a crossword using key words from the key points, e.g. yield.

C2 3.6

Reversible reactions

Teaching suggestions

- **Special needs.** The sections to form the flow chart to explain the equilibrium system could be made into a cut and stick activity.

- **Learning styles**

  Kinaesthetic: Moving to show the answers to the 'true or false' plenary.

  Visual: Creating a flow chart to explain an equilibrium system.

  Auditory: Listening to the true or false statements.

  Interpersonal: Working in pairs to match key words with their definitions.

  Intrapersonal: Reflecting on their own learning.

- **Homework.** Ask students to find one further example of an equilibrium reaction and write a word and symbol equation to represent it.

Answers to in-text questions

a) The reaction goes in the forward direction only.

b) The reaction is reversible.

c) The two rates are equal.

SPECIFICATION LINK-UP   Unit: Chemistry 2.12.3

- *In some chemical reactions, the products of the reaction can react to produce the original reactants. Such reactions are called reversible reactions and are represented by:*

  $$A + B \rightleftharpoons C + D$$

  For example: ammonium chloride $\rightleftharpoons$ ammonia + hydrogen chloride

- *When a reversible reaction occurs in a closed system, equilibrium is reached when the reactions occur at exactly the same rate in each direction. [HT only]*

- *The relative amounts of all the reacting substances at equilibrium depends on the conditions of the reaction. [HT only]*

Lesson structure

STARTER

Card sort – Create a card sort for the students to match the key words with their definitions. Put the cards into envelopes and give each pair of students a set to sort out on their desk. Then ask students to pick three new words and write them in their book, including the definition.

Reactants – starting substances in a chemical reaction.

Products – substances left at the end of a chemical reaction.

Reversible reaction – where the reactants make the products and the products make the reactants.

Closed system – where no reactants or products can get in or out.

Equilibrium – when the reactants are making the products at the same rate as the products making the reactants. (10 minutes)

Reflection – Ask students to draw a table with three columns headed: 'What I already know', 'What I want to know', 'What I know now'. Encourage the students to look at the title of the page and the objectives. Then ask them to fill in the first column with bullet points of facts they already know about the topic. Then ask them to think of questions that they think they need to have answered by the end of the lesson and note these in the second column. (10 minutes)

MAIN

- Heating ammonium chloride causes thermal decomposition to form ammonia and hydrogen chloride. This reaction can be completed experimentally in the lab by heating ammonium chloride in a boiling tube, then relating this to reversible reactions. Encourage the students to focus their attention on the cool part of the boiling tube, and ask them to explain in the form of a flow chart what is happening in the boiling tube.

- Hydrated copper sulfate is blue, and on heating it loses its water of crystallisation. This is a reversible reaction on the addition of water. Students could complete this practical and then explain why it is a reversible reaction.

- Show students the Animation C3 3.6 'Reversible energy' from the Additional Science CD ROM.

PLENARIES

Reflection – Ask students to review their starter table ('Reflection') and use a different colour pen/pencil to correct any misconceptions from the start of the lesson. Then ask the students to answer the questions that they posed. If they can't, encourage them to talk in small groups, consult the Student Book, and if necessary ask you. Finally, students should record, in bullet-point format, any other facts that they have picked up during the lesson, in the last column. (10 minutes)

True or false – On separate sheets of sugar paper, write the words 'true' and 'false'. Then stick them on opposite sides of the classroom. Read out statements. Students should stand next to the wall to represent their answer. If they don't know, they should stand in the centre of the room.

All chemical reactions are reversible. [False]

A closed system has no mass change. [True]

Equilibrium can only happen in closed systems. [True]

A double-headed arrow in an equation shows that it is a non-reversible reaction. [False]

In a reversible reaction, reactants make products and products make reactants. [True]

(5 minutes)

Practical support

Heating ammonium chloride

Equipment and materials required

A boiling tube, boiling tube holder, Bunsen burner and safety equipment, mineral wool, spatula, ammonium chloride, eye protection.

Details

Put about half a spatula of ammonium chloride into a boiling tube and insert a mineral wool plug at the top. Gently heat in a Bunsen flame.

Safety: Eye protection should be worn at all times. As acidic hydrogen chloride gas and alkaline ammonia gas are produced, the mineral plug must be used and the reaction should be carried out in a well-ventilated room. Ammonium chloride is harmful – CLEAPSS Hazcard 9.

Heating copper sulfate

Equipment and materials required

A boiling tube, boiling tube holder, Bunsen burner and safety equipment, spatula, hydrated copper sulfate, wash bottle, eye protection.

Details

- Put about half a spatula of hydrated copper sulfate into a boiling tube and heat gently on a Bunsen flame until the colour change to white is complete. Remove from the heat and allow the boiling tube to cool. Then add a few drops of water and observe.

- **Safety:** Be careful to allow the boiling tube to cool before adding water as the glass could crack. Eye protection should be worn throughout this experiment. Copper sulfate is harmful – CLEAPSS Hazcard 27.

ACTIVITY & EXTENSION IDEAS

- The colour changes produced by indicators are reversible reactions. Students could find out (experimentally or using secondary resources) the colours different indicators go in acidic/neutral/alkaline solutions.

- Chromate ions form an equilibrium mixture with dichromate ions. These substances were used in the first breathalysers. Encourage students to find out the chemical reactions that occurred in these early testers.

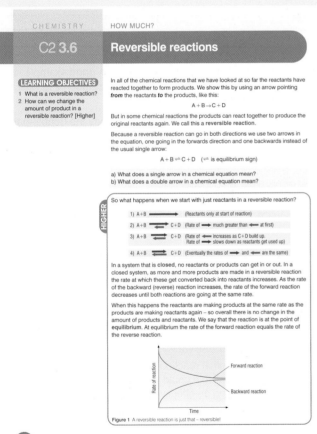

CHEMISTRY   HOW MUCH?

C2 3.6   Reversible reactions

LEARNING OBJECTIVES

1 What is a reversible reaction?
2 How can we change the amount of product in a reversible reaction? [Higher]

In all of the chemical reactions that we have looked at so far the reactants have reacted together to form products. We show this by using an arrow pointing *from* the reactants *to* the products, like this:

$$A + B \rightarrow C + D$$

But in some chemical reactions the products can react together to produce the original reactants again. We call this a **reversible reaction**.

Because a reversible reaction can go in both directions we use two arrows in the equation, one going in the forwards direction and one backwards instead of the usual single arrow:

$$A + B \rightleftharpoons C + D \quad (\rightleftharpoons \text{ is equilibrium sign})$$

a) What does a single arrow in a chemical equation mean?
b) What does a double arrow in a chemical equation mean?

HIGHER

So what happens when we start with just reactants in a reversible reaction?

1) $A + B \longrightarrow$ (Reactants only at start of reaction)

2) $A + B \rightleftharpoons C + D$ (Rate of $\longrightarrow$ much greater than $\longleftarrow$ at first)

3) $A + B \rightleftharpoons C + D$ (Rate of $\longrightarrow$ increases as C+D build up.
Rate of $\longrightarrow$ slows down as reactants get used up)

4) $A + B \rightleftharpoons C + D$ (Eventually the rates of $\longrightarrow$ and $\longleftarrow$ are the same)

In a system that is **closed**, no reactants or products can get in or out. In a closed system, as more and more products are made in a reversible reaction the rate at which these get converted back into reactants increases. As the rate of the backward (reverse) reaction increases, the rate of the forward reaction decreases until both reactions are going at the same rate.

When this happens the reactants are making products at the same rate as the products are making reactants again – so overall there is no change in the amount of products and reactants. We say that the reaction is at the point of **equilibrium**. At equilibrium the rate of the forward reaction equals the rate of the reverse reaction.

Rate of reaction

Forward reaction

Backward reaction

Time

Figure 1 A reversible reaction is just that – reversible!

c) How does the rate of the backward reaction compare to the rate of the forward reaction at equilibrium?

One example of a reversible reaction is the reaction between iodine monochloride (ICl) and chlorine gas. Iodine monochloride is a brown liquid, while chlorine is a green gas. We can react these substances together to make yellow crystals of iodine trichloride (ICl_3).

When there is plenty of chlorine gas the forward reaction makes iodine trichloride crystals which are quite stable. But if we lower the concentration of chlorine gas the backward (reverse) reaction turns iodine trichloride back to iodine monochloride and chlorine.

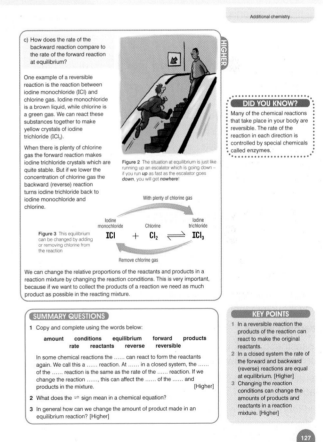

Figure 2 The situation at equilibrium is just like running up an escalator which is going down – if you run *up* as fast as the escalator goes *down*, you will get *nowhere*!

With plenty of chlorine gas

iodine   Chlorine   Iodine
monochloride   trichloride

$$ICl + Cl_2 \rightleftharpoons ICl_3$$

Figure 3 This equilibrium can be changed by adding or removing chlorine from the reaction

Remove chlorine gas

We can change the relative proportions of the reactants and products in a reaction mixture by changing the reaction conditions. This is very important, because if we want to collect the products of a reaction we need as much product as possible in the reacting mixture.

HIGHER

DID YOU KNOW?

Many of the chemical reactions that take place in your body are reversible. The rate of the reaction in each direction is controlled by special chemicals called enzymes.

SUMMARY QUESTIONS

1 Copy and complete using the words below:

> amount   conditions   equilibrium   forward   products
> rate   reactants   reverse   reversible

In some chemical reactions the ...... can react to form the reactants again. We call this a ...... reaction. At ...... in a closed system, the ...... of the ...... reaction is the same as the rate of the ...... reaction. If we change the reaction ......, this can affect the ...... of the ...... and products in the mixture. [Higher]

2 What does the $\rightleftharpoons$ sign mean in a chemical equation?

3 In general how can we change the amount of product made in an equilibrium reaction? [Higher]

KEY POINTS

1 In a reversible reaction the products of the reaction can react to make the original reactants.

2 In a closed system the rate of the forward and backward (reverse) reactions are equal at equilibrium. [Higher]

3 Changing the reaction conditions can change the amounts of products and reactants in a reaction mixture. [Higher]

SUMMARY ANSWERS

1 Products, reversible, equilibrium, rate, forward (reverse), reverse (forward), conditions, amount, reactants.

2 The reaction is reversible.

3 Change the conditions or add reactants and/or remove products.

DID YOU KNOW?

Enzymes are biological catalysts made of proteins. Proteins work best in optimum conditions, if the body strays too far from this ideal the enzyme proteins denature and no longer have an effective active site.

KEY POINTS

Split the class into three groups and give each group a key point. They should generate reasons to why their point is the most important of the three. Then encourage the students to debate the issue.

C2 3.7

Making ammonia – the Haber process

(See pages 152–3)

LEARNING OBJECTIVES

Students should learn that:

- Ammonia is an important chemical.

- How ammonia can be made.

- How waste from ammonia production can be minimised.

LEARNING OUTCOMES

Most students should be able to:

- Give a use for ammonia.

- Name the raw materials for the Haber process.

- Write the word equation for the production of ammonia.

- Quote the reaction conditions to make ammonia.

- Explain how waste is minimised.

Some students should also be able to:

- Complete a balanced symbol equation for the production of ammonia. [**HT** only]

- Explain the choice of reaction conditions for the production of ammonia. [**HT** only]

Teaching suggestions

- **Special needs.** A simple script for the factory tour could be provided to the students. However, the paragraphs could be in the wrong order. Students should then order the information and copy it out into their own work.

- **Learning styles**

  Kinaesthetic: Finding the partners for questions and answers.

  Visual: Watching a video about the Haber process.

  Auditory: Preparing and listening to audio revision.

  Interpersonal: Working in small groups to make a script for a factory tour.

  Intrapersonal: Finding elements and compounds in text.

- **Homework.** Ammonia is an important chemical: ask students to find three uses for ammonia.

- **ICT link-up.** There are a number of models for the Haber process available. In some of them, it is possible for students to vary conditions and view the effect that it has on yield.

SPECIFICATION LINK-UP   Unit: Chemistry 2.12.3

- *Although reversible reactions may not go to completion they can still be used efficiently in continuous industrial processes, such as the Haber process that is used to manufacture ammonia.*

- *The raw materials for the Haber process are nitrogen and hydrogen. Nitrogen is obtained from the air and hydrogen may be obtained from natural gas or other sources.*

- *The purified gases are passed over a catalyst of iron at a high temperature (about 450°C) and high pressure (about 200 atmospheres). Some of the hydrogen and nitrogen reacts to form ammonia. The reaction is reversible so ammonia breaks down again into nitrogen and hydrogen:*

$$nitrogen + hydrogen \rightleftharpoons ammonia$$

- *On cooling, the ammonia liquefies and is removed. The remaining hydrogen and nitrogen is re-cycled.*

- *The reaction conditions are chosen to produce a reasonable yield of ammonia quickly.* [**HT** only] (See pages 152–3)

Lesson structure

STARTER

Video – Show a video about the industrial production of ammonia. A good example is the RSC *Industrial Chemistry* video (from RSC www.rsc.org). Ask the students to note down the raw materials and reaction conditions. (10 minutes)

DART (Directed Activity Relating to Text) – Ask the students to study the double-page spread and make a list of all the elements and compounds that are mentioned. [**Elements** – nitrogen, hydrogen, iron; **Compounds** – ammonia, nitrates, methane.] (5 minutes)

MAIN

- Show students the Simulation C2 3.7 'Making Ammonia' and allow them to explore the resource if possible.

- Ask students if they have ever been to a factory tour like 'Cadbury World' or 'Wedgwood'. Ask a few students to recall their experiences of the visit. Split the class into small groups and ask them to prepare a tour guide for a factory tour of an ammonia plant.

- Encourage them to write a script for the guide including what they should point out to the guests. They could even include diagrams or images of certain sections.

- The students could extend this activity by making a visitor guidebook.

- The Haber process in an important industrial reaction met at many levels in chemistry. Other scientific posters commercially available could be shown to students to give them ideas on how to approach designing an effective poster.

- Encourage them to make a poster to highlight the important aspects of the Haber process, including a balanced symbol equation.

- Encourage students to create their own script for an audio revision guide. Their section should last no more than 3 minutes.

- NB The Higher Tier statement in the specification regarding choice of operating conditions for the Haber process is covered in more detail on pages 152–3 in the Student Book. The concepts introduced in Chapters 4 and 5 really need to be covered before students can understand fully the conditions chosen. Then higher attaining students can discuss in detail the sometimes conflicting factors affecting rate of reaction, yield, safety and economics of the process.

PLENARIES

Questions and answers – Give each student a slip of paper (about A5 in size). Ask them to write a question and its answer on the paper about the Haber process and reversible reactions. Then ask them to cut each answer free from the question and give them to you. Now give a question and answer to each student but they should not match. Read the first question out, the student with the correct answer should read it out, then read their question and so on around the room. (10 minutes)

Flow chart – Give the students an outline of a flow chart to show the process of making ammonia. Encourage them to add labels to summarise the reaction. (5 minutes)

Performance – Students could perform their own audio revision piece for the Haber process. They could record theirs using digital technology and this could be put onto the school web site to help others with revision. (15 minutes)

Before the Haber process was invented, ammonia had already been discovered and was being used for a variety of things including fertilisers. Ask the students to research where this ammonia came from [urine].

CHEMISTRY   HOW MUCH?

C2 3.7 Making ammonia – the Haber process

LEARNING OBJECTIVES

1 Why is ammonia important?
2 How do we make ammonia?
3 How can we make ammonia without wasting raw materials?

We need plants – for food, and as a way of providing the oxygen that we breathe. Plants need nitrogen to grow, and although this gas makes up about 80% of the air around us, plants cannot use it because it is very unreactive.

Instead, plants absorb soluble nitrates from the soil through their roots. When we harvest plants these nitrates are lost – so we need to replace them. Nowadays we usually do this by adding nitrate fertilisers to the soil. We make these fertilisers using a process invented nearly 100 years ago by a young German chemist called Fritz Haber.

a) Why can't plants use the nitrogen from the air?
b) Where do plants get their nitrogen from?

Figure 1 Plants are surrounded by nitrogen in the air. They cannot use this nitrogen, and rely on soluble nitrates in the soil instead. We supply these by spreading fertiliser on the soil.

The Haber process

The Haber process provides us with a way of turning the nitrogen in the air into ammonia. We can use ammonia in many different ways. One of the most important of these is to make fertilisers.

The raw materials for making ammonia are:

• nitrogen from the air, and
• hydrogen which we get from natural gas (containing mainly methane, CH_4).

The nitrogen and hydrogen are purified and then passed over an iron catalyst at high temperatures (about 450°C) and pressures (about 200 atmospheres). The product of this chemical reaction is ammonia.

c) What are the two raw materials needed to make ammonia?

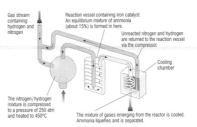

Gas stream containing hydrogen and nitrogen

Reaction vessel containing iron catalyst. An equilibrium mixture of ammonia (about 15%) is formed in here.

Unreacted nitrogen and hydrogen are returned to the reaction vessel via the compressor.

Cooling chamber

The nitrogen/hydrogen mixture is compressed to a pressure of 250 atm and heated to 450°C

The mixture of gases emerging from the reactor is cooled. Ammonia liquefies and is separated.

Figure 2 The Haber process

The reaction used in the Haber process is reversible, which means that the ammonia breaks down again into hydrogen and nitrogen. To reduce this, we have to remove the ammonia by cooling and liquefying it as soon as it is formed. We can then recycle any hydrogen and nitrogen that is left so that it has a chance to react again.

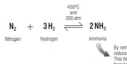

$$N_2 + 3H_2 \rightleftharpoons 2NH_3$$

Nitrogen   Hydrogen   Ammonia

450°C and 200 atm

By removing the ammonia that forms we can reduce the rate of the backwards reaction. This helps to stop the ammonia that is formed from breaking down into nitrogen and hydrogen.

We carry out the Haber process in conditions that have been carefully chosen to give a reasonable yield of ammonia as quickly as possible. (See pages 152–3.)

d) How is ammonia removed from the reaction mixture?
e) How do we make sure the reactants are not wasted?

SUMMARY QUESTIONS

1 Copy and complete using the words below:

air   fertilisers   gas   450   hydrogen   iron   liquefying
nitrogen   removed   200

Ammonia is an important chemical used for making .... The raw materials are ...... from the ...... and ...... from natural .... These are reacted at about ...... °C and ...... atmospheres pressure using an ...... catalyst. Ammonia is ...... from the reaction mixture before it can break down into the reactants again by ...... the gas.

2 Draw a flow diagram to show how the Haber process is used to make ammonia.

KEY POINTS

1 Ammonia is an important chemical for making other chemicals, including fertilisers.
2 Ammonia is made from nitrogen and hydrogen in the Haber process.
3 We carry out the Haber process under conditions which are chosen to give a reasonable yield of ammonia as quickly as possible.
4 Any unused nitrogen and hydrogen are recycled in the Haber process.

128   129

SUMMARY ANSWERS

1 Fertilisers, nitrogen, air, hydrogen, gas, 450, 200, iron, removed, liquefying.

2

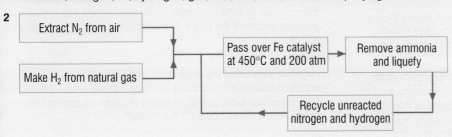

Answers to in-text questions

a) Because it is very unreactive.

b) From nitrates in the soil, absorbed through their roots.

c) Nitrogen and hydrogen.

d) The gases are cooled down and ammonia is liquefied/condensed and run off.

e) The unreacted nitrogen and hydrogen are recycled into the reaction vessel.

KEY POINTS

Give each key word an action, e.g. for Haber clap hands. Then read out the passage and the students can put in the actions.

C2 3.8 Aspects of the Haber process

Students should use their skills, knowledge and understanding of 'How Science Works':

- ... to evaluate sustainable development issues related to atom economy. [**HT** only]

This spread can be used to revisit the following substantive content already covered in this chapter:

- *Although reversible reactions may not go to completion they can still be used efficiently in continuous industrial processes, such as the Haber process that is used to manufacture ammonia.*

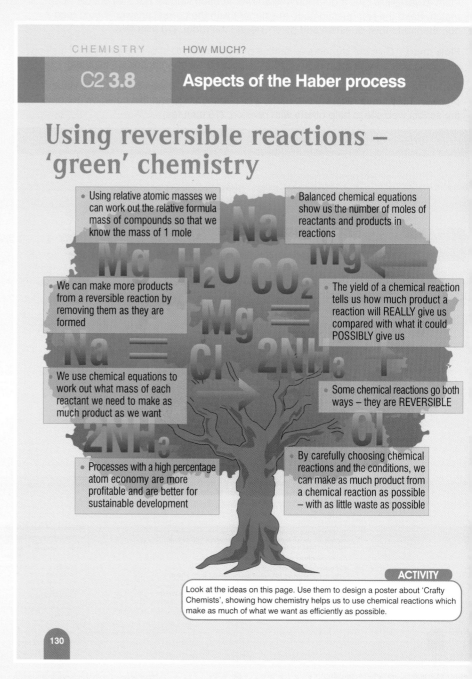

Using reversible reactions – 'green' chemistry

- Using relative atomic masses we can work out the relative formula mass of compounds so that we know the mass of 1 mole

- Balanced chemical equations show us the number of moles of reactants and products in reactions

- We can make more products from a reversible reaction by removing them as they are formed

- The yield of a chemical reaction tells us how much product a reaction will REALLY give us compared with what it could POSSIBLY give us

- We use chemical equations to work out what mass of each reactant we need to make as much product as we want

- Some chemical reactions go both ways – they are REVERSIBLE

- Processes with a high percentage atom economy are more profitable and are better for sustainable development

- By carefully choosing chemical reactions and the conditions, we can make as much product from a chemical reaction as possible – with as little waste as possible

ACTIVITY

Look at the ideas on this page. Use them to design a poster about 'Crafty Chemists', showing how chemistry helps us to use chemical reactions which make as much of what we want as efficiently as possible.

130

Teaching suggestions

Activities

- **Poster** – Show the students some thought-provoking posters about innovative use of chemistry, e.g. upd8 (at upd8.org.uk) or RSC (at www.rsc.org). Encourage them to make a poster to highlight the use of chemistry to maximise yields. They could make their poster using a desktop publishing package on the computer.

- **Letter/e-mail** – Show the students images of different scientific laboratories from modern-day research facilities. Encourage them to work out a list of reasons why it is important to complete weapons research and a converse list of why weapons research should be halted. Ask the students to imagine that they are either:
  - A brilliant young chemist, and write an e-mail or letter explaining to a friend that you will be taking this position.
  - A friend of a scientist working in the facility, and write an e-mail or letter outlining why you do not think they should work in this job.

If the student is writing a letter, encourage them to use correct letter format and they could even write their letter onto paper. If they choose to write an e-mail, they could type it into their e-mail account and print the page. The writing could then be used as a display.

- **Discuss** – Groups of five or six could discuss the positive and negative aspects of the work done by Fritz Haber. Further research following the articles on page 131 will reveal the societal influences on Haber at that time and his disillusionment before death. Show PhotoPLUS C2 3.8 'Haber'.

Homework

- **Location** – Ask the students to find a location of an ammonia plant and detail the reasons why it is positioned there.

Fritz Haber – a good life or a bad one?

Der Newsweb

Donnerstag 14. Oktober 1920

Fritz Haber - German Patriot

Early on in the First World War both sides became bogged down in trench warfare. Fritz Haber focused on what he could do to bring about German victory. He thought that poison gas would penetrate the strongest defences, allowing Germany to win the war.

Poison gases were already available as unwanted by-products of chemical processes. Haber experimented with these gases to find those suitable to use on the battlefield. He focused on chlorine gas.

The Germans used chlorine for the first time on 22nd April 1915, against French and Algerian troops in Belgium. They released 200 tonnes of gas which rolled into the allied lines. The allied soldiers choked

in agony, and slowly died. The gas cloud tinted everything a sickly green. Those who could escape the cloud fled in panic.

The soldier Wilfrid Owen wrote:

GAS! Gas! Quick, boys! – An ecstasy of fumbling,
Fitting the clumsy helmets just in time;
But someone still was yelling out and stumbling
And floundering like a man in fire or lime.
Dim, through the misty panes and thick green light
As under a green sea, I saw him drowning.
In all my dreams, before my helpless sight,
He plunges at me, guttering, choking, drowning.

19th November 1920 1d — Palestine becomes British mandate - page 4

Tragedy of Clara Haber

Clara Haber had graduated as the first woman from the University of Breslau in Germany in 1900. At this time many professors were still against female students. She married Fritz Haber in 1901. Clara could not continue her research work because she was a woman. Instead, she contributed to her husband's work, although her support was never mentioned. Because of her support Haber was promoted very quickly.

Clara was deeply opposed to warfare, and especially to the use of science in war. She called Haber's work a 'perversion of science'. Unable to stop him, Clara committed suicide in May 1915. Her death was never announced in the newspapers.

League of Nations holds first meeting in Geneva, Switzerland

ACTIVITY

A new laboratory has been set up to develop a new chemical to be used as a weapon.

Either: As a brilliant young chemist you have been invited to go and work in this laboratory. Write a letter or e-mail to a friend explaining why you are planning to accept this invitation.

Or: A friend has been invited to go and work in this laboratory. Write a letter or e-mail to this friend explaining why you think they should not go and work in this laboratory.

131

Extension

Spot the difference – Show the students images of different scientific laboratories throughout the ages, including modern-day research facilities. Ask them to work in pairs and note down all the similarities and all the differences. Feedback to the class using question and answer session.

Learning styles

Visual: Looking at different images of laboratories.

Auditory: Listening to other students' work.

Interpersonal: Working in pairs on posters.

Intrapersonal: Penning letters and e-mails.

ICT link-up

Get images of different laboratories from a Google image search. Then project them onto the interactive whiteboard and mark the differences (perhaps in red) and the similarities (maybe in green).

Gifted and talented

Split the class into groups of about six. They are to imagine that they are being commissioned by an international chemical company to site an ammonia plant and decide on its working conditions. The chemical company is multinational, so the group can site the plant anywhere in the world, but they need to reason out all of their decisions, including running conditions of the plant. The group could then create a persuasive 5-minute presentation of their proposal.

SUMMARY ANSWERS

1 **a)** B **b)** A **c)** D **d)** C

2 **a)** 44 g

b) 28 g

c) 100 g

d) 94 g

e) 206 g

3 **a)** 0.5

b) 0.1

c) 0.01

4 $AlBr_3$ [**HT** only]

5 56% [**HT** only]

6 **a)** A reaction that can go in either direction, i.e. products→reactants as well as reactants→products.

b) An 'ordinary' reaction is normally regarded as going in one direction only, i.e. the 'forward' direction.

c) 450°C; 200 atm; iron catalyst

Summary teaching suggestions

- **Special needs** – Question 1 could be made into a card sort, allowing the students to match up the start and end of sentences and then writing them out once they make sense.

- **When to use the questions?**
  - These questions could be used for revision at the end of the topic.
  - Question 6 could make a good extended homework piece. The students could be encouraged to answer this question in an essay style. Then the following lesson, they could swap their scripts with another student who could be provided with a marking scheme. Students could then assess each others' work.
  - Questions 2, 3, 4 and 5 are further examples of calculation questions, and could be used as an extension or for homework during lessons 3.2–3.4.

- **Learning styles**
  Kinaesthetic: Question 1 lends itself to being completed with a card sort.
  Interpersonal: Question 6 could be completed through a class discussion before students pen their own answers.
  Intrapersonal: Questions 2, 3, 4 and 5 lend themselves to individuals completing their own work.

- **Misconceptions** – Question 4 requires students to generate the formula of a compound after being given the mass of each element. Students often forget to calculate the number of moles of each element first and just complete a formula based on the ratio of the masses instead.

EXAM-STYLE ANSWERS

1 **a)** *One each for:*
- Atoms of the same element/with the same number of protons/same atomic number.
- But different numbers of neutrons/different mass numbers.
(2 marks)

b) 1 proton *(1 mark)*, 1 electron *(1 mark)*, 2 neutrons *(1 mark)*

c) 20 – *correct answer gains 2 marks.*
One mark can be gained for showing correct working: $(2 \times 2) + 16$

2 **a)** 152 – *correct answer gains 2 marks.*
One mark can be gained for showing correct working:
$56 + 32 + (16 \times 4)$

b) 36.8% – *correct answer gains 2 marks (accept 37% or 36.84%)*
One mark can be gained for showing correct working:
$56 \times 100/152$

SUMMARY QUESTIONS

1 Match up the parts of the sentences:

a) Neutrons have a relative mass of	A ...... negligible mass compared to protons and neutrons.
b) Electrons have	B ...... 1 compared to protons.
c) Protons have a relative mass of	C ...... found in its nucleus.
d) Nearly all of an atom's mass is	D ...... 1 compared to neutrons.

2 Calculate the mass of 1 mole of each of the following compounds:
a) CO_2
b) B_2H_6
c) $CaCO_3$
d) K_2O
e) $KMnO_4$
(A_r values: C = 12, O = 16, B = 11, H = 1, Ca = 40, K = 39, Mn = 55)

3 How many moles of
a) Ag atoms are there in 54 g of silver,
b) P atoms are there in 3.1 g of phosphorus,
c) Fe atoms are there in 0.56 g of iron?
(A_r values: Ag = 108, P = 31, Fe = 56)

4 When aluminium reacts with bromine, 1.35 g of aluminium reacts with 12.0 g of bromine. What is the empirical formula of aluminium bromide?
(A_r values: Al = 27, Br = 80)   [Higher]

5 In a lime kiln, calcium carbonate is decomposed to calcium oxide:
$CaCO_3 \rightarrow CaO + CO_2$
Calculate the percentage atom economy for the process (assuming 100% conversion).
(A_r values: Ca = 40, O = 16, C = 12)   [Higher]

6 a) What is a reversible reaction?
b) How does a reversible reaction differ from an 'ordinary' reaction?
c) State the conditions chosen for the Haber process to convert nitrogen and hydrogen into ammonia.

EXAM-STYLE QUESTIONS

1 Hydrogen has three isotopes, ^1_1H, ^2_1H, and ^3_1H.
(a) What are isotopes?
(b) How many protons, neutrons and electrons are there in an atom of ^2_1H?
(c) Heavy water contains atoms of the isotope ^2_1H instead of ^1_1H. It has the formula $^2_1H_2O$. What is the mass of one mole of heavy water?

2 Tablets taken by people with iron deficiency anaemia contain 0.200 g of anhydrous iron(II) sulfate, $FeSO_4$.
(a) Calculate the relative formula mass of iron(II) sulfate, $FeSO_4$.
(b) Calculate the percentage of iron in iron(II) sulfate.
(c) Calculate the mass of iron in each tablet.

3 The equation for the main reaction to make ammonia is
$$N_2 + 3H_2 \rightleftharpoons 2NH_3$$
(a) What does the symbol $\rightleftharpoons$ tell you about this reaction?
(b) The flow diagram shows the main stages in making ammonia.

(i) Name the two raw materials **A** and **B**.
(ii) What is the purpose of the iron in the reactor?
(iii) Why do the nitrogen and hydrogen not react completely?
(iv) How is wastage of unreacted nitrogen and hydrogen prevented?

4 The equation for the reaction of calcium carbonate with hydrochloric acid is:
$$CaCO_3 + 2HCl \rightarrow CaCl_2 + CO_2 + H_2O$$

---

c) 0.074 g – *correct answer gains 2 marks (accept 0.0737 g or 0.07 g or correct answer based on answer to part (b) – error carried forward)*
One mark can be gained for showing correct working:
e.g. $0.2 \times 36.8/100$

3 **a)** Reversible reaction.   *(1 mark)*

b) i)   A is air *(1 mark)* B is methane or natural gas.   *(1 mark)*
ii) Catalyst.   *(1 mark)*
iii) *One from:*
- Reverse reaction takes place.
- Ammonia breaks down to form nitrogen and hydrogen.   *(1 mark)*
iv) They are recycled/returned to the reactor.   *(1 mark)*

4 **a)** 2   *(1 mark)*

b) 1   *(1 mark)*

c) 111 g – *correct answer gains 2 marks.*
One mark can be gained for showing correct working: e.g.
$40 + (35.5 \times 2)$

d) 100 g – *correct answer gains 2 marks.*
One mark can be gained for showing correct working:
e.g. $40 + 12 + (16 \times 3)$

e) 66.7% – *correct answer gains 2 marks (accept 66.67 or 67 or correct answer based on answers to part d) and part c) – error carried forward).*
One mark can be gained for correct working:
e.g. $(7.4 \times 100)/(10 \times 111/100)$ [**HT** only]

5 **a)** 104 g – *correct answer gains 2 marks.*
One mark can be gained for showing correct working: e.g. 2×52

b) Using aluminium: 50.5% – *correct answer gains 2 marks.*
One mark can be gained for correct working:
e.g. $(104 \times 100)/(104 + 102)$
Using carbon: 61.2% – *correct answer gains 2 marks.*
One mark can be gained for correct working:
e.g. $(208 \times 100)/(208 + 132)$

HOW SCIENCE WORKS QUESTIONS

(a) How many moles of hydrochloric acid react with one mole of calcium carbonate? (1)

(b) How many moles of calcium chloride are produced from one mole of calcium carbonate? (1)

(c) What is the mass of calcium chloride that can be made from one mole of calcium carbonate? (2)

(d) What is the mass of one mole of calcium carbonate? (2)

(e) A student reacted 10 g of calcium carbonate with hydrochloric acid and collected 7.4 g of calcium chloride. What was the percentage yield? (2)
[Higher]

Chromium can be obtained from chromium oxide, Cr_2O_3, by reduction with aluminium or carbon. For the first reaction, chromium is mixed with aluminium and ignited in a crucible. The reaction using carbon is done at high temperatures in a low-pressure furnace. The equations for the reactions are:

$$Cr_2O_3 + 2Al \rightarrow 2Cr + Al_2O_3$$
$$2Cr_2O_3 + 3C \rightarrow 4Cr + 3CO_2$$

(a) Calculate the maximum mass of chromium that can be obtained from one mole of chromium oxide. (2)

(b) Calculate the percentage atom economy for both reactions to show which reaction has the better atom economy. (4)

(c) Suggest one advantage and one disadvantage of using carbon to manufacture chromium. (2)
[Higher]

Ibuprofen is used as a pain killer throughout the world. You might know it as Nurofen or Ibuleve. The traditional way to manufacture ibuprofen involved a lot of chemical reactions and produced a lot of waste. The atom economy was just 32%.
Recently it became possible for any pharmaceutical (drug) company to make ibuprofen. As there was a lot of money to be made, the race was on to find the most economic way to make it. This meant cutting down waste. The new method involves catalysts, some of which can be completely recovered and do not go out as waste. The atom economy is increased to 77%, partly because only the active form of ibuprofen is made. This also means that lower doses are needed and they take a shorter time to kill any pain.
Evaluate the two methods of manufacture in terms of the social, economic and environmental issues involved.
[Higher] (6)

A class of students were given the task of finding out how much hydrogen would be produced by different amounts of calcium reacting with water. The hydrogen was collected in an upturned measuring cylinder. The apparatus was set up as is shown.

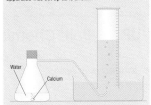

Water   Calcium

Different amounts of calcium were weighed . Each piece was put separately into the flask and the bung put on as quickly as possible. The reaction was left to finish and the volume of hydrogen measured.

The results of the different groups are in the table below.

Mass of Ca (g)	Volume of hydrogen (cm³)				
	A	B	C	D	E
0.05	25	26	27	18	26
0.10	55	53	55	55	52
0.15	85	86	81	89	84
0.20	115	117	109	116	113
0.25	145	146	148	141	140

a) Produce a table to show the mean for all of the groups for each mass of calcium used. (5)

b) Why is the mean often a more useful set of results than any one group? (1)

c) What is the range of volumes when 0.25 grams of calcium are used? (1)

d) What is the sensitivity of the balance used to weigh out the calcium? (1)

e) How could you determine which group had the most accurate results? (1)

f) Look at the method described. Is there any possibility of a systematic error? If so, say how this error could arise. (1)

133

• Percentage atom economies can be calculated from the relative mass of useful product compared with the relative mass of all the atoms in either the reactants or the products, because equations are balanced. Students should be aware that this could be done by either method. Calculating atom economies of different routes to products is a good basis for research and discussion.

HOW SCIENCE WORKS ANSWERS

a)

Mass of Ca (g)	Mean volume, hydrogen (cm³)
0.05	26
0.1	54
0.15	85
0.2	114
0.25	144

Note D for 0.05 g is an anomaly and has been omitted from the calculation.

b) The mean is a more useful result because it is likely to be more accurate.

c) The range of volumes when 0.25 grams of calcium are used – 140 cm³ to 148 cm³.

d) The sensitivity of the balance used to weigh out the calcium is at least 0.05 g.

e) The group which was closest to the mean could be considered the one with the most accurate results. A better way would be to calculate the theoretical volume produced and then compare the different groups.

f) Placing the bung on the flask after the reaction has started will produce a systematic error.

How science works teaching suggestions

• **Literacy guidance.** Key terms that should be clearly understood: mean, range, sensitivity, accuracy, systematic error.

• **Higher- and lower-level answers.** Question e) is a higher-level question and the answers provided above are also at this level. Question b) is lower level and the answer provided is also lower level.

• **Gifted and talented.** Able students could consider how to calculate a theoretical value and whether they have enough information to do this.

• **How and when to use these questions.** When wishing to develop table skills and range and mean calculations. How to assess accuracy. The questions could be part individual and part class discussion depending on the level of understanding of the ideas.

• **Misconceptions.** That all results must be used to calculate a mean. To address this: give an example where this would be obviously incorrect. For example, a student investigating a candle burning under a beaker gets the timings 39 seconds, 43 seconds, 40 seconds and 3 seconds. In fact, on the last repeat test the beaker accidently knocked the candle over into the sand tray. Should the student add $39 + 43 + 40 + 3$, then divide by 4 to get the mean value? Would it be 'cheating' to leave out the last result?

Another misconception is that range is quoted as a single figure. To address this stress how much more information quoting the minimum and maximum values gives us. For example, ask a student the range of ages of their brothers and/or sisters. An answer such as '11 years' is not as useful as 'From 8 years old to 19 years old'.

• **Homework.** Question a) could be set as homework.

• **Special needs.** For these students the table could be reduced to columns C, D and E.

---

c) *One advantage from:*
   • Better atom economy.
   • More economical/carbon costs less than aluminium/ aluminium has to be produced by electrolysis.
   • No solid waste to dispose of.   *(1 mark)*
   One disadvantage from:
   • Produces carbon dioxide/greenhouse gas/global warming.
   • Needs more vigorous conditions for the reduction to take place.   *(1 mark)*
                    [HT only]

6 Social e.g. lower doses OR quicker action in stopping pain *(2 marks)*
   economic e.g. cheaper to manufacture, therefore more profits or cheaper to buy   *(2 marks)*
   environmental e.g. higher atom economy   *(2 marks)*
   The above could be explained by reference to the two methods of manufacture of ibuprofen. If a non-comparative statement is made then maximum 1 mark for each.   **[HT only]**

Exam teaching suggestions

• Allow 40 minutes for the questions on this chapter, which have a total of 41 marks. Q1 could be set after 3.2, Q2 after 3.3, Q4 and Q5 after 3.5, and Q3 at the end of the chapter.

• Most candidates are able to calculate relative formula masses successfully. Questions similar to Q2 invariably appear as parts of larger structured questions in examinations, and candidates should be encouraged to look for and attempt these straightforward calculations. To give additional practice and variety, get pairs or small groups to set each other similar questions on substances for which they have found the formulas in books or on the Internet. The competition can get quite fierce! They can also be used as the basis for comparing the usefulness of compounds such as metal ores, fertilisers and food supplements.

• Students should be encouraged to read calculation questions carefully to check if answers need to include units. Units may be given in the answer space for lower demand questions, but are often not given in higher-tier questions. If a relative mass is asked for, there will be no units, as in Q2a). The mass of an amount in moles requires units, usually grams, as in Q4, parts c) and d).

133

C2 4.1

How fast?

LEARNING OBJECTIVES

Students should learn:

- That chemical reactions can happen at different rates.
- That the rate of a chemical reaction can be measured.

LEARNING OUTCOMES

Most students should be able to:

- State a definition for the rate of reaction.
- List ways that the rate can be measured.

Some students should also be able to:

- Suggest a method for measuring the rate in a specified reaction.
- Explain why a particular method of measuring the rate is suitable for a specified reaction.

Teaching suggestions

- **Special needs.** Graph paper can be confusing for these students. Therefore supply them with squared paper, with the scales already drawn on. Once the students have plotted their graph, you could supply these statements (in the wrong order) for students to copy onto their graph.
  - Start of reaction.
  - Fast rate of reaction.
  - Slow rate of reaction.
  - End of reaction.
- **Learning styles**

  Kinaesthetic: Completing the gas collection practical.

  Visual: Watching the disappearing cross.

  Auditory: Listening to discussions in groups.

  Intrapersonal: Finding the definition for rate of reaction.

  Interpersonal: Working in groups discussing decisions.

- **ICT link-up.** The disappearing cross experiment relies on a person deciding when they think the cross disappears and this introduces errors. A light sensor and data logger could be set up, where a plot of the light intensity could be made. When the light intensity gets to a certain level the result (time) is noted by reading off the graph. (See www.rogerfrost.com.)

SPECIFICATION LINK-UP   Unit: Chemistry 2.12.4

- *The rate of a chemical reaction can be found by measuring the amount of a reactant used or the amount of product formed over time:*

$$\text{Rate of reaction} = \frac{\text{Amount of reactant used or amount of product formed}}{\text{Time}}$$

Students should use their skills, knowledge and understanding of 'How Science Works':

- *to interpret graphs showing the amount of product formed (or reactant used up) with time, in terms of the rate of the reaction.*

Lesson structure

STARTER

Fast or slow – Give each student a piece of paper with 'fast' on one side and 'slow' on the other. Then show them different images of chemical reactions, e.g. rusting, baking a cake, cooking an egg, magnesium reacting with acid, neutralisation, etc. They should look at the image and decide if the rate is fast or slow and hold up the card to demonstrate their answer. Images could be shown using a data projector and having a separate image per PowerPoint® slide. (5 minutes)

Cut and stick – Explain to students what 'rate of reaction' is. Then give the students different magazines and catalogues. Their task is to cut out an example of a reaction with a fast rate and a slow rate. They then compare their findings with a small group (about five students), and they choose the best from their selection. Students could then make a class montage on sugar paper. (15 minutes)

MAIN

- In most chemical reactions that are used to study rate, a gas is made. In order for students to interpret information about a reaction a graph should be produced. Using the reaction between magnesium and acid, get students to plot a graph to show the production of hydrogen over two minutes. Ask them to then annotate their graph to explain the shape. They should include information as to why the graph starts at $0\,cm^3$ of gas and about the shape of the graph.

- The reaction between hydrochloric acid and sodium thiosulfate is the classic example used to highlight how light can be used to measure the rate of reaction. Students could complete this experiment themselves and reflect on the technique. Alternatively, this could be completed as a class demonstration. Draw the black cross onto an OHT and put onto an OHP. Choose a student to be in charge of the stopwatch. Then put the reaction vessel onto the cross, and ask students to raise their hands when they think the cross has gone. When most of the hands are raised, stop the watch and note the time.

- Let class interact with the Simulation C2 4.1 'How fast?' from the Additional Science CD ROM.

PLENARIES

Card sort – Make a set of eight cards, four with diagrams showing how rate of reaction can be measured (mass change, gas collection by displacement in a measuring cylinder, gas collection in a gas syringe, disappearing cross), four with examples of reactions that can be measured using these techniques (magnesium + acid, calcium carbonate + acid, sodium thiosulfate + acid, hydrogen peroxide + manganese dioxide). Ask the students to match the methods with reactions, encourage them to discuss their work in small groups, then feedback to the class in a question and answer session. [Note: Only the sodium thiosulfate reaction can be measured using the disappearing cross, however the other three reactions can be measured with any of the remaining methods.] (15 minutes)

Graph interpretation – Show students a graph of rate of reaction of a particular reaction. Ask them to interpret the graph and explain the shape of the curve. (5 minutes)

Practical support

Measuring the mass of a reaction mixture

Equipment and materials required

Marble chips, 1 M hydrochloric acid (irritant – CLEAPSS Hazcard 47), 250 ml conical flask, top-pan balance, cotton wool, stopwatch, measuring cylinder, eye protection.

Measuring the volume of gas given off

Equipment and materials required

Marble chips, 1 M hydrochloric acid (irritant – CLEAPSS Hazcard 47), 250 ml conical flask, bung fitted with delivery tube, about 50 cm length of rubber tubing, 100 ml gas syringe (ensure syringe plunger is free-moving), gas syringe holder, boss, stand, stopwatch, measuring cylinder, eye protection.

Measuring the light transmitted through a solution

Equipment and materials required

Two measuring cylinders, stopwatch, paper with large cross in the centre, conical flask, beaker, 0.2 M sodium thiosulfate, 0.2 M hydrochloric acid (irritant), eye protection.

Safety: During this experiment, sulfur dioxide is produced which is toxic and can trigger asthmatic attacks, therefore this should be completed in a well-ventilated room. Once the reaction is complete, the mixture should be disposed of down a well-flushed sink, preferably in a fume cupboard.

Demonstration of the reaction between magnesium and acid

Equipment and materials required

1 M hydrochloric acid (irritant – CLEAPSS Hazcard 47), strips of 1 cm magnesium (flammable – CLEAPSS Hazcard 59), test tube, eye protection.

ACTIVITY & EXTENSION IDEAS

After the students have watched the demonstration of the reaction between magnesium and acid, allow them to experiment with the different methods for measuring rate of reaction detailed in 'Practical support'. They will need a supply of the hydrochloric acid and magnesium strips (and eye protection). The aim of this activity is for the students to decide which is the most informative method. [Hopefully they will realise that the balances available are not sensitive enough, there is not a precipitate formed so the disappearing cross is useless, but collection of gas is the most accurate if a gas syringe is used.]

Answers to in-text questions

a) How fast the reactants are turned into products.

b) In order to understand (and control) how fast chemicals are made.

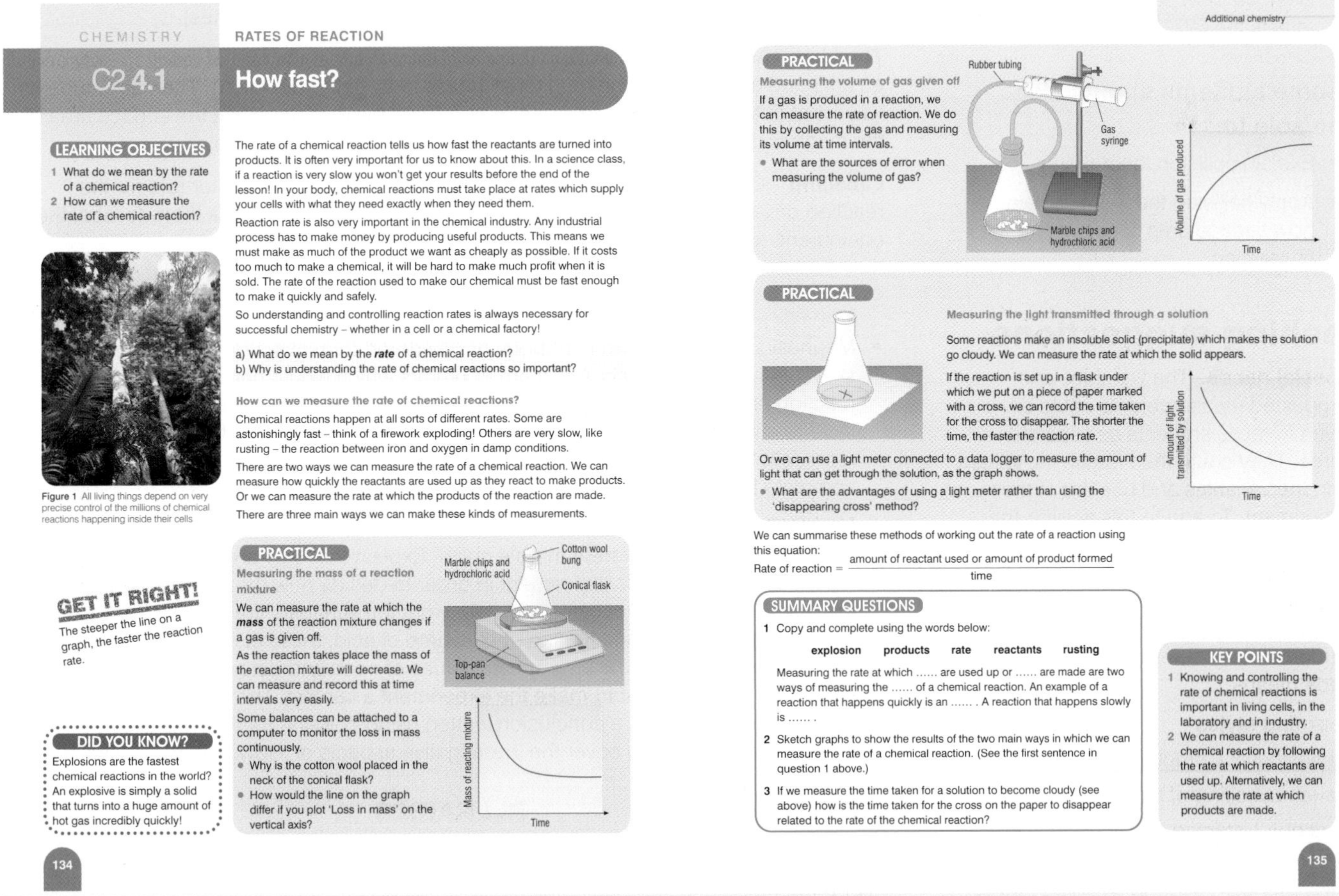
CHEMISTRY

RATES OF REACTION

C2 4.1 How fast?

LEARNING OBJECTIVES

1 What do we mean by the rate of a chemical reaction?
2 How can we measure the rate of a chemical reaction?

The rate of a chemical reaction tells us how fast the reactants are turned into products. It is often very important for us to know about this. In a science class, if a reaction is very slow you won't get your results before the end of the lesson! In your body, chemical reactions must take place at rates which supply your cells with what they need exactly when they need them.

Reaction rate is also very important in the chemical industry. Any industrial process has to make money by producing useful products. This means we must make as much of the product we want as cheaply as possible. If it costs too much to make a chemical, it will be hard to make much profit when it is sold. The rate of the reaction used to make our chemical must be fast enough to make it quickly and safely.

So understanding and controlling reaction rates is always necessary for successful chemistry – whether in a cell or a chemical factory!

a) What do we mean by the ***rate*** of a chemical reaction?
b) Why is understanding the rate of chemical reactions so important?

Figure 1 All living things depend on very precise control of the millions of chemical reactions happening inside their cells

How can we measure the rate of chemical reactions?

Chemical reactions happen at all sorts of different rates. Some are astonishingly fast – think of a firework exploding! Others are very slow, like rusting – the reaction between iron and oxygen in damp conditions.

There are two ways we can measure the rate of a chemical reaction. We can measure how quickly the reactants are used up as they react to make products. Or we can measure the rate at which the products of the reaction are made.

There are three main ways we can make these kinds of measurements.

GET IT RIGHT!
The steeper the line on a graph, the faster the reaction rate.

DID YOU KNOW?
Explosions are the fastest chemical reactions in the world? An explosive is simply a solid that turns into a huge amount of hot gas incredibly quickly!

PRACTICAL
Measuring the mass of a reaction mixture

We can measure the rate at which the ***mass*** of the reaction mixture changes if a gas is given off.

As the reaction takes place the mass of the reaction mixture will decrease. We can measure and record this at time intervals very easily.

Some balances can be attached to a computer to monitor the loss in mass continuously.

- Why is the cotton wool placed in the neck of the conical flask?
- How would the line on the graph differ if you plot 'Loss in mass' on the vertical axis?

Marble chips and hydrochloric acid; Cotton wool bung; Conical flask; Top-pan balance; Mass of reacting mixture; Time

134

Additional chemistry

PRACTICAL
Measuring the volume of gas given off

If a gas is produced in a reaction, we can measure the rate of reaction. We do this by collecting the gas and measuring its volume at time intervals.

- What are the sources of error when measuring the volume of gas?

Rubber tubing; Gas syringe; Marble chips and hydrochloric acid; Volume of gas produced; Time

PRACTICAL
Measuring the light transmitted through a solution

Some reactions make an insoluble solid (precipitate) which makes the solution go cloudy. We can measure the rate at which the solid appears.

If the reaction is set up in a flask under which we put on a piece of paper marked with a cross, we can record the time taken for the cross to disappear. The shorter the time, the faster the reaction rate.

Or we can use a light meter connected to a data logger to measure the amount of light that can get through the solution, as the graph shows.

- What are the advantages of using a light meter rather than using the 'disappearing cross' method?

Amount of light transmitted by solution; Time

We can summarise these methods of working out the rate of a reaction using this equation:

$$\text{Rate of reaction} = \frac{\text{amount of reactant used or amount of product formed}}{\text{time}}$$

SUMMARY QUESTIONS

1 Copy and complete using the words below:

explosion products rate reactants rusting

Measuring the rate at which ...... are used up or ...... are made are two ways of measuring the ...... of a chemical reaction. An example of a reaction that happens quickly is an .... A reaction that happens slowly is ....

2 Sketch graphs to show the results of the two main ways in which we can measure the rate of a chemical reaction. (See the first sentence in question 1 above.)

3 If we measure the time taken for a solution to become cloudy (see above) how is the time taken for the cross on the paper to disappear related to the rate of the chemical reaction?

KEY POINTS

1 Knowing and controlling the rate of chemical reactions is important in living cells, in the laboratory and in industry.
2 We can measure the rate of a chemical reaction by following the rate at which reactants are used up. Alternatively, we can measure the rate at which products are made.

135

SUMMARY ANSWERS

1 Reactants, products, rate, explosion, rusting.

2 Graphs like those at bottom of page 134 and top of page 135 in Student Book.

3 The shorter the time taken for the cross to disappear, the faster the rate of the reaction.

KEY POINTS

Students could start a spider diagram using the key points from this spread. Then at the end of each lesson during this chapter, encourage students to add the new key points to their diagram.

DID YOU KNOW?

The biggest conventional bomb has a mass of 9752 kg and is known as 'MOAB' (Massive Ordnance Air Blast). It differs from most bombs as it doesn't explode on impact, it has its own parachute and explodes just above the ground.

C2 4.2

Collision theory

SPECIFICATION LINK-UP   Unit: Chemistry 2.12.4

- *The rate of a chemical reaction increases:*
  - *– if the temperature increases*
  - *– if the concentration of dissolved reactants or the pressure of gases increases*
  - *– if solid reactants are in smaller pieces (greater surface area)*
  - *– if a catalyst is used.*
- *Chemical reactions can only occur when reacting particles collide with each other with sufficient energy. The minimum amount of energy particles must have to react is the activation energy.*

LEARNING OBJECTIVES

Students should learn:

- That different factors affect the rate of reaction.
- That rates of reaction can be explained using collision theory.
- That collision theory can be used to explain the effect of surface area on the rate of reaction.

LEARNING OUTCOMES

Most students should be able to:

- List the factors that affect the rate of reaction.
- Recall a definition for collision theory.
- Describe how surface area affects the rate of reaction.

Some students should also be able to:

- Explain collision theory.
- Apply collision theory to explain how surface area affects the rate of reaction.

Teaching suggestions

- **Special needs.** The variables and suggested measurements could be given to these students as separate cards. They could then match the values with the variables and use this in their experiment. To add to this activity, the variable that must be kept constant could be written in one colour, and the independent and dependent variables could be in another colour. Then the students could be asked what the colour code means.
- **Learning styles**
  Kinaesthetic: Completing the practicals.
  Visual: Labelling of a diagram.
  Auditory: Listening to discussions in groups.
  Intrapersonal: Creating a bullet-point list about collision theory.
  Interpersonal: Working in groups and discussing decisions.
- **Homework.** A bath bomb is mainly a metal carbonate and an acid. When they are put into water a neutralisation reaction happens. As the two reactants dissolve, they can collide and react. Ask students to explain why a bath bomb takes a long time to react with water, but if it is crumbled up it reacts more quickly.

Lesson structure

STARTER

Word search – Create a word search using key words that students will use in this lesson spread ('collision theory', 'temperature', 'concentration', 'surface area', 'catalyst', 'particle', 'activation', 'energy'). This activity could be extended by asking students to write eight sentences each involving one of the key words. (10 minutes)

Thinking – Ask students to work in pairs and list ways that the rate of reaction between an acid and a metal could be monitored [mass loss, gas production]. Then ask students ways that this reaction could be speeded up [heat the acid, increase the surface area of the magnesium, increase the concentration of the acid]. (10 minutes)

Labelling – Give students a diagram of the equipment used to monitor rate for the reaction of marble with acid, when mass loss is being measured. Ask them to label the equipment. (5–10 minutes)

MAIN

- Magnesium is often found in ribbons or powdered form in schools. Show the students samples of each. Ask them to predict which would have the fastest rate of reaction and why (using collision theory to explain). In their prediction, they should include a word equation (balanced symbol equation for higher attaining students) to represent the reaction and what observations they would expect. They could then complete the experiment and see if their prediction was correct.

- Marble chips come in a variety of sizes, but each size is within a range. Show the students samples of different marble chips. Explain that they are going to investigate the mass lost during this experiment in order to decide how the surface area affects the rate. Encourage students to consider what the variables are in the experiment [time, temperature, concentration and volume of acid, mass of marble]. Students should then decide on the appropriate values of each and detail which variables should be kept constant to make the experiment a fair test. The investigation should then be completed and a conclusion written using collision theory. This provides an excellent opportunity to cover the investigative aspects of 'How Science Works'.

PLENARIES

Demonstration – For this demo you will need an iron nail, iron wool, iron filings, tongs, heat-proof mat, Bunsen burner, spatula, eye protection. Show students the iron nail, iron wool and iron filings. Ask them what reaction will happen when the iron is put in the flame and ask for a volunteer to write the word equation on the board [iron + oxygen → iron oxide]. Ask the students to predict which will combust most quickly and why. Then demonstrate each type of iron in the flame, i.e. hold the nail into the blue flame using tongs; then hold a small piece of iron wool into the flame using tongs; finally sprinkle a few iron filings from a spatula into the flame. (10 minutes)

Summarise – Ask the students to make a bullet-point list of facts about the collision theory. (5 minutes)

Practical support

Which burns faster – ribbon or powder?

Equipment and materials required

Bunsen burner and safety equipment, 2 cm length of magnesium ribbon (flammable – CLEAPSS Hazcard 59), magnesium powder (flammable), spatula, tongs, stopwatch, eye protection.

Details

Hold the end of the magnesium ribbon with tongs. Put the tip of the ribbon in the top of the blue gas cone. As soon as the ribbon ignites, remove from the flame and observe. Then sprinkle about half a spatula of magnesium directly into the blue flame (held at an angle) and observe.

Safety: Eye protection should be worn throughout this practical. Magnesium oxide powder will be made and may enter the air; this could irritate airways and therefore the reaction should be completed in a well-ventilated room. When magnesium ribbon burns, a very bright white light is produced. This can blind if people look at it directly. Therefore encourage students to look past the reaction or alternatively use specialised blue glass/plastic to mute the light.

Investigating surface area

Equipment and materials required

Conical flask, dilute hydrochloric acid (1M – irritant – CLEAPSS Hazcard 47), cotton wool, top-pan balance, marble chips of different sizes, measuring cylinder, stopwatch, eye protection.

Details

Wash and dry the marble chips (to remove the powder from the surface). Measure out about 1 g of marble chips of a certain size into a conical flask. Eye protection should be worn at this point. Add 25 ml of acid and put in the cotton wool plug. Put the reaction vessel onto the top-pan balance and observe the mass change over time. Repeat the experiment with different-sized marble chips.

- Control variables are: Concentration of acid, volume of acid, time, temperature.

ACTIVITY & EXTENSION IDEAS

- Students could complete an evaluation about the calcium carbonate and acid reaction. For example, the problems that they might have found may have been: 'the same mass of marble in each experiment could not be achieved due to natural variation in the marble', 'mass was lost before the reaction vessel was put on the balance', 'the balances aren't very accurate in order to get enough information to draw graphs', etc. Students could then consider ways to change the method to try to reduce these problems and ultimately the errors in the experiment.

- Get sports bibs for students to wear, representing different reactant particles. Then ask them to create and act out a play to describe collision theory.

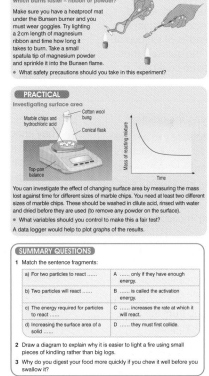

CHEMISTRY · RATES OF REACTION

C2 4.2 Collision theory

LEARNING OBJECTIVES

1 What affects the rate of a chemical reaction?
2 What is collision theory?
3 How does collision theory explain the effect of surface area on reaction rate?

The rate at which chemical reactions happen is very different, depending on the reaction. There are four main factors which affect the rate of chemical reactions:

- temperature,
- concentration or pressure,
- surface area,
- presence of a catalyst.

Reactions can only take place when the particles (atoms, ions or molecules) that make up the reactants come together. But the reacting particles don't just have to bump into each other. They need to collide with enough energy too, otherwise they will not react. This is known as **collision theory**.

The smallest amount of energy that particles must have before they will react is known as the **activation energy**. So anything which increases the chance of reacting particles bumping into each other, or which increases the energy that they have when they collide will make it more likely that reactions will happen. If we increase the chance of individual particles reacting, we will also increase the rate of reaction.

a) What must happen before two particles can stand a chance of reacting?
b) Particles must have a certain amount of energy before they will react – what is this energy called?

In everyday life we control the rates of chemical reactions often without any idea what we are doing and why! For example, cooking cakes in ovens or spraying a mixture of fuel and air into our car engines. But in chemistry we need to know exactly how to control the rate of chemical reactions and why our method works.

Surface area and reaction rate

If we want to light a fire we don't pile large logs together and try to set them alight. We use small pieces of kindling to begin with. Doing this increases the surface area of the logs, so there is more wood that can react with the air.

When a solid reactant reacts with a solution, the size of the pieces of the solid material make a big difference to the rate of the reaction. The inside of a large piece of solid is not in contact with the solution it is reacting with, so it can't react. It has to wait for the outside to react first.

In smaller lumps, or in a powder, each tiny piece is surrounded by solution. This means that reactions can take place much more easily.

c) How does the surface area of a solid affect its rate of reaction?

Figure 1 There is no doubt that the chemicals in these fireworks have reacted – but how do we explain what happens in a chemical reaction?

Figure 2 Cooking – an excellent example of controlling reaction rates!

Figure 3 When a solid reacts, the size of its pieces make a big difference to the rate of the reaction – the smaller the pieces, the faster the reaction

PRACTICAL

Which burns faster – ribbon or powder?

Make sure you have a heatproof mat under the Bunsen burner and you must wear goggles. Try lighting a 2 cm length of magnesium ribbon and time how long it takes to burn. Take a small spatula tip of magnesium powder and sprinkle it into the Bunsen flame.

- What safety precautions should you take in this experiment?

PRACTICAL

Investigating surface area

You can investigate the effect of changing surface area by measuring the mass lost against time for different sizes of marble chips. You need at least two different sizes of marble chips. These should be washed in dilute acid, rinsed with water and dried before they are used (to remove any powder on the surface).

- What variables should you control to make this a fair test?

A data logger would help to plot graphs of the results.

GET IT RIGHT!

Particles collide all the time, but only some collisions lead to reactions.
Increasing the number of collisions and the energy of collisions produces faster rates.
Larger surface area does not result in collisions with more energy but does increase the frequency of collisions.

SUMMARY QUESTIONS

1 Match the sentence fragments:

a) For two particles to react	A ...... only if they have enough energy.
b) Two particles will react	B ...... is called the activation energy.
c) The energy required for particles to react	C ...... increases the rate at which it will react.
d) Increasing the surface area of a solid	D ...... they must first collide.

2 Draw a diagram to explain why it is easier to light a fire using small pieces of kindling rather than big logs.

3 Why do you digest your food more quickly if you chew it well before you swallow it?

KEY POINTS

1 The minimum amount of energy that particles must have in order to react is called the activation energy.
2 The rate of a chemical reaction increases if the surface area of any solid reactants is increased.

Surface area of one side = 3 × 3 = 9 cm²
Surface area of whole cube = 6 × 9 = 54 cm²
3 cm 3 cm 3 cm
Volume = 27 cm³

Surface area of one side = 1 × 1 = 1 cm²
Surface area of whole cube = 6 × 1 = 6 cm²
1 cm 1 cm 1 cm
27 of these small cubes have the same volume as the large cube
Surface area of 27 small cubes = 27 × 6 = 162 cm²

136

137

SUMMARY ANSWERS

1 a) D b) A c) B d) C

2 [Students should draw a diagram clearly explaining/showing that cutting a solid into smaller pieces increases its surface area.]

3 Because you have increased its surface area.

Answers to in-text questions

a) The particles must collide.

b) The activation energy.

c) Increasing the surface area increases the rate of the reaction.

KEY POINTS

Students could copy out the key points, representing them in the form of a labelled diagram.

C2 4.3

The effect of temperature

LEARNING OBJECTIVES

Students should learn:

- That changing temperature affects the rate of reaction.

LEARNING OUTCOMES

Most students should be able to:

- Describe how increasing the temperature of a reaction increases the rate.
- List reasons why increasing the temperature increases the rate.

Some students should also be able to:

- Explain how and why changing the temperature changes the rate of reaction.

Teaching suggestions

- **Special needs.** Link temperature and rate of reaction with dissolving sugar into tea. Ask students to predict which cup of tea will dissolve sugar the quickest [hot tea]. This physical change could be demonstrated or completed by the class.

- **Learning styles**

  Kinaesthetic: Completing the practical.

  Visual: Creating a cartoon to explain the effect of temperature on rate of reaction.

  Auditory: Listening to finished sentences.

  Intrapersonal: Spotting the mistake in a sentence.

  Interpersonal: Working in pairs to play 'Pictionary'.

- **Homework.** Ask students to write a brief account in terms of being a reactant particle in a 50°C thiosulfate reaction, from the start to the completion of the reaction.

- **ICT link-up.** Each group from the class could put their results from the thiosulfate experiment into an Excel spreadsheet. This could then be used to calculate a class mean quickly and plot a graph of these results. (See www.rogerfrost.com.)

Answers to in-text questions

a) Because the particles collide more often and have more energy, so when they collide it is more likely that they will have at least the activation energy required for the reaction.

b) The rate roughly doubles.

c) The time decreases.

SPECIFICATION LINK-UP   Unit: Chemistry 2.12.4

- *The rate of reaction increases if the temperature increases.*
- *Increasing the temperature increases the speed of the reacting particles so that they collide more frequently and more energetically. This increases the rate of reaction.*

Students should use their skills, knowledge and understanding of 'How Science Works':

- *to interpret graphs showing the amount of product formed (or reactant used up) with time, in terms of the rate of reaction.*

Lesson structure

STARTER

What is in the bag? – In a brightly coloured bag, put in key words on separate pieces of paper: 'collision theory', 'temperature', 'particles', 'collision', 'rate'. Then ask for a volunteer to come to the front and remove a key word. They can then explain what that words means. If the student struggles, allow them to go back to their seat and look through the Student Book and talk to neighbours; invite them back at the end of the starter. In total, ask five volunteers to explain each of the words in turn. (10 minutes)

Pictionary – Create packs of cards with these statements on: 'increase temperature', 'collision', 'particle', 'reactant', 'product', 'rate', 'chemical reaction'. Split the students into pairs and give them a pack of cards. Ask them to take it in turns to pick up the card and draw a picture (with no text, symbols or numbers) to get their partner to say the statement or word. (10 minutes)

MAIN

- Students could experimentally determine the effect of temperature on rate of reaction by using the sodium thiosulfate reaction. As a class decide on five temperatures that will be used. In small groups each temperature is completed once, but then three groups (or the whole class) could pool their results and take a mean, making the results more reliable. Students could plot a scatter graph, drawing a line of best fit. They should then use their graph and their knowledge of collision theory to draw a conclusion. This provides another opportunity to cover the investigative aspects of 'How Science Works'.

- Ask students to draw a cartoon to show the effect of heating up a reaction in terms of its rate. Students could be encouraged to personify the particles and make a fun depiction of the reaction. To help them, the cartoon framework could be given with statements to include in a box below their images, in order to explain what is happening.

PLENARIES

Sentences – In small groups ask the students to finish the following sentence:

- 'As you heat up a reaction . . .'

After a few minutes ask the groups to read out their finished sentences. Then choose the most accurate and scientific sentence and give that group a prize. (10 minutes)

Spot the mistake – Ask students to spot the error in the following sentence:

- 'When temperature is dropped, particles have more energy but move around less and so the rate of reaction stays the same.' [When temperature is dropped, the particles have less energy and the rate of reaction will reduce.] (5 minutes)

SUMMARY ANSWERS

1 Rate, quickly, collide, energy, rise, doubles, reducing, decreases, chemical, off.

2 Because it is at a higher temperature in the pressure cooker which speeds up the chemical reactions that make food cook.

3 Muscles rely on chemical reactions to produce movement, so a reduction in temperature reduces the rate of these reactions, making the animal move more slowly.

Practical support

Reacting magnesium and hydrochloric acid at different temperatures

Equipment and materials required

Ice bath, test tube rack, hot water bath, 1 M hydrochloric acid (irritant – CLEAPSS Hazcard 47), 1 cm magnesium strips (flammable – CLEAPSS Hazcard 59), calcium carbonate, two measuring cylinders, six test tubes, thermometer, eye protection.

Details

Wearing eye protection, measure out 2 ml of acid into each test-tube, put two test tubes in an ice bath, two in a test tube rack and two in a hot water bath. Allow the test tubes to rest in the water/ice baths for about 5 minutes to get to the appropriate temperature. Students can check the temperature of the acid using the thermometer. Add one strip of magnesium to each of the different temperatures of acid. Allow the students to observe the reaction and comment on the rate at different temperatures, encouraging them to decide how they are determining the rate [amount of bubbles produced]. Keep the lab well ventilated.

Repeat the reaction with one marble chip (calcium carbonate) in each test tube.

The effect of temperature on rate of reaction

Equipment and materials required

Two measuring cylinders, stopwatch, paper with large cross in the centre, conical flask, beaker, 0.2 M sodium thiosulfate, 0.2 M hydrochloric acid (irritant), ice bath, water bath/hot plate, thermometer, eye protection.

Details

Measure 10 ml of acid (eye protection should be worn) and 10 ml of sodium thiosulfate in separate clean measuring cylinders and reduce or increase the temperatures of these solutions using ice baths/water baths/hot plates. Choose temperatures that are easy to attain, e.g. 10°C, 20°C, 30°C, 40°C, 50°C; at least five need to be completed in order that a graph can be drawn. Place the beaker on the centre of the large cross; first add the sodium thiosulfate to the beaker. Then add the acid and start the stopwatch and swirl to mix the solutions. Stop the clock when the cross disappears and note the time.

Safety: During this experiment, sulfur dioxide is produced which is toxic and can trigger asthmatic attacks, therefore this should be completed in a well-ventilated room. Once the reaction is complete, the mixture should be disposed of down a well-flushed sink, preferably in a fume cupboard. Also acid will be warmed making it more dangerous.

ACTIVITY & EXTENSION IDEAS

- **Studying more reactions** – Other reactions could be studied at three different temperatures, e.g. magnesium and acid, calcium carbonate and acid. A circus of the three practicals could be set up and students could rotate around them finding out that rate of reaction is always increased on heating the reactions.

KEY POINTS

If there are any EFL (English as a Foreign Language) students present, the key points could be translated into another language. Alternatively you could ask the Modern Foreign Languages department to translate them into a different language, and students could then read each statement and see if they can match it to the English version.

C2 4.3   The effect of temperature

LEARNING OBJECTIVES

1 How does changing temperature affect the rate of reactions?

When we increase the temperature of a reaction it always increases the rate of the reaction. Collision theory tells us why this happens – there are two reasons.

Both of these reasons are related to the fact that when we heat up a mixture of reactants the particles in the mixture move more quickly.

1 Particles collide more often

When we heat up a substance, energy is transferred to the particles that make up the substance. This means that they move faster. And when particles move faster they have more collisions. Imagine a lot of people walking around in the school playground. They may bump into each other occasionally – but if they start running around, they will bump into each other even more often!

2 Particles collide with more energy

Particles that are moving quickly have more energy, which means that the collisions they have are much more energetic. It's just like two people who collide when they are running about as opposed to just walking into each other!

When we increase the temperature of a reaction, the particles have more collisions and they have more energy. This speeds up the reaction in two ways – the particles will collide more often and they have more energy when they do collide.

Figure 1 Moving faster means it's more likely that you'll bump into someone else – and the bump will be harder too!

Both of these changes increase the chance that two molecules will react. Around room temperature, if we increase the temperature of the reaction by 10°C the rate of the reaction will roughly double.

a) Why does increasing the temperature increase the rate of a reaction?
b) How much does a 10°C rise in temperature increase reaction rate at room temperature?

Cold – slow movement, few collisions, little energy

Hot – fast movement, more collisions, more energy

Figure 2 More collisions with more energy – both of these increase the rate of a chemical reaction as the temperature increases

This change in reaction rate is why we use fridges and freezers – because reducing the temperature slows down the rate of a chemical reaction. When food goes bad it is because of chemical reactions. Reducing the temperature slows down these reactions, so the food goes off much less quickly.

PRACTICAL

The effect of temperature on rate of reaction

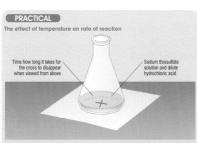

Time how long it takes for the cross to disappear when viewed from above

Sodium thiosulfate solution and dilute hydrochloric acid

When we react sodium thiosulfate solution and hydrochloric acid it produces sulfur. This makes the solution go cloudy. We can record the length of time it takes for the solution to go cloudy at different temperatures.

- Which variables do you have to control to make this a fair test?
- Why is it difficult to get accurate timings by eye in this investigation?
- How can you improve the reliability of the data you collect?

The results of an investigation like this can be plotted on a graph:

The graph shows how the time for the solution to go cloudy changes with temperature.

c) What happens to the time it takes the solution to go cloudy as the temperature increases?

SUMMARY QUESTIONS

1 Copy and complete using the words below:

chemical	collide	decreases	doubles	energy	off
	quickly	rate	reducing	rise	

When we increase the temperature of a reaction, we increase its .... This makes the particles move more .... so they .... more often and they have more .... At room temperature, a temperature .... of about 10°C roughly .... the reaction rate. This explains why we use fridges and freezers – because .... the temperature .... the rate of the .... reactions which make food go ....

2 Water in a pressure cooker boils at a much higher temperature than water in a saucepan because it is under pressure. Why does food take longer to cook in a saucepan than it does in a pressure cooker?

3 Use your knowledge of the effect of temperature on chemical reactions to explain why cold-blooded animals like reptiles or insects may move very slowly in cold weather.

NEXT TIME YOU...

... turn the heat up when you're cooking a meal, remember that you're increasing the rate at which chemical reactions are happening!

Time taken for solution to go cloudy

Temperature

KEY POINTS

1 Reactions happen more quickly as the temperature increases.

2 A 10°C increase in temperature at room temperature roughly doubles the rate of a reaction.

3 The rate of a chemical reaction increases with temperature because the particles collide more often and they have more energy.

C2 4.4

The effect of concentration

Students should learn:

- That changing the concentration of reactants changes the rate of reaction.
- That changing the pressure of reacting gases changes the rate of reaction.

LEARNING OUTCOMES

Most students should be able to:

- State the effect on the rate if the concentration of reactants is increased or decreased.
- Describe what we mean by gas pressure.
- State the effect on the rate if pressure is changed in a reaction involving gases.

Some students should also be able to:

- Recall a definition for concentration. [**HT** only]
- Explain the effect of changing concentration on the rate in terms of collision theory.
- Explain that equal volumes of gases at the same temperature and pressure contain equal numbers of particles. [**HT** only]
- Explain the effect of changing pressure on the rate in terms of collision theory.

Teaching suggestions

- **Learning styles**

   Kinaesthetic: Completing the practical.

   Visual: Completing the graph in the starter activity.

   Auditory: Listening to other student's definitions.

   Intrapersonal: Creating a poster.

   Interpersonal: Working in groups to discuss the merits of different posters.

- **Homework.** Ask students to explain how pressure affects rate of reaction.

- **ICT link-up.** Arrange for class to use a selection of the simulations available on the Additional Science CD ROM that cover the effect of concentration on rates of reaction.

SPECIFICATION LINK-UP   Unit: Chemistry 2.12.4

- *The rate of a chemical reaction increases if the concentration of dissolved reactants or the pressure of gases increases.*
- *Increasing the concentration of reactants in solutions and increasing the pressure of reacting gases also increases the frequency of collisions and this increases the rate of reaction.*
- *Concentrations of solutions are given in moles per cubic decimetre (mol/dm³). Equal volumes of solutions of the same molar concentration contain the same number of moles of solute, i.e. the same number of particles. [**HT** only]*
- *Equal volumes of gases at the same temperature and pressure contain the same number of molecules. (Candidates will not be expected to find concentrations of solutions or volumes of gases in this unit.) [**HT** only]*

Students should use their skills, knowledge and understanding of 'How Science Works':

- *to interpret graphs showing the amount of product formed (or reactant used up) with time in terms of the rate of reaction.*

Lesson structure

STARTER

Demonstration – Show the students a bottle of undiluted squash. Then put half into a large beaker and add water. Ask the students which container has the most concentrated drink in and how they know. Then ask the students to work in pairs to come up with a definition of concentration. Ask each pair to come to the board and write down their definition. Ask the whole class to consider the definitions and refer to the Student Book to write their own definition of concentration into their notes. (10 minutes)

Graph – Give students an unfinished graph (time, concentration) with two curved lines to show reactants and products. Ask students to complete the axis labels (including units) and briefly explain the shape of the two curves. (5 minutes)

MAIN

- Students can experimentally determine the effect of concentration on rate by observing the reaction between marble chips and acid. At this point, moles have been introduced to students but not their calculation in volume. Therefore to change the concentration the volume of the acid should be diluted with water, but the volume of the mixture should remain constant in order that the reaction is a fair test. Encourage the students to plot all the curves on the same axis. Then ask students to explain their results using collision theory. (This offers another excellent opportunity to cover any investigative aspect of 'How Science Works'.)

- Give students an A4 sheet of paper and ask them to split in it half. On one side they should explain how concentration affects rate and on the other how pressure affects rate. In each section they should define the key word (concentration/pressure) and include one labelled diagram. Ensure that students do not put their name on the front of the poster. (See plenary 'Exhibition'.)

PLENARIES

Act – Split students into small groups of about five, and ask them to design a sketch to highlight that by raising concentration the rate of reaction increases. Circulate around the room and pick two groups to share their sketch with the whole class. (20 minutes)

Demonstration – For this demonstration iron wool, tongs, deflagration spoon, a gas jar of oxygen and a Bunsen burner and safety equipment is needed. Using a safety screen between the class and the demonstration (plus eye protection), hold some iron wool into a blue Bunsen flame using tongs. Then put some iron wool on a deflagration spoon, heat until it is glowing in the top of a blue gas cone. Then quickly put the wool into a gas jar of oxygen. Ask students, in small groups, to explain which reaction was more vigorous and why. Then choose a few students to feedback into the class. (10 minutes)

Exhibition – Get all the students' posters and lay them out on the side benches, and give each a number. Put students in small groups and ask them to rate each poster out of 10 in terms of presentation, accuracy of science and easiest to understand. Then ask them to total up the scores and feedback which is the best poster overall and that student could get a prize. (15 minutes)

ACTIVITY & EXTENSION IDEAS

- Ask students to explain why changing the pressure of a reaction mixture only affects a reaction with gas phase chemicals.

- Once the graph of the production of gas has been drawn, students could be shown how to calculate a numerical value for rate. The graph should be a curve, they choose a particular time and draw a tangent to this point on the curve. Then they work out the gradient (change in vertical value/change in horizontal value) and this is the rate measured in units that refer to volume of gas/time.

- Introduce the idea that [chemical] means the concentration of the chemical.

- Use Simulation C2 4.5 'Rates of Reactions' from the Additional Science CD ROM.

Practical support

Investigating the effect of concentration on rate of reaction

Equipment and materials required

Marble chips, 1 M hydrochloric acid (irritant – CLEAPSS Hazcard 47), 250 ml conical flask, top-pan balance, cotton wool, stopwatch, measuring cylinder, eye protection.

Details

Put about 5 marble chips into the bottom of a conical flask. Measure out 25 ml of acid (wear eye protection), and put into the conical flask, and put a piece of cotton wool in the neck. Quickly place on the balance and take a reading, start the stopwatch. Measure the mass of the conical flask every 10 seconds for 2 minutes.

Repeat for different concentrations.

CHEMISTRY   RATES OF REACTION

C2 4.4   The effect of concentration

LEARNING OBJECTIVES

1 How does changing the concentration of reactants affect the rate of reactions?

2 How does changing the pressure of reacting gases affect the rate of reactions?

Some of our most beautiful buildings are made of limestone or marble. These buildings have stood for centuries, but in the last 50 years or so they have begun crumbling away increasingly fast. This is because limestone and marble both contain calcium carbonate. This reacts with acids, leaving the stone soft and crumbly.

We think that the rate of this reaction has speeded up because the concentration of sulfuric and nitric acids found in rainwater has been steadily increasing.

Increasing the concentration of reactants in a solution, increases reaction rate because there are more particles of the reactants moving around in the same volume. The more 'crowded' together the reactant particles are, the more likely it is that they will bump into each other and a reaction will take place.

Increasing the pressure of a reaction involving gases has the same effect. It squashes the gas particles more closely together. This increases the chance that they will collide and react and so speeds up the rate of the reaction.

a) Why does increasing concentration or pressure increase reaction rate?

Low concentration/low pressure   High concentration/high pressure

Figure 1 Limestone statues are damaged by acid rain. This damage increases as the concentration of the acids in rainwater increases.

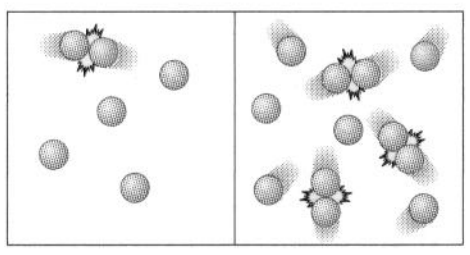

Figure 2 Increasing concentration and pressure both mean that particles are closer together. This increases the number of collisions between particles, so the reaction rate increases.

The concentration of a solution tells us how many particles of solute we have dissolved in a certain volume of the solution. Concentration is measured in moles per cubic decimetre, which is shortened to mol/dm³. Solutions with the same concentration always contain the same number of particles of solute in the same volume.

b) What unit do we use to measure the concentration of solute in a solution?

We never talk about the concentration of a gas – but the number of particles in a certain volume of gas depends on its temperature and its pressure. At the same temperature and pressure, equal volumes of gases all contain the same number of particles.

c) Two identical containers of gas are at the same temperature and pressure. What can we say about the number of particles in the two containers?

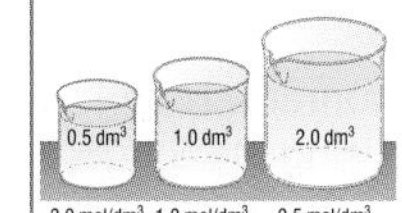

0.5 dm³   1.0 dm³   2.0 dm³
2.0 mol/dm³   1.0 mol/dm³   0.5 mol/dm³

Figure 3 These different volumes of solution all contain the same amount of solute – but at different concentrations

HIGHER

PRACTICAL

Investigating the effect of concentration on rate of reaction

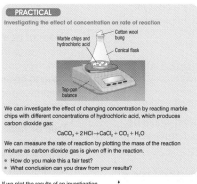

Marble chips and hydrochloric acid — Cotton wool bung
Conical flask
Top-pan balance

We can investigate the effect of changing concentration by reacting marble chips with different concentrations of hydrochloric acid, which produces carbon dioxide gas:

$$CaCO_3 + 2HCl \rightarrow CaCl_2 + CO_2 + H_2O$$

We can measure the rate of reaction by plotting the mass of the reaction mixture as carbon dioxide gas is given off in the reaction.

- How do you make this a fair test?
- What conclusion can you draw from your results?

If we plot the results of an investigation like the one above on a graph they look like this:

The graph shows how the rate at which the mass of the reaction mixture decreases changes with concentration.

Mass

Lower acid concentration

Higher acid concentration

Time

d) Which line on the graph shows the fastest reaction? How could you tell?

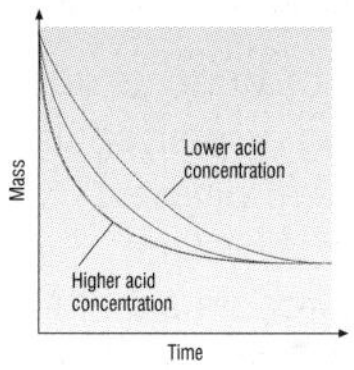

GET IT RIGHT!

Increasing concentration or pressure does not increase the energy with which the particles collide. It does increase the frequency of collisions

SUMMARY QUESTIONS

1 Copy and complete using the words below:

collisions   concentration   faster   gases   increases
number   pressure   rate   volume

The ...... of a chemical reaction is affected by the ...... of reactants in solution and by ...... if the reactants are ...... Both of these tell us the ...... of particles that there are in a certain ...... of the reaction mixture. Increasing this ...... the number of ...... that particles make with each other, making reactions happen ....

2 Acidic cleaners are designed to remove limescale when they are used neat. They do not work so well when they are diluted. Using your knowledge of collision theory, explain why this is.

3 How are the 'concentration of a solution' and the 'pressure of a gas' similar? [Higher]

KEY POINTS

1 Increasing the concentration of reactants increases the frequency of collisions between particles, increasing the rate of reaction.

2 Increasing the pressure of reacting gases results in particles colliding more often, increasing the rate of reaction.

SUMMARY ANSWERS

1 Rate, concentration, pressure, gases, number, volume, increases, collisions, faster.

2 There are more particles in the acid to collide with limescale particles when the cleaner is more concentrated, so increasing the rate of reaction.

3 Both concentration of a solution and pressure of a gas give an indication of the number of particles (of solute or gas) present in a given volume. [**HT** only]

Answers to in-text questions

a) Because there are more particles in the same volume, making collisions more likely.

b) Moles per cubic decimetre (mol/dm³).

c) They are the same.

d) The higher acid concentration (green line) showed the fastest reaction because the line is steepest initially (or it finished reacting first).

KEY POINTS

Ask students to summarise the points further, maybe using arrows, chemical shorthand and mathematical symbols to represent words e.g.:

$$\uparrow [\text{reactants}] \Rightarrow \uparrow \text{collisions} \Rightarrow \uparrow \text{rate}$$

C2 4.5

The effect of catalysts

LEARNING OBJECTIVES

Students should learn:

- That catalysts affect the rate of reaction.
- That catalysts are used in many industrial reactions.

LEARNING OUTCOMES

Most students should be able to:

- Give a definition for a catalyst.
- Give an example of an industrial process that uses a catalyst.
- List the reasons why a catalyst may be used in an industrial process.

Some students should also be able to:

- Explain how a catalyst works.
- Explain why a catalyst would be used in an industrial process.

Teaching suggestions

- **Special needs.** A line of students could be formed (representing a catalyst), then other students could wear different coloured sports bibs to represent reactant particles. They could act out how a catalyst works, i.e. the reactants get held by the catalyst and then they can link to form the compound more easily. When they have linked, the 'product' then leaves.

- **Learning styles**

  Kinaesthetic: Completing the practicals.

  Visual: Completing the graph.

  Auditory: Listening to other student's poems.

  Intrapersonal: Creating a question and answer sheet.

  Interpersonal: Working in pairs to reflect on each other's work.

- **ICT link-up.** Excel could be used to plot a graph quickly of the different results.

- **Homework.** Students could find out the name of one catalyst and the reaction it is used in.

SPECIFICATION LINK-UP   Unit: Chemistry 2.12.4

  • *The rate of a chemical reaction increases if a catalyst is used.*

- *Catalysts change the rate of chemical reactions but are not used up during the reaction. Different reactions need different catalysts.*

- *Catalysts are important in increasing the rates of chemical reactions used in industrial processes to reduce costs.*

Students should use their skills, knowledge and understanding of 'How Science Works':

- *to interpret graphs showing the amount of product formed (or reactant used up) with time, in terms of the rate of the reaction.*

Lesson structure

STARTER

Foam of death – Write the formula of hydrogen peroxide (H_2O_2) on the board and ask the students to think about what the products of the decomposition reaction could be and how they could be tested [water, tested with cobalt chloride paper; oxygen tested with a glowing splint]. See 'Practical support'; when the foam has dried slightly, allow students to come up to the foam and re-light a glowing splint. Explain that the manganese dioxide did not get used up in the reaction, but sped it up and this is a catalyst. (15 minutes)

True or false – Give each student a statement about catalysts. Then they must walk around the room and ask five people if they think the statement is true or false. Based on these answers, the student should decide if the statement is true or false. Each student should then read their statement to the class and say if they think it is true or false and then you give feedback. (10 minutes)

MAIN

- Hydrogen peroxide is unstable in sunlight and will decompose into oxygen and water. This process is relatively slow, but a number of catalysts can be used to speed up this reaction: chopped fresh celery; chopped fresh liver; manganese dioxide. Encourage students to investigate the gas production using the different catalysts to decide which is the best. They should take a set of results for each catalyst and draw all the lines of best fit on the same graph, giving more coverage of the investigative aspects of 'How Science Works'.

- Give students a sheet of A4 paper and ask them to fold it in half (portrait). They should create 10 questions on the left-hand side about catalysts, using the Student Book for inspiration. Then on the right-hand side, they should write the answers.

PLENARIES

Catalytic converter – Get an old catalytic converter (from a scrap yard) and have it cut into slices (maybe in technology). Clean out the deposits then hand out the slices (they look like a honey comb) to the students and let them handle the pieces. The students should be encouraged to discuss in small groups what the visual aid could be used for. Ask each group to feedback their thoughts and then share with the students that it is a catalytic converter used on a car exhaust to remove pollutant gases. (10 minutes)

Poem – Encourage the students to create an eight-line poem, where the first letters of each line spell 'catalyst'. Then choose some students to read their poem to the rest of the class. (20 minutes)

AfL (Assessment for Learning) – To continue the poem activity, ask students to swap their poem with a partner. If the student feels that there is some incorrect science, they should amend the work using a pencil. Once they have worked on the poem, it should be returned to its owner and they should then review any comments that have been made. (10 minutes)

Practical support

Foam of death

Equipment and materials required

100 vol. hydrogen peroxide (corrosive – CLEAPSS Hazcard 50), one-litre measuring cylinder, washing-up bowl, washing-up liquid, manganese dioxide (harmful), spatula, cobalt chloride paper, splints, eye protection and gloves.

Details

Stand a one-litre measuring cylinder in a washing-up bowl. Add a good dash of washing-up liquid, and about 100 ml of 100 vol. H_2O_2. Add a spatula of manganese(IV) oxide and allow the students to observe.

Safety: Wear eye protection and be aware of skin burns. Manganese(IV) oxide – see CLEAPSS Hazcard 60.

Investigating catalysis

Equipment and materials required

Stand, boss, gas syringe holder, gas syringe, 10 vol. hydrogen peroxide (irritant), manganese dioxide (harmful), celery, liver, white tile, knife, stopwatch, conical flask, bung, delivery tube, about a 25 cm length of rubber tube, measuring cylinder, spatula, eye protection.

Details

Measure out 25 ml of hydrogen peroxide and put it into the conical flask, eye protection should be worn. Finely chop some celery and put into the flask. Quickly connect the bung to the gas syringe and note the volume of gas produced every 10 seconds for 2 minutes. Repeat with chopped liver, and repeat with a spatula of manganese(IV) oxide. Other transition metal oxides can also be investigated.

- The catalyst.
- Bar chart because the independent variable is categoric (and dependent variable is continuous).

Safety: Be aware of irritation caused by the hydrogen peroxide, wash under cold water and it should dissipate. Make sure the syringe plunger is free-moving.

CHEMISTRY   RATES OF REACTION

C2 4.5 — The effect of catalysts

LEARNING OBJECTIVES

1 How do catalysts affect the rate of chemical reactions?
2 Why are catalysts used in so many industrial reactions?

Figure 1 Catalysts are all around us, in the natural world and in industry. Our planet would be very different without them.

Sometimes we need to change the rate of a reaction but this is impossible using any of the ways we have looked at so far. Or sometimes a reaction might be possible only if we use very high temperatures or pressures – which can be very expensive. However we can speed chemical reactions up another way – by using a special substance called a catalyst.

a) Apart from using a catalyst, what other ways are there of speeding up a chemical reaction?

A catalyst is a substance which increases the rate of a chemical reaction but it is not affected chemically itself at the end of the reaction. It is not used up in the reaction, so it can be used over and over again to speed up the conversion of reactants to products.

We need to use different catalysts with different reactions. Many of the catalysts we use in industry are transition metals or their compounds. For example, iron is used in the Haber process, while platinum is used in the production of nitric acid.

Catalysts are often very expensive because they are made of precious metals. But it is often cheaper to use a catalyst than to pay for all the energy needed for higher temperatures or pressures in a reaction.

b) How is a catalyst affected by a chemical reaction?

Figure 2 The transition metals platinum and palladium are used in the catalytic converters in cars

Some catalysts work by providing a surface for the reacting particles to come together. They lower the activation energy needed for the particles to react. This means that more of the collisions between particles result in a reaction taking place. We normally use catalysts in the form of powders, pellets or fine gauzes. This gives the biggest possible surface area for them to work.

c) Why is a catalyst divided up into pellets more effective than a whole lump of the catalyst?

PRACTICAL

Investigating catalysis

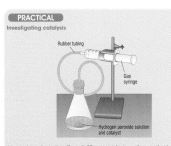

Hydrogen peroxide solution and catalyst

We can investigate the effect of different catalysts on the rate that hydrogen peroxide solution decomposes:

$$2H_2O_2 \rightarrow 2H_2O + O_2$$

The reaction produces oxygen. We can collect this in a gas syringe using the apparatus shown above.

We can investigate the effect of many different substances on the rate of this reaction. Examples include manganese(IV) oxide and potassium iodide.

- State the independent variable in this investigation. (See page 276.)

A simple table of the time taken to produce a certain volume of oxygen can then tell us which catalyst makes the reaction go fastest.

- What type of graph would you use to show the results of your investigation? Why? (See page 280.)

Apart from speeding up a chemical reaction, the most important thing about a catalyst is that it does not get used up in the chemical reaction. We can use a tiny amount of catalyst to speed up a chemical reaction over and over again.

SUMMARY QUESTIONS

1 Copy and complete using the words below:

    activation   energy   increases   more   react

A catalyst ...... the rate of a chemical reaction. It does this by reducing the ...... energy needed for the reaction. This means that ...... particles have enough ...... to ....

2 Solid catalysts used in chemical plants are often shaped as tiny beads or cylinders with holes through them. Why are they made in this shape?

3 Why is the number of moles of catalyst needed to speed up a chemical reaction very small compared to the number of moles of reactants?

DID YOU KNOW?

The catalysts used in chemical plants eventually become 'poisoned' so that they don't work any more. This happens because impurities in the reaction mixture combine with the catalyst and stop it working properly.

KEY POINTS

1 A catalyst speeds up the rate of a chemical reaction.
2 A catalyst is not used up during a chemical reaction.

SUMMARY ANSWERS

1 Increases, activation, more, energy, react.

2 This increases their surface area.

3 Because the catalyst is not used up in the reaction.

Answers to in-text questions

a) Increasing temperature, surface area, concentration (if reactants are in solution) or pressure (if reactants are gases).

b) It is unaffected.

c) Because it has greater surface area.

KEY POINTS

Put the key points onto an index card, underlining the key words. As an extension, a key for the important words could be given to the students, e.g. always write catalyst in red etc.

C2 4.6   Catalysts in action

CHEMISTRY   RATES OF REACTION

C2 4.6   Catalysts in action

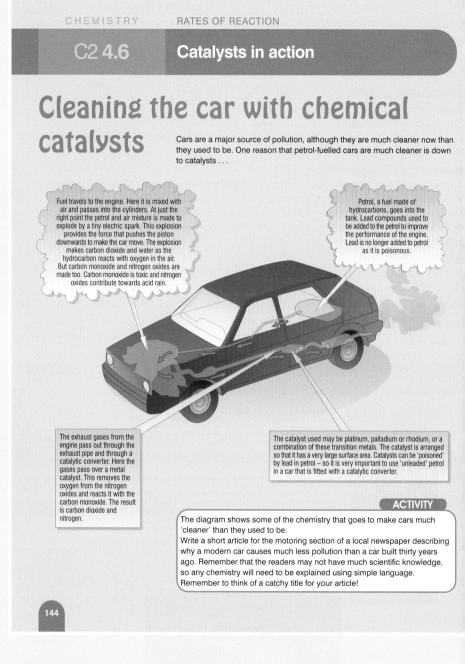

Cleaning the car with chemical catalysts

Cars are a major source of pollution, although they are much cleaner now than they used to be. One reason that petrol-fuelled cars are much cleaner is down to catalysts ...

Fuel travels to the engine. Here it is mixed with air and passes into the cylinders. At just the right point the petrol and air mixture is made to explode by a tiny electric spark. This explosion provides the force that pushes the piston downwards to make the car move. The explosion makes carbon dioxide and water as the hydrocarbon reacts with oxygen in the air. But carbon monoxide and nitrogen oxides are made too. Carbon monoxide is toxic and nitrogen oxides contribute towards acid rain.

Petrol, a fuel made of hydrocarbons, goes into the tank. Lead compounds used to be added to the petrol to improve the performance of the engine. Lead is no longer added to petrol as it is poisonous.

The exhaust gases from the engine pass out through the exhaust pipe and through a catalytic converter. Here the gases pass over a metal catalyst. This removes the oxygen from the nitrogen oxides and reacts it with the carbon monoxide. The result is carbon dioxide and nitrogen.

The catalyst used may be platinum, palladium or rhodium, or a combination of these transition metals. The catalyst is arranged so that it has a very large surface area. Catalysts can be 'poisoned' by lead in petrol – so it is very important to use 'unleaded' petrol in a car that is fitted with a catalytic converter.

ACTIVITY

The diagram shows some of the chemistry that goes to make cars much 'cleaner' than they used to be.
Write a short article for the motoring section of a local newspaper describing why a modern car causes much less pollution than a car built thirty years ago. Remember that the readers may not have much scientific knowledge, so any chemistry will need to be explained using simple language. Remember to think of a catchy title for your article!

144

SPECIFICATION LINK-UP

Unit: Chemistry 2.12.4

Students should use their skills, knowledge and understanding of 'How Science Works':

- *to explain and evaluate the development, advantages and disadvantages of using catalysts in industrial processes.*

This spread can also be used to revisit the following substantive content already covered in this chapter:

- *Catalysts change the rate of chemical reactions but are not used up during the reaction. Different reactions need different catalysts.*

- *Catalysts are important in increasing the rate of chemical reactions used in industrial processes to reduce costs.*

Teaching suggestions

Activities

- **Newspaper article** – Show students the car sections of a local or national newspaper (or search an online newspaper). Ask the students to imagine that they have been commissioned to write an article about pollution due to cars. Explain that the article should be biased, stating why motorcars of today are not as bad for the environment as previous models. Remind students that they should 'tone down' the science as the audience of the newspaper may not have a scientific background. Some students could then produce their article on a desktop publishing package.

- **News broadcast** – Encourage students to read the news reports carefully. Then split the class into small groups of about three students. Their task is to produce a small news piece (no more than 5 minutes) looking at the future of enzymes in industry. Students could complete some of their own research on enzymes using the Internet. They could then complete their broadcast while being recorded using a camcorder. The video could then be uploaded onto the school's Internet site, or used as a starter in future lessons about enzymes.

- **Presentation** – Split the class into four groups and give each team a different title from these: 'What are enzymes and how are they used in an industrial process?'; 'Enzymes and foods'; 'Enzymes and cleaning'; 'Enzymes and babies'.

Each group should produce an A5 informative leaflet about their topic and a short presentation to highlight the key points of their topic. The leaflets should be collected and photocopied, so that each student has a full record of how the enzyme works. The groups could give their presentations to the rest of the class. Assessment for Learning (AfL) could be incorporated into this activity, by giving students a sheet of marking points to award each group. These sheets can then be given to the relevant groups to inform them about their work.

ENZYMES – CLEVER CATALYSTS THAT ARE GETTING EVERYWHERE

ENZYMES MAKE CLOTHES CLEANER AND CLASSIER!

For years we've been used to enzymes helping to get our clothes clean. Biological washing powders contain tiny molecules that help to literally 'break apart' dirt molecules such as proteins at low temperatures. But why stop there? Why not make washing powders that help to repair clothes and make them like new? Searching the surface of fabric for any tears or breaks in the fibres, enzymes could join these back together, while other enzymes might look for frayed or 'furry' bits of fabric and could makes these smooth again. And not only that . . . . . .

ENZYMES TO THE RESCUE

Everyone knows how upsetting it is to cut yourself. And it can be a pain to have to wear a sticking plaster until your body has repaired your skin. But enzymes may be the answer to this. By choosing the right enzyme mixture we may one day be able to mend cuts and other damage to our skin simply by painting a liquid onto our skin. But until then . . . . . .

SAY 'AAAHH' FOR THE ENZYME!

Those lengthy waits for the results of a blood test to come back could soon be a thing of the past. By combining biological molecules like enzymes with electronics, scientists reckon that they can make tiny measuring probes that will enable doctors to get an instant readout of the level of chemicals in your blood. These sensors are so tiny that it is possible to take more than a dozen measurements at the same time, doing away with the need for lots of tests.

SCIENTISTS MAKE ENZYMES MAKE COMPUTER

Scientists announced today that they are close to making a biological computer made of enzymes and DNA. The tiny device could change the face of computing in the future, which up until now has been based on electronic devices made from silicon. The idea of using DNA in computers first took off in 1994, when a scientist in California used it to solve a maths problem. Computers made from DNA would be so tiny that a trillion of them could fit in a single drop of water.

ACTIVITY

There is more than a grain of truth in all of these ideas about enzymes. Use some or all of these news reports to produce a short piece for the 'and finally' slot in a TV news broadcast. Remember to use your knowledge of catalysts to explain why enzymes are important in all of these developments.

Homework

- **Enzymes** – Ask students to create a spider diagram about the effects of using an enzyme in an industrial process. If the class have studied Unit Biology 2 11.6 in the Specification on enzymes, they could be asked to integrate that work into their spider diagram.

Extension

- **Making yoghurt** – Enzymes are used to make yoghurt. If a room swap can be arranged to a food technology room, students could experiment with making yoghurt: many recipes are available from the Internet, although some schools may have their own yoghurt-making machine, which contains its own instructions.

Learning styles

Kinaesthetic: Completing the 'Making yoghurt' extension activity.

Visual: Preparing a spider diagram about the use of enzymes in industry.

Auditory: Listening to other students' presentations.

Intrapersonal: Writing a newspaper article.

Interpersonal: Working as a group to produce broadcasts.

ICT link-up

The Internet can be used to gain additional information about enzymes. Search in Google for 'uses of enzymes'. Show Animation C2 4.6 'Catalytic converter' from Additional Science CD ROM.

Special needs

Give the students cards with pros and cons of using enzymes in an industrial process. They should then sort them into two lists and stick them into their notes.

Gifted and talented

Encourage these students to research how enzymes actually work (link with the biology component), in particular how active sites make the protein specific.

SUMMARY ANSWERS

1 Lines drawn to link left-hand side and right-hand side columns as follows:

a) A and C   **b)** A   **c)** B   **d)** B

2 a) Measure volume of gas or mass of reaction mixture.

b) Three of: increase concentration of acid; increase surface area of magnesium; increase temperature of reaction mixture; add a catalyst.

c) Increasing concentration/surface area increases number of collisions between reactants; increasing temperature increases number of collisions between reactants and the energy possessed by reacting particles; catalyst lowers activation energy.

3 a) [Graph.]

b) It is double.

c) It is double.

d) Investigation 2 uses acid with twice the concentration of that in investigation 1 (rate and volume of gas double) with at least enough marble chips to react fully with the acid in each case.

Summary teaching suggestions

- **ICT link up** – Question 3 could be used with a graphing package, e.g. Excel, allowing the students to plot a graph using ICT. Alternatively, the graph could be created in advance and then displayed so that students can check their own work.

- **Special needs** – Question 1 could be prepared as a cut and paste question. However, there should be as many reactions as methods of measuring (i.e. some of the second column needs to be repeated), as this could lead to confusion.

- **Misconceptions** – Students often use the terms: 'molecules', 'ions', 'particles', 'elements' and 'compounds' interchangeably. It is important that they realise that the term 'particles' is generic, but the other words have specific meaning. Thus, if they are used incorrectly, they can make answers chemically wrong even if the student is well aware of the collision theory response.

- **Learning styles**
  Auditory: Questions 2 and 3 lend themselves to a class discussion before each student pens their own answer.
  Visual: Question 3 allows the production of a graph.
  Kinaesthetic: Using a card sort, or cut and stick activity, to answer question 1 allows this activity to appeal to these learners.

- **When to use the questions?**
  - As a revision aid at the end of the topic.
  - Question 1 could be used as homework or a plenary to lesson 4.1.
  - Questions 2 and 3 could be used as homework to consolidate learning from lessons 4.2–4.
  - Students could be encouraged not to answer the questions but to create a mark scheme. They should critically consider all the answers that could be awarded a mark and also answers that are close but should not be given any credit.

RATES OF REACTION: C2 4.1 – C2 4.6

SUMMARY QUESTIONS

1 Select from A, B and C to show how the rate of each reaction, a) to d), could be measured.

a) Gas evolved from reaction mixture	A Measure mass
b) Mass of reaction mixture changes	B Measure light transmitted
c) Precipitate produced	C Measure volume
d) Colour of solution changes	

2 A student carried out a reaction in which she dropped a piece of magnesium ribbon in sulfuric acid with a concentration of 1 mol/dm³.

a) Suggest **one** way in which the student could measure the rate of this reaction.

b) Suggest **three** ways in which the student could increase the rate of this reaction.

c) Explain how each of these methods changes the rate of the reaction.

3 The following results show what happened when two students investigated the reaction of some marble chips with acid.

Time (seconds)	Investigation 1 Volume of gas produced (cm³)	Investigation 2 Volume of gas produced (cm³)
0	0	0
30	5	10
60	10	20
90	15	30
120	20	40
150	25	50
180	28	57
210	30	59
240	30	60

a) Plot a graph of these results with time on the *x*-axis.

b) After 30 seconds, how does the rate of the reaction in investigation 2 compare with the rate of reaction in investigation 1?

c) How does the final volume of gas produced in investigation 2 compare with the final volume of gas produced in investigation 1?

d) Suggest how the reaction in investigation 2 differs from the reaction in investigation 1. Explain your answer.

146

EXAM-STYLE QUESTIONS

1 Marble chips (calcium carbonate) react with hydrochloric acid as shown in the equation.

$$CaCO_3(s) + 2HCl(aq) \rightarrow CaCl_2(aq) + H_2O(l) + CO_2(g)$$

Some students investigated the effect of the size of marble chips on the rate of this reaction. They did the reactions in a conical flask, which they put onto a balance connected to a computer to record their results. They used three different sizes of marble chips and kept all of the other conditions the same. The graphs show the total mass of the flask and reaction mixture plotted against time for the three experiments.

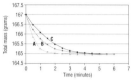

(a) Which curve, **A**, **B** or **C**, shows the results for the fastest reaction? (1

(b) Which curve, **A**, **B** or **C**, shows the results for the largest marble chips? (1

(c) Explain, using collision theory, why changing the size of marble chips changes the rate of reaction. (2

(d) (i) Use curve **A** to describe how the rate of reactio changes from the start to the finish of the reaction.
(3

(ii) Explain why the rate of reaction changes in this way. (2

2 A student investigated the reaction between magnesiun ribbon and hydrochloric acid.

$$Mg(s) + 2HCl(aq) \rightarrow MgCl_2(aq) + H_2(g)$$

The student reacted 20 cm³ of two different concentrations of hydrochloric acid with 0.050 g of magnesium. All other conditions were kept the same. The student's results are shown in the table on the next page.

EXAM-STYLE ANSWERS

1 a) A   *(1 mark)*

b) C   *(1 mark)*

c) *One mark each for:*
  - Smaller chips have larger surface area.
  - So more (acid) particles collide with the solid/more collisions.
  Accept converse explanation.   *(2 marks)*

d) i) *One mark each for:*
  - Begins rapidly/high rate at start.
  - Rate decreases with time/gets slower.
  - Until it stops/stops after 3 minutes.   *(3 marks)*

  ii) *Two from:*
  - Concentration of acid greatest at start so highest rate.
  - Concentration of acid decreases as it is used up, so rate decreases.
  - Reaction stops when all acid has been used.   *(2 marks)*

2 a) Volume of gas   *(1 mark)*

b) e.g. volume of acid/magnesium; temperature of acid   *(1 mark)*

c) Suggestion linked to b) e.g. use same volume of acid for each concentration of acid.   *(1 mark)*

d) Suitable scales for axes chosen and both labelled.   *(1 mark)*
Correct plotting of points for both concentrations ($+/-$ half small square).   *(2 marks)*
Smooth lines drawn through all points on each curve (no daylight).   *(1 mark)*

e) i) Doubles the rate/goes twice as fast.   *(1 mark)*
  ii) Slope/gradient of line for concentration 2 mol per dm³ is twice as steep as slope/gradient of other line.   *(2 marks)*
  Accept slope/gradient is steeper for 1 mark.
  Accept reaction with concentration 2 mol per dm³ stopped after 4–5 minutes, other reaction after 9 minutes for 1 mark.
  Accept after one minute reaction with concentration 2 mol per dm³ produced 15 cm³ of gas, other reaction 30 cm³ or similar comparison for 1 mark.

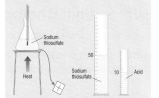

HOW SCIENCE WORKS QUESTIONS

This student's account of an investigation into the effect of temperature on the rate of a reaction was found on the Internet.

I investigated the effect of temperature on the rate of a reaction. The reaction was between sodium thiosulfate and hydrochloric acid. I set up my apparatus as in this diagram.

Sodium thiosulfate

Heat

50

Sodium thiosulfate

10 Acid

The cross was put under the flask. I heated the sodium thiosulfate to the temperature I wanted and then added the hydrochloric acid to the flask. I immediately started the watch and timed how long it took for the cross to disappear.

My results are below.

Temperature of the sodium thiosulfate	Time taken for the cross to disappear
15	110
30	40
45	21

My conclusion is that the reaction goes faster the higher the temperature.

a) Suggest a suitable prediction for this investigation. (1)

b) Describe one safety feature that is not mentioned in the method. (1)

c) Suggest some ways in which this method could be improved. For each suggestion, say why it is an improvement. (10)

d) Suggest how the table of results could be improved. (1)

e) Despite all of the problems with this investigation, is the conclusion appropriate? Explain your answer. (1)

147

Concentration and time table:

Concentration of acid (moles per dm³)	Time (minutes)	0	1	2	3	4	5	6	7	8	9	10
1.0	Volume of gas (cm³)	0	15	24	31	37	41	44	46	47	48	48
2.0	Volume of gas (cm³)	0	30	39	45	47	48	48	48	48	48	48

(a) Name the dependent variable. (1)

(b) Suggest a control variable. (1)

(c) Suggest how the student might have controlled this variable. (1)

(d) Plot these results on the same axes, with time on the horizontal axis and volume of gas on the vertical axis. Draw a smooth line for each concentration. Label each line with the concentration of acid. (4)

(e) (i) What is the effect of doubling the concentration on the rate of reaction? (1)
(ii) Explain how the graphs show this effect. (2)
(iii) Explain this effect in terms of particles and collision theory. (2)

(f) Explain why the total volume of hydrogen is the same for both reactions. (2)

(g) Draw a labelled diagram of the apparatus you would use to do this experiment. (3)

3 Hydrogen peroxide solution is colourless and decomposes very slowly at 20°C.

$$2H_2O_2(aq) \rightarrow 2H_2O(l) + O_2(g)$$

Manganese(IV) oxide, a black powder, is a catalyst for the reaction.

(a) Explain what the word catalyst means. (2)

(b) What would you **see** if manganese(IV) oxide was added to hydrogen peroxide solution? (1)

(c) Describe briefly one way that you could show that manganese(IV) oxide was acting as a catalyst. (2)

(d) Explain, using particle and collision theory, how a solid catalyst works. (2)

(e) Hydrogen peroxide solution stored at 10°C decomposes at half the rate compared to when it is stored at 20°C. Explain, in terms of particles, why the rate of the reaction changes in this way. (3)

- Q1, parts b) and c) can be used to check that students are clear about the relationship between the size of pieces of reagents and their surface area. Part d) probes their understanding of rate. They should have been taught that rate is an amount divided by time and is the slope of amount versus time graphs. Some students only think in terms of overall rate of a reaction, i.e. the time it takes to go to completion, but they should understand that rates may be calculated at any time during a reaction.

- In Q2 it is the difference in the initial rates that allows the comparison of rate at different concentrations. The concentration of the second reaction is double that of the first reaction at the start of the reactions. It remains so over a short time period, about one minute in this case, and this is sometimes used to measure initial rates in investigations such as the reaction of sodium thiosulfate with hydrochloric acid and iodine clock experiments. Q2 parts a) to c) relate to 'How Science Works'.

- Literacy skills are important in answers requiring explanations. When explaining how the rate of a reaction depends upon collisions, as in Q2e)(iii), many students do not make it clear in their answers that it is an increase in the frequency of collisions that causes an increase in the rate. Commonly, students simply refer to more collisions without mentioning time, leaving examiners to infer that they mean frequency. Definitions, like that of a catalyst in Q3a), should be well rehearsed. A common slip here is for students to write that catalysts 'are not used in the reaction', when they mean 'not used up in the reaction'. It may be better to say that the catalyst remains at the end of the reaction.

HOW SCIENCE WORKS ANSWERS

a) e.g. The higher the temperature, the more quickly the cross will disappear.

b) e.g. Wear eye protection or do not heat solution above 50°C or dispose of solutions in fume cupboard.

c) Ways in which the method could have been improved include:
- There should have been more temperatures chosen, so that the pattern could have been seen in the results.
- The range could have been wider, so that the effect of higher and lower temperatures could have been noted.
- The volume and concentration of the two reactants should be known, to make sure that the method is valid.
- The hydrochloric acid should have been heated to the desired temperature as well, to ensure that the reaction took place at the stated temperature.
- Data logging could have been used to detect the end point, it is difficult to tell accurately when the cross disappears.
- The solutions should be continually stirred, to ensure validity.
- A water bath should have been used to control the temperature.

d) Include units in the table.

e) It is not possible to tell because the evidence is not reliable. (Also accept an answer that indicates that the conclusion is appropriate because there are large differences between the results at different temperatures (assuming the timings were taken in seconds.)

---

iii) Increasing concentration means more particles per cm³ *(1 mark)* so the frequency of collisions increases. *(1 mark)*

f) All of the magnesium was used up in both reactions *(1 mark)* because there was excess hydrochloric acid. *(1 mark)*

g) *One mark each for:*
- Side arm test tube or conical flask containing reactants.
- Gas syringe or inverted measuring cylinder/burette full of water in trough of water.
- Sealed system with bung and delivery tube correctly connected. *(3 marks)*

3 a) A substance that speeds up a chemical reaction *(1 mark)* but is not used up in the reaction/remains at the end of the reaction. *(1 mark)*

b) Rapid fizzing/effervescence/lots of bubbles of gas. *(1 mark)*

c) *One mark each for:*
- Remove/filter catalyst from products/water.
- Add it to fresh hydrogen peroxide to show it will work again OR dry it and weigh it to show none has been used up. *(2 marks)*

d) It provides a surface for the reactants to come together. *(1 mark)* It lowers the activation energy needed for the particles to react. *(1 mark)*

e) *One mark each for:*
- Increasing temperature causes particles to move faster
- so they collide more frequently
- and they collide with more energy. *(3 marks)*

Exam teaching suggestions

- The questions on this chapter total 36 marks, and should take students about 35 minutes to complete in a single session. Q1 could be used after completing spread 4.2, Q2 after 4.4 and Q3 after 4.5.

How science works teaching suggestions

- **Literacy guidance**
  - Key terms that should be clearly understood: controls, validity.
  - Question c) expects a longer answer, where students can practise their literacy skills.

- **Higher- and lower-level answers.** Question c) is a higher-level question and the answers provided above are also at this level. Question d) is lower level and the answer provided is also lower level.

- **Homework.** High attaining students could tackle the questions for homework. Others could bring in suggestions for the brainstorming session.

- **Special needs.** You could take these students through the practical as a demonstration and ask them how they would set up the experiment.

C2 5.1

Exothermic and endothermic reactions

Students should learn:

- That energy is involved in chemical reactions.
- That energy changes in a chemical reaction can be measured.

Most students should be able to:

- State a definition for exothermic and endothermic reactions.
- List one example of an exothermic and endothermic reaction.
- Recognise an endothermic or exothermic reaction when data is given.
- Describe how a reaction can be monitored for its energy changes.

Some students should also be able to:

- Explain the difference between exothermic and endothermic reactions.

Teaching suggestions

- **Special needs.** The information needed to be detailed on the posters could be given to the students. However, they would need to decide which poster it is referring to, before copying it out onto their work.

- **Learning styles**

  Kinaesthetic: Using a calorimeter to record the energy changes of a reaction.

  Visual: Preparing posters about energy changes in a reaction.

  Auditory: Listening to different reactions and deciding whether they are exothermic or endothermic.

  Intrapersonal: Making detailed observations about the sherbet reaction.

  Interpersonal: Working as a group to explain observations from the neutralisation experiment.

- **Homework.** Students could list one exothermic reaction and one endothermic reaction that they could not live without and state why.

SPECIFICATION LINK-UP Unit: Chemistry 2.12.5

- *When chemical reactions occur, energy is transferred to or from the surroundings.*
- *An exothermic reaction is one that transfers energy, often as heat, to the surroundings. Examples of exothermic reactions include combustion, many oxidation reactions and neutralisation.*
- *An endothermic reaction is one that takes in energy, often as heat, from the surroundings. Endothermic reactions include thermal decompositions.*

Lesson structure

STARTER

Sherbet – Give students a sherbet sweet before they enter the room. Ask students to detail what their observations are as they eat it. Then, using questions and answers, get feedback from the students and ask them if they think the reaction is chemical/physical and exo-/endothermic (these words should be defined by the students looking back at their previous work and using the Student Book). (5 minutes)

Cut and stick – Pictures of different reactions could be given to students. They firstly need to make themselves aware of the definitions of exothermic and endothermic reactions. They could then cut up the pictures and arrange them in a table to detail the energy changes shown in the reactions. (10 minutes)

MAIN

- The energy changes of a reaction can be recorded using a coffee cup calorimeter. Explain to the students that most reactions show their energy change in the form of heat, and that the reaction needs to be well insulated to prevent heat loss to the surroundings. Then ask students to complete the displacement reaction between zinc powder and copper sulfate solution. Students should design their own results table and record their results in order to draw a graph. They should be reminded that the scales do not have to start at 0 (and the y-axis will probably start at about 20°C). Students may struggle in drawing the line of best fit for this reaction; you could show how to do this on the board. There are many whole investigations that this can be developed into to extend the 'How Science Works' concepts already covered.

- Students could be given an A5 sheet of blue paper. They should then write a definition of endothermic onto the blue paper and include examples of endothermic reactions. A similar poster could then be created for exothermic reactions on red paper.

PLENARIES

Exo-/endothermic – Give the students a blue card with the word 'endothermic' written on, and a red card with the word 'exothermic' printed on. Then read out these reactions and ask the students to decide if they are exo- or endothermic, displaying the card to represent their answer:

- Thermal decomposition of marble. [Endothermic]
- Combustion of methane. [Exothermic]
- Neutralisation of hydrochloric acid and sodium hydroxide. [Exothermic]
- Rusting of an iron nail. [Exothermic]
- Thermal decomposition of copper carbonate. [Endothermic]

This activity could be extended by asking the students to complete word or symbol equations for the reactions. Also these reactions could be demonstrated by you, or they could be shown using photographs or a video via a digital projector. (5 minutes)

Demonstration – Use a data logger to plot the temperature changes in a neutralisation reaction. Display the temperature graph using a digital projector. In small groups, students should decide whether the reaction is exothermic or endothermic and say how they could tell. Then choose a few students to feedback to the class. (10 minutes)

Practical support
Investigating energy changes
Equipment and materials required
Polystyrene coffee cup, polystyrene lid with two holes in, a mercury thermometer (0–50°C), copper sulfate 1 M (harmful), zinc powder (flammable), spatula, balance, measuring cylinder, stopwatch, stirrer, eye protection.

Details
Wear eye protection and measure 25 ml of copper sulfate solution into the coffee cup. Measure the temperature every 30 seconds for 5 minutes. Then add 1 g of zinc to the cup and quickly put on the lid and stir constantly. Take the temperature every 10 seconds for 10 minutes.

- Repeat the measurements more than once or repeat using a different thermometer or a temperature sensor or check your results with those of another group.

Safety: Make students aware that they are using a mercury thermometer for accuracy, but that this contains a risk and they should be careful not to leave them by the edge of the bench. You should be aware of where the mercury spillage kit is and how to use it. Copper sulfate is harmful – CLEAPSS Hazcard 27. Zinc powder is flammable – CLEAPSS Hazcard 107.

Demonstration of neutralisation reaction
Equipment and materials
Burette, measuring cylinder, burette holder, stand, 1 M sodium hydroxide (corrosive), 1 M hydrochloric acid (irritant), universal indicator (flammable), magnetic stirrer, conical flask, magnetic stirrer bar, temperature probe, interface, computer, digital projector, white tile, filter funnel, eye protection.

Details
Measure 25 ml of sodium hydroxide into a conical flask and add a few drops of indicator. Place the flask onto the magnetic stirrer and add the bar. Fill the burette with hydrochloric acid using the filter funnel. Position the burette over the conical flask and add the temperature probe to the flask, taking care that it doesn't hit the stirrer. Set the graph to take data for about 2 minutes and begin stirring. Start the data collection. Turn on the flow of acid to the flask and observe.

This activity can be extended by adding a pH probe and comparing the temperature rise with the pH of the solution.

DID YOU KNOW?
When people suffer sports injuries cold packs can be used to alleviate the pain. These also rely on a reaction, but it takes in heat energy from its surroundings. Cold packs work by having two reactants that are separated and when you break an inner bag, it allows them to mix and the associated temperature change is then given.

Answers to in-text questions
a) Exothermic.
b) Endothermic.
c) Respiration, burning (or other reaction releasing energy).
d) Thermal decomposition, photosynthesis (or other reaction that absorbs energy).

KEY POINTS
Ask the students to imagine that they work for a marketing company. They are to make a poster to encourage students to think about science in their everyday lives (like the RSC posters 'scientists don't always wear white coats'). Their poster should include all the key points.

CHEMISTRY   ENERGY AND REACTIONS

C2 5.1 — Exothermic and endothermic reactions

LEARNING OBJECTIVES
1 How is energy involved in chemical reactions?
2 How can we measure the energy transferred in a chemical reaction?

Whenever chemical reactions take place, energy is involved. That's because energy is always transferred as chemical bonds are broken and formed.

Some reactions transfer energy *from* the reacting chemicals *to* the surroundings. We call these exothermic reactions. The energy transferred from the reacting chemicals often heats up the surroundings. This means that we can measure a rise in temperature as the reaction happens.

Some reactions transfer energy *from* the surroundings *to* the reacting chemicals. We call these endothermic reactions. Because they take in energy from their surroundings, these reactions cause a drop in temperature as they happen.

a) What do we call a chemical reaction that gives out heat?
b) What do we call a chemical reaction that absorbs heat from its surroundings?

Exothermic reactions
Fuels burning are an obvious example of exothermic reactions, but there are others which we often meet in the chemistry lab.

Neutralisation reactions between acids and alkalis are exothermic. We can easily measure the rise in temperature using simple apparatus (see opposite).

Similarly, heat is released when we add water to white anhydrous copper(II) sulfate (anhydrous means 'without water'). This reaction makes blue hydrated copper(II) sulfate crystals. The reaction gives out heat – it is an exothermic reaction.

Respiration is a very special kind of burning. It involves reacting sugar with oxygen inside the cells of every living thing. This makes the energy needed for all the reactions of life, and also makes water and carbon dioxide as waste products. Respiration is another exothermic reaction.

c) Give two examples of exothermic reactions.

Figure 1 When a fuel burns in oxygen, energy is transferred to the surroundings. We usually don't need a thermometer to know that there is a temperature change!

DID YOU KNOW?
Chemical handwarmers use an exothermic chemical reaction to keep your hands warm on cold days.

Figure 2 All warm-blooded animals rely on exothermic reactions to keep their body temperatures steady

Endothermic reactions
Endothermic reactions are much less common than exothermic ones.

When we dissolve some ionic compounds like potassium chloride or ammonium nitrate in water the temperature of the solution drops.

Thermal decomposition reactions are also endothermic. An example is the decomposition of calcium carbonate to form calcium oxide and carbon dioxide. This reaction only takes place if we keep heating the calcium carbonate strongly. It takes in a great deal of energy from the surroundings.

The most important endothermic reaction of all is **photosynthesis**. This is the reaction in which plants turn carbon dioxide and water into sugar and oxygen, using energy from the Sun.

d) Name two endothermic reactions.

Figure 3 When we eat sherbet we can feel an endothermic reaction! Sherbet dissolving in the water in your mouth takes in energy – giving a slight cooling effect.

PRACTICAL
Investigating energy changes

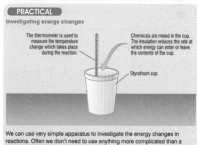

The thermometer is used to measure the temperature change which takes place during the reaction.

Chemicals are mixed in the cup. The insulation reduces the rate at which energy can enter or leave the contents of the cup.

Styrofoam cup

We can use very simple apparatus to investigate the energy changes in reactions. Often we don't need to use anything more complicated than a Styrofoam drinks cup and a thermometer.

- State two ways in which you could make the data you collect more reliable.

GET IT RIGHT!
Remember that exothermic reactions involve energy EXiting (leaving) the reacting chemicals so the surroundings get hotter. In endothermic reactions energy moves INTO (sounds like 'endo'!) the reacting chemicals, so the surroundings get colder.

SUMMARY QUESTIONS
1 Copy and complete using the words below:

   broken   endothermic   exothermic   made   neutralisation
   photosynthesis   respiration   thermal decomposition

Chemical reactions involve energy changes as bonds are ...... and .... When a chemical reaction releases energy we say that it is an ...... reaction. Two important examples of this kind of reaction are ...... and .... When a chemical reaction takes in energy we say that it is an ...... reaction. Two important examples of this kind of reaction are ...... and ....

2 Potassium chloride dissolving in water is an endothermic process. What might you expect to observe when potassium chloride dissolves in water?

KEY POINTS
1 Energy may be transferred to or from the reacting substances in a chemical reaction.
2 A reaction where energy is transferred from the reacting substances is called an exothermic reaction.
3 A reaction where energy is transferred to the reacting substances is called an endothermic reaction.

148   149

SUMMARY ANSWERS

1 Broken, made, exothermic, neutralisation, respiration, endothermic, thermal decomposition, photosynthesis.

2 Condensation forming on outside of the walls of the container in which the solution is being made as a result of the decrease in temperature.

C2 5.2   Energy and reversible reactions

LEARNING OBJECTIVES

Students should learn:

- That energy is involved in reversible reactions.
- How altering the temperature when reactions are at equilibrium produces a change. [**HT** only]

LEARNING OUTCOMES

Most students should be able to:

- Recall the test for water.
- Recognise that if the forward reaction is exothermic, the reverse reaction will be endothermic.
- Recognise that if the forward reaction is endothermic, the reverse reaction will be exothermic.
- That the energy used or released in either direction are the same amount.

Some students should also be able to:

- Explain how temperature changes will affect the equilibrium mixture. [**HT** only]

Teaching suggestions

- **Learning styles**

  Kinaesthetic: Completing the practical.

  Visual: Creating a revision book page.

  Auditory: Listening to others during group work.

  Intrapersonal: Writing own answers to questions.

  Interpersonal: Working as a group and considering group dynamics.

- **ICT link-up.** Set up a flexi-cam or video camera. This can be used to show exemplar work quickly and easily to the rest of the class.

- **Homework.** Students could tackle each group's exemplar question from their revision page.

SPECIFICATION LINK-UP   Unit: Chemistry 2.12.5

- *If a reversible reaction is exothermic in one direction it is endothermic in the opposite direction. The same amount of energy is transferred in each case. For example:*

  hydrated   endothermic   anhydrous
  copper sulfate $\rightleftharpoons$ copper sulfate + water
  (blue)   exothermic   (white)

  The reverse reaction can be used to test for water.

- *When a reversible reaction occurs in a closed system, equilibrium is reached when the reactions occur at exactly the same rate in each direction. [**HT** only]*

- *The relative amounts of all the reacting substances at equilibrium depend on the conditions of the reaction. [**HT** only]*

- *If the temperature is raised, the yield from the endothermic reaction increases and the yield from the exothermic reaction decreases. [**HT** only]*

- *If the temperature is lowered, the yield from the endothermic reaction decreases and the yield from the exothermic reaction increases. [**HT** only]*

Lesson structure

STARTER

Group dynamics – Give each student a questionnaire to find out what type of team player they are, e.g. leader, recorder, ideas generator, etc. These sorts of questionnaires are available from management recruitment books and courses. Explain to students what type of group works and set them the task of forming their own group with at least one of each type of person. (15 minutes)

Questions – Give each student an A4 whiteboard (or laminated sheet of paper), a washable pen and eraser. Then ask them the following series of questions, the student should note down their answer and show you for immediate assessment. If the student is unsure of the answer, they could refer to the Student Book or wait for other students to hold up their answer and then use these responses to inform their answer.

- What is the symbol to show a reversible reaction? [$\rightleftharpoons$]
- Give an example of a reversible reaction. [The Haber process, hydration of dehydrated copper sulfate, thermal decomposition of ammonium chloride.]
- What does exothermic mean? [Energy is given out in the reaction.]
- What happens to the temperature in an endothermic reaction? [Temperature decreases.] (10 minutes)

MAIN

- The students can experimentally complete the reversible reaction of hydration/dehydration of copper sulfate crystals. Before the experiment is completed, encourage the students to think about how they will record their results (table, diagram, flow chart, paragraphs, bullet points, etc.). Once the practical is completed, show the exemplar work to the rest of the class and explain why it is a good way to record the results.

- Ask students to imagine that they have been commissioned by a top publisher to create a GCSE science revision book. Show students a selection of revision materials and ask them to discuss in groups what they like and dislike about the material. Explain that they have an A4 page spread in a book to explain energy and reversible reactions. They must include a worked examination question and an extra question for the reader to attempt, with the answers upside down on the page. Students could work in small teams to complete this task, allowing them to calve up the task as they desire.

PLENARIES

Objectives – Ask students to try to answer the questions posed by the objectives. (10 minutes)

Crossword – Create a crossword with the answers taken from this double-page spread (words could include: 'reversible', 'endothermic', 'exothermic', 'energy', 'equilibrium', 'closed', 'hydrated', 'water'). There are many free sites via the Internet, which can be used to create your own crossword. Then ask students to complete the crossword. (10–15 minutes)

Practical support

Energy changes in a reversible reaction

Equipment and materials required

Hydrated copper sulfate (harmful – CLEAPSS Hazcard 27), spatula, Bunsen burner and safety equipment, dropping pipette, water, boiling tube, boiling tube holder, eye protection.

Details

Eye protection should be worn throughout this practical. Put a spatula of copper sulfate crystals into a boiling tube. Using the boiling tube holder, hold the boiling tube just above the blue flame of the Bunsen burner. The tube should be held at an angle and out of the direction of people's faces. Do not overheat. Once the visible change is complete, allow the tube to cool. Add a few drops of water. Be aware that water added directly to the boiling tube, may crack it.

Demonstration of making cobalt chloride paper

Equipment and materials required

Filter paper, cobalt chloride (toxic), 50 ml beaker, stirring rod, wash bottle and water and a spatula, Bunsen burner, (desiccator), eye protection.

Details

Add half a spatula of cobalt chloride crystals, add water and stir until it dissolves. Soak some filter paper in the solution. Take care drying the paper using a yellow Bunsen flame and it will become blue (dehydrated), add water and it will become pink (hydrated).

Explain that the paper should be kept out of air in a desiccator as the air contains water and will turn the paper pink. A desiccator could be shown to the students and they could research how it works.

Safety: Wear eye protection. Keep cobalt chloride off skin (avoid handling papers with fingers.) Wash hands after use. (See CLEAPSS Hazcard 25.)

ACTIVITY & EXTENSION IDEAS

- Add state symbols to the symbol equation for the dehydration/hydration of cobalt chloride/copper sulfate.
- Cobalt chloride is usually made into paper for use in practicals to test for water. This can be shown to the students. See 'Practical support'.

Answers to in-text questions

a) Amount of energy released in one direction is the same as the amount of energy absorbed in the other direction.

b) Water.

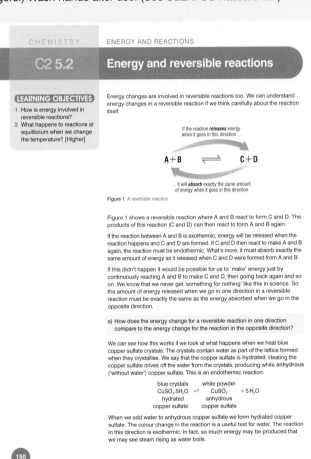

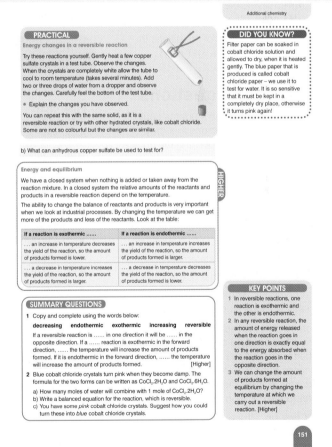

SUMMARY ANSWERS

1 Exothermic (endothermic), endothermic (exothermic), reversible, decreasing, increasing. [**HT** only after first sentence]

2 a) 4

b) $CoCl_2.2H_2O + 4H_2O \rightleftharpoons CoCl_2.6H_2O$

c) Heat them (gently) to drive off the water.

KEY POINTS

Encourage the students to copy out the key points onto flash cards. They can then create a bank of the key points on separate cards to use for revision.

C2 5.3

More about the Haber process

LEARNING OBJECTIVES

Students should learn:

- The conditions used in the Haber process. (See C2 3.7 for students taking the Foundation Paper.)

- Why these conditions are chosen. [**HT** only]

LEARNING OUTCOMES

Most students should be able to:

- State the operating temperature and pressure used in the Haber process. (See C2 3.7 for students taking the Foundation Paper.)

Some students should also be able to:

- Explain the effects of changing temperature and pressure in a given reversible reaction. [**HT** only]

- Justify the choice of conditions in the Haber process. [**HT** only]

Teaching suggestions

- **Special needs.** These students could be given a set of questions that they must answer when explaining the choice of temperature and pressure.

- **Learning styles**

  Kinaesthetic: Moving the true/false sign to show the answer.

  Visual: Completing a flow chart to show the Haber process.

  Auditory: Listening to statements.

  Intrapersonal: Drawing a graph.

  Interpersonal: Working in a group to assess fictitious student answers.

- **Homework.** Ask students to explain why a temperature of 0°C would achieve a better percentage yield in the Haber process but it would not be used by industry. In their answer they need to refer to the collision theory.

- **ICT link-up.** There are a number of simulations available for the Haber process. These allow students to change the conditions to investigate the affect on yield. One such simulation could be projected onto an interactive whiteboard, teams could then come to the board and change the temperature and pressure separately in order to get their own set of results to plot the graphs.

SPECIFICATION LINK-UP   Unit: Chemistry 2.12.5

- *The relative amounts of all the reacting substances at equilibrium depend on the conditions of the reaction.* [**HT** only]

- *If the temperature is raised, the yield from the endothermic reaction increases and the yield from the exothermic reaction decreases.* [**HT** only]

- *If the temperature is lowered the yield from the endothermic reaction decreases and the yield from the exothermic reaction increases.* [**HT** only]

- *In gaseous reactions, an increase in pressure will favour the reaction that produces the least number of molecules as shown by the symbol equation for that reaction.* [**HT** only]

- *These factors, together with reaction rates, are important when determining the optimum conditions in industrial processes, including the Haber process.* [**HT** only]

- *It is important for sustainable development as well as economic reasons to minimise energy requirements and energy wasted in industrial processes. Non-vigorous conditions means less energy is used and less is released into the environment.*

Students should use their skills, knowledge and understanding of 'How Science Works':

- *to describe the effects of changing the conditions of temperature and pressure on a given reaction or process.*

- *to evaluate the conditions used in an industrial process in terms of energy requirements.*

Lesson structure

STARTER

Flow chart – Students have already encountered the Haber process. To refresh their memory, give the students an unfinished flow chart of the industrial process for them to complete. (5 minutes)

True or false – Create two A4 sheets of paper, one with 'True' written on and the other with 'False'. Then secure these onto each side of the classroom. Read out the following statements and students should then stand by the poster that shows their response. If they are unsure, they could stand in the centre or move more towards one side than the other to show how sure they are of their answer.

- The Haber process makes ammonia. [True]
- The Haber Process is a reversible reaction. [True]
- The reactants for the Haber process are natural gas and air. [False]
- The Haber process is carried out at room temperature and pressure. [False]
- There are more moles of gas on the products' side than the reactants' side in the Haber process. [False] (10–15 minutes)

MAIN

- Give the students data for the yield of the Haber process at different temperatures and different pressures. Students could then plot two graphs to show the trend in yield as these variables change. Higher attaining students could have two *x*-axis scales and plot the data onto one graph. They could then be encouraged to use the graphs to make conclusions about how temperature and pressure affects this reaction. Students could then be encouraged to explain these trends using information from the Student Book.

- Split the class into two teams. One group should explain the choice of temperature in the industrial Haber process and the other should describe the choice of pressure. The groups should decide how they will present their explanations to the class – as a presentation, using the board, just speaking, as a poster, etc. It is up to the group to decide.

PLENARIES

Explanations – Each half of the class should explain the choice of temperature and pressure in the industrial Haber process. (10 minutes)

AfL (Assessment for Learning) – Give students an examination question on this topic and three fictitious student answers. Students should work in small groups discussing the responses and put them in order according to the number of marks that they would give. Then using question and answer you could gain feedback from the whole class and reveal the positive and negative points of the answers. (15 minutes)

ACTIVITY & EXTENSION IDEAS

- Industrial Chemistry (from www.rsc.org) which includes the Haber process could be shown to remind students of the reaction.

CHEMISTRY   ENERGY AND REACTIONS

C2 5.3   More about the Haber process

LEARNING OBJECTIVES

1 Why do we use a temperature of 450°C for the Haber process?
2 Why do we use a pressure of about 200 atmospheres for the Haber process?

We saw on the previous page that the temperature at which we carry out a reversible reaction can affect the amount of the products formed at equilibrium. But if the reaction we are carrying out involves gases, pressure can be very important too.

Many reversible reactions which involve gases have more moles of gas on one side of the equation than on the other. By changing the pressure at which we carry out the reaction we can change the amount of products that we produce. Look at the table below:

If a reaction produces a larger volume of gases	If a reaction produces a smaller volume of gases ......
... an increase in pressure decreases the yield of the reaction, so the amount of products formed is lower.	... an increase in pressure increases the yield of the reaction, so the amount of products formed is larger.
... a decrease in pressure increases the yield of the reaction, so the amount of products formed is larger.	... a decrease in pressure decreases the yield of the reaction, so the amount of products formed is lower.

To see how this is useful we can look at the Haber process which we met earlier.

a) Look at the table above. How does increasing the pressure affect the amount of products formed in a reaction which produces a larger volume of gas?

The economics of the Haber process

The Haber process involves the reversible reaction between nitrogen and hydrogen to make ammonia:

$$N_2 + 3H_2 \rightleftharpoons 2NH_3 \quad (\rightleftharpoons \text{ is the equilibrium symbol})$$

Energy is released during this reaction, so it is exothermic. As the chemical equation shows, there are 4 moles of gas ($N_2 + 3H_2$) on the left-hand side of the equation. But on the right-hand side there are only 2 moles of gas ($2NH_3$). This means that the volume of the reactants is much greater than the volume of the products. So an increase in pressure will tend to produce more ammonia.

b) How does the volume of the products in the Haber process compare to the volume of the reactants?

To get the maximum possible yield of ammonia in the Haber process, we need to make the pressure as high as possible. But high pressures need expensive reaction vessels and pipes which are strong enough to withstand the pressure. Otherwise there is always the danger that an explosion may happen.

In the Haber process we have to make a compromise between using very high pressures (which would produce a lot of ammonia) and the expense of building a chemical plant which can withstand those high pressures. This compromise means that we usually carry out the Haber process at between 200 and 350 atmospheres pressure.

Figure 1 It is expensive to build chemical plants that operate at high pressures

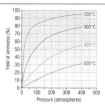

Figure 2 The conditions for the Haber process are a compromise between getting the maximum amount of product in the equilibrium mixture and getting the reaction to take place at a reasonable rate

DID YOU KNOW?

The Haber process is really called the Haber-Bosch process, since Fritz Haber found out how to make ammonia from nitrogen and hydrogen but Carl Bosch carried out the work to find the best conditions for the reaction. Bosch carried out 6500 experiments to find the best catalyst for the reaction.

The effect of temperature on the Haber process is more complicated than the effect of pressure. The forward reaction is exothermic. So if we carry it out at low temperature this would increase the amount of ammonia in the reaction mixture at equilibrium.

But at a low temperature, the rate of the reaction would be very slow. That's because the particles would collide less often and would have less energy. To make ammonia commercially we must get the reaction to go as fast as possible. We don't want to have to wait for the ammonia to be produced!

To do this we need another compromise. A reasonably high temperature is used to get the reaction going at a reasonable rate, even though this reduces the amount of ammonia in the equilibrium mixture.

We also use an iron catalyst to speed up the reaction. (Since this affects the rate of reaction in both directions, it does not affect the amount of ammonia in the equilibrium mixture.)

SUMMARY QUESTIONS

1 Copy and complete using the words below:

**decreases   exothermic   fewer   increasing   left
pressure   released**

The Haber process is ...... so energy is ...... during the reaction. This means that ...... the temperature ...... the amount of ammonia formed. Increasing the ...... will increase the amount of ammonia formed, because there are ...... moles of gas on the right-hand side of the equation than on the ......-hand side.

2 Look at Figure 2.

a) What is the approximate yield of ammonia at a temperature of 500°C and 400 atmospheres pressure?
b) What is the approximate yield of ammonia at a temperature of 500°C and 100 atmospheres pressure?
c) What is the approximate yield of ammonia at a temperature of 200°C and 400 atmospheres pressure?
d) What is the approximate yield of ammonia at a temperature of 200°C and 100 atmospheres pressure?
e) Why is the Haber process carried out at around 200 to 350 atmospheres and 450°C?

KEY POINTS

1 The Haber process uses a pressure of around 200 to 350 atmospheres to increase the amount of ammonia produced.
2 Although higher pressures would produce more ammonia, they would make the chemical plant too expensive to build.
3 A temperature of about 450°C is used for the reaction. Although lower temperatures would increase the amount of ammonia at equilibrium, the ammonia would be produced too slowly.

152   153

SUMMARY ANSWERS

1 Exothermic, released, increasing, decreases, pressure, fewer, left.
[**HT** only]

2 a) 32%
   b) 10%
   c) 95%
   d) 82%
   e) This combines optimum conditions for rate of reaction, amount of ammonia at equilibrium and cost.
   [**HT** only]

Answers to in-text questions

a) It decreases the amount of product formed.

b) It is smaller.

KEY POINTS

Create a word search involving key words from this section. However, do not share the words with the students, they should refer to the key points section to decide on which words that they could find. For lower ability students the number of words to be found in the search could be given, along with their first letter.

CHEMISTRY   ENERGY AND REACTIONS

C2 5.4   Industrial dilemmas

SPECIFICATION LINK-UP

Unit: Chemistry 2.12.5

Students should use their skills, knowledge and understanding of 'How Science Works':

- *to describe the effects of changing the conditions of temperature and pressure on a given reaction or process.*

- *to evaluate the conditions used in an industrial process in terms of energy requirements.*

This spread can also be used to revisit the following substantive content already covered in this chapter:

- *It is important for sustainable development as well as economic reasons to minimise energy requirements and energy wasted in industrial processes. Non-vigorous conditions means less energy is used and less is released into the environment.*

How can we make as much chemical as possible . . .

ABC Laboratory Consultants

Haber House • Drudge Street • Anywhere • AD13 4FU

Dear Sirs

We are planning to build a factory to produce our new chemical, which has the secret formula AB. We are including some data sheets giving details of the reaction we shall be using to produce this chemical, and would like you to advise us about the best reaction conditions (temperature, pressure etc) to use to get as much AB as we can as cheaply as possible. We should like you to present your ideas in a short presentation to be held in your offices in two weeks' time.

Signed

BRIEFING SHEET 1

Project number: 45AB/L1670-J4550K
Specification: R MST3K 65 L7

Brief prepared by   J K Rolling
Checked by   L Skywalker
CHECKED

The equation for the reaction is:

$$A_2B_2 \rightleftharpoons 2AB$$

Both A_2B_2 and AB are gases. These are not their real formulae, which are secret. But the reaction does involve making two moles of product from one mole of reactants.

BRIEFING SHEET 2

Project number: 45AB/L1670-J4550K
Specification: R MST3K 6... CHECKED

Brief prepared by   J K Rolling
Checked by   L Skywalker

The graph shows the amount of AB in the equilibrium mixture at different temperatures.

(graph: y-axis "% of AB at equilibrium" ranging 0–80; x-axis "Temperature (°C)" ranging 0–400)

ACTIVITY

Working in teams, decide what you will advise Consolidated Chemicals to do about the conditions for the reaction. Prepare a presentation with your advice – the whole team should contribute to this. The following questions may help you:

- How does the amount of product change with temperature?
- How does the volume of the gases in the reaction change as AB is made from A_2B_2?
- What conditions may affect the reaction, and how?

154

Teaching suggestions

Activities

- **Presentation** – Split the class into groups of about five and ask all but one group to imagine that they are a group of chemical consultants. Their job is to use the brief set out in the Student Book to generate a proposal for what the chemical conditions should be for this reaction. Their proposal should include a bullet-pointed list to summarise their recommendations. Students could be encouraged to use a presentation package such as PowerPoint® to enhance their proposal. The remaining group should be told to imagine that they are the chemical company; they should write a list of what they are looking for from their contractors. This team could be encouraged to design a pro forma to help judge the presentations and come up with a list of questions that they could ask the groups. Their final job is to decide, with reasons, which group they would employ. Students could then give the presentations, while the company director group takes notes and gives at least one question to the group, which they must respond to. Finally the company director group could give feedback to each team and announce the winners of the contract. You may wish to give a prize for the winning team.

- **Report** – Students should work in small groups of about three. Their task is to consider whether or not it would be possible to go to other worlds and bring back resources for use on Earth. Students should be encouraged to brainstorm their ideas, maybe on a large piece of sugar paper. They could use secondary resources, such as the Internet and library books, for this task; a room swap to the library could be advantageous. Students should continue their discussions and research until they have a clear idea of whether it would be possible, and higher attaining students may like to predict which resources we could bring back from where and the timescale for this to occur. Each team could then compile a report on their work. Some students may struggle writing a report and it may be worth consulting with the English department to see if they have any help sheets to give guidance for this task.

... and what happens when the raw materials run out?!

NO MORE TINNED FOOD IN STOCK

Due to the world shortage of metals our suppliers have told us that there will be no more deliveries of tinned food. Until further notice.

'What do we do when our resources run low?'

The world population grows all the time. It grows in its demands for a better lifestyle as well. Why shouldn't everyone have access to cars, computers and the latest electrical goodies? Yet all this growth means greater use of our natural resources – chemicals, minerals, oil. Minerals and metals don't replace themselves as carefully managed living resources do. So either we will have to find alternative materials, or alternative sources of the minerals we have been using . . .

London today saw some of the worst rioting as people struggled to get their hands on the last deliveries to be made to the shops. The world shortage of minerals has really begun to bite now, with the supplies of raw materials like copper and zinc running low and prices going through the roof. As oil supplies dwindle too, the lights are going out all over London . . .

'SPACE IS THE ANSWER!!'

The **Bugle** says 'get into space to find more minerals!!' It must be obvious even to our dim-witted leaders that we need to go and explore. Just as explorers in the past found new lands and new riches, we must go into space to find minerals on other planets! We can then bring them back to Earth so that we can make the things we need!'

ACTIVITY

There are many technical problems that have to be solved to allow us to travel to other planets in the Solar System. But imagine that they could be overcome. Could we really travel to other worlds to find new resources and bring them back to Earth?

Work in teams. You have been asked to produce a report for a government department about the possibility of using the Moon and nearby planets as a source of minerals. You need to consider not only the practical aspects of this but also the economics and the politics too. For example, in 1969 American astronauts landed on the Moon. So does this mean that the USA owns the Moon? Who will decide who owns the minerals on Mars or on the Moon?

155

Homework

Find out – The higher the pressure, the more product is formed in the Haber process. Show students images of pressure vessels used in the lab and by industry. Encourage students to find out the safety and cost implications of running a system under high pressure.

Extension

Find out – Ask students to find out about another industrial process and its reaction conditions (e.g. metal extractions or The Contact Process). Higher attaining students could be encouraged to explain the choice of these reaction conditions.

Learning styles

Visual: Creating the presentation on chemical conditions.

Auditory: Listening to presentations by other students.

Intrapersonal: Discovering the cost and safety implications of using pressure vessels.

Interpersonal: Working as small groups in the report writing or presentation activities.

Special needs

- Give these students a pack of cards with details about the AB reaction. The cards should include explanations for temperature and pressure changes, information about costs and safety. Students can then use these as prompts to create their presentation.

- A similar set of cards could be used with prompts about the exploitation of other worlds for their resources, or a part-finished spider diagram to help them form their ideas.

Gifted and talented

Split the class in half, one side is to argue that humans will exploit other planets' resources and the other will argue that they will not. Allow the students to research the facts and then hold a debate on the matter.

ICT link-up

Students could use a word-processing package to type up their report.

SUMMARY ANSWERS

1 Lines drawn to link left-hand and right-hand columns as follows:

a) B and C **b)** A and D

2 [Students should describe a way in which the temperature change can be measured when known amounts of sherbet dissolve in water.]

3 a) and **b)**

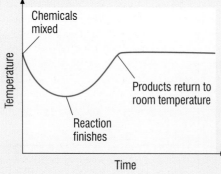

Chemicals mixed

Temperature

Products return to room temperature

Reaction finishes

Time

4 a) $X(g) + 2Y(g) \rightleftharpoons 3Z(g)$

  b) i) No change.

    ii) Increase.

  c) i) Decrease.

    ii) Increase.

  d) Better (because it would cost less) to get 10% of product in 25 seconds rather than waiting 3 times as long to get twice the amount of product. [**HT** only]

Summary teaching suggestions

- **Special needs** – Prepare a table with two columns – exothermic and endothermic. On a separate sheet of paper create a cut and paste activity using the statements from question 1. Students can then cut out the sentences and put them in the correct column of the table.

- **Learning styles**
  Visual: Question 2 involves the drawing of a diagram and question 3 involves the drawing of a graph.
  Auditory: Question 4 could be read out to students, and they note their answers on A4 whiteboards (or laminated paper) and hold them up to you for assessment.
  Interpersonal: Question 2 lends itself to a discussion before each student pens their own answer.

- **When to use the questions?**
  - As a revision resource.
  - Questions 1 and 4 could be turned into multiple-choice questions and displayed on slides. The answers could then be colour-coded, and each student could be given different coloured cards to correspond to the answers. Then you could refer to the question and the students hold up their cards to represent their answer.

SUMMARY QUESTIONS

1 Select from A, B, C and/or D to describe correctly exothermic and endothermic reactions.

a) In an exothermic reaction ...... A ...... we may notice a decrease in temperature.

b) In an endothermic reaction ...... B ...... energy is released by the chemicals.

  C ...... we may notice an increase in temperature.

  D ...... energy is absorbed by the chemicals.

2 'When sherbet sweets dissolve in your mouth this is an endothermic process.' Devise an experiment to test your statement. Use words and diagrams to describe clearly what you would do.

3 Two chemicals are mixed and react endothermically. When the reaction has finished, the reaction mixture is allowed to stand until it has returned to its starting temperature.

a) Sketch a graph of temperature (y-axis) v time (x-axis) to show how the temperature of the reaction mixture changes.

b) Label the graph clearly and explain what is happening wherever you have shown the temperature changing.

4 A chemical reaction can make product Z from reactants X and Y. Under the reaction conditions, X, Y and Z are gases.

X, Y and Z react in the proportions 1 : 2 : 3. The reaction is carried out at 250°C and 100 atmospheres. The reaction is reversible, and it is exothermic in the forward direction.

a) Write an equation for this (reversible) reaction.

b) How would increasing the pressure affect
  i) the amount of Z formed,
  ii) the rate at which Z is formed?

c) How would increasing the temperature affect
  i) the amount of Z formed,
  ii) the rate at which Z is formed?

d) A 10% yield of Z is obtained in 25 seconds under the reaction conditions. To get a 20% yield of Z under the same conditions takes 75 seconds. Explain why it makes more sense economically to set the reaction up to obtain a 10% yield rather than a 20% yield. [Higher]

EXAM-STYLE QUESTIONS

1 Match each of (a) to (g) with one of the following:

**endothermic reaction exothermic reaction
no reaction**

(a) Burning petrol in a car engine.

(b) Respiration in living cells.

(c) Boiling water.

(d) Converting limestone into calcium oxide.

(e) Switching on an electric light bulb.

(f) Reducing lead oxide with carbon to produce lead.

(g) Carbon dioxide combining with water in cells of green plants.

2 When heated continuously, pink cobalt chloride crystals can be changed into blue crystals .

$$CoCl_2.6H_2O \rightleftharpoons CoCl_2.2H_2O + 4H_2O$$
pink   blue

(a) What does the symbol $\rightleftharpoons$ tell you about this reaction?

(b) How can you tell that the reaction to produce blue crystals is endothermic?

(c) (i) How could you change the blue crystals to pink crystals?

    (ii) What temperature change would you observe when this is done?

(d) Suggest how the colour changes of these crystals could be used.

3 The equation for the main reaction in the Haber process to make ammonia is:

$$N_2 + 3H_2 \rightleftharpoons 2NH_3$$

The table shows the percentage yield of the Haber process at different temperatures and pressures.

Pressure (atm)	Temp. (°C) 0	100	200	300	400	500
400	99	91	78	55	32	20
200	96	87	66	40	21	12
100	94	79	50	25	13	6
50	92	71	36	16	5	2

(a) Why does the yield of ammonia decrease with increased temperature?

(b) Why does the yield of ammonia increase with increased pressure?

EXAM-STYLE ANSWERS

1 a) Exothermic reaction. *(1 mark)*

  b) Exothermic reaction. *(1 mark)*

  c) No reaction. *(1 mark)*

  d) Endothermic reaction. *(1 mark)*

  e) No reaction. *(1 mark)*

  f) Exothermic reaction. *(1 mark)*

  g) Endothermic reaction. *(1 mark)*

2 a) It is reversible. *(1 mark)*

  b) It has to be heated continuously. *(1 mark)*

  c) i) Add water. *(1 mark)*

    ii) It would get hot/temperature rises. *(1 mark)*

  d) As a test for water. *(1 mark)*

3 a) Formation of ammonia is exothermic/forward reaction is exothermic. *(1 mark)*
So increase in temperature favours reverse reaction/increase in temperature causes more ammonia to decompose. *(1 mark)*

  b) For forward reaction, 4 moles of gas produces 2 moles of gas. *(1 mark)*

An increase in pressure favours reaction that produces smaller number of molecules of gas. *(1 mark)*

  c) These are compromise conditions (explained somewhere in answer). *(1 mark)*
200 atm is as high as economically possible/higher pressure would need much stronger plant/need more energy/would be more dangerous. *(1 mark)*
450°C is needed so that reaction is quite fast/so that catalyst works. *(1 mark)*

  d) Better as line graphs on the same axes. *(1 mark)*
[**HT** only]

c) Why are conditions of 200 atm pressure and 450°C used in the industrial process? (3)

d) Suggest a better way than a table to present this data. (1)

[Higher]

The reaction to produce poly(ethene) is exothermic.

$$n\,C_2H_4 \rightarrow -\!\!(CH_2\!-\!CH_2)\!\!-_n$$

ethene poly(ethene)

The conditions used in two processes to make poly(ethene) are shown in the table.

Process	Temperature (°C)	Pressure (atm)	Catalyst
A	150–300	1000–3000	no
B	40–80	1–50	yes

(a) What enables process **B** to be operated under less vigorous conditions? (1)

(b) Suggest one way to keep the energy used to a minimum in both processes. (1)

(c) Suggest **two** environmental advantages of using process **B** to make poly(ethene). (2)

A student had learned that the reaction between hydrochloric acid and sodium hydroxide solution was exothermic. She, therefore, predicted that when she added more acid to the alkali more heat would be produced. She used a burette to deliver exact amounts of hydrochloric acid to 20 cm³ of alkali in a flask. She used a thermometer to measure the temperature. Her results are in this table:

Volume of acid added (cm³)	Temperature recorded (°C)
0	17
10	21
20	24
30	21
40	21
50	20

(a) How should she have insulated the flask? (1)

(b) Explain why she should have taken the temperature of the acid before adding it to the sodium hydroxide solution. (2)

(c) Did she actually measure the heat produced by the reaction? Explain your answer. (1)

(d) How might she have used an indicator to increase the accuracy of her method? (1)

HOW SCIENCE WORKS QUESTIONS

Jack set up some apparatus to see the effect of temperature on the rate of a reaction between calcium carbonate and hydrochloric acid.

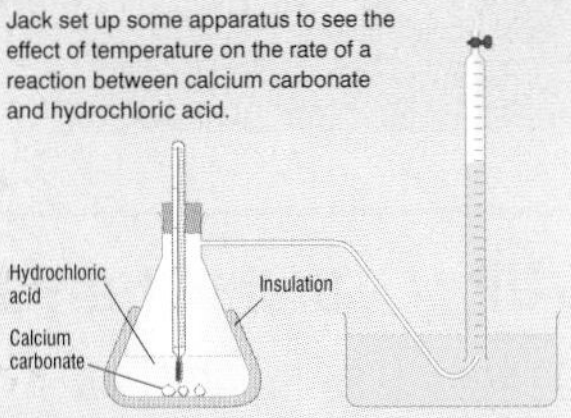

Jack was careful to ensure that the mass of the calcium carbonate, the concentration and the volume of the hydrochloric acid were kept the same for the start of each experiment. He also ensured that the temperature of the reactants was checked after the carbon dioxide had been collected. He timed how long it took, at each temperature, to fill the burette.

Here are his results:

Temperature of reactants (°C)	Average time taken (s)	Average temperature change (°C)
15	145	+1
20	105	+1
25	73	+3
30	51	+3
35	30	+4

a) Plot a graph of the temperature of the reactants against the average time taken. (3)

b) Describe the pattern that you think is shown by these results. (2)

c) List three variables that Jack controlled in this investigation. (3)

d) Name a variable that Jack could not control, but did take account of. (1)

e) What type of error was the changing temperature? Explain your answer. (1)

f) Was the sensitivity of the thermometer good enough? Explain your answer. (1)

g) Why is it not possible to judge the precision of Jack's results? (2)

h) Do you doubt the reliability of Jack's results? Explain your answer. (1)

4 a) The catalyst. *(1 mark)*

b) Use heat from (exothermic) reaction to heat reactants/use heat produced elsewhere in the chemical plant, e.g. to make steam to drive pumps. *(1 mark)*

c) It uses less energy/uses smaller amounts of finite resources to produce energy. *(1 mark)*
Less energy is released into the environment. *(1 mark)*

5 a) Any reasonable suggestion – wrapped in cotton wool. *(1 mark)*

b) It is a variable she has not controlled. *(1 mark)*
OR she does not know if it is the heat in the acid that is raising the temperature. *(2 marks)*

c) No she measured the temperature of the two liquids. *(1 mark)*

d) She could have used the indicator to note when the reaction had finished. *(1 mark)*

Exam teaching suggestions

- Allow about 30 minutes for the four questions on this chapter, totalling 29 marks. Q1 and Q2 could be done after 5.2 and the other questions when the chapter has been completed. Q3 would appear only on a higher-tier paper.
- In Q1, students should be familiar with common examples of exothermic and endothermic reactions and should be able to differentiate physical changes from chemical reactions. Students could be encouraged to suggest and classify other everyday changes, perhaps in the form of a 'day in my life' sequence, listing things that happen from getting up in the morning until going to bed at night.
- Some students find questions on reversible reactions difficult, or avoid them in exams because they look complicated. Familiarity and consistent logic help students to understand what happens in these reactions. Simulations can be helpful for many students, especially when considering the effects of changes in conditions.
- The Haber process is used as an example again in this part of the specification, but questions will be set on other industrial processes that candidates are not expected to be familiar with. This will assess their understanding of the principles in this part of the specification and their ability to apply them in new situations (Assessment Objective 2).
- Q5 is based on concepts embedded in 'How Science Works'.

HOW SCIENCE WORKS ANSWERS

a) Graph drawn should be fully labelled, with units. The plots need to be correct and a line of best fit drawn. The temperature needs to be on the *x*-axis and time taken on the *y*-axis.

b) As the temperature increases, the time taken decreases. The reduction in time gets less as the temperature gets higher.

c) Jack controlled the mass of the calcium carbonate, the concentration and the volume of the hydrochloric acid.

d) Jack could not control the temperature change.

e) The changing temperature could be called a systematic error. It is related to the rate of the reaction, it being exothermic. Students might argue that it is a random error because it is not constant. The difference is not greatly important, but for able students might be worthy of discussion.

f) No because the pattern is difficult to detect.

g) It is not possible to judge the precision of results because there are no actual results shown, (he has only shown the average time taken) the variation of which would indicate precision.

h) Yes. There is no other data, e.g., from secondary sources to establish reliability. However the pattern shown looks convincing and fits in with accepted theory.

How science works teaching suggestions

- **Literacy guidance**
  - Key terms that should be clearly understood: control, error, precision, reliability.
  - Question h) expects a longer answer, where students can practise their literacy skills.
- **Higher- and lower-level answers.** Questions b), e), f), g) and h) are higher-level questions. The answers for these have been provided at this level. Question d) is lower level and the answer provided is also at this level.
- **Gifted and talented.** Able students could suggest how the variable temperature might be taken into account, for example in the plotting of the graph.
- **How and when to use these questions.** The questions could be used when wishing to develop graph-drawing skills or when an understanding of sensitivity, precision and reliability needs to be developed.
  The questions should be tackled for homework and reviewed in a class plenary.
- **Homework.** For lower-ability students, the graph might be drawn for homework.
- **Special needs.** For these students the axes of the graph could be drawn and labelled to get them started.

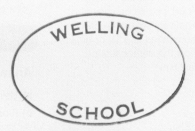

C2 6.1

Electrolysis – the basics

Unit: Chemistry 2.12.6

LEARNING OBJECTIVES

Students should learn:

- That ionic compounds can undergo electrolysis.
- Which substances can be electrolysed.
- The products of electrolysis.

LEARNING OUTCOMES

Most students should be able to:

- State a definition for electrolysis.
- Recognise which compounds will undergo electrolysis.
- Add state symbols to an equation.
- Predict the products of molten electrolysis.

Some students should also be able to:

- Explain how electrolysis occurs.

Teaching suggestions

- **Special needs.** Give the students the parts of the flow chart for the decomposition of lead bromide, but in the wrong order. These students can then cut them up and stick them into their own diagram in their notes.

- **Learning styles**

  Kinaesthetic: Completing the electrolysis practical.

  Visual: Drawing a labelled diagram of the electrolysis equipment.

  Auditory: Listening to explanations of different words.

  Intrapersonal: Defining key words.

  Interpersonal: Working in pairs to note information about chemicals.

- **Homework.** Ask students to find out two different materials that can be used to make electrodes and then give examples of a use for each electrode material.

- **ICT link-up.** Often it is difficult for students to see a demonstration in a fume cupboard. If the reaction can be filmed beforehand it could be shown to students. Alternatively set up flexicam or a camcorder connected to a TV or digital projector to show the demonstration magnified in real time.

SPECIFICATION LINK-UP   Unit: Chemistry 2.12.6

- The state symbols in equations are (s), (l), (g) and (aq).
- When an ionic substance is melted or dissolved in water, the ions are free to move about within the liquid or solution.
- Passing an electric current through ionic substances that are molten or in solution breaks them down into elements. This process is called electrolysis.
- During electrolysis, positively charged ions move to the negative electrode, and negatively charged ions move to the positive electrode.

Lesson structure

STARTER

Anagram – As a title write: 'cysistrollee'. Explain to the students that they are going to study this topic, but the letters are jumbled up. Encourage them to find out the word [electrolysis] and write this as the title, followed by a brief definition [splitting-up a compound using electricity]. (10 minutes)

Observations – In sealed containers show the students an ampoule of bromine, a sample of lead and lead bromide. In pairs, ask students to make a list about everything that they know about these chemicals and encourage them to use the periodic table and list the mass etc. Draw a three-column table on the board, each headed with the different chemical and ask groups for pieces of information to fill in the table. Then ask the students how lead and bromine could be made from lead bromide. (10 minutes)

MAIN

- A classic demonstration of electrolysis involved the decomposition of lead bromide. This is chosen, as it is an ionic solid with a relatively low melting point. The reaction does produce lead and bromine and therefore should be completed in a fume cupboard. Demonstrate the experiment and use questions and answers to extract observations from the students. Then ask them to draw a diagrammatic flow chart, including a symbol equation to represent the demonstration.

- Students could complete their own electrolysis experiment, however this cannot be completed for a molten liquid, a solution must be used. To prevent any confusion due to water producing oxygen or hydrogen, copper chloride solution should be used. Students could be given a set of questions to consider as they complete the reaction to channel their thoughts.

- Use Simulation C2 6.1 'Electrolysis' from the Additional Science CD ROM.

PLENARIES

Taboo – Create a set of cards with the key words: 'electricity', 'electrolysis', 'electrolyte', 'electrode', 'decompose'. Below each key word list three further words that would aid in explaining the main word. Give the pack of cards to groups of three. Each person should take it in turns to pick a card and try to explain the main word, without using the taboo words. The person who managed to explain the most words (without using any taboo words) is the winner. (10 minutes)

Definitions – Ask students to define the key words: 'electrolysis', 'electrolyte', 'decompose', 'anode', 'cathode', 'electrode' in their books. Higher attaining students could define the term, then use it correctly in a sentence. (10 minutes)

Diagram – Ask students to draw a labelled diagram of the equipment needed to complete a simple electrolysis. (5 minutes)

Answers to in-text questions

a) Using an electric current to break down a substance.

b) Electrolyte.   c) Negative electrode (Cathode).   d) Positive electrode (Anode).

Practical support

Demonstration of the electrolysis of lead bromide

Equipment and materials required

Ceramic evaporating basin, lead bromide (toxic – CLEAPSS Hazcard 57), spatula, tongs, Bunsen burner and safety equipment, tongs, two carbon electrodes, lamp, three wires, two crocodile clips, lab pack, fume cupboard, tripod, pipe-clay triangle, eye protection, protective gloves.

Details

Half-fill the evaporation basin with lead bromide and submerge the ends of the electrodes. Connect the electrodes into the circuit involving the lamp and the lab pack. Put the evaporation basin on the pipe-clay triangle above the Bunsen burner. Ignite the Bunsen burner and heat the lead bromide strongly, turn on the lab pack and observe. Once the lamp is on, the electricity is flowing, this will only occur when the ions are free to move, i.e. the lead bromide is molten. Point out the vapour (bromine is toxic – CLEAPSS Hazcard 15). The reaction is heated so the halogen is released as a gas not as a liquid, which is its state at room temperature. The molten lead will collect at the bottom of the basin. Switch off the Bunsen and use the tongs to tip the molten lead onto the flame-proof mat to show the students.

Safety: Eye protection should be worn during this demonstration and it should be completed in a fume cupboard. Pregnant women should not use lead bromide. Anhydrous zinc chloride (corrosive – CLEAPSS Hazcard 108) melts at a lower temperature than lead bromide so can be used as an alternative.

Electrolysis of copper chloride solution

Equipment and materials required

Beaker, two carbon electrodes, lamp, three wires, two crocodile clips, lab pack, 1 M copper chloride solution (harmful – CLEAPSS Hazcard 27), eye protection.

Details

Half-fill the beaker with copper chloride solution and immerse the tips of the electrodes. Connect the electrodes in a simple circuit with the lab pack and lamp. Start the current and observe, chlorine (toxic) should be smelt at the anode, and copper should be deposited at the cathode. As soon as the observations are complete the lab pack should be switched off.

Safety: Eye protection should be worn throughout the practical. This experiment should be completed in a well-ventilated room as the chlorine could irritate asthmatics.

ACTIVITY & EXTENSION IDEAS

- Show students a simulation of the reaction detailing the particles.
- Students could complete electrolysis of other halides that involve a metal below hydrogen in the reactivity series, e.g. zinc chloride. By using this select group of compounds, students do not need to use the table of discharge to determine the products. The experiment is identical to that for copper chloride, as detailed in 'Practical support'.

SUMMARY ANSWERS

1 Anode, cathode, negative, ions, move, solution, molten.

2 a) Copper at −; iodine at +.

   b) Potassium at −; bromine at +.

   c) Sodium at −; fluorine at +.

3 [Words/diagrams explain how ions carry charge.] If ions are not free to move (as they are not in a solid because they are held in position by strong electrostatic forces) no current can flow in the circuit.

KEY POINTS

Ask students to copy out the objectives with the key point that best answers the question alongside it.

C2 6.1   Electrolysis – the basics

LEARNING OBJECTIVES

1 What is electrolysis?
2 What types of substances can we electrolyse?
3 What is made when we electrolyse substances?

Figure 1 The first person to explain electrolysis was Michael Faraday, who worked on this and many other problems in science nearly 200 years ago. His work formed the basis of an understanding of electrolysis that we still use today.

The word electrolysis means 'splitting up using electricity'. In electrolysis we use an electric current to break down (or **decompose**) a substance made of ions into simpler substances. We call the substance broken down by electrolysis the **electrolyte**.

a) What is electrolysis?
b) What do we call the substance broken down by electrolysis?

We set up an electrical circuit for electrolysis that has two electrodes which dip into the electrolyte. The electrodes are conducting rods. One of these is connected to the positive terminal of a power supply, the other is connected to the negative terminal.

We normally make the electrodes out of an unreactive (or **inert**) substance like graphite or platinum. This is so they do not react with either the electrolyte or the products made during electrolysis. We use the name **anode** for positive electrode, while we call the negative electrode the **cathode**.

During electrolysis, positively charged ions move to the negative electrode (cathode) and negative ions move to the positive electrode (anode).

When the ions reach the electrodes they can lose their charge and be deposited as elements. Depending on the compound being electrolysed, gases may be given off or metals deposited at the electrodes.

DEMONSTRATION

The electrolysis of lead bromide

This demonstration needs a fume cupboard because bromine is toxic and corrosive.

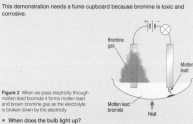

Figure 2 When we pass electricity through molten lead bromide it forms molten lead and brown bromine gas as the electrolyte is broken down by the electricity

- When does the bulb light up?

Figure 2 shows how electricity breaks down lead bromide into lead and bromine:

$$lead\ bromide \rightarrow lead + bromine$$
$$PbBr_2\ (l) \rightarrow Pb\ (l) + Br_2\ (g)$$

Lead bromide is an ionic substance which does not conduct electricity when it is solid. But when we melt it the ions can move freely towards the electrodes.

The positive lead ions move towards the cathode, while the negatively charged bromide ions move towards the anode. Notice how the state symbols in the equation tell us that the lead bromide and the lead are molten. The '(l)' stands for 'liquid', while bromine is given off as a gas, shown as '(g)'.

c) Which electrode do positive ions move towards during electrolysis?
d) Which electrode do negative ions move towards during electrolysis?

Many ionic substances have very high melting points. This can make electrolysis very difficult or even impossible. But some ionic substances dissolve in water, and when this happens the ions can move freely.

When we dissolve ionic substances in water to electrolyse them it is more difficult to predict what will be formed. This is because water also forms ions, and so the product at the anode and the cathode is not always exactly what we expect.

When we electrolyse a solution of copper bromide in water, copper ions move to the negative electrode (cathode) and the bromide ions move to the positive electrode (anode). Copper bromide is split into its two elements at the electrodes:

$$copper\ bromide \rightarrow copper + bromine$$
$$CuBr_2\ (aq) \rightarrow Cu\ (s) + Br_2\ (aq)$$

In this case the state symbols in the equation tell us that the copper bromide is dissolved in water, shown as '(aq)'. The elements that are produced are solid copper, shown as '(s)', and bromine which remains dissolved in the water – '(aq)'.

Covalent compounds cannot be split by electrolysis.

SUMMARY QUESTIONS

1 Copy and complete using the words below:

     anode   cathode   ions   molten   move
         negative   solution

   In electrolysis the ...... is the positive electrode while the ...... is the ...... electrode. For the current to flow, the ...... must be able to ...... between the electrodes. This can only happen if the substance is in ...... or if it is ....

2 Predict the products formed at each electrode when the following compounds are melted and then electrolysed:

   a) copper iodide
   b) potassium bromide
   c) sodium fluoride

3 Solid ionic substances do not conduct electricity. Using words and diagrams explain why they conduct electricity when molten or in solution.

FOUL FACTS

Electrolysis is also a way of getting rid of unwanted body hair. A small electric current is passed through the base of each individual hair to be removed. The hair is destroyed by chemical changes caused by the electric current which destroy the cells that make the hair grow.

Figure 3 If we dissolve copper bromide in water we can decompose it by electrolysis. Copper metal is formed at the cathode, while brown bromine appears in solution around the anode

KEY POINTS

1 Electrolysis involves splitting up a substance using electricity.
2 Ionic substances can be electrolysed when they are molten or in solution.
3 In electrolysis positive ions move to the negative electrode (cathode) and negative ions move to the positive electrode (anode).

C2 6.2

Changes at the electrodes

LEARNING OBJECTIVES

Students should learn:

- That electrons are transferred during electrolysis.
- That electrolysis can be represented in half equations. [**HT** only]
- That water affects electrolysis.

LEARNING OUTCOMES

Most students should be able to:

- Recall the transfer of electrons at the anode and cathode.
- Recognise oxidation and reduction at electrodes.
- Predict the products of electrolysis.

Some students should also be able to:

- Explain the transfer of electrons in electrolysis.
- Construct half equations. [**HT** only]
- Explain how water affects the products of electrolysis.

Teaching suggestions

- **Learning styles**

  Kinaesthetic: Completing a card sort activity.

  Visual: Annotating the digital photograph of the electrolysis play.

  Auditory: Listening to questions and answers to guess a key word.

  Intrapersonal: Completing half equations.

  Interpersonal: Working as a class to act out the particle movement in electrolysis.

- **Homework.** Ask students to complete the following symbol equation and half equations:
  $2FeCl_3(aq) \rightarrow [2Fe(s)] + [3Cl_2(g)]$
  Anode: $[2Cl^-(aq) \rightarrow Cl_2(g) + 2e^-]$
  Cathode: $[Fe^{3+}(aq) + 3e^- \rightarrow Fe(s)]$

- **ICT link-up.** Digital photographs could be taken of the electrolysis play. These could then be used in the classroom to remind students of the play. If a photograph is displayed on an interactive whiteboard, then annotations could be added in front of the class.

SPECIFICATION LINK-UP   Unit: Chemistry 2.12.6

- *At the negative electrode positively charged ions gain electrons (reduction) and at the positive electrode negatively charged ions lose electrons (oxidation).*
- *If there is a mixture of ions, the products formed depend on the reactivity of the elements involved.*
- *Reactions at electrodes can be represented by half equations, for example:*

$$2Cl^- \rightarrow Cl_2 + 2e^-$$ [*HT* only]

Students should use their skills, knowledge and understanding of 'How Science Works':

- *to predict the products of electrolysing solutions of ions.*
- *to complete and balance supplied half equations for the reactions occurring at the electrodes during electrolysis. [HT only]*

Lesson structure

STARTER

Card sort – Give the key words (oxidation, reduction and redox) and their definitions on separate cards. Students should sort the cards to match the key words with their definitions. (5 minutes)

Poem – Encourage the students to create a little poem or saying to help them remember that oxidation is the loss of electrons and happens at the anode, meanwhile reduction is the gain of electrons and occurs at the cathode. To help students, direct their attention to the 'Get it right section' of the Student Book. Encourage a few students to read out their work. The best one could then be copied by all the students into their notes. (15 minutes)

MAIN

- Show the students a sample of potassium chloride and ask them to predict the products of the reaction if the compound was molten. Encourage a student to write the balanced symbol equation on the board.

- Now ask pairs of students to predict the products if a solution of potassium chloride were electrolysed. Ask each group their thoughts and why they came to this idea. Then allow the students to complete the experiment to find out it they were correct. Encourage students to note their work in the form of a fully labelled diagram, including half equations and brief notes to explain where the hydrogen comes from. (Note that half equations are Higher Tier content.)

- Students could act out an electrolysis experiment. They could wear black bibs and make a line to represent the electrodes and wires in the circuit. Polystyrene balls could be used as electrons, two students could stand by a bucket of balls – one student giving them out and one putting them into the bucket (this represents the power source). Different coloured bibs (blue – cations, red – anions) could be used to create the solution. The circuit could then 'run' under your instructions. Students could then use the play to describe what happens in terms of particles at the anode and cathode.

PLENARIES

What am I? – On sticky labels write the following words: 'redox', 'reduction', 'oxidation', 'reduced', 'oxidised', 'half equation'. Split the students into teams of six and give each a word and ask them to stick it on their forehead (but they should not know what their word is). Each student then takes it in turns to ask his or her group questions, which the team can only respond with 'yes' or 'no'. The aim is for each student to guess their word. (10 minutes)

Half equations – Ask students to complete the half equations as detailed in question 2 of the summary questions. Then encourage the students to create three more examples of half equations of their choice. [**HT** only] (10 minutes)

Practical support

Electrolysis of potassium chloride

Equipment and materials required

Beaker, two carbon electrodes, lamp, three wires, two crocodile clips, lab pack, saturated solution of potassium chloride, test tube, splint, eye protection.

Details

Half-fill the beaker with potassium chloride solution and immerse the tips of the electrodes. Connect the electrodes in a simple circuit with the lab pack and lamp. Start the current and observe, chlorine (toxic – CLEAPSS Hazcard 22) should be smelt at the anode, and bubbles (hydrogen – flammable – CLEAPSS Hazcard 48) should be observed at the cathode. As soon as the observations are complete the lab pack should be switched off. The hydrogen could be collected in a test tube under displacement, and tested with a lighted splint.

Safety: Eye protection should be worn throughout the practical. This experiment should be completed in a well-ventilated room as the chlorine could irritate asthmatics.

ACTIVITY & EXTENSION IDEAS

Use Simulation C2 6.1 from the Additional Science CD ROM which shows particle movement in electrolysis.

Answers to in-text questions

a) Electron(s) are transferred from the ion to the electrode.

b) Electron(s) are transferred to the ion from the electrode.

C2 6.2 — Changes at the electrodes

LEARNING OBJECTIVES

1 What happens during electrolysis?
2 How can we represent what happens in electrolysis? [Higher]
3 How does water affect the products of electrolysis?

During electrolysis ions move towards the electrodes. The direction they move in depends on their charge. As we saw on the previous page, positive ions move towards the negative electrode (the cathode). Negative ions move towards the positive electrode (the anode).

When ions reach an electrode, they either lose or gain electrons depending on their charge.

Negatively charged ions *lose* electrons to become neutral atoms. Positively charged ions form neutral atoms by *gaining* electrons.

a) How do negatively charged ions become neutral atoms in electrolysis?
b) How do positively charged ions become neutral atoms in electrolysis?

The easiest way to think about this is to look at an example:

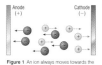

Figure 1 An ion always moves towards the oppositely charged electrode

In the electrolysis of molten lead bromide, positively charged lead ions (Pb^{2+}) move towards the cathode (−). When they get there, each ion gains **two** electrons to become a neutral lead atom.

Gaining electrons is called **reduction** – we say that the lead ions are *reduced*. 'Reduction' is simply another way of saying 'gaining electrons'.

When molten lead bromide is electrolysed, negatively charged bromide ions (Br^-) move towards the anode (+). When they get there, each ion loses *one* electron to become a neutral bromine atom. Two bromine atoms then form a covalent bond to make a bromine molecule, Br_2.

Losing electrons is called **oxidation** – we say that the bromide ions are *oxidised*. 'Oxidation' is another way of saying 'losing electrons'.

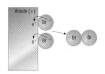

We represent what is happening at the electrodes using *half equations*. We call them this because what happens at one electrode is only half the story – we need to know what is happening at both electrodes to know what is happening in the whole reaction.

At the negative electrode:

$$Pb^{2+} + 2e^- \rightarrow Pb$$ (notice how an electron is written as 'e⁻')

At the positive electrode:

$$2Br^- \rightarrow Br_2 + 2e^-$$

Sometimes half equations are written showing the electrons being removed from negative ions, like this:

$$2Br - 2e^- \rightarrow Br_2$$

Neither method is more 'right' than the other – it just depends on how you want to write the half equation.

Because **RED**uction and **OX**idation take place at the same time in electrolysis (reduction at the cathode (−), oxidation at the anode (+)), it is sometimes called a **redox** reaction.

The effect of water

When we carry out electrolysis in water the situation is made more complicated by the fact that water contains ions. The rule for working out what will happen is to remember that if two elements can be produced at an electrode, the less reactive element will usually be formed.

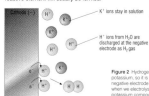

Figure 2 Hydrogen is less reactive than potassium, so it is produced at the negative electrode rather than potassium when we electrolyse a solution of a potassium compound

GET IT RIGHT!

Remember OILRIG –
Oxidation **I**s **L**oss (of electrons), **R**eduction **I**s **G**ain (of electrons).

KEY POINTS

1 In electrolysis, the ions move towards the oppositely charged electrodes.
2 At the electrodes, negative ions are oxidised while positive ions are reduced.
3 Reactions where reduction and oxidation happen are called redox reactions.
4 When electrolysis happens in water, the less reactive element is usually produced at an electrode.

SUMMARY QUESTIONS

1 Copy and complete using the words below:

> anode (+)   cathode (−)   electrodes   gain   less   lose
> ions   oxidised   reduced

During electrolysis ...... move towards the .... At the ...... positively charged ions are ...... and ...... electrons. At the ...... negatively charged ions are ...... and ...... electrons. When electrolysis is carried out in water, the ...... reactive element is usually produced.

2 Copy and complete the following half-equations where necessary:

a) $Cl^- \rightarrow Cl_2 + e^-$
b) $O^{2-} \rightarrow O_2 + e^-$
c) $Ca^{2+} + e^- \rightarrow Ca$
d) $Al^{3+} + e^- \rightarrow Al$
e) $Na^+ + e^- \rightarrow Na$
f) $H^+ + e^- \rightarrow H_2$ [Higher]

SUMMARY ANSWERS

1 Ions, electrodes, cathode (−), reduced, gain, anode (+), oxidised, lose, less.

2 a) $2Cl^- \rightarrow Cl_2 + 2e^-$
b) $2O^{2-} \rightarrow O_2 + 4e^-$
c) $Ca^{2+} + 2e^- \rightarrow Ca$
d) $Al^{3+} + 3e^- \rightarrow Al$
e) $Na^+ + e^- \rightarrow Na$
f) $2H^+ + 2e^- \rightarrow H_2$ [**HT** only]

KEY POINTS

Ask students to copy the key points and to write any word that has a positive charge in red (e.g. oxidation, positive, anode,) and any with a negative charge in blue.

C2 6.3

Electrolysing brine

Teaching suggestions

- **Gifted and talented.** The Solvay process uses sodium chloride. Students could research the industrial production of sodium carbonate and sodium hydrogencarbonate using this method.

- **Learning styles**

  Kinaesthetic: Completing the electrolysis of sodium chloride practical.

  Visual: Writing and assembling a magazine article.

  Auditory: Listening to uses of the products of electrolysis of brine, then deciding which product it refers to.

  Intrapersonal: Spotting the difference in two different pictures.

  Interpersonal: Working in pairs to predict the products of the electrolysis of sodium chloride.

- **Homework.** Ask the students to find out the different uses of chlorine in the UK, represented as percentages. Then ask the students to display the information as a pie chart. For lower ability students, the data could be given and they could plot a bar chart.

- **ICT link-up.** Students could use desktop publishing packages to produce their article. They could be encouraged to use photographs of the industrial processes using the Internet, or they could use a digital camera to take images in the lab to be used in their article.

Lesson structure

STARTER

Predict – Ask students to work in pairs to predict the products of electrolysis of molten sodium chloride and a solution of sodium chloride. Higher attaining students could also complete half equations to show the formation of the products. (10 minutes)

Spot the difference – Show the students two images of the electrolysis of sodium chloride solution from the Additional Science CD ROM. Students should ring the changes in the second picture, e.g. labels missing/incorrect. (5 minutes)

MAIN

- Students can complete their own electrolysis of sodium chloride. They could record their observations in a colourful diagram of the apparatus. They could also annotate the formation of the products and detail their uses.

- Show students different popular science magazines, from *New Scientist* to *Horrible Science*. Ask the students to write a magazine article for a popular science magazine to explain the importance of the chloro-alkali industry (search for 'electrolysis of salt' or 'chloro-alkali').

PLENARIES

Demonstration – Show the electrolysis of sodium chloride solution in a Petri dish. This could be completed on an OHP and the colours of the universal indicator solution can be clearly seen. Take care not to spill solution into OHP. Ask the students to explain the observations. (10 minutes)

Uses – Give the students separate cards with the words 'hydrogen', 'chlorine' and 'sodium hydroxide' printed on. Read out the following uses of the products of electrolysis of sodium chloride solution, students should then hold up the card to show which product is used for that specific use:

- Margarine [hydrogen]
- PVC [chlorine]
- Bleach [sodium hydroxide, chlorine]
- Soap [sodium hydroxide]
- Paper [chlorine, sodium hydroxide]
- Rayon fibres [sodium hydroxide]
- Detergents [sodium hydroxide, chlorine]
- Purification of aluminium ore [sodium hydroxide]
- Hydrochloric acid manufacture [chlorine, hydrogen] (10 minutes)

Practical support

Electrolysing brine in the lab

Equipment and materials required

Beaker or electrolysis cell, saturated sodium chloride solution, two carbon electrodes, two crocodile clips, two wires, lab pack, litmus paper, water, 2 test tubes, splint, matches, gloves, eye protection.

Details

Half-fill the beaker with the sodium chloride solution and submerge one end of the carbon electrodes. Using the wires and crocodile clips, connect to the lab pack. Wearing gloves, fill the test-tube with the solution and hold, inverted with the neck in the solution over the cathode (the carbon electrode attached to the black terminal of the lab pack). Put on eye protection and start the electrolysis. Once the test-tube is full of gas, put a gloved finger to seal the tube, and remove from the water, test the gas with a lighted splint (a pop should be heard). While the gas is being collected, using a damp piece of litmus paper, test the gas at the anode. Hold the litmus paper over the anode and observe.

Safety: This practical produces chlorine gas (CLEAPSS Hazcard 22 – could irritate asthmatics) and should only be completed in a well-ventilated area, and once the products have been tested the equipment should be switched off. The solution produces sodium hydroxide and this is why gloves should be worn to collect the gas by displacement.

ACTIVITY & EXTENSION IDEAS

- Show students the industrial electrolysis of brine using a video, e.g. RSC *Industrial Chemistry*.
- Electrolysis of brine occurs in two main ways: membrane cell, and mercury cathode cell. Students could research these methods using the Internet.
- Students could complete the electrolysis of sodium chloride in a beaker and collect the gas produced at the cathode under displacement. This gas could be tested with a lighted split. A damp piece of litmus paper can be used to test the gas at the anode. See 'Practical support'.

C2 6.3 Electrolysing brine

LEARNING OBJECTIVES

1 What is produced when we electrolyse brine?
2 How do we use these products?

DID YOU KNOW?

Smelly drains, dustbins and other 'pongs' in hot summer weather mean that we use far more bleach in summer than in winter.

The electrolysis of brine (sodium chloride solution) is an enormously important industrial process. When we pass an electric current through brine we get three products. Chlorine gas is produced at the positive electrode, hydrogen gas is made at the negative electrode, and a solution of sodium hydroxide is also formed:

sodium chloride solution $\xrightarrow{\text{electrolysis}}$ hydrogen + chlorine + sodium hydroxide solution

a) What are the three products made when we electrolyse brine?

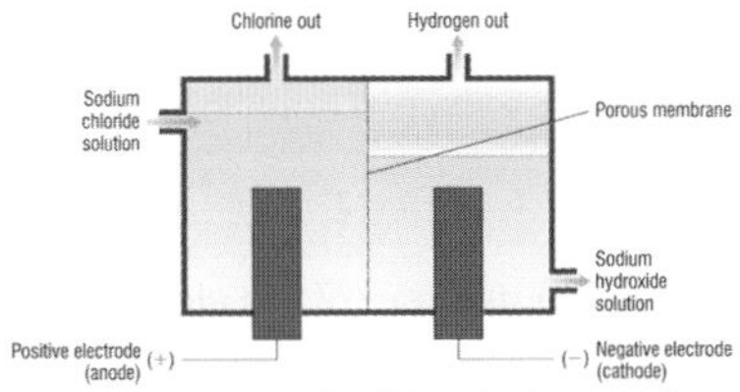

Figure 1 Brine can be electrolysed in a cell in which the two electrodes are separated by a porous membrane. This is called a **diaphragm cell**.

The half equations for what happens in the electrolysis of brine are:

At the positive electrode, $2Cl^-(aq) \rightarrow Cl_2(g) + 2e^-$

At the negative electrode, $2H^+(aq) + 2e^- \rightarrow H_2(g)$

This leaves a solution containing Na^+ and OH^- ions, i.e. a solution of sodium hydroxide.

Using chlorine

Chlorine is a poisonous green gas which causes great damage to our bodies if it is inhaled in even tiny quantities. But it is also a tremendously useful chemical. The chlorine made when we electrolyse brine plays a vital role in public health. It is used to kill bacteria in drinking water and in swimming pools.

We can also react chlorine with the sodium hydroxide produced in the electrolysis of brine. This makes a solution called *bleach* (sodium chlorate(I)). Bleach is a strong oxidising agent which is very good at killing bacteria. We use it widely in homes, hospitals and industry to maintain good hygiene.

Chlorine is also an important part of many other disinfectants as well as the plastic (polymer) known as PVC.

b) What is chlorine used for?

PRACTICAL

Electrolysing brine in the lab

Turn off the electricity once the tubes are nearly full of gas to avoid inhaling chlorine gas (toxic).

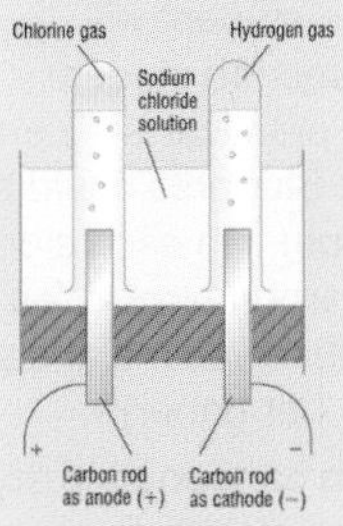

- How can you positively test for the gases collected?

Using hydrogen

The hydrogen that we make by electrolysing brine is particularly pure. This makes it very useful in the food industry. We make margarine by reacting hydrogen with vegetable oils under pressure and with a catalyst to turn the oil into a soft spreadable solid.

We can also react hydrogen with the chlorine made by the electrolysis of brine to make hydrogen chloride gas. We can then dissolve this gas in water to make hydrochloric acid. This very pure acid is used widely by the food and pharmaceutical industries.

c) What is hydrogen used for?

Using sodium hydroxide

The sodium hydroxide which is made when we electrolyse brine is used to make soap and paper. It is also used to control the pH in many industrial processes. The other major use of sodium hydroxide is to combine it with the chlorine produced to make bleach (see previous page).

d) What is sodium hydroxide used for?

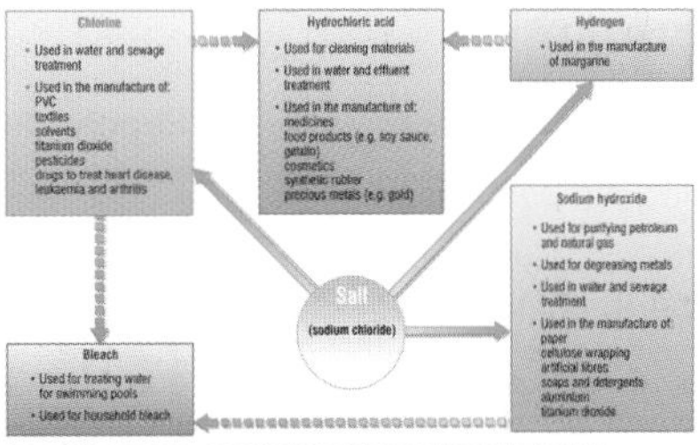

Figure 2 Chlorine brings us clean, disease-free drinking water and helps to keep our homes, schools and hospitals free from disease

Figure 3 There are many uses for the chemicals that we get from salt by electrolysis

SUMMARY QUESTIONS

1 Copy and complete using the words below:

chlorine   hydrochloric   hydrogen   sodium chlorate(I)
sodium hydroxide

When we pass an electric current through brine we make ...... gas, ... gas and .... solution. These products are also used to make .... solution (bleach) and ...... acid.

2 a) Write a balanced chemical equation to show the production of chlorine, hydrogen and sodium hydroxide from salt solution by electrolysis. The equation is started off for you below:
NaCl + H₂O → ?   [Higher]

b) We can also electrolyse *molten* sodium chloride. Compare the products formed with those from the electrolysis of sodium chloride solution. What are the differences?

KEY POINTS

1 When we electrolyse brine we get three products – chlorine gas, hydrogen gas and sodium hydroxide solution.
2 Chlorine is used to kill microbes in drinking water and swimming pools, and to make hydrochloric acid, disinfectants, bleach and plastics.
3 Hydrogen is used to make margarine and hydrochloric acid.
4 Sodium hydroxide is used to make bleach, paper and soap.

SUMMARY ANSWERS

1 Hydrogen (chlorine), chlorine (hydrogen), sodium hydroxide, sodium chlorate(I), hydrochloric.

2 a) $2NaCl(aq) + 2H_2O(l) \rightarrow 2NaOH(aq) + Cl_2(g) + H_2(g)$ [**HT** only]

b) Sodium is formed at the negative electrode with molten sodium chloride whereas hydrogen is formed there with sodium chloride solution. We also get sodium hydroxide solution formed when we electrolyse the solution.

Answers to in-text questions

a) Chlorine, hydrogen, sodium hydroxide solution.

b) Water treatment, making bleach, making plastics (PVC).

c) Hardening vegetable oils, making hydrochloric acid.

d) Making soap and paper, making bleach (with chlorine), pH control.

KEY POINTS

Give students a diagram of the electrolysis of brine. They should then annotate their diagram so that it contains all the information from the key points.

C2 6.4   Purifying copper

LEARNING OBJECTIVES

Students should learn that:

- Copper needs to be purified.
- Electrolysis is used to purify copper.

LEARNING OUTCOMES

Most students should be able to:

- State how copper is purified using electrolysis.

Some students should also be able to:

- Explain what happens at the electrodes during purification of copper.
- Construct the half equations for the purification of copper. [**HT** only]

Teaching suggestions

- **Special needs.** Students could be given the labels to cut and stick onto their diagram of the electrolysis of copper.

- **Learning styles**

  Kinaesthetic: Completing the purification of copper activity.

  Visual: Creating a poster to contrast the observations from the experiment.

  Auditory: Listening to predictions of products from each group.

  Intrapersonal: Assessing other students' work.

  Interpersonal: Working in pairs to generate a labelled diagram of copper purification.

- **Homework.** Ask students to use the AfL (Assessment for Learning) feedback to make any corrections to their work.

SPECIFICATION LINK-UP   Unit: Chemistry 2.12.6

- *The state symbols in equations are (s), (l), (g) and (aq).*
- *Copper can be purified by electrolysis using a positive electrode made of impure copper and a negative electrode of pure copper in a solution containing copper ions.*

Students should use their skills, knowledge and understanding of 'How Science Works':

- *to predict the products of electrolysing solutions of ions.*
- *to explain and evaluate processes that use the principles described in this unit.*
- *to complete and balance supplied half equations for the reactions occurring at the electrodes during electrolysis. [**HT** only]*

Lesson structure

STARTER

Connections – Show the students three photographs of copper-containing objects (search the Internet for water pipes, an electrical circuit and a copper roof). Ask the students to consider what all the pictures have in common. Then feedback to the class with questions and answers. (5–10 minutes)

Prediction – Students could predict the products of electrolysis of copper sulfate if:

- Graphite electrodes are used. [Copper and oxygen]
- Copper electrodes are used. [Copper and copper ions]

Ask students to talk in small groups about their predictions and then encourage each group to feedback to the whole class, in order to generate a whole class prediction. To extend students further, ask them to attempt to write half equations for each electrode. (10 minutes)

MAIN

- Supply students with the parts of a diagram of the electrolysis of copper for purification. They should assemble the full diagram from the pieces and then label the image, including explanations to explain how copper is purified in this process.

- Students can complete their own purification of copper, in order to compare active and inert electrodes; encourage the students to work in pairs. One student will complete the electrolysis with carbon electrodes, meanwhile the second student could complete the electrolysis with copper electrodes. Once the practical is up and running, the pair can make observations and comments together. Students could be given an A4 sheet of paper, which they could fold in half (landscape). On each side they should draw a labelled diagram of the apparatus (one with carbon electrodes and one with copper electrodes). Then they need to explain the observations at each electrode (including half equations for students taking the Higher Tier paper).

- Students could be encouraged to draw how copper is purified in a cartoon-strip style. To guide students, ask them to use the key words, e.g. electrolysis, electrode, electron, sludge, at least once. More artistic students may wish to personify the ions and electrons to make the cartoon more amusing.

- Use Simulation C2 6.4 'Purifying copper' from the Additional Science CD ROM.

- The electrolysis of copper sulfate solution provides a good opportunity to develop investigative aspects of 'How Science Works'. For example, students could investigate the factors that might affect the rate of electrolysis.

PLENARIES

I went to the shops . . . – Sit the students in a circle, the first student says 'I went to the shops to buy...' (insert a copper object here). The next student repeats the first and adds another copper-containing item onto their list. This continues around the circle. (5 minutes)

AfL (Assessment for Learning) – Lay the cartoons on the side bench of the room, with an A4 sheet of paper at one side. Ask each student to study all the cartoon strips and comment on the scientific accuracy of the work, by noting their thoughts on the paper. (10–15 minutes)

Practical support

Comparing electrodes

Equipment and materials required

Two beakers, 1 M copper sulfate solution (harmful), two carbon electrodes, two copper electrodes, six wires, two lab packs, four crocodile clips, eye protection.

Details

Wear eye protection throughout this practical. Half-fill each beaker with copper sulfate solution. Add the electrodes to each beaker, ensuring that one end is submerged into the liquid, while the other is free of the solution. The two carbon electrodes should be added to the first beaker and, using the wires and crocodile clips, connected to the lab pack. Meanwhile, add the two copper electrodes to the second beaker and connect to the second lab pack.

Safety: Copper sulfate is harmful – CLEAPSS Hazcard 27.

CHEMISTRY   ELECTROLYSIS

C2 6.4 Purifying copper

LEARNING OBJECTIVES

1 Why do we need to purify copper?
2 How do we use electrolysis to purify copper?

When we remove copper from its ore it is possible to get copper that is about 99% pure. The impurities include precious metals like gold, silver and platinum. These affect the conductivity of the copper, and must be removed before we can use the copper for electrical wires.

a) What impurities may be found in copper after it has been removed from its ore?
b) Why must these be removed?

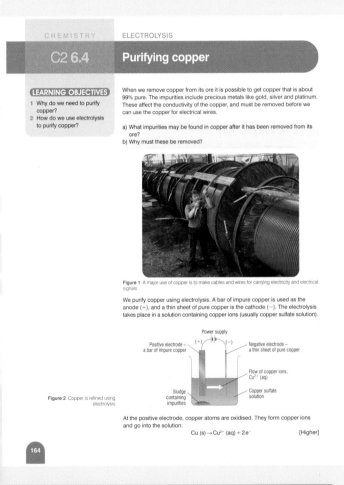

Figure 1 A major use of copper is to make cables and wires for carrying electricity and electrical signals

We purify copper using electrolysis. A bar of impure copper is used as the anode (+), and a thin sheet of pure copper is the cathode (−). The electrolysis takes place in a solution containing copper ions (usually copper sulfate solution).

Figure 2 Copper is refined using electrolysis

At the positive electrode, copper atoms are oxidised. They form copper ions and go into the solution:

$$Cu\,(s) \rightarrow Cu^{2+}\,(aq) + 2e^-$$ [Higher]

At the negative electrode, copper ions are reduced. They form copper atoms which are deposited on the electrode:

$$Cu^{2+}\,(aq) + 2e^- \rightarrow Cu\,(s)$$ [Higher]

c) Where are the copper atoms oxidised?
d) What is formed when copper atoms are oxidised?

Once we have purified the copper in the electrolytic cell, it is removed, melted and then formed into bars or ingots.

The sludge, containing precious metal impurities, is periodically removed from the electrolysis cell to collect the precious metals from it.

DID YOU KNOW?
The Statue of Liberty in the USA is covered with nearly 100 tonnes of copper metal.

PRACTICAL

Comparing electrodes

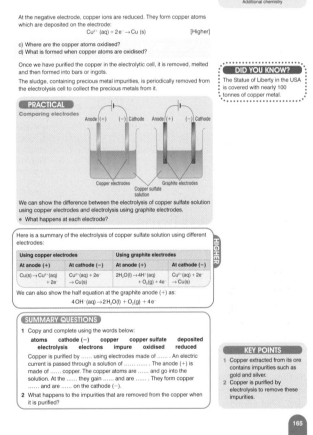

We can show the difference between the electrolysis of copper sulfate solution using copper electrodes and electrolysis using graphite electrodes.
- What happens at each electrode?

Here is a summary of the electrolysis of copper sulfate solution using different electrodes:

Using copper electrodes		Using graphite electrodes	
At anode (+)	At cathode (−)	At anode (+)	At cathode (−)
$Cu(s) \rightarrow Cu^{2+}(aq) + 2e^-$	$Cu^{2+}(aq) + 2e^- \rightarrow Cu(s)$	$2H_2O(l) \rightarrow 4H^+(aq) + O_2(g) + 4e^-$	$Cu^{2+}(aq) + 2e^- \rightarrow Cu(s)$

We can also show the half equation at the graphite anode (+) as:

$$4OH^-\,(aq) \rightarrow 2H_2O(l) + O_2(g) + 4e^-$$

SUMMARY QUESTIONS

1 Copy and complete using the words below:

   atoms   cathode (−)   copper   copper sulfate   deposited
   electrolysis   electrons   impure   oxidised   reduced

   Copper is purified by ...... using electrodes made of .... An electric current is passed through a solution of .... The anode (+) is made of ...... copper. The copper atoms are ...... and go into the solution. At the ...... they gain ...... and are .... They form copper ...... and are ...... on the cathode (−).

2 What happens to the impurities that are removed from the copper when it is purified?

KEY POINTS

1 Copper extracted from its ore contains impurities such as gold and silver.
2 Copper is purified by electrolysis to remove these impurities.

SUMMARY ANSWERS

1 Electrolysis, copper, copper sulfate, impure, oxidised, cathode (−), electrons, reduced, atoms, deposited.

2 They are removed from the sludge, purified and sold.

DID YOU KNOW?

The depth of the copper on the Statue of Liberty is 2.5 mm, and the monument has a height from base to torch of 46 m. In addition to copper, the Statue of Liberty also contains 125 tonnes of steel, making its total mass 225 tonnes.

Answers to in-text questions

a) Precious metals like gold, silver and platinum.

b) These metals affect the electrical conductivity of the copper.

c) At the anode (+)/positive electrode.

d) Copper ions (Cu^{2+})

KEY POINTS

Ask students to add information to the key points so that they produce two paragraphs about these topics.

C2 6.5

To build or not to build?

SPECIFICATION LINK-UP

Unit: Chemistry 2.12.6

Students should use their skills, knowledge and understanding of 'How Science Works':

* *To explain and evaluate processes that use the principles described in this unit.*

This spread can be used to revisit the following substantive content covered in this chapter:

* *Passing an electric current through ionic substances that are molten or in solution breaks them down into elements. This process is called electrolysis.*

Teaching suggestions

Activities

* **Directed activity relating to text** – Encourage students to read the two biased pieces of writing – one from BrineCo and the other from a pressure group. Ask students to complete questions 1–3 in note form. Then put the students into pairs and ask them to compare their responses. Using question and answer, feedback from the class to form a complete answer on the board. This section could be lead by one pair (a scribe and a person fielding the comments from the rest of the class).

* **Newspaper article** – Students should be reminded that news items should be impartial, and that newspapers and broadcasters risk prosecutions if they are found to be bias. Show students examples of articles and get them to underline in different colours the two sides of the argument. This could be completed using an OHT or interactive whiteboard. Then encourage students to use information from the book to write their own page lead in a local newspaper (about 250 words) about BrineCo. They should also consider the type of images that they would like to use in their article. Encourage students to take quotes from the book to use in their articles.

Unemployment in Newtown may rise!

Two big local employers say that concerns over supplies of chemicals that they need for their factories mean that they may have to close. This will lead to hundreds of Newtown jobs being slashed.

A director of Allied Fats said 'We have been worried about supplies of hydrogen to our plant for some time since the cost of transporting this chemical is so high. We may have to close and relocate our business somewhere nearer to our present suppliers.'

Consolidated Paper are also worried about supplies of sodium hydroxide and chlorine to their paper mill in the town. Tracey Wiggins, the MP for Newtown, said 'This would be a tragedy for the town.'

Hope for new employment!

Following concerns about supplies of chemicals to two big local employers, we can exclusively reveal that a deal is being struck that would bring a manufacturer of these chemicals to Newtown.

BrineCo, one of the largest chemical companies in the country, is currently in talks with the council about building a big new plant to produce chemicals in a new factory near the town. BrineCo already manufacture chlorine and sodium hydroxide at other plants in the UK.

Local MP Tracey Wiggins said 'This would be a wonderful opportunity for workers and their families in Newtown and the surrounding area.'

QUESTIONS

Look at the two leaflets produced by BrineCo and by the local pressure group GREEN.

1 Make a list of the differences between the two maps on the leaflets.
2 How is BrineCo trying to persuade people that their factory is a good idea?
3 How is GREEN trying to persuade people that the factory is *not* a good idea?

ACTIVITY

Write an editorial for the local newspaper in which you examine both sides of the argument for bringing the BrineCo chemical factory to the town. The final part of your editorial should come down on one side or the other – but you must argue your point logically. You may also decide that the factory should go ahead, but on a different site. Can *you* persuade local people that *you* are the voice of reason?

* **Debate** – Split the class into half, one group should be acting as the brine company and the other as the protestors. Give the students time to conduct further research about the impact of such a plant in a local area. Then hold a debate on the issue. Following the debate, ask all the students to vote on whether they think that the plant should/should not get permission to trade.

Homework

* **Hydrogen as a fuel** – Hydrogen is another product of the electrolysis of brine. Encourage students to find out how it can be used as a fuel, and the environmental implications of doing this.

Extensions

* **Research** – Ask students to find out the location of one brine electrolysis plant (anywhere in the world). They could then list the benefits of the chosen site.

* **Saponification** – Sodium hydroxide is used to make soap. Students could research how to do this (using the Internet) and they could make their own soaps.

BrineCo
working for you!

BrineCo produce chlorine and sodium hydroxide solution by passing electricity through brine (salt solution). This is called *electrolysis*.

The chlorine that we make is used to make paper, chemicals and plastics, and for treating water to kill bacteria. Sodium hydroxide solution is sold to companies making paper, artificial fibres, soaps and detergents.

Our new factory can bring many benefits to Newtown. Consolidated Paper will be a major user of BrineCo's chemicals, and Allied Fats will buy the hydrogen produced by our factory.

This will give both companies a cheaper supply of raw materials than they have at present. *Think carefully about BrineCo's proposals – they mean a secure future for you and your children.*

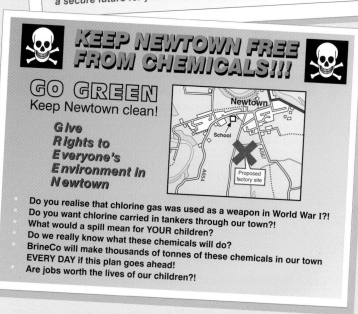

KEEP NEWTOWN FREE FROM CHEMICALS!!!

GO GREEN
Keep Newtown clean!

Give
Rights to
Everyone's
Environment in
Newtown

Do you realise that chlorine gas was used as a weapon in World War I?!
Do you want chlorine carried in tankers through our town?!
What would a spill mean for YOUR children?
Do we really know what these chemicals will do?
BrineCo will make thousands of tonnes of these chemicals in our town EVERY DAY if this plan goes ahead!
Are jobs worth the lives of our children?!

167

Learning styles

Kinaesthetic: Making soap.

Visual: Preparing a newspaper article.

Intrapersonal: Researching into hydrogen as a fuel.

Interpersonal: Working as a team in a debate.

ICT link-up

Desktop publishing packages could be used by students to create their newspaper articles. The Internet could be used, to add images. The work could then be printed and put on display.

Special needs

All the advantages and disadvantages of the electrolysis plant could be written on separate cards. These students could then sort them into two lists before jotting them down in their notes.

Teaching assistant

The teaching assistant could be the team leader of half of the class, meanwhile the teacher could lead the other half. This would aid the students in preparing their arguments for their debate.

SUMMARY ANSWERS

1 Lines drawn to link left-hand to right-hand columns as follows:

a) B **b)** A **c)** B **d)** A **e)** B **f)** A

2 **Negative electrode:** sodium, calcium, zinc, aluminium.
Positive electrode: iodide, fluoride, oxide, bromide.

3 **a)** $2H_2O \rightarrow 2H_2 + O_2$

b) Cathode (−): $2H^+ + 2e^- \rightarrow H_2$
Anode (+): $4OH^- \rightarrow O_2 + 2H_2O + 4e^-$

c) 1 mole.

d) The power supply. **[HT only]**

4 **a)** $K^+ + e^- \rightarrow K$

b) $Ba^{2+} + 2e^- \rightarrow Ba$

c) $2I^- \rightarrow I_2 + 2e^-$

d) $2O^{2-} \rightarrow O_2 + 4e^-$ **[HT only]**

5 Description with object to be plated made negative (cathode) in solution containing metal ions (e.g. $CuSO_4$ solution for copper plating). To keep concentration of metal ions in solution constant, an anode made of the metal to be plated should be used. **[HT only]**
Half equation: $Cu^{2+} + 2e^- \rightarrow Cu$

Summary teaching suggestions

- **Special needs** – Question 1 could be prepared as a cut and stick activity. A blank table with two columns – anode and cathode could be supplied to the students. Then the statements could be given on a separate sheet of paper. Students could cut up the statements and stick them into the appropriate column in the table. To extend this activity, all positive words (e.g. anode) could be underlined in red, whereas all negative words could be underlined in blue.

- **Gifted and talented** – Students could be encouraged to write a full method, including safety, for question 5. These students may also be allowed to complete their practical.

- **Learning styles**
  Auditory: Question 5 lends itself to a class discussion before each student tries to write their own answer.
  Visual: Questions 2 and 5 involve creating a table or diagrams.
  Kinaesthetic: If question 1 is turned into a cut and stick activity, this will appeal to these learners.

- **When to use the questions?**
  - These questions could be used as a test preparation, where for half of the lesson the students attempt the questions. Then, in the second half, answers are given out and students mark each others' work.
  - Question 1 is a good review question to check understanding of electrolysis. This could be used after lesson 6.2 as a plenary or homework.
  - Both questions 1 and 2 could be used as a kinaesthetic activity. Stick the two column headings on opposite sides of the room (e.g. for question 1, anode and cathode). Then give each student a statement and they should stand in the group that they think they belong to.

ELECTROLYSIS: C2 6.1 – C2 6.5

SUMMARY QUESTIONS

1 Select A or B to describe correctly what happens at the positive electrode and negative electrode in electrolysis for a) to f).

a) Positive ions move towards this.   A Positive electrode

b) Negative ions move towards this.   B Negative electrode

c) Reduction happens here.

d) Oxidation happens here.

e) Connected to the negative terminal of the power supply.

f) Connected to the positive terminal of the power supply.

2 Make a table to show which of the following ions would move towards the positive electrode and which towards the negative electrode during electrolysis. (You may need to use a copy of the periodic table to help you.)
sodium, iodide, calcium, fluoride, zinc, oxide, aluminium, bromide

3 Water can be split into hydrogen and oxygen using electrolysis. The word equation for this reaction is:
water → hydrogen + oxygen
a) Write a balanced equation for this reaction using the correct chemical symbols.
b) Write half-equations to show what happens at the positive and negative electrodes.
c) When some water is electrolysed it produces 2 moles of hydrogen. How much oxygen is produced?
d) Where does the energy needed to split water into hydrogen and oxygen come from during electrolysis?
[Higher]

4 Copy and complete the following half-equations:
a) $K^+ \rightarrow K$ b) $Ba^{2+} \rightarrow Ba$
c) $I^- \rightarrow I_2$ d) $O^{2-} \rightarrow O_2$
[Higher]

5 Electrolysis can be used to produce a thin layer of metal on the surface of a metal object. Using words and diagrams, describe how you would cover a small piece of steel with copper. Make sure that you write down the half equation that describes what happens at the surface of the steel.
[Higher]

EXAM-STYLE QUESTIONS

1 The table shows the results of passing electricity through some substances. Carbon electrodes were used

Substance	Product at negative electrode	Product at positive electrode
Molten lead bromide	lead	A
Molten B	magnesium	chlorine
Aqueous sodium sulfate solution	C	oxygen
Aqueous copper sulfate solution	D	E

(a) Name **A**, **B**, **C**, **D** and **E**. (5)

(b) What is the name used for substances that conduct electricity and are decomposed by it? (1)

(c) Why must the substances be molten or in solution? (1)

(d) Explain why reduction takes place at the negative electrode. (2)

2 The diagram shows a cell used for the electrolysis of brine. Brine is a solution of sodium chloride in water.

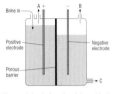

(a) Name and give the formulae of the positive ions in brine. (2)

(b) Name and give the formulae of the negative ions in brine. (2)

(c) Name gases **A** and **B**. (2)

(d) Explain as fully as you can how gas B is produced. (4)

(e) Name the product in solution C. (1)

168

EXAM-STYLE ANSWERS

1 a) **A** bromine, **B** magnesium chloride, **C** hydrogen, **D** copper, **E** copper ions. *(5 marks)*

b) Electrolyte. *(1 mark)*

c) So that the ions can move (*'ions cannot move in solids' is not sufficient for the mark*). *(1 mark)*

d) Positive ions gain electrons at the negative electrode. *(1 mark)*
Reduction is gaining electrons. *(1 mark)*

2 a) Sodium ions, Na^+ and hydrogen ions, H^+ (*one mark for both names, one mark for both formulae OR one mark for one name and formula – ignore (aq) state symbols*). *(2 marks)*

b) Chloride ions, Cl^-, and hydroxide ions OH^- (*mark as for part (a)*). *(2 marks)*

c) A is chlorine (*1 mark*) B is hydrogen (*1 mark*) *(2 marks)*

d) *Four from:*
- Positive (hydrogen and sodium) ions are attracted to negative electrode.
- Hydrogen is less reactive than sodium.
- Hydrogen ions are reduced/gain electrons to hydrogen atoms.
- Two hydrogen atoms combine to form hydrogen molecules.
- Hydrogen ions are replaced by more water ionising.
(4 marks)

e) Sodium hydroxide. *(1 mark)*

3 a) *One mark each for:*
- Tin ions (Sn^{2+}) from solution gain electrons/are reduced.
- Tin atoms are formed.
- Tin is deposited on the electrode. *(3 marks)*

b) *One mark each for:*
- Tin atoms lose electrons/are oxidised.
- Tin ions (Sn^{2+}) are formed.
- Tin ions (Sn^{2+}) go into the solution/electrolyte. *(3 marks)*

HOW SCIENCE WORKS QUESTIONS

Mild steel can be electroplated with tin in the laboratory. The diagram shows the apparatus used.

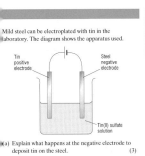

(a) Explain what happens at the negative electrode to deposit tin on the steel. (3)

(b) What happens to tin at the positive electrode? (3)

(c) Why does the concentration of the tin(II) sulfate solution not change during the electrolysis? (2)

(d) Some food cans are made of mild steel coated with tin. Suggest **two** reasons why tin plated steel is chosen for this use. (2)

A student was interested in electrolysis. He knew that a current passes through a copper sulfate solution. With copper electrodes some of the copper would come away from one electrode and move to the other. He thought that there would be the same amount of copper leaving one electrode as attached to the other electrode. He set up his equipment and weighed each electrode several times over a 25 minute period. His results are in this table:

Loss in mass of positive electrode in 5 minutes (g)	Gain in mass of negative electrode in 5 minutes (g)	Time (mins)
0.027	0.021	5
0.022	0.027	10
0.061	0.030	15
0.001	0.025	20
0.025	0.027	25

(a) What evidence is there for an anomalous result? (1)

(b) What was the range for the results at the negative electrode? (1)

(c) What evidence is there to support the student's prediction? (1)

(d) Comment on the reliability of the results. (1)

Hydrogen – the new petrol?

Hydrogen could be a very important fuel for personal transport. However, there are many practical problems to be solved.

Mikael came up with the idea of using the Sun's energy to produce hydrogen from sea water. The apparatus used was similar to what you might have seen in your school laboratory. However, he used a solar cell to produce a voltage to drive the electrolysis. Mikael left the electrolysis for the same time for each solution used.

The results are shown below.

Solution used	Volume of hydrogen (cm³)		mean
Sea water	33	27	45

a) Calculate the mean volume of hydrogen produced. (1)

b) What do these results tell us about the precision of the method used? Explain your answer. (1)

c) What probably caused the variation in the student's results? (1)

d) Mikael's teacher dismissed the research saying, 'It could never come to anything that might produce large volumes of hydrogen.' Why do you think the teacher thought this? (1)

e) Mikael's dad thought it was a brilliant idea and a chance to make some money! He pictured a huge factory turning out millions of tonnes of hydrogen and millions of pounds of money! He quizzed Mikael about his results. He asked Mikael if he was telling the whole truth about his results. Why was it important that Mikael was telling the whole truth about his investigation? (1)

f) What might be Mikael's next step towards becoming a millionaire? (1)

169

- State symbols are not essential in Q2, because the focus is on the ions. There is effectively half a mark for each answer to parts a) and b) of this question, but half marks are not used in GCSE, so the mark scheme reflects this. Part d) has a maximum of four marks, but there are five marking points available. Students could discuss and produce exemplar answers to this question. Questions of this type are often used to assess quality of written communication, and this could be applied here, using the correct scientific terms or correct sequencing of ideas as the criteria.

- Candidates are not expected to have met tin plating before, but should apply their knowledge and understanding of the electrolysis of copper(II) sulfate to this process. Q4 is based on concepts drawn from the 'How Science Works' content in the specification.

HOW SCIENCE WORKS ANSWERS

a) The mean volume of hydrogen produced is 35 cm³.

b) The precision is not good. The results are too widely spread around the mean.

c) The variation in the level of sunlight is likely to have caused the variation in the student's results.

d) The results are on a very small scale and do not necessarily indicate that they could be used on a large scale.

e) The results are more credible if the whole truth is told.

f) Mikael should get someone else to repeat his results, to increase their reliability.

How science works teaching suggestions

- **Literacy guidance**
  - Key terms that should be clearly understood: precision, conclusions, credibility of data.
  - The question expecting a longer answer, where students can practise their literacy skills is: d).

- **Higher- and lower-level answers.** Question b) is a higher-level question and the answer provided above is also at this level. Question a) is lower level and the answer provided is also lower level.

- **Gifted and talented.** Able students could suggest how the reliability of Mikael's results might be further enhanced by using a different technique to collect more gas.

- **How and when to use these questions.** When wishing to encourage students to see their own work as being part of a bigger picture. The questions could be tackled in small discussion groups.

- **Homework.** The questions could be used for homework.

- **Special needs.** A teacher-controlled discussion could be conducted to lead through the ideas.

---

c) As tin ions are removed from the solution at the negative electrode they are replaced from the positive electrode *(1 mark)* by equal numbers of ions going into the solution. *(1 mark)*

d) *Any two from:*
- Tin prevents iron from rusting.
- Tin is not corroded by the atmosphere/water.
- Tin is not attacked/corroded by food/no toxic substances go into food.
- Tin plate is cheaper than pure tin.
- Mild steel is stronger than tin (so cans can be thinner/use less metal). *(2 marks)*

4 a) For the +ve electrode the reading at 15 minutes is very high and that at 20 minutes very low. *(1 mark)*

b) 0.021 g to 0.030 g *(1 mark)*

c) After 25 minutes the +ve electrode has lost the same mass as the −ve electrode has gained. *(1 mark)*

d) The repeats are not similar over each 5 minute period and therefore the reliability is not good. *(1 mark)*

Exam teaching suggestions

- The questions on this chapter have a total of 34 marks and should take students about 35 minutes to complete. Q1 could be set after completing spread 6.2, Q2 after 6.3, and Q3 after 6.4.

- In Q1, students should be encouraged to look at all of the information in the table and not just focus on the missing parts. The other information should help them to predict or confirm any answers they are unsure about. This applies to all questions that require a table to be completed.

C2 7.1

Acids and alkalis

LEARNING OBJECTIVES

Students should learn:

- How solutions can be acidic or alkaline.
- That acidity can be measured.

LEARNING OUTCOMES

Most students should be able to:

- List the properties of acids and alkalis.
- Give an example of an acid and alkali.
- Recognise if a chemical is an acid or alkali if the pH is given.
- Recognise a neutralisation reaction.

Some students should also be able to:

- Explain in terms of ions what an acid and alkali are.

Teaching suggestions

- **Special needs.** The method to test the alkalinity of different household chemicals could be given in labelled diagrams to these students, but in the wrong order. They could sort out the steps before completing the practical.

- **Learning styles**

  Kinaesthetic: Completing the practical testing of pH.

  Visual: Putting data into a table.

  Auditory: Listening to people's explanations about the cryptic sentence.

  Intrapersonal: Creating a poster about the pH scale.

  Interpersonal: Designing an investigation in pairs.

- **Homework.** Ask students to find out how to make an indicator at home and write a bullet-point method on how to make it, e.g. using elderberries, cranberries or red cabbage.

- **ICT link-up.** Make a coloured universal indicator pH scale on interactive whiteboard software or PowerPoint®. Invite the students to label weak/strong acid/alkali and neutral chemicals. Then show images of different things, e.g. stomach acid, then drag and drop the images onto the pH scale.

SPECIFICATION LINK-UP   Unit: Chemistry 2.12.6

- *Hydrogen ions H+(aq) make solutions acidic and hydroxide ions OH−(aq) make solutions alkaline. The pH scale is a measure of the acidity or alkalinity of a solution.*
- *The state symbols in equations are (s), (l), (g) and (aq).*

Lesson structure

STARTER

Table – Ask students to draw a three-columned table, with titles: 'acid', 'base', 'neutral'. They should then list as many things about each group as they can, including examples. Then draw a similar table on the board, and ask each student in turn to write a piece of information into the table. (5–10 minutes)

Think – On the board, write the sentence: 'All alkalis are bases but not all bases are alkali.' Ask students to work in pairs to explain this sentence. Feedback ideas from the class. (10–15 minutes)

MAIN

- Ask students to create a colourful poster to display the universal indicator chart. A common misconception is starting the chart from pH1, but it should actually start from pH0 and point out that we can also have negative pH values. Students could then use secondary sources of data to put everyday and lab examples of chemicals onto their poster.

- Students could test a variety of chemicals using universal indicator to find out their pH. Encourage them to design their own results table for the experiment. Then ask them to draw conclusions from their results. Hopefully, they will realise that, with everyday chemicals, some acids can be eaten, whereas most alkalis are cleaning products.

- Students could design and carry out their own investigation to determine the alkalinity of different household cleaning products. Encourage students to work in pairs to plan their experiment. They could use a variety of methods, including universal indicator, digital pH probes or data loggers.

PLENARIES

5,4,3,2,1 – Ask students to list the names of 5 everyday acids, 4 lab based bases, 3 properties of acids, 2 properties of alkalis and 1 example of a neutral chemical. (5–10 minutes)

Review – Show students the table that the class made. Ask them to look carefully and consider any mistakes. Discuss the mistakes and make amendments. Then ask students to copy out three facts from the table and add a new fact that they have learned from the lesson into their notes. (10–15 minutes)

Practical support

Testing pH of various chemicals

Equipment and materials required

Dimple tiles, beaker of water, dropping pipettes, samples of acids (irritants/harmful), alkalis (irritants/harmful), neutral chemicals and buffer solutions (irritants/harmful), universal indicator solution (flammable), universal indicator paper, scissors, eye protection.

Details

Wear eye protection throughout the practical, and wash hands in cold water if any of the solutions get onto the skin. Be aware that universal indicator will stain the skin for about three days.

Put a few drops of each type of solution in separate dimples. Either add a few drops of universal indicator solution or a small square of universal indicator paper. Compare the colour of the paper or solution with the given colour chart (each brand of universal indicator will go a different colour at each pH value, so it is important to compare with the appropriate chart). Put dropping pipette into beaker of water when finished.

Investigating household cleaning products

Equipment and materials required

Different cleaning products (irritant/harmful), beakers, stirring rods, pH probes, pH data logger and equipment, universal indicator (flammable), dropping pipette, dimple tile, eye protection.

Details

Wear eye protection and put a small amount of cleaning product on a dimple tile. Add a few drops of water if the product is a solid. Then add universal indictor and compare with the colour chart. Alternatively, put the cleaning product into a beaker and submerge the calibrated pH probe (either digital or data logger) and note the reading.

Safety: If the cleaning product gets onto skin, wash well with cold water. Be aware that some cleaning products may be 'corrosive' and 'toxic' – avoid these.

ACTIVITY & EXTENSION IDEAS

- Ask students to find out how electricity can be used to measure pH.

- Ask students to research and find out different indicators that can be used to test for acids and bases.

- Students could complete mole calculations on the balanced symbol equations.

Answers to in-text questions

a) A base is a chemical that can neutralise acids.

b) An alkali is a base that is soluble in water.

c) H$^+$ ions/hydrogen ions.

d) OH$^-$ ions/hydroxide ions.

CHEMISTRY

ACIDS, ALKALIS AND SALTS

C2 7.1 Acids and alkalis

LEARNING OBJECTIVES

1 Why are solutions acidic or alkaline?
2 How do we measure acidity?

Acids and bases are an important part of our understanding of chemistry. They play a vital part inside us and for all other living things too.

What are acids and bases?

When we dissolve a substance in water we make an **aqueous solution**. The solution may be acidic, alkaline or neutral, depending on the chemical we have dissolved. **Bases** are chemicals which can neutralise **acids**.

Alkalis are bases which dissolve in water. Pure water is **neutral**.

a) What is a base?
b) What is an alkali?

Acids include chemicals like citric acid, sulfuric acid and ethanoic acid. All acids taste very sour, although many acids are far too dangerous to put in your mouth. We use acids in many chemical reactions in the laboratory. Ethanoic acid (vinegar) and citric acid (the sour taste in citric fruit, fizzy drinks and squashes) are acids which we regularly eat.

One acid that we use in the laboratory is hydrochloric acid. This is formed when the gas hydrogen chloride (HCl) dissolves in water:

$$HCl\ (g) \xrightarrow{\text{water}} H^+\ (aq) + Cl^-\ (aq)$$

All acids form H$^+$ ions when we add them to water – it is hydrogen ions that make a solution acidic. Hydrogen chloride also forms chloride ions (Cl$^-$). The '(aq)' symbol shows that the ions are in an 'aqueous solution'. In other words, they are dissolved in water.

c) What ions do all acids form when we add them to water?

Bases are the opposite of acids in the way they react. Because alkalis are bases which dissolve in water they are the bases which we use most commonly. For example, sodium hydroxide solution is often found in our school laboratories. Sodium hydroxide solution is formed when we dissolve solid sodium hydroxide in water:

$$NaOH\ (s) \xrightarrow{\text{water}} Na^+\ (aq) + OH^-\ (aq)$$

All alkalis form hydroxide ions (OH$^-$) when we add them to water. It is hydroxide ions that make a solution alkaline.

d) What ions do all alkalis form when we add them to water?

Measuring acidity

Indicators are special chemicals which change colour when we add them to acids and alkalis. Litmus paper is one well-known indicator, but there are many more. These include some natural ones like the juice of red cabbage or beetroot.

Figure 1 Acids and bases are all around us, in many of the things we buy at the shops, in our schools and factories – and inside us too

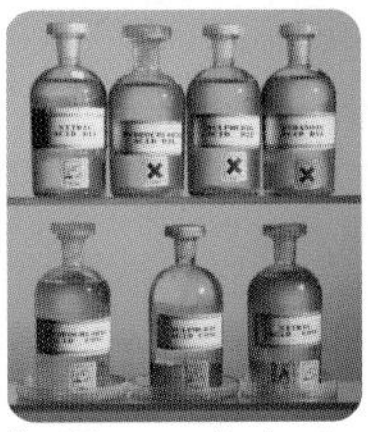

Figure 2 Some common laboratory acids

We use the pH scale to show how acid or alkaline a solution is. The scale runs from 0 (most acidic) to 14 (most alkaline). **Universal indicator** is a very special indicator made from a number of dyes. It turns different colours at different values of pH. Anything in the middle of the pH scale (pH 7) is neutral, neither acid nor alkali.

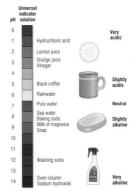
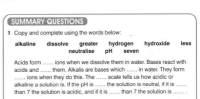

Universal indicator pH solution	
0	
1	Hydrochloric acid — Very acidic
2	Lemon juice
3	Orange juice / Vinegar
4	
5	Black coffee — Slightly acidic
6	Rainwater
7	Pure water — Neutral
8	Sea water / Baking soda — Slightly alkaline
9	Milk of magnesia / Soap
10	
11	
12	Washing soda
13	
14	Oven cleaner / Sodium hydroxide — Very alkaline

Figure 3 The pH scale tells us how acid or alkaline a solution is

A H$^+$ ion is simply a hydrogen atom that has lost an electron – in other words a proton. So another way of describing an acid is to say that it is a 'proton donor'.

SUMMARY QUESTIONS

1 Copy and complete using the words below:

alkaline	dissolve	greater	hydrogen	hydroxide	less
	neutralise	pH	seven		

Acids form ...... ions when we dissolve them in water. Bases react with acids and ...... them. Alkalis are bases which ...... in water. They form ...... ions when they do this. The ...... scale tells us how acidic or alkaline a solution is. If the pH is ...... the solution is neutral, if it is ...... than 7 the solution is acidic, and if it is ...... than 7 the solution is ....

2 How could you use paper containing universal indicator as a way of distinguishing between pure water, sodium hydroxide solution and citric acid solution?

PRACTICAL

Which is the most alkaline product?

Compare the alkalinity of various cleaning products.

You can test washing-up liquids, shampoos, soaps, hand-washing liquids, washing powders/liquids and dishwasher powders/tablets.

You might be able to use a pH sensor and data logger to collect your data.

• What are the advantages of using a pH sensor instead of universal indicator solution or paper?

KEY POINTS

1 Acids are substances which produce H$^+$ ions when we add them to water.
2 Bases are substances that will neutralise acids.
3 An alkali is a soluble base. Alkalis produce OH$^-$ ions when we add them to water.
4 We use the pH scale to show how acidic or alkaline a solution is.

170 / 171

SUMMARY ANSWERS

1 Hydrogen, neutralise, dissolve, hydroxide, pH, seven, less, greater, alkaline.

2 The paper would turn green in water, blue in sodium hydroxide solution and red/orange in citric acid solution.

KEY POINTS

Ask students to copy out the key points, but to colour-code them. Each word that is a base, colour in blue or purple, each acid word colour in red, yellow or orange and each neutral word colour in green.

C2 7.2 Making salts from metals and bases

LEARNING OBJECTIVES

Students should learn:

- That acids and bases can be neutralised.
- Which products are made in a neutralisation reaction.
- That salts can be made using neutralisation.

LEARNING OUTCOMES

Most students should be able to:

- Define neutralisation.
- Name the salt formed if the acid and alkali are given.
- Complete symbol equations including state symbols.
- Write the ionic equation for neutralisation.
- Write general word equations for neutralisation reactions.

Teaching suggestions

- **Special needs.** Provide these students with a skeleton structure of the equations. Then each additional piece of information could be made into a card. Each card should have a separate chemical and then the students try to create the equations, using Blu-tack to secure the cards.

- **Learning styles**

  Kinaesthetic: Completing a neutralisation practical.

  Visual: Creating A6 revision cards.

  Auditory: Listening to other student's answers.

  Intrapersonal: Completing equations.

  Interpersonal: Trying to complete a neutralisation in pairs.

- **Homework.** Students to find three uses for a neutralisation reaction (e.g. antacids, reduction of acidity of soils, to remove harmful gases from factory emissions).

- **ICT link-up**

  There are many simulations of neutralisation. Search Google for 'neutralisation/animation/simulation'.

SPECIFICATION LINK-UP   Unit: Chemistry 2.12.6

- *Soluble salts can be made from acids by reacting them with:*
  - *metals – not all metals are suitable, some are too reactive and others are not reactive enough.*
  - *insoluble bases – the base is added to the acid until no more will react and the excess solid is filtered off.*
  - *alkalis – an indicator can be used to show when the acid and alkali have completely reacted to produce a salt solution.*

- *The particular salt produced in any reaction between an acid and a base or alkali depends on:*
  - *the acid used (hydrochloric acid produces chlorides, nitric acid produces nitrates, sulfuric acid produces sulfates).*
  - *the metal or base or alkali.*

- *Salt solutions can be crystallised to produce solid salts.*

- *Metal oxides and hydroxides are bases. Soluble hydroxides are called alkalis.*

Students should use their skills, knowledge and understanding of 'How Science Works':

- *to suggest methods to make a named salt.*

Lesson structure

STARTER

Table – Ask students to complete the following table:

Name of acid	Name in salt	Example
Hydrochloric	[Chloride]	[Sodium chloride]
[Nitric]	Nitrate	[Copper nitrate]
Sulfuric	Sulfate	[Calcium sulfate]

Show the incomplete table on the board and ask different students to fill in the missing data. (10 minutes)

Experiment – Ask students to complete a neutralisation reaction in pairs. The first group to get exactly green is the winner and a prize could be given. (10 minutes)

MAIN

- Students have frequently had the experience of neutralisation of an acid with an alkali. However, they may not have had the experience using an insoluble base. Show the students some copper oxide and allow them to try to dissolve it in water. Then allow students to prepare copper sulfate crystals (toxic) using this method. Encourage the students to write up the method in a brief bullet-point format and summarise the reaction in a general word equation.

- Give each student three index cards. These can be made out of three different coloured pieces of card about A6 in size. In the top right-hand corner hole-punch all the cards. On the front of each card the student should write a general word equation. Then on the reverse a specific example, including a method and an equation for the reaction. Once all of the cards have been completed, they can be joined together with a treasury tag or a piece of string. These can then be tied to their notes and used for revision for examination.

PLENARIES

Copy and complete – Ask students to copy and complete the following prose. Students should be encouraged to use the most scientific word they can think of to complete the paragraph.

'Soluble [salts] can be made by reacting [acids] and bases or [alkalis]. Metal oxides and hydroxides are [bases]. Alkalis are [soluble] hydroxides.' (5 minutes)

Chemical equations – Ask students to complete the following equations (they get progressively more difficult). Time the students for five minutes and assure them that it doesn't matter how far they get. When the notes are marked it will give an idea of the level that each student is working at:

- Acid + alkali → [salt] + [water]
- [Acid] + [metal] → metal salt + hydrogen
- Acid + [base] → salt + [water]
- [Sodium hydroxide] + [nitric acid] → sodium nitrate + water
- Sulfuric acid + zinc → [zinc sulfate] + hydrogen
- $[2HCl(aq)] + [Ca(s)] → CaCl_2 [(aq)] + H_2 [(g)]$ (5–15 minutes)

Practical support

Preparing copper sulfate crystals

Equipment and materials required

Copper oxide (harmful), 1 M sulfuric acid (irritant), stirring rod, beaker, Bunsen burner, tripod, gauze, filter funnel, filter paper, evaporating basin, spatula, measuring cylinder, conical flask, eye protection.

Details

Add a spatula of copper oxide to a beaker, then add 25 ml of sulfuric acid. Stir the reaction mixture well and note any observations [colour change of liquid from colourless to blue]. Warm the mixture gently on a tripod and gauze. Do not allow to boil. Let the mixture containing excess black copper oxide cool down. Fold the filter paper and put into the funnel in the neck of a conical flask. Filter the mixture. Collect the filtrate and put into an evaporating basin. Leave the liquid in a warm place for a few days to allow the crystals to form.

Safety: Eye protection should be worn throughout this practical. This reaction makes copper sulfate which is harmful – CLEAPSS Hazcard 27. (Sulfuric acid – CLEAPSS Hazcard 98.)

ACTIVITY & EXTENSION IDEAS

- Students could be encouraged to generate general symbol equations using M as any metal.
- Students could be shown how to generate the ionic equation for neutralisation from first principles. They could then use the method to check other examples and prove that the same ionic equation is always generated.
- Students could complete mole calculations on the balanced symbol equations.

Answers to in-text questions

a) Salt and hydrogen.

b) Salt and water.

c) Zinc sulfate.

KEY POINTS

Split the class into three groups and give each group a different key point. They then need to come up with reasons why their key point is the most important. Then hold the debate!

C2 7.2   Making salts from metals or bases

LEARNING OBJECTIVES

1 What do we make when we react acids and metals?
2 What do we make when we react acids and bases?
3 What salts can we make?

Acids + metals

We can make salts by reacting acids with metals. This is only possible if the metal is above hydrogen in the reactivity series. If it is, then hydrogen gas is produced when the acid reacts with the metal, and a salt is also produced:

acid + metal → salt + hydrogen

$$2HCl\ (aq) + Mg\ (s) → MgCl_2\ (aq) + H_2\ (g)$$
hydrochloric acid + magnesium → magnesium chloride + hydrogen solution

a) What does the reaction between an acid and a metal produce?

Acid + insoluble base

When we react an acid with a base we produce a solution which contains a salt and water.

The general equation which describes all reactions of this type is:

acid + base → salt + water

b) What two substances are formed when an acid and a base react?

The salt that we make depends on the metal or the base that we use in the reaction and the acid. So bases that contain sodium ions will always make sodium salts, while those that contain potassium ions will always make potassium salts.

In a similar way:

- the salts formed when we neutralise hydrochloric acid are always *chlorides*
- sulfuric acid always makes salts which are *sulfates*, and
- nitric acid always makes *nitrates*.

The oxide of a transition metal, such as iron(III) oxide, is an example of a base that we can use to make a salt in this way:

acid + base → salt + water

$$6HCl\ (aq) + Fe_2O_3\ (s) → 2FeCl_3\ (aq) + 3H_2O\ (l)$$
hydrochloric acid + solid iron(III) oxide → iron(III) chloride + water solution

c) Name the salt formed when dilute sulfuric acid reacts with zinc oxide.

DID YOU KNOW?

Chalk or limestone is added to lakes that are badly affected by acid rain to increase the pH of the water.

PRACTICAL

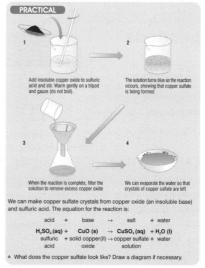

Add insoluble copper oxide to sulfuric acid and stir. Warm gently on a tripod and gauze (do not boil).

The solution turns blue as the reaction occurs, showing that copper sulfate is being formed

When the reaction is complete, filter the solution to remove excess copper oxide

We can evaporate the water so that crystals of copper sulfate are left

We can make copper sulfate crystals from copper oxide (an insoluble base) and sulfuric acid. The equation for the reaction is:

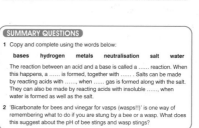

acid + base → salt + water

$$H_2SO_4\ (aq) + CuO\ (s) → CuSO_4\ (aq) + H_2O\ (l)$$
sulfuric acid + solid copper(II) oxide → copper sulfate solution + water

- What does the copper sulfate look like? Draw a diagram if necessary.

SUMMARY QUESTIONS

1 Copy and complete using the words below:

bases   hydrogen   metals   neutralisation   salt   water

The reaction between an acid and a base is called a ...... reaction. When this happens, a ...... is formed, together with .... Salts can be made by reacting acids with ......, when ...... gas is formed along with the salt. They can also be made by reacting acids with insoluble ......, when water is formed as well as the salt.

2 'Bicarbonate for bees and vinegar for vasps (wasps!!)' is one way of remembering what to do if you are stung by a bee or a wasp. What does this suggest about the pH of bee stings and wasp stings?

KEY POINTS

1 When we react an acid with a base a neutralisation reaction occurs.
2 The reaction between an acid and a base produces a salt and water.
3 Salts can also be made by reacting a metal with an acid. This reaction also produces hydrogen gas as well as a salt.

SUMMARY ANSWERS

1 Neutralisation, salt, water, metals, hydrogen, bases.

2 Bee stings are acidic and wasp stings are alkaline.

C2 7.3

Making salts from solutions

LEARNING OBJECTIVES

Students should learn that:

- Salts can be made from an acid and alkali.
- Insoluble salts can be made.
- Unwanted ions can be removed from solutions.

LEARNING OUTCOMES

Most students should be able to:

- Record a method to make soluble salts.
- Record a method to make insoluble salts.
- State what a precipitation reaction is and recognise examples.

Some students should also be able to:

- Suggest a method for making a named salt.
- Explain what precipitation is in terms of ions involved.

Teaching suggestions

- **Learning styles**

   Kinaesthetic: Making an insoluble salt.

   Visual: Drawing a labelled diagram.

   Auditory: Listening to definitions.

   Intrapersonal: Finding key words in a word search.

   Interpersonal: Working as a group to determine definitions.

- **Homework.** Ask students to define the term 'precipitation reaction' and find out two uses of this reaction.

- **ICT link-up.** Search the web for 'word search generator' e.g. www.puzzlemaker.school.discovery.com, to make an exercise about acids and bases.

FOUL FACTS

Nitrogen is needed by plants, to synthesis the proteins in stalks and leaves.

Answers to in-text questions

a) acid + alkali → salt + water

b) A precipitation reaction.

SPECIFICATION LINK-UP   Unit: Chemistry 2.12.6

- *In neutralisation reactions, hydrogen ions react with hydroxide ions to produce water. This reaction can be represented by the equation:*

$$H^+(aq) + OH^-(aq) \rightarrow H_2O(l)$$

- *Insoluble salts can be made by mixing appropriate solutions of ions so that a precipitate is formed. Precipitation can be used to remove unwanted ions from solutions, for example in treating water for drinking or in treating effluent.*

- *Soluble salts can be made from acids by reacting them with:*
   - *metals – not all metals are suitable, some are too reactive and others not reactive enough.*
   - *insoluble bases – the base is added to the acid until no more will react and the excess solid is filtered off.*
   - *alkalis – an indicator can be used to show when the acid and alkali have completely reacted to produce a salt solution.*

- *Ammonia dissolves in water to produce an alkaline solution. It is used to produce ammonium salts. Ammonium salts are important as fertilisers.*

- *The state symbols in equations are (s), (l), (g) and (aq).*

- *The particular salt produced in any reaction between an acid and a base or alkali depends on:*
   - *the acid used (hydrochloric acid produces chlorides, nitric acid produces nitrates, sulfuric acid produces sulfates).*
   - *the metal or base or alkali.*

Students should use their skills, knowledge and understanding of 'How Science Works':

- *to suggest methods to make a named salt.*

- *to explain and evaluate processes that use the principles described in this unit.*

Lesson structure

STARTER

Demonstration – The solubility of ammonia can be shown using the fountain reactions (see 'Practical support'). Show the students and ask them to note their observations – perhaps use a scribe to jot them onto the board as you complete the demonstration. Then the observations can be used as a starting point for discussion about solubility. (10 minutes)

Definitions – Ask students to define the terms 'soluble' and 'insoluble'. Then ask them to write two sentences each using one of the key words. After about five minutes split the class into four groups and ask each group to come up with their definitive definitions and two sentences. Then ask each group to feedback to the class their work. (10 minutes)

MAIN

- Students could show experimentally that ammonia is very soluble and makes an alkali. They could then record this experiment with a fully labelled diagram to explain the observations. Then encourage them to include information about what ammonium hydroxide can be used for.

- Students could make an insoluble salt. Encourage them to record this in a step-by-step method including an equipment list. Also the students could generate the word equation or balanced symbol equation.

PLENARIES

Method – Ask students to briefly explain how they would make the following salts:

- Sodium chloride [Neutralisation between sodium hydroxide and hydrochloric acid, then evaporate the water.]

- Lead iodide [Reaction between lead nitrate and sodium iodide, filter and collect the solid wash with distilled water and dry.] (10 minutes)

Practical support

Making an insoluble salt

Equipment and materials required

0.01 M lead nitrate solution (toxic), sodium chloride solution, beaker, measuring cylinder, conical flask, filter funnel, filter paper, distilled water, eye protection.

Details

Measure 10 ml of sodium chloride and 5 ml of lead nitrate into a test tube. Gently shake, and then filter the mixture and wash through with distilled water. Remove the filter paper and allow the solid to dry. This is the insoluble salt.

Safety: Eye protection should be worn throughout, and hands should be thoroughly washed after the experiment has been completed. Pregnant women should be aware that lead salts can affect unborn children – CLEAPSS Hazcard 57.

ACTIVITY & EXTENSION IDEAS

- Students could act out a precipitation reaction, where each student represents an ion.
- Mole calculations could be completed from balanced symbol equations.
- Students could test the solubility of salts at different temperatures and plot solubility curves (see 'Practical support'). Secondary data could be obtained to compare the solubility of different chemicals, e.g. from *RSC Data book* or search the Internet for 'solubility data'.

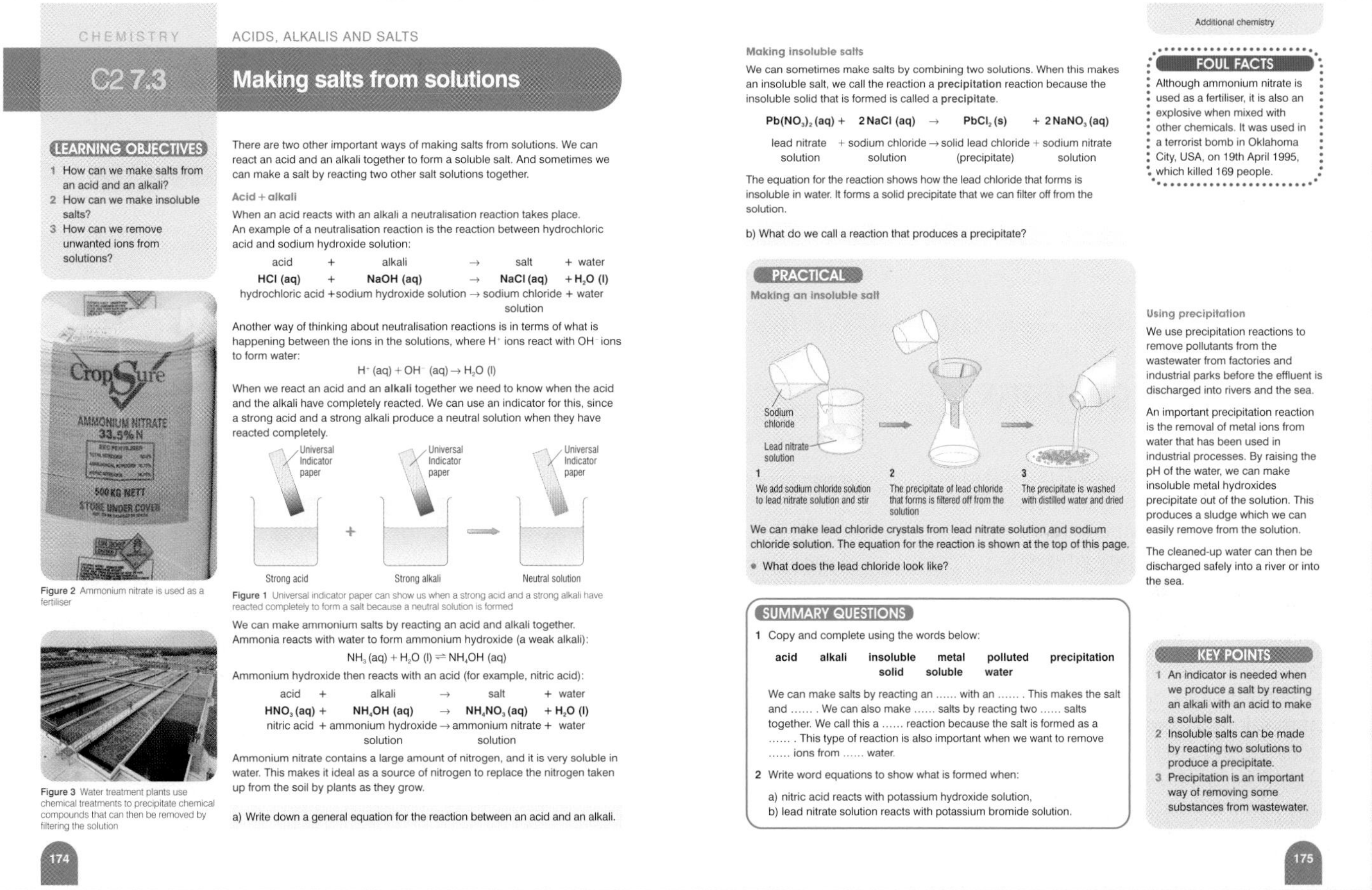

C2 7.3 — Making salts from solutions

LEARNING OBJECTIVES

1 How can we make salts from an acid and an alkali?
2 How can we make insoluble salts?
3 How can we remove unwanted ions from solutions?

Figure 2 Ammonium nitrate is used as a fertiliser

Figure 3 Water treatment plants use chemical treatments to precipitate chemical compounds that can then be removed by filtering the solution

There are two other important ways of making salts from solutions. We can react an acid and an alkali together to form a soluble salt. And sometimes we can make a salt by reacting two other salt solutions together.

Acid + alkali

When an acid reacts with an alkali a neutralisation reaction takes place. An example of a neutralisation reaction is the reaction between hydrochloric acid and sodium hydroxide solution:

acid	+	alkali	→	salt	+ water
HCl (aq)	+	NaOH (aq)	→	NaCl (aq)	+ H₂O (l)

hydrochloric acid + sodium hydroxide solution → sodium chloride solution + water

Another way of thinking about neutralisation reactions is in terms of what is happening between the ions in the solutions, where H⁺ ions react with OH⁻ ions to form water:

$$H^+ (aq) + OH^- (aq) \rightarrow H_2O (l)$$

When we react an acid and an **alkali** together we need to know when the acid and the alkali have completely reacted. We can use an indicator for this, since a strong acid and a strong alkali produce a neutral solution when they have reacted completely.

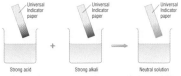

Strong acid   Strong alkali   Neutral solution

Figure 1 Universal indicator paper can show us when a strong acid and a strong alkali have reacted completely to form a salt because a neutral solution is formed

We can make ammonium salts by reacting an acid and alkali together. Ammonia reacts with water to form ammonium hydroxide (a weak alkali):

$$NH_3 (aq) + H_2O (l) \rightleftharpoons NH_4OH (aq)$$

Ammonium hydroxide then reacts with an acid (for example, nitric acid):

acid	+	alkali	→	salt	+ water
HNO₃ (aq)	+	NH₄OH (aq)	→	NH₄NO₃ (aq)	+ H₂O (l)

nitric acid + ammonium hydroxide solution → ammonium nitrate solution + water

Ammonium nitrate contains a large amount of nitrogen, and it is very soluble in water. This makes it ideal as a source of nitrogen to replace the nitrogen taken up from the soil by plants as they grow.

a) Write down a general equation for the reaction between an acid and an alkali.

Making insoluble salts

We can sometimes make salts by combining two solutions. When this makes an insoluble salt, we call the reaction a **precipitation** reaction because the insoluble solid that is formed is called a **precipitate**.

Pb(NO₃)₂ (aq) +	2 NaCl (aq)	→	PbCl₂ (s)	+ 2 NaNO₃ (aq)
lead nitrate solution	+ sodium chloride solution	→ solid lead chloride (precipitate)	+ sodium nitrate solution	

The equation for the reaction shows how the lead chloride that forms is insoluble in water. It forms a solid precipitate that we can filter off from the solution.

b) What do we call a reaction that produces a precipitate?

PRACTICAL
Making an insoluble salt

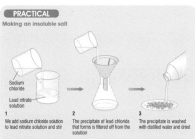

Sodium chloride
Lead nitrate solution

1 We add sodium chloride solution to lead nitrate solution and stir

2 The precipitate of lead chloride that forms is filtered off from the solution

3 The precipitate is washed with distilled water and dried

We can make lead chloride crystals from lead nitrate solution and sodium chloride solution. The equation for the reaction is shown at the top of this page.

• What does the lead chloride look like?

SUMMARY QUESTIONS

1 Copy and complete using the words below:

acid   alkali   insoluble   metal   polluted   precipitation
solid   soluble   water

We can make salts by reacting an ...... with an .... This makes the salt and .... We can also make ...... salts by reacting two ...... salts together. We call this a ...... reaction because the salt is formed as a .... This type of reaction is also important when we want to remove ...... ions from ...... water.

2 Write word equations to show what is formed when:
a) nitric acid reacts with potassium hydroxide solution,
b) lead nitrate solution reacts with potassium bromide solution.

FOUL FACTS
Although ammonium nitrate is used as a fertiliser, it is also an explosive when mixed with other chemicals. It was used in a terrorist bomb in Oklahoma City, USA, on 19th April 1995, which killed 169 people.

Using precipitation
We use precipitation reactions to remove pollutants from the wastewater from factories and industrial parks before the effluent is discharged into rivers and the sea.

An important precipitation reaction is the removal of metal ions from water that has been used in industrial processes. By raising the pH of the water, we can make insoluble metal hydroxides precipitate out of the solution. This produces a sludge which we can easily remove from the solution.

The cleaned-up water can then be discharged safely into a river or into the sea.

KEY POINTS

1 An indicator is needed when we produce a salt by reacting an alkali with an acid to make a soluble salt.
2 Insoluble salts can be made by reacting two solutions to produce a precipitate.
3 Precipitation is an important way of removing some substances from wastewater.

Word search – Create a word search, but students need to answer questions to determine the words that they need to find:

- A method for removing pollutants from water. [Precipitation]
- When a solute will dissolve into a solvent, it is described as . . . [Soluble]
- Chalk is described as this it will not dissolve in water. [Insoluble]
- A chemical with a pH < 7 [Acid]
- A soluble base. [Alkali]
- The name of the chemical reaction between a hydrogen ion and hydroxide ion. [Neutralisation] (10 minutes)

SUMMARY ANSWERS

1 Acid (Alkali), alkali (acid), water, insoluble, soluble, precipitation, solid, metal, polluted.

2 a) nitric acid + potassium hydroxide → potassium nitrate + water

b) lead nitrate + potassium bromide → lead bromide + potassium nitrate

KEY POINTS

Ask students to make three questions that could be answered by each key point.

C2 7.4

It's all in the soil

SPECIFICATION LINK-UP

Unit: Chemistry 2.12.6

Students should use their skills, knowledge and understanding of 'How Science Works':

- *To explain and evaluate processes that use principles described in this unit.*

This spread can be used to revisit the substantive content below:

- *... Precipitation can be used to remove unwanted ions from solutions, for example in treating water for drinking or in treating effluent.*

Teaching suggestions

Activities

- **Article** – Science knowledge is used in a lot of different jobs and aspects of life. Gardeners often put lime onto the soil (to increase pH) and add fertilisers. Gardeners know from past experience that these methods create healthier plants, but may not be aware of the science behind this. Ask students to imagine that they have been commissioned to write an article explaining the science of gardening. To help students, show them the gardening section in the local newspaper or some information leaflets from the local gardening centre.

- **Report** – A blue flag award for a beach is prestigious and helps tourism in an area. However, beaches can be polluted in a variety of different ways, heavy metals are just one form of pollution. Split the class into small groups of about three. They are to write a report to advise a council on how to remove heavy metals from polluted water. Students should include methods for this, but also a simplified explanation for non-scientists. Cleaning up pollution is an expensive task; therefore students could also consider how the pollution occurred and thus how it can be prevented. Students should also build into their reports a cost structure and whom they recommend should pay.

CHEMISTRY   ACIDS, ALKALIS AND SALTS

C2 7.4   It's all in the soil

The importance of rotation

No, nothing to do with rotating YOU! This is about not growing the same vegetables in the same place two years running. If you do this you are likely to find two problems.

First, pests and diseases which live on the particular vegetables will increase, and you will have real problems.

Second, growing the same crop in the same place year after year will lead to the soil becoming unbalanced, with the level of some nutrients becoming too low.

Getting the right amount of acid

When the soil in your garden is too acid or alkaline, nutrients present in the soil become locked-up or unavailable. Acidic soil has a 'pH' that is too low (less than 7) while alkaline soil has a 'pH' that is too high. In fact, a decrease of just one pH unit means that the soil is ten times more acidic!

Getting the pH right is the same as applying fertiliser since it 'unlocks' plant nutrients which are already present.

ACTIVITY

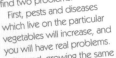

Although there is a lot of chemistry in gardening, it is not often that it is explained clearly (or correctly!). Your job is to write an article for a gardening newspaper or a leaflet for a local garden centre.

It should describe the chemistry behind getting the pH of the soil correct by testing it and then adding the necessary chemicals. You can even use simple chemical equations (especially word equations) if this helps you to explain things more clearly.

Testing your soil

You can find out the pH of your soil by testing it with a simple soil testing kit. This will tell you how acidic or alkaline your soil is.

Follow the instructions in the kit, which usually involves mixing a little soil with some water and testing it with some special paper. The colour that the paper turns will tell you if your soil has a 'pH' that is too low or too high.

What to add . . . ?

If your soil has the wrong 'pH' you'll need to do something about it. Unless you live on chalky soil it's very unusual for the pH of soil to be too high. This is because adding fertiliser usually makes soil acidic. So the most common thing that you'll need to do every so often to keep your soil with a 'neutral pH' is to add lime.

Lime is made by heating limestone to decompose it. Lime reacts with acid in the soil, making it neutral. You can buy lime from your local garden centre.

176

Homework

- **Research** – Encourage students to find out the chemical processes involved in purifying water for drinking purposes. They could display the processes as a flow chart.

Extension

- **Making a fertiliser** – Students could make ammonium sulfate, see 'Practical support'.

- **Natural fertilisers** – A number of plants have nitrogen-fixing bacteria in root nodules. Encourage students to find out how these plants provide their own fertilisers and how farmers can utilise them in crop rotations.

- **Which is the best fertiliser?** – Ask students to research the active chemical in a number of fertilisers (e.g. ammonium nitrate, ammonium phosphate). Also students could find out which minerals plants need and why. They should then decide which is the best fertiliser and why. Higher attaining students could complete mole calculations to show the percentage composition of nitrogen in different fertilisers, in order to find out which is the best fertiliser.

Blue flag beaches

The idea of a way of showing clearly that a beach is clean was put forward in 1987, when 244 beaches from 10 countries were awarded a flag to show that the beach met certain standards. As far as water quality goes, these standards include:

- the cleanliness of the water must comply with the EU Bathing Water Directive,
- no industrial effluent or sewage discharges may affect the beach area,
- there must be local emergency plans to cope with pollution accidents.

In 2005 there were nearly 2500 blue flag beaches worldwide.

ACTIVITY

The town council of a seaside resort wishes to apply for a 'blue flag' for their beach. However, they have been told that they must get rid of a large amount of heavy metal pollution in the water discharged through the town's sewage system. The heavy metals come from a large factory near the town, which is a very important local employer.

Your job is to act as a consultant to the town council to advise them of the best way to go about cleaning up the effluent in order to be able to apply for a blue flag.

Write a report to the council explaining what they should do. You will need to explain the chemistry to them in simple terms (they should be able to understand simple word equations), and you will need to suggest who will pay for the treatment – whether this should be the local people (through their local taxes), the factory producing the pollution, or even the visitors to the town (through higher prices for their accommodation and other holiday costs).

Cleaning up industrial effluent

A lot of wastewater from industry contains salts of heavy (transition) metals dissolved in it. Before this can be discharged these must be removed. The simplest way of removing the metal ions is to raise the pH of the solution. The hydroxide ions in the alkaline solution then react with the metal ions, producing metal hydroxides. The hydroxides of most heavy metals are very insoluble. So these form a precipitate which can be removed from the wastewater before it is discharged into a river or into the sea.

177

Learning styles

Kinaesthetic: Making a fertiliser.

Visual: Creating a flow chart to show the purification of drinking water.

Intrapersonal: Completing calculations on percentage composition of different fertilisers.

Interpersonal: Working as a small group to prepare a report.

ICT link-up

A data logger could be used to show the pH changes in the neutralisation reaction to make the fertiliser ammonium sulfate.

Special needs

Instead of writing an article about the science behind gardening, the class could be split into groups of three. Each group could be given the task to make three posters with different focuses: soil pH, rotation, and fertilisers. Students could arrange their own group as they wish, e.g. each student taking responsibility for a poster, or splitting each poster into tasks and each student working on all the posters.

Practical support

Making ammonium sulfate

Equipment and materials required

A burette, stand, boss, clamp, conical flask, measuring cylinder, 1 M ammonia solution (CLEAPSS Hazcard 6), 1 M sulfuric acid (irritant – CLEAPSS Hazcard 98), glass rod, litmus paper, evaporating dish, funnel, eye protection.

Details

Wearing eye protection, students should measure 25 ml of ammonia solution into a conical flask and fill the burette with sulfuric acid. Add 1 ml of the acid into the conical flask and swirl the mixture. Then they remove a drop on a glass rod and touch litmus paper and observe the colour. Keep adding 1 ml of acid at a time until the litmus paper just turns pink, then the reaction is complete. Transfer the reaction mixture to an evaporating dish and allow the water to evaporate. The white crystals left behind are the ammonium sulfate fertiliser.

SUMMARY ANSWERS

1 a) C **b)** A **c)** E **d)** B **e)** F **f)** D

2 Beaker 1: OH^- and H^+
Beaker 2: O^{2-} and $2H^+$
Beaker 3: Pb^{2+} and $2Cl^-$

3 a) Hydrogen.

b) and **c)**

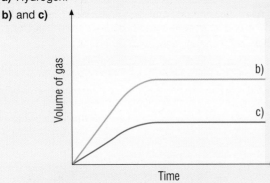

[Line on graph has half the slope of the first line, producing half as much hydrogen.]

4 a) $2KOH(aq) + H_2SO_4(aq) \rightarrow K_2SO_4(aq) + 2H_2O(l)$

b) $ZnO(s) + 2HNO_3(aq) \rightarrow Zn(NO_3)_2(aq) + H_2O(l)$

c) $Ca(s) + 2HCl(aq) \rightarrow CaCl_2(aq) + H_2(g)$

d) $Ba(NO_3)_2(aq) + Na_2SO_4(aq) \rightarrow BaSO_4(s) + 2NaNO_3(aq)$

Summary teaching suggestions

- **Special needs** – Question 4 could have the reactants already written out on a worksheet in the form of a word equation. There should be two lines for each product. Then a list of the chemicals should be displayed to the students. Each student then uses the list to decide which chemical should go on which line.

- **Gifted and talented** – Students could write balanced symbol equations, including state symbols for the reactions in question 2.

- **Learning styles**
  Kinaesthetic: Question 1 could be turned into a card sort.
  Visual: Question 3 allows students to sketch a graph.
  Auditory: Question 2 lends itself to a discussion before students try to answer the question.
  Intrapersonal: Question 4 allows students to work on chemical equations as individuals.

- **When to use the questions?**
  - Question 1 is a good indicator of language used in this section. It would be useful as a plenary or homework after lesson 7.1 had been taught.
  - Students could attempt the questions in the first half of the lesson. They could then swap their work with a neighbour, who should then try to mark the work, putting on suggestions for amendments. In the last ten minutes of the lesson, the work could be returned to the owner in order to make amendments and additions.
  - Question 4 is a good question to use after lessons 7.2 and 7.3 have been taught, as this utilises the general equations introduced in these two lessons.
  - Question 1 could be used to verbally assess the understanding of the key words.

SUMMARY QUESTIONS

1 Match the halves of the sentences together:

a) A base that is soluble in water	A ...... a pH of exactly 7.
b) Pure water is neutral with	B ...... form OH⁻ ions when they dissolve in water.
c) Acids are substances that	C ...... is called an alkali.
d) Alkalis are substances that	D ...... is acidic.
e) Indicators are substances that	E ...... produce H⁺ ions when they dissolve in water.
f) A solution with a pH less than 7	F ...... change colour when we add them to acids and alkalis.

2 The table shows the ions in substances in three pairs of beakers. Copy the table and draw lines between the ions that react in each beaker.

Beaker 1	Na⁺	OH⁻		H⁺	Cl⁻	
Beaker 2	Cu²⁺	O²⁻		H⁺	H⁺	SO₄²⁻
Beaker 3	Pb²⁺	NO₃⁻	NO₃⁻	Cu²⁺	Cl⁻	Cl⁻

3 A student carried out an investigation in which she dropped a piece of magnesium ribbon into some acid. She measured the total amount of gas that had been produced every 10 seconds and plotted this on a graph. At the end of the reaction some magnesium ribbon remained that had not reacted.
a) What gas does this reaction produce?
b) Sketch a graph of volume of gas (y-axis) against time (x-axis) that this student could have obtained.
c) Sketch another line on the graph to show the results that might be obtained if the student repeated this investigation, using the same acid but diluted so that its concentration was half of that used in the first investigation.

4 Write chemical equations to describe the following chemical reactions. (Each reaction forms a salt.)
a) Potassium hydroxide (an alkali) and sulfuric acid.
b) Zinc oxide (an insoluble base) and nitric acid.
c) Calcium metal and hydrochloric acid.
d) Barium nitrate and sodium sulfate (this reaction produces an insoluble salt – **hint:** all sodium salts are soluble).

EXAM-STYLE QUESTIONS

1 Magnesium hydroxide, $Mg(OH)_2$, is used in many antacids for relieving acid indigestion.
(a) Magnesium hydroxide is slightly soluble in water.
(i) Give the formulae of the ions produced when it dissolves. (2
(ii) Give a value for the pH of the solution it forms. (1
(b) Write a word equation for the reaction of magnesium hydroxide with hydrochloric acid. (2
(c) Write a balanced symbol equation for the reaction. (2
(d) Suggest why sodium hydroxide would not be suitable for use as a cure for indigestion. (2

2 Copper(II) sulfate crystals can be made from an insoluble base and sulfuric acid.
(a) Name the insoluble base that can be used to make copper(II) sulfate. (1
(b) Describe how to make a solution of copper(II) sulfate from 25 cm³ of dilute sulfuric acid so that all of the acid is used. (3
(c) Describe how you could make crystals of copper(II) sulfate from the solution. (3

3 Salts are formed when acids react with alkalis.
(a) Complete the word equation:
acid + alkali → .... + ... (2
(b) What type of reaction takes place when an acid reacts with an alkali? (1
(c) (i) Name the acid and alkali used to make potassium nitrate. (2
(ii) What would you use to show when the acid had completely reacted with the alkali? (1
(iii) Write a balanced symbol equation for the reaction that takes place. (2

EXAM-STYLE ANSWERS

1 a) i) $OH^-(aq)$ and $Mg^{2+}(aq)$ *(2 marks)*
ii) Any value between 8 and 12. *(1 mark)*

b) magnesium hydroxide + hydrochloric acid → magnesium chloride + water.
(1 mark for reactants, 1 mark for products) *(2 marks)*

c) $Mg(OH)_2 + 2HCl \rightarrow MgCl_2 + 2H_2O$
(1 mark for all correct formulae, 1 mark for balancing) *(2 marks)*

d) Sodium hydroxide is very (strongly) alkaline/has very high pH. *(1 mark)*
It is corrosive/it will damage skin or flesh *(1 mark)*
(do not accept just 'dangerous' or 'harmful').

2 a) Copper Oxide (copper(II) oxide). *(1 mark)*

b) *One mark each for:*
- Add copper(II) oxide to (warm) acid a little at a time.
- Until no more will dissolve/excess solid remains.
- Filter off the (excess) solid. *(3 marks)*

c) *One mark each for:*
- Heat/boil the solution.
- To evaporate some (but not all) of the water.
- Allow to cool.
- Filter off crystals.
- Allow to dry at room temperature/allow water to evaporate at room temperature. *(3 marks)*

3 a) Salt *(1 mark)* + water *(1 mark)* *(2 marks)*

b) Neutralisation *(1 mark)*

c) i) Potassium hydroxide *(1 mark)* + nitric acid *(1 mark)* *(2 marks)*

ii) An indicator. *(1 mark)*
iii) $KOH + HNO_3 \rightarrow KNO_3 + H_2O$ *(2 marks all correct, 1 mark for correct formulae with incorrect balancing).*

HOW SCIENCE WORKS QUESTIONS

The effluent from nickel plating works is treated with sodium carbonate to precipitate nickel ions from the solution. The precipitate is separated from the solution by settlement in a tank. Filtration is not usually used as the main method of removing the precipitate, but can be used to remove small amounts of solids from the effluent after settlement.

(a) Write a word equation for the reaction between nickel sulfate solution and sodium carbonate solution. (2)

(b) Name the precipitate that is formed. (1)

(c) How is most of the precipitate removed from the effluent? (1)

(d) Suggest one reason why filtration is not used to remove most of the precipitate. (1)

(e) Why is it necessary to remove metal ions like nickel from effluents? (1)

There are four main methods of making salts:

A Acid + metal
B Acid + insoluble base
C Acid + alkali
D Solution of salt A + solution of salt B

(a) A student wanted to make some sodium sulfate.
  (i) Which method would be the best one to use? (1)
  (ii) Explain why you chose this method. (3)
  (iii) Name the reagents you would use. (2)
  (iv) Write a word equation for the reaction. (1)

(b) Another student wanted to make some magnesium carbonate.
  (i) Which method would you use for this salt? (1)
  (ii) Explain why you chose this method. (2)
  (iii) Name the reagents you would use. (2)
  (iv) Write a word equation for the reaction. (1)

Chemistry to help!

Modern living produces enormous quantities of wastewater. Most of this can be treated in sewage works by biological processes. Sometimes biology cannot solve all of the problems. Chemistry is needed.

Phosphates are one such problem. You might have seen patches of stinging nettles near to old farms. These are due to the high concentrations of phosphates produced in animal (and human!) waste. This is a real problem when you have farms producing beef. In parts of USA they rear cattle with very little land.

The waste would normally be put on the land. It would cost a lot of money to transport the waste back to the farms that produced the feed. The waste is therefore dumped. The problem is that the high concentration of the phosphates causes water pollution problems.

Removing the phosphates at the sewage works by adding iron(III) chloride is also expensive. The wastewater therefore is treated with struvite, a magnesium salt that precipitates the phosphates.

Use these notes and your experience to answer these questions.

a) What are the economic issues associated with the disposal of animal waste? (2)

b) What are the environmental issues associated with the disposal of animal waste? (2)

c) What are the ethical issues associated with the use of chemistry to solve the problems of pollution? (1)

d) Who should be making the decisions about using chemistry to solve these problems? Explain your answer. (1)

e) Struvite can become a problem by precipitating out and blocking water pipes.
What extra information would be useful to those using struvite? (1)

179

---

4 a) nickel sulfate + sodium carbonate → nickel carbonate + sodium sulfate.
(1 mark for reactants, 1 mark for products) (2 marks)

b) Nickel carbonate (1 mark)

c) By allowing it to settle/settlement in a tank. (1 mark)

d) Filters will clog up/need frequently changing/filters are more expensive. (1 mark)

e) (Nickel) metal ions are toxic/poisonous/harmful to living things. (1 mark)

5 a) i) C; acid + alkali (1 mark)
  ii) *Three from:*
  • Sodium sulfate is soluble (so cannot use D).
  • Sodium oxide is soluble in water/a soluble base (so cannot use B).
  • Sodium hydroxide is an alkali (so C is suitable).
  • Sodium metal is too reactive (to use safely with acid, so cannot use A). (3 marks)
  iii) Sodium hydroxide (1 mark)
    Sulfuric acid (1 mark)
  iv) sodium hydroxide + sulfuric acid → sodium sulfate + water (1 mark)

b) i) D; solution of salt A + solution of salt B (1 mark)
  ii) *Two from:*
  • Magnesium carbonate is insoluble.
  • Magnesium carbonate reacts with acids.
  • There is no suitable acid that can be used. (2 marks)
  iii) Any soluble magnesium salt e.g. magnesium chloride. (1 mark)
    Any soluble carbonate (alkali metal carbonate) e.g. sodium carbonate. (1 mark)
  iv) Depends on their choice of reactants. (1 mark)

Exam teaching suggestions

- Allow students 40 minutes to do all five questions, with a total of 43 marks. Q1, Q2 and Q3 could be set after completing 7.2, Q4 after 7.3.

- In Q1, students are expected to apply their knowledge of acids and bases. Writing word equations and balanced symbol equations for reactions should be practised as often as possible and there are plenty of opportunities in teaching this topic. In part d) students should know that specific reasons are expected rather than simple ideas, such as 'it is harmful'.

- The preparation of a salt is separated into two parts in Q2. This approach could be helpful in teaching and revising this topic, making the learning more manageable, more bite-sized. Using bulleted answers to questions of this type can help students ensure that they are writing the required number of marking points and can help them focus on the essential steps, cutting out unnecessary statements.

- Summary equations, like that in Q3a) should be thoroughly learnt by students. Small cards or posters displayed in the room where they work or revise will help them remember such essential facts. These can be prepared in class and students can help each other to produce very effective learning aids.

- Q4 requires students to apply their knowledge to a new situation. They should be encouraged to attempt questions like this and not be put off by the unknown. Focusing on the key words helps. Any reasonable answer will usually gain credit.

HOW SCIENCE WORKS ANSWERS

a) Economic issues: cost of transport of waste away from farm to where it can be used; cost of treating the waste on the farm; cost of treatment if it leaks into the water supply; is it still profitable to rear the cattle in this way?

b) Environmental issues: pollution of water supplies; survival of plants where it is dumped; use of fossil fuels to transport waste to where it can be used.

c) Ethical issues: should humans be using animals in such an artificial way to produce 'cheap' food?

d) Scientists should provide the evidence, and society in the shape of government should make the decisions.

e) Exactly how much struvite is needed to remove a quantity of phosphates – then none is left to block up the drains.

How science works teaching suggestions

- **Literacy guidance.** Key terms that should be clearly understood: ethical, environmental, economic.

- **Higher- and lower-level answers**
  - Higher-level answers are expected from c).
  - Lower-level answers are expected from d).

- **Gifted and talented.** Able students could review the responsibility of chemists for the environment.

- **How and when to use these questions.** When wishing to develop the meaning of ethical, economic and environmental issues. Also, the limitations of science in answering some important questions.
  The questions should be a stimulus for whole-class discussion.

- **Homework.** For homework, ask students to research one other topic that relates to the role of the chemist in either improving or reducing the quality of the environment.

- **ICT link-up.** The Internet could be a source for further information to research the economic, environmental and ethical issues.

C2 Examination-Style Questions

Examiner's comments

Allow 40 minutes to complete all of the questions if done in a single session. Q1 and Q2 could be set after completing C2 2, Q3 after C2 3, Q4 after C2 4 and Q5 after C2 6.

Q6 is best left until the end of the unit.

Questions will be set in contexts that are unfamiliar to candidates. These questions will provide candidates with information so that they can apply their skills, knowledge and understanding

(Assessment Objective 2). Candidates do not need to learn any substantive content outside the current specifications that appear in questions given as examples in specimen assessment materials, or from previous examination papers.

Many candidates do not attempt calculations or they give up at the first problem they encounter. Encourage students to attempt all parts of a problem, and to use whatever answer they get for the next step to benefit from error carried forward (e.c.f.) marks.

Answers to Questions

1 (a) hydrogen chloride

   (b) neon

   (c) diamond

   (d) sodium chloride

   (e) magnesium   *(1 mark each, total 5 marks)*

2 (a) Li or dot at centre of two concentric circles, inner circle with two dots/crosses, outer circle with one dot/cross. *(all correct = 2 marks, one error or omission = 1 mark)*

   (b) F or dot at centre of two concentric circles, inner circle with two dots/crosses, outer circle with seven dots/crosses. *(all correct = 2 marks, one error or omission = 1 mark)*

   (c) Lithium ion: EITHER Li^+ or $[Li]^+$ OR Li at centre of circle with two dots/crosses (with brackets) and $^+$ at top right-hand side.   *(1 mark)*
   Fluoride ion: EITHER F at centre of two concentric circles with two dots/crosses on inner circle and eight dots/crosses on outer circle (surrounded by brackets) with $^-$ at top right-hand side OR F surrounded by eight dots/crosses with $^-$ at top right-hand side.   *(2 marks)*
   (It is acceptable to show only the outer electrons in bonding diagrams)

3 (a) 13

   (b) 2,8,3

   (c) 8

   (d) $[2,8]^{2-}$ *(allow 2,8)*

   (e) 39

   (f) K^+

   (g) 18

   (h) $[2,8,8]^-$ *(allow 2,8,8)*   *(1 mark each, total 8 marks)*
   continues opposite ❯

EXAMINATION-STYLE QUESTIONS

1 Match these substances with the descriptions (a) to (e):

   diamond, hydrogen chloride, magnesium, neon, sodium chloride

   See pages 104–11

   (a) A compound made of small molecules.

   (b) A gas at room temperature made of single atoms.

   (c) A giant lattice of atoms that are covalently bonded.

   (d) An ionic solid with a high melting point.

   (e) A giant lattice that conducts electricity when it is solid.   *(5 marks)*

2 (a) Draw a dot and cross diagram to show the electron arrangement of a lithium atom, atomic number 3.   *(2 marks)*

   See pages 90–3

   (b) Draw a dot and cross diagram to show the electron arrangement of a fluorine atom, atomic number 9.   *(2 marks)*

   (c) Draw dot and cross diagrams to show the ions in lithium fluoride.   *(3 marks)*

3 Complete the table that shows information about some atoms.

   See pages 88–95, 116

Symbol	Atomic number	Mass number	Number of protons	Number of neutrons	Electron arrangement of atom	Formula of ion	Electron arrangement of ion
Al	13	27	(a)	14	(b)	Al^{3+}	$[2,8]^+$
O	8	16	8	(c)	2,6	O^{2-}	(d)
K	19	(e)	19	20	2,8,8,1	(f)	$[2,8,8]^+$
Cl	17	35	17	(g)	2,8,7	Cl^-	(h)

   (8 marks)

4 A student added 20 g of marble chips to 50 cm³ of dilute hydrochloric acid in a conical flask. The flask was put onto a balance. The table shows the mass of gas that was given off. Some marble chips were left in the flask at the end of the reaction.

   See pages 137–9

Mass of gas given off (g)	0	0.14	0.27	0.38	0.47	0.51	0.57	0.59	0.60
Time (minutes)	0	1.0	2.0	3.0	4.0	5.0	6.0	7.0	8.0

   (a) Plot a graph of the results. Put time on the horizontal axis and mass lost on the vertical axis. Draw a smooth line through the points, omitting any result that is anomalous.   *(5 marks)*

   (b) The rate of this reaction decreases with time. Explain how you can tell this from the graph.   *(1 mark)*

   The student decided to extend his work to see if temperature affected the rate at which the gas was produced.

   (c) (i) Suggest one control variable he should use.

GET IT RIGH

It is important to express yourself clearly in answe that require explanation: Question 4(b), you shou make it clear that the gr or slope of the graph sh the rate of reaction at th time. Also, if you are as how collisions affect th of reaction, it is not en say there are more co It is the frequency of collisions (the numbe collisions per second the rate depends upo

---

BUMP UP THE GRADE

Students should be encouraged to read and attempt all parts of each question. Questions do not necessarily become more difficult towards the end, and may contain some easier parts. These should not be missed!

GET IT RIGHT!

It is important that students express themselves clearly in answers that require explanations. They do not always make it clear in their answers that they understand it is the gradient or slope of the graph that shows the rate of reaction at a particular time, and that the rate decreases as the reaction proceeds. Also, when explaining how collisions affect the rate of reaction, it is not enough to say there are more collisions. It is the frequency of collisions (the number of collisions per second) that the rate depends upon, and so the number of collisions needs to be related to the time for full marks.

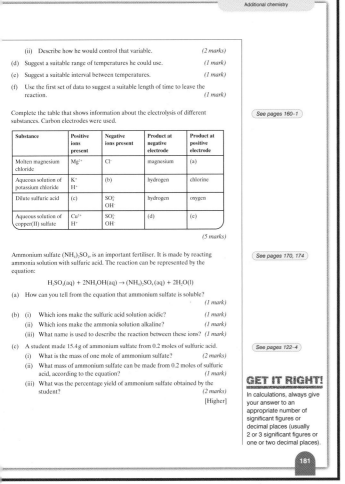

> continues from previous page

4 (a) *One mark each for:*
  - Both axes labelled.
  - Suitable scales used.
  - All points correctly plotted (+/− half small square).
  - Smooth line through points.
  - Omitting point at 5 minutes. *(5 marks)*

(b) Slope/gradient decreases with time OR slope/gradient/line is steeper at the beginning or becomes less steep or levels off. *(1 mark)*

(c) (i) E.g. concentration of acid; size of marble chips. *(1 mark)*

  (ii) Linked to the above e.g. ensure that the same concentration of acid is used for each temperature. *(1 mark)*

(d) E.g. 20°C to 60°C – reasonable within practical and safety limits. *(1 mark)*

(e) At least five, equally spaced. *(1 mark)*

(f) About four minutes. *(1 mark)*

5 (a) chlorine *(1 mark)*

(b) Cl^- and OH^- *(accept with correct state symbols, i.e. aq)* *(1 mark)*

(c) H^+ *(accept H_3O^+, H^+(aq), H_3O^+(aq))* *(1 mark)*

(d) copper *(1 mark)*

(e) oxygen *(1 mark)*

6 (a) Its state symbol is (aq)/it is aqueous. *(1 mark)*

(b) (i) Hydrogen ions/H^+/H^+(aq)/H_3O^+/H_3O^+(aq). *(1 mark)*

  (ii) Hydroxide ions/OH^-/OH^-(aq). *(1 mark)*

  (iii) Neutralisation. *(1 mark)*

(c) (i) 132 g *(2 marks for correct answer with units)* *(correct working, e.g. $(14 + 4) \times 2 + 32 + (16 \times 4)$ gains 1 mark)*

  (ii) 26.4 g *(1 mark)*

  (iii) 58.3% *(2 marks for correct answer)* *(correct working, e.g. $15.4 \times 100/26.4$ (e.c.f. from (ii) can gain 2 marks)*

[HT only]

Key Stage 3 curriculum links

The following link to **'What you already know'**:

- How to determine the speed of a moving object and to use the quantitative relationship between speed, distance and time.

- That the weight of an object on Earth is the result of the gravitational attraction between its mass and that of the Earth.

- That unbalanced forces change the speed or direction of movement of objects and that balanced forces produce no change in the movement of an object.

- Ways in which frictional forces, including air resistance, affect motion [for example, streamlining cars, friction between tyre and road].

- How to design and construct series and parallel circuits, and how to measure current and voltage.

- That the current in a series circuit depends on the number of cells and the number and nature of other components and that current is not 'used up' by components.

- That energy is transferred from batteries and other sources to other components in electrical circuits.

Scheme of work
7J Electrical circuits
7K Forces and their effects
9I Energy and electricity
9K Speeding up

RECAP ANSWERS

1 **a)** Conductors: brass, copper; Insulators: air, plastic, wood.

   b) Two of: The battery might be 'flat'. The lamp might have 'blown'. A wire might have broken.

2 **a)** The force of gravity on you (i.e. your weight), the support force from the seat.

   b) i) The forces are balanced.

      ii) You would drop onto the floor.

3 **a)** Microwaves.

   b) X-radiation and γ radiation.

4 **a) i)** A charged atom.

      ii) X-radiation, α, β and γ radiation.

   b) i) α radiation.

      ii) The nucleus.

5 **a)** km for kilometres (distance), s for seconds (time).

Making connections

Each of these vignettes provides you with an opportunity to discuss important scientific developments linked to exploration and would best be tackled as the story of our general urge to explore. Use the ideas to show the students why scientific developments are key in technological progress and that new ideas and discoveries will be needed if we are to reach further out into space. There are several space exploration missions active at one time; some more successful than others. You can provide the students with up-to-date information on the latest space probe. It is hard to predict the breakthroughs that could happen before 2099, but they might like to consider these possibilities:

- **Matter transmitters:** Could we 'beam' ourselves across the world?

- **Artificial intelligence:** Machines with the ability to think; they could potentially be smarter than humans.

- **Digitised humans:** One day we could leave our flesh bodies behind and our minds could run on smaller and more long-lasting hardware. This would be ideal for the long-time scale of space exploration.

- **Alien contact:** We might finally contact another intelligent species. Would it be friend or foe?

PHYSICS

P2 | Additional physics

What you already know

Here is a quick reminder of previous work that you will find useful in this unit:

Figure 1 Spot the units!

Electricity
- In an electric circuit, energy is transferred from a voltage supply to the other parts of the circuit.
- Current passes round an electric circuit if the circuit is complete.
- Insulators do not conduct electricity.

Force
- If the forces acting on an object are not balanced, they will change the motion of the object.
- Weight is caused by the force of gravity on a mass.
- Friction acts between two surfaces in contact with each other when they slide or try to slide past each other.

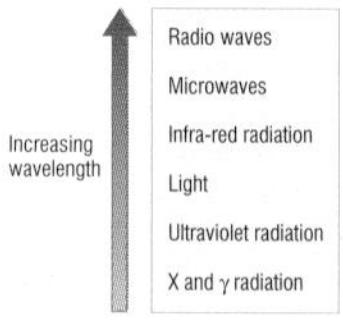

Energy
- Energy cannot be created or destroyed. It can only be transformed from one form to another form.
- Power is the rate of transfer of energy.

Radiation
- Radioactive substances decay because the nuclei of some atoms are unstable. An unstable nucleus emits α, β or γ radiation when it decays.
- X-rays and α, β and γ radiation ionise substances they pass through.

Increasing wavelength →

Radio waves
Microwaves
Infra-red radiation
Light
Ultraviolet radiation
X and γ radiation

Figure 2 The electromagnetic spectrum

RECAP QUESTIONS

1 a) Sort the materials below into two lists – electrical conductors and insulators.

    air   brass   copper   plastic   wood

   b) A student replaces a battery in an electric torch but the torch still doesn't work. Suggest two possible reasons why it doesn't work.

2 a) List the forces acting on you at this moment, assuming you are sitting still.

   b) i) When you are sitting still, what can you say about the forces acting on you?

      ii) If the force your seat exerts on you suddenly decreased, what would happen to you?

3 a) Which has the longer wavelength, γ radiation or microwaves?

   b) Which electromagnetic waves can pass through the body?

4 a) i) What is an ion?

      ii) List four different types of ionising radiation.

   b) i) Which is most easily absorbed, α, β or γ radiation?

      ii) Where in the atom does α, β or γ radiation come from?

5 What are the units in the cartoon at the top of this page used to measure?

182

SPECIFICATION LINK-UP
Unit: Physics 2

How can we describe the way things move?

Even when things are moving in a straight line, describing their movement is not easy. They can move with different speeds and can also change their speed and/or direction (accelerate). Graphs can help us to describe the movement of the body. These may be distance–time graphs or velocity–time graphs.

How do we make things speed up or slow down?

To change the speed of a body an unbalanced force must act on it.

What happens to the movement energy when things speed up or slow down?

When a body speeds up or slows down, its kinetic energy increases or decreases. The forces that cause the change in speed do so by transferring energy to, or from, the body.

What is momentum?

The faster a body is moving the more kinetic energy it has. It also has momentum. When working out what happens to bodies as a result of explosions or collisions it is more useful to think in terms of momentum than in terms of energy.

What is static electricity, how can it be used and what is the connection between static electricity and electric currents?

Static electricity can be explained in terms of electrical charges. When electrical charges move we get an electric current.

What does the current through an electrical circuit depend on?

The size of the current in a circuit depends on how hard the supply tries to push charge through the circuit and how hard the circuit resists having charge pushed through it.

What is mains electricity and how can it be used safely?

Mains electricity is useful but can be very dangerous. It is important to know how to use it safely.

Why do we need to know the power of electrical appliances?

Electrical appliances transform energy. The power of an electrical appliance is the rate at which it transforms energy. Most appliances have their power and the potential difference of the supply they need printed on them. From this we calculate their current and the fuse they need.

What happens to radioactive substances when they decay?

To understand what happens to radioactive substances when they decay we need to understand the structure of the atoms from which they are made.

What are nuclear fission and nuclear fusion?

Nuclear fission is the splitting of atomic nuclei and is used in nuclear reactors as a source of heat energy that can be transformed to electrical energy. Nuclear fusion is the joining together of atomic nuclei and is the process by which energy is released in stars.

Making connections
Taking off!

To fly high, you need to take off first. The first powered flight was by the Wright brothers in 1903. Now planes can carry hundreds of people for thousands of miles in a few hours. We can send space probes far into space. Where will people have got to by the end of this century? Read on to find out where the physics in this module can take you.

Jets and rockets

The first jet engine was invented by a British engineer, Frank Whittle. He worked out how to create a jet of hot gases by burning aviation fuel. He used his scientific knowledge of materials, energy and forces to design and test the first jet engine.

On the launch pad

Space is only a few miles above your head but gravity stops you going there – unless you are in a rocket. A rocket is a jet engine with its own oxygen supply. Jet planes don't need to carry oxygen to burn aviation fuel in their engines because they use oxygen in the atmosphere. But a single-stage rocket can't get far enough into space to escape from the Earth. The Russian physicist, Konstanin Tsiolovsky predicted in 1895 that space rockets would need to be multistage.

Keeping in touch

Space travel would be impossible without electronic circuits for control and communications. A radio signal from a space probe is weaker than the light from a torch lamp on the Moon. The communication circuits in a space probe detect and process very weak signals. On-board cameras and sensors collect and send information back to Earth. Control circuits operate on-board rockets to change the path of a space probe. The electronic circuits in a space probe need to be totally reliable.

Interstellar travel

Voyager 2 was launched in 1975. Now it is on its way out of the Solar System after sending back amazing pictures of the outer planets and their moons. Space probes and satellites need power supplies that last for many years.

Space travel by astronauts far from the Sun would need powerful electricity generators powered by nuclear reactors. Nuclear submarines carry small nuclear reactors for their electricity. New types of nuclear reactors such as fusion reactors would be better. The probes and the reactors would probably need to be built on the Moon, using local materials.

ACTIVITY
Discuss:
What things do you think people will be able to do in the year 2099 that we can't do today? What breakthroughs in science will these rely on?

Chapters in this unit

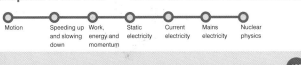

Motion | Speeding up and slowing down | Work, energy and momentum | Static electricity | Current electricity | Mains electricity | Nuclear physics

183

Teaching suggestions

Misconceptions

Motion of objects

- Many students will be used to describing speeds in miles per hour. It is hard to discourage them from this and no matter what you do, some will still be giving answers in m.p.h. on the final exam paper. Just try to minimise this number by not giving example of cars moving in miles per hour in the unit. Unfortunately you don't really have this option for the braking distance charts.

- Some will think that a force is required for an object to keep moving at a steady velocity. Because of friction and air resistance it is hard to demonstrate that the object will keep going unless a force is applied. Air tracks and lots of space-based examples may help.

- There are bound to be problems with the confusion between mass and weight. You may also find that students are confused about gravity and say things like 'the downward force on me is gravity' instead of 'the downward force is my weight'.

Electrical circuits

- Often students have the misconception that a battery produces electrons and then some of them are used up as they travel through components. It can be hard to discourage this idea; try to get across the picture of electrons as energy carriers; some computer animations are exceptionally helpful here.

- Incorrect positioning of voltmeters and ammeters is common; try to talk about the potential difference **across** a component and the current **through** it.

Chapters in this unit

- Motion
- Speeding up and slowing down
- Work, energy and momentum
- Static electricity
- Current electricity
- Mains electricity
- Nuclear physics

P2 1.1

Distance–time graphs

LEARNING OBJECTIVES

Students should learn:

- How to interpret the slope of a distance–time graph.

- How to calculate the speed of a body using the speed equation.

- How to use a distance–time graph to compare the speed of a body.

LEARNING OUTCOMES

Most students should be able to:

- State that the slope of a distance–time graph represents the speed.

- Use the speed equation to calculate the average speed of an object.

Some students should also be able to:

- Rearrange and use the speed equation.

- Compare the speed of an object using the slope of a distance–time graph.

Teaching suggestions

- **Gifted and talented.** Using the details from the train timetable (see 'Homework') the students can plot graphs to compare the speeds of local trains and expresses.

- **Learning styles**

  Kinaesthetic: Researching into speed records.

  Visual: Observing and presenting speed data.

  Auditory: Explaining ideas about motion.

  Interpersonal: Reporting changes in speed records.

  Intrapersonal: Interpreting data from graphs.

- **Homework**

  - Provide the students with a graph and ask them to describe the motion of the object. Higher attaining students should calculate the speed of the object during each stage of the motion.

  - Ask the students to get a bus or train timetable and a map. They should use the information in these to work out the average speed of the trains or buses between different locations.

SPECIFICATION LINK-UP   Unit: Physics 2.13.1

- *The slope of a distance–time graph represents speed.*

Students should use their skills, knowledge and understanding of 'How Science Works':

- *to construct distance–time graphs for a body moving in a straight line when the body is stationary or moving with a constant speed.*

Lesson structure

STARTER

Speedy start – Give the students a set of cards showing different moving objects and ask them to put them in order from fastest to slowest. (5 minutes)

Understanding graphs – Show the students slides of a range of graphs showing the relationship between two variables and ask them to describe what is happening. Alternatively, show Animation P2 1.1 'Distance–time graphs' from the Additional Science CD ROM. (5–10 minutes)

A quick quiz – Give the students a quick verbal quiz to check their understanding of the terms 'speed', 'distance' and 'time' and to find out if they remember how to calculate speed. (5 minutes)

MAIN

- Some students have difficulty understanding what you mean by the terms 'object' or 'body' and you will have to exemplify these ideas by talking about cars, trains or runners.

- Students can also have difficulty with the whole ideas of a 'time axis'. You might like to show time as moving on by revealing the graph from left to right, and discussing what is happening to the distance the object has moved over each second.

- There are quite a few that fail to understand that the flat (horizontal) portions of the graph show that the object is stationary. Emphasise that the distance isn't changing, even though time is; 'the object hasn't got any further away during this second so it must be still'.

- You should use additional simple graphs to discuss the motion of several objects until you are sure that the students can identify when the objects are moving fastest.

- The students should be familiar with the speed equation, but it may have been some time since they used it in Key Stage 3. A few practice questions should remind them of the basic idea.

- Be cautious of students using inappropriate units for speed such as 'm.p.h.' or even 'mps' (metres per second). If students find 'per' difficult, then just use 'each'.

- With higher attaining students, you can get them to read information off the graphs to calculate speed although this is covered in detail on page 190 in the Student Book at an appropriate level. They should be able to calculate the overall average speed and the speed during individual phases of the motion.

- With higher attaining students, you may like to discuss displacement instead of distance or you could leave this until you are discussing velocity in the next topic.

- The practical activity is a good way to round off the lesson, and it can be as brief as ten minutes long if bicycles are not involved.

PLENARIES

Interpreting a graph – Ask students to describe the motion represented in some graphs. Examples are found on page 185 links on the CD or on Animation P2 1.1 'Distance–time graphs'.

A driving story – Give the students a paragraph describing the motion of a car through a town, including moving at different speeds and stopping at traffic lights etc. Ask them to sketch a graph of the described motion. (10 minutes)

Oscillations – Show the students a pendulum swinging from side to side and ask them to sketch a distance–time graph of the motion. (5–10 minutes)

ACTIVITY & EXTENSION IDEAS

Detailed speed measurements

To make more detailed measurements of the speed of an object a distance sensor can be used.

Equipment and materials required

Distance sensor, data logger and a simple moving object.

Details

The distance sensor should be mounted in a fixed position and the object moves in front of it while the data logger records. You can use this to measure your distance in front of the meter while you walk back and forth at different speeds. The students can then analyse the graphs and see if they can describe the motion from them.

A need for speed

The students could find out about how the land speed record has changed over the past 150 years (from trains to rocket cars). They could plot a graph of the record speed against the year and see if they can extrapolate to find what the record will be in 50 years' time. A similar activity can be carried out for the air and water speed records.

DID YOU KNOW?

The fastest moving man-made object was the Helios 2 space probe. It travelled at about 67 km/s (67 000 m/s), which is Mach 203 (not that sound can travel in space). Space probes can travel so quickly, because there is no air resistance so they do not lose any of their kinetic energy. The probe Voyager 1 is travelling at 17.5 km/s and has been travelling for around 30 years. Ask: 'How far away is it?'

Practical support

Be a distance recorder!

Measuring speed is a simple activity and livens up what can be a fairly dry start to the motion unit.

Equipment and materials required

For each group: stopwatch, metre wheel. Clipboards and marker cones are also useful.

Details

The students should measure out distances first and then time each other walking, running, hopping or riding over these fixed distances. An outdoor netball court, or similar, can provide a set of straight and curved lines for the students to follow. You may like to see if the students travel faster along the straight edges or if they follow the curves on the court. If you intend to use bicycles, then a lot more space will be needed and the students must wear the appropriate safety gear. Check with the PE department to see if they have cones to mark out the distances and if they mind bicycles on their running tracks or shoes on their indoor courts!

PHYSICS | MOTION

P2 1.1 | Distance–time graphs

LEARNING OBJECTIVES

1 How can we tell from a distance–time graph if an object is stationary?
2 How can we tell from a distance–time graph if an object is moving at constant speed?
3 How do we calculate the speed of a body?

Figure 1 Capturing the land speed record

DID YOU KNOW?

- A top sprinter can travel a distance of about 10 metres every second.
- A cheetah is faster than any other animal. It can run about 30 metres every second – but only for about 20 seconds!
- A vehicle travelling at the speed limit of 70 miles per hour (mph) on a UK motorway travels a distance of 31 metres every second.
- The land speed record at present is 763 mph, which is more than Mach 1, the speed of sound.
- The air speed record was broken in November 2004 by X-43A, an experimental scram-jet plane. It reached 6600 mph or Mach 9.6! Whoosh …

Some motorways have marker posts every kilometre. If you are a passenger in a car on a motorway, you can use these posts to check the speed of the car. You need to time the car as it passes each post. The table below shows some measurements made on a car journey:

Distance (metres, m)	0	1000	2000	3000	4000	5000	6000
Time (seconds, s)	0	40	80	120	160	200	240

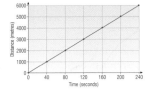

Figure 2 A distance–time graph

Look at the readings plotted on a graph of distance against time in Figure 2.

The graph shows that:

- the car took 40 s to go from each marker post to the next. So its speed was **constant**.
- the car went a distance of 25 metres every second (= 1000 metres ÷ 40 seconds). So its speed was 25 metres per second.

If the car had travelled faster, it would have gone further than 1000 metres every 40 seconds. So the line on the graph would have been **steeper**.

The slope on a distance–time graph represents speed.

a) What can you say about the steepness of the line if the car had travelled slower than 25 metres per second?

Speed

For an object moving at constant speed, we can calculate its speed using the equation:

$$\text{speed (metre/second, m/s)} = \frac{\text{distance travelled (metre, m)}}{\text{time taken (second, s)}}$$

The scientific unit of speed is the metre per second, usually written as metre/second or m/s.

Speed in action

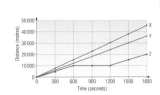

Figure 3 Comparing distance–time graphs

Long-distance vehicles are fitted with recorders that can check that their drivers don't drive for too long. The information from a recorder may be used to plot a distance–time graph.

Look at the distance–time graph above for three lorries, X, Y and Z, on the same motorway.

- X went fastest because it travelled furthest in the same time.
- Y travelled more slowly than X. From the graph, you can see it travelled 30 000 metres in 1500 seconds. So its speed was 20 m/s (= 30 000 m ÷ 1500 s).

b) Calculate the speed of X.

- Z stopped for some of the time. Its speed was zero in this time.

c) How long did Z stop for?
d) Calculate the **average** speed of Z.

PRACTICAL

Be a distance recorder!

Take the measurements needed to plot distance–time graphs for a person:

- walking,
- running, and
- riding a bike.

Remember that you must always label the graph axes, which includes units.

- Compare the slopes of the lines and work out average speeds.

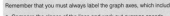

SUMMARY QUESTIONS

1 Choose the correct word from the list to complete a) to c) below.

    distance   speed   time

a) The unit of …… is the metre/second.
b) An object moving at steady …… travels the same …… every second.
c) The steeper the line on a distance–time graph of a moving object, the greater its …… is.

2 A vehicle on a motorway travels 1800 m in 60 seconds. Calculate:

a) the speed of the vehicle in m/s.
b) how far it would travel at this speed in 300 seconds.

KEY POINTS

1 The steeper the line on a distance–time graph, the greater the speed it represents.
2 Speed (metre/second, m/s) =
$$\frac{\text{distance travelled (metre, m)}}{\text{time taken (second, s)}}$$

SUMMARY ANSWERS

1 a) Speed.
  b) Speed, distance.
  c) Speed.

2 a) 30 m/s
  b) 9000 m

Answers to in-text questions

a) It would not have been as steep.

b) 25 m/s

c) 600 s

d) 11.1 m/s

KEY POINTS

The students can be given the opportunity to describe a journey in detail from a distance–time graph.

P2 1.2   Velocity and acceleration

Students should learn that:

- Velocity is the speed in a particular direction.
- Acceleration is the rate of change of velocity.

Most students should be able to:

- Explain the difference between the velocity of an object and the speed.
- Calculate the acceleration of an object using the acceleration equation.

Some students should also be able to:

- Rearrange and use the acceleration equation.

Teaching suggestions

- **Gifted and talented.** These students may like to look into the details of the concepts of displacement and velocity. Ask: 'What is the average speed of a Formula One car over one whole lap? What is the average velocity for the complete lap?' The students could draw a diagram to explain the difference.

- **Learning styles**

  Visual: Observing and presenting graphical data.

  Auditory: Discussing and explaining experiences on fairground rides, etc.

  Interpersonal: Giving feedback about results.

  Intrapersonal: Evaluating outcome of experiment.

- **ICT link-up**

  - Distance sensors need to be used to measure velocity and changes in velocity accurately.

  - Motion can also be monitored with video equipment and frame by frame playback. (This relates to 'How Science Works': making measurements.)

SPECIFICATION LINK-UP   Unit: Physics 2.13.1

- *The velocity of a body is its speed in a given direction.*
- *The acceleration of a body is given by:*

$$\text{acceleration (metre second squared, } m/s^2) = \frac{\text{change in velocity (metre/second, } m/s)}{\text{time taken for change (second, } s)}$$

Students should use their skills, knowledge and understanding of 'How Science Works':

- *to construct velocity–time graphs for a body moving with a constant velocity or a constant acceleration.*

Lesson structure

STARTER

In the right direction – Give the students a map and ask them how to get from one location to another. They need to include distances and directions. (5 minutes)

Treasure island – Give the students a scaled map with hidden treasure, but at first only give them the times they have to walk for, then the speeds they must go at, and finally the matching directions. This shows how important direction is. (5 minutes)

Getting nowhere fast – A racing driver completes a full circuit of a 3 km racecourse in 90 seconds. Ask: 'What is his average speed? Why isn't he 3 km away from where he started?' (5 minutes)

MAIN

- Talking about fairground rides or roundabouts helps to get across the idea that you can be moving at a constant speed but be feeling a force. You can link this experience into the idea that unbalanced forces cause acceleration, see later topics.

- Some students will not see the difference between speed and velocity clearly and a few examples are needed. These can include simply walking around the room and describing your velocity.

- You might like to discuss a collision between two objects travelling at 30 and 31 km/h. If they collide while travelling in opposite directions the impact will be devastating, because the relative velocity is 61 km/h. If they collide when they are travelling in the same direction only a 'nudge' will be felt, because their relative velocity is only 1 km/h. Clearly the direction is very important.

- Check that all of the students can give an example of a velocity.

- Velocity–time graphs look similar enough to distance–time graphs to cause a great deal of confusion for students. Because they have just learned that the 'flat' region on a distance–time graph shows that the object is stationary, they will probably feel that this is true for the velocity–time graph too. Time should be taken to explain that the object is moving at a steady velocity.

- Many students are unclear of the units for acceleration (m/s^2) and ask what the 'squared bit' is. If they are mathematically strong, you might like to show where the unit comes from using the equation but otherwise they should not worry about it.

- There may be some confusion with the terms 'acceleration', 'deceleration' and 'negative acceleration', especially if you consider objects that move backwards as well as forwards. For higher attaining students you should show a graph of the motion of an object moving forwards then backwards, and describe the acceleration in detail.

PLENARIES

One graph to another – Give the students a velocity–time graph, showing the movement of a car and asking them to sketch a matching distance–time graph. For higher attaining students you could use a challenging graph, where the car reverses for part of the movement. (5–10 minutes)

Comparing graphs – Ask the students to make a comparison of what a distance–time graph and a velocity–time graph show. (5–10 minutes)

Rolling, rolling, rolling – Three balls of the same size are rolled down the same slope. One is iron, one wood and one is a football. Ask: 'Which will reach the bottom first?' The students should explain their ideas. (5–10 minutes)

ACTIVITY & EXTENSION IDEAS

- **Acceleration, power and mass in vehicles** – The students could find out about what makes a vehicle good at accelerating. By finding out the power output (bhp or kW) and mass of some vehicles (include motorcycles), they could investigate if there is a relationship between mass, power and acceleration. They could explain how well the data fits any pattern.

PHYSICS   MOTION

P2 1.2   Velocity and acceleration

LEARNING OBJECTIVES

1 What is the difference between speed and velocity?
2 What is acceleration and what are its units?
3 What is deceleration?

Figure 1 You experience plenty of changes in velocity on a corkscrew ride!

When you visit a fairground, do you like the rides that throw you round? Your speed and your direction of motion keep changing. We use the word **velocity** for speed in a given direction. An exciting ride would be one that changes your velocity often and unexpectedly!

Velocity is speed in a given direction.

- An object moving steadily round in a circle has a constant speed. Its direction of motion changes as it goes round so its velocity is not constant.

- Two moving objects can have the same speed but different velocities. For example, a car travelling north at 30 m/s on a motorway has the same speed as a car travelling south at 30 m/s. But their velocities are not the same because they are moving in opposite directions.

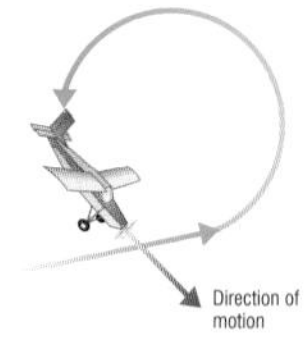

Direction of motion

Figure 2 Speed and velocity

a) How far apart are the two cars 10 seconds after they pass each other?

Acceleration

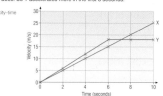

Figure 3 On a test circuit

A car maker claims their new car 'accelerates more quickly than any other new car'. A rival car maker is not pleased by this claim and issues a challenge. Each car in turn is tested on a straight track with a velocity recorder fitted.

The results are shown in the table:

Time from a standing start (seconds, s)	0	2	4	6	8	10
Velocity of car X (metre/second, m/s)	0	5	10	15	20	25
Velocity of car Y (metre/second, m/s)	0	6	12	18	18	18

Which car accelerates more? The results are plotted on the velocity–time graph in Figure 4. You can see the velocity of Y goes up from zero faster than the velocity of X does. So Y accelerates more in the first 6 seconds.

Figure 4 Velocity–time graphs

The acceleration of an object is its change of velocity per second. The unit of acceleration is the metre per second squared, abbreviated to m/s^2.

Any object with a changing velocity is accelerating. We can work out its acceleration using the equation:

$$\text{Acceleration (metre/second squared, } m/s^2) = \frac{\text{change in velocity (metre/second, m/s)}}{\text{time taken for the change (second, s)}}$$

Worked example
In Figure 4, the velocity of Y increases from zero to 18 m/s in 6 seconds. Calculate its acceleration.

Solution
Change of velocity = 18 m/s – 0 m/s = 18 m/s
Time taken = 6.0 s

$$\text{Acceleration} = \frac{\text{change in velocity (metre/second, m/s)}}{\text{time taken for the change (second, s)}} = \frac{18 \, m/s}{6.0 \, s} = 3.0 \, m/s^2$$

b) Calculate the acceleration of X in Figure 4.

Deceleration

A car decelerates when the driver brakes. We use the term **deceleration** or *negative acceleration* for any situation where an object slows down.

SUMMARY QUESTIONS

1 Complete a) to c) using the words below:

acceleration   speed   velocity

a) An object moving steadily round in a circle has a constant ....
b) If the velocity of an object increases by the same amount every second, its ...... is constant.
c) Deceleration is when the ...... of an object decreases.

2 The velocity of a car increased from 8 m/s to 28 m/s in 8 s without change of direction. Calculate:

a) its change of velocity,   b) its acceleration.

NEXT TIME YOU...

... go 'skateboarding', go round in a circle and think about how your velocity is changing.

KEY POINTS

1 Velocity is speed in a given direction.
2 Acceleration is change of velocity per second.
3 A body travelling at a steady speed is accelerating if its direction is changing.

186   187

SUMMARY ANSWERS

1 a) Speed.
  b) Acceleration.
  c) Velocity.

2 a) 20 m/s   b) 2.5 m/s²

Answers to in-text questions

a) 600 m
b) 2.5 m/s²

KEY POINTS

The students could describe the movement of objects as represented by velocity–time graphs by labelling parts on an interactive whiteboard.

P2 1.3 More about velocity–time graphs

Teaching suggestions

- **Learning styles**

  Kinaesthetic: Carrying out a range of experiments.

  Visual: Obtaining precise results.

  Auditory: Explaining and listening to the outcomes of experiments from different groups.

  Interpersonal: Evaluating the quality of results as a group.

  Intrapersonal: Interpreting graphical information.

- **Homework.** The students could calculate the distance travelled by an object using a velocity–time graph.

- **ICT link-up.** Using route planner software, the students can find the distances between points on their journey to school or other locations. (see www.multimap.co.uk or maps.google.com.) They can time themselves travelling between these points and work out their average speed. Sharing this information will allow them to compare different modes of transport.

Answers to in-text questions

a) Less steep.

b) It would not be as steep.

c) Greater.

Lesson structure

STARTER

Comparing graphs – Ask the students to describe the differences in the movement of three cars as shown on the same velocity–time graph. You can also use distance–time graphs. (5–10 minutes)

Measuring speed – Ask: 'How many different ways can you think of to measure the speed of an object?' These could be techniques or devices like radar, sonar etc. (What about red shift?) (5 minutes)

Late again? – Give the students the distance from their last class to the laboratory and ask them to work out their speed on the journey to you, using the time it took them to arrive. Anybody travelling at less than 1 m/s clearly isn't keen enough! (5 minutes)

MAIN

- Demonstrate the results produced for test A in the Student Book. If you do not get a straight line, you might want to discuss air resistance as a force opposing the movement of the trolley.

- The investigation into the motion of an object is a good one if you have sufficient equipment. Alternatives using light gates do not give a simple comparison of the accelerations, but you may be able to demonstrate that the velocity has increased. (This relates to: 'How Science Works': types of variable; fair testing; relationship between variables.)

- As before, time should be taken to ensure that the students understand what the gradients of the different graphs mean. They should be encouraged to break the graph down and just look at one section at a time, in order to explain what is happening between these sections.

- There should be no difficulty explaining that braking will reduce the velocity of the car, but you might like to ask what braking would look like on the graph if the car was in reverse.

- When calculating the area under the graph, ensure that the students are not giving their answers as 'distance = 15 cm²' or similar. This can happen when they 'count boxes' or do their calculations based on the area being measured in centimetres. Make sure that they are reading the distances and times off the graph, not the actual dimensions of the shapes.

- Finally you could show what would happen if the deceleration took longer, by superimposing the new gradient over the old one and showing that the area is greater.

PLENARIES

Busy teacher – Wear a pedometer throughout the lesson, calculate your average step distance and then ask the students to work out how far you have moved and your average speed. (5 minutes)

Slow motion – If you have a movement sensor alarm in your lab, you could see if the students sit so still that the sensor light goes off. Can they move so slowly that the alarm does not trigger? (5 minutes)

Practical support

Movement and trolleys

Dynamics trolleys are an excellent way of studying motion, but class sets are very expensive. If none are available, then fairly large toy cars can be used for the basic experiments. Velocity sensors are also expensive and you may need to modify this experiment into a demonstration.

Equipment and materials required

Dynamics trolley, adjustable slope, protractor, and data-logging equipment including a velocity sensor.

Details

Set up the equipment so that the angle of the ramp can be adjusted and easily measured. Make sure that the sensor is pointing along the path of the slope, otherwise the velocity will not be measured accurately. The students activate the sensor and then release the trolley.

Repeating this for a range of slope angles should give the result that the steeper the slope the greater the acceleration.

Alternative equipment

Light gates

As an alternative to a velocity sensor, a set of light gates can be used in experiments. This involves mounting a card of known length on top of the trolley so that it interrupts the beam, and the sensor measures the time for this to take place. This data can be used to determine the velocity; some software will do this for you directly. To determine acceleration, you can use a slotted card that interrupts the beam twice. This allows you to determine acceleration by looking at the speed the trolley was travelling when it first interrupted the beam and the speed the second time. Several sets of light gates can be used to measure the velocity at different stages of the motion.

Distance sensors

These use ultrasound or infra-red to measure the distance to an object. Some software will convert these distance values into speed values and plot the required graphs.

ACTIVITY & EXTENSION IDEAS

Trolley aerodynamics

The ramp experiment can be expanded to look into the aerodynamic properties of the trolleys.

Equipment and materials required

Dynamics trolley, adjustable slope, protractor, stiff cardboard, scissors and data-logging equipment including a velocity sensor.

Details

Set up the equipment as in the earlier trolley experiment, but fix the ramp in one position. Mount various sized pieces of card on the back of the trolley for each run, and compare the accelerations. The trolley should accelerate less with larger pieces of card mounted on it. You may also find that the acceleration of the trolley gets less the faster it goes; shown by a curved velocity–time graph. This is due to the air resistance increasing at larger velocities; an important concept in car design.

PHYSICS | MOTION

P2 1.3 — More about velocity–time graphs

LEARNING OBJECTIVES

1 How can we tell from a velocity–time graph if an object is accelerating or decelerating?

2 What does the area under a velocity–time graph represent?

Figure 2 Measuring motion using a computer

Investigating acceleration

We can use a motion sensor linked to a computer to record how the velocity of an object changes. Figure 1 shows how we can do this, using a trolley as the moving object. The computer can also be used to display the measurements as a velocity–time graph.

Test A: If we let the trolley accelerate down the runway, its velocity increases with time. Look at the velocity–time graph from a test run in Figure 2.

Figure 1 A velocity–time graph on a computer

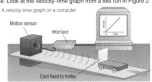

- The line goes up because the velocity increases with time. So it shows the trolley was accelerating as it ran down the runway.
- The line is straight which tells us that the increase in velocity was the same every second. In other words, the acceleration of the trolley was constant (or uniform).

Test B: If we make the runway steeper, the trolley accelerates faster. This would make the line on the graph in Figure 2 steeper than for test A. So the acceleration in test B is greater.

The slope on a graph is a measure of its steepness. The tests shows that:

the slope of the line on a velocity–time graph represents acceleration.

a) If you made the runway less steep than in test A, would the line on the graph be steeper or less steep than in A?

PRACTICAL

Investigating acceleration

Use a motion sensor and a computer to find out how the slope of a runway affects a trolley's acceleration.

- Name i) the independent variable, and ii) the dependent variable in this investigation. (See page 276.)
- What relationship do you find between the variables? (See page 280.)

Braking

Braking reduces the velocity of a vehicle. Look at the graph in Figure 3. It is the velocity–time graph for a vehicle that brakes to a standstill at a set of traffic lights. The velocity is constant until the driver applies the brakes.

Using the slope of the line:

- The section of the graph for constant velocity is flat. The line's slope is zero so the acceleration in this section is zero.
- When the brakes are applied, the velocity decreases to zero and the vehicle decelerates. The slope of the line is negative in this section.

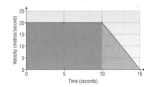

Figure 3 Braking

b) How would the slope of the line differ if the deceleration had taken longer?

Look at the graph in Figure 3 again.

Using the area under the line:

- Before the brakes are applied, the vehicle moves at a velocity of 20 m/s for 10 s. It therefore travels 200 m in this time (= 20 m/s × 10 s). This distance is represented on the graph by the area under the line from 0 s to 10 s. This is the shaded rectangle on the graph.
- When the vehicle decelerates in Figure 3, its velocity drops from 20 m/s to zero in 5 s. We can work out the distance travelled in this time from the area of the purple triangle in Figure 3. This area is $\frac{1}{2}$ × the height × the base of the triangle. So the vehicle must have travelled a distance of 50 m when it was decelerating.

The area under the line on a velocity–time graph represents distance travelled.

c) Would the total distance travelled be greater or smaller if the deceleration had taken longer?

SUMMARY QUESTIONS

1 Match each of the following descriptions to one of the lines, labelled A, B, C and D, on the velocity–time graph.

1 Accelerated motion throughout
2 Zero acceleration
3 Accelerated motion, then decelerated motion
4 Deceleration

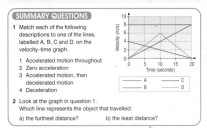

2 Look at the graph in question 1. Which line represents the object that travelled:
a) the furthest distance?   b) the least distance?

DID YOU KNOW?

A speed camera flashes when a vehicle travelling over the speed limit has gone past. Some speed cameras flash twice and measure the distance the car travels between flashes.

KEY POINTS

1 The slope of the line on a velocity–time graph represents acceleration.
2 The area under the line on a velocity–time graph represents distance travelled.

SUMMARY ANSWERS

1 1. B 2. A 3. D 4. C

2 a) A b) C

KEY POINTS

- Give the students a velocity–time graph and ask them to calculate the distance travelled.
- For higher attaining students this could include backwards motion.

P2 1.4

Using graphs

LEARNING OBJECTIVES

Students should learn:

- How to calculate the speed from a distance–time graph. [**HT** only]

- How to calculate the distance travelled from a velocity–time graph. [**HT** only]

- How to calculate the acceleration of an object from a velocity–time graph. [**HT** only]

LEARNING OUTCOMES

Most Higher Tier students should be able to:

- Calculate the slope of a distance–time graph and relate this to the speed of an object. [**HT** only]

- Calculate the slope of a velocity–time graph and hence the acceleration. [**HT** only]

- Find the area under a velocity–time graph for constant velocity and use this to calculate the distance travelled by an object. [**HT** only]

- Find the area under a velocity–time graph for constant acceleration and use this to calculate the distance travelled by an object. [**HT** only]

Teaching suggestions

- **Learning styles**

  Kinaesthetic: Making convection mobiles.

  Visual: Viewing and obtaining information from graphs.

  Auditory: Explaining what the graphs show about movement.

  Intrapersonal: Interpreting information.

- **Homework.** Follow-up work can be set on analysing or plotting a range of graphs of motion.

- **ICT link-up.** Simulation software can be used to investigate motion and to plot graphs of the behaviour. These can be either quite simple or rather complex, so you should be able to find something suitable for all ranges of ability. (See sunflowerlearning.com; www.fable.co.uk.

SPECIFICATION LINK-UP   Unit: Physics 2.13.1

Students should use their skills, knowledge and understanding of 'How Science Works':

- *to calculate the speed of a body from a distance–time graph. (**HT** only)*

- *to calculate the acceleration of a body from a velocity–time graph. (**HT** only)*

- *to calculate the distance travelled by a body from a velocity–time graph. (**HT** only)*

Lesson structure

STARTER

Finding areas – Get the students to calculate the total area of a shape made up of rectangles and triangles. (5–10 minutes)

Plot – Give the students a set of velocity–time data for a moving object, and ask them to plot a graph of displacement–time. (10 minutes)

Graph matching – The students have to match the description of the movement of objects with graphs of distance–time and velocity–time. (5–10 minutes)

MAIN

- This topic is for higher attaining students only, but you can use some ideas to reinforce the learning of middle abilities.

- Some students will prefer the term 'gradient' to 'slope'. As 'gradient' is the more correct term, it should be encouraged; but if the students are used to 'slope', then don't confuse them with two terms.

- With a bit of practice, they should have no difficulty determining slopes. Watch out for students reading off the total distance and total time instead of the change in distance and change in time.

- Get the students to describe what is happening to the speed of a range of objects. You might like to show graphs, followed by video clips, of objects doing what was shown in the graph, e.g. cars accelerating from 0–60 m.p.h. or balls bouncing, etc. (Search at video.google.com or altavista.com).

- When you move on to velocity–time graphs, yet again emphasise that these show something different. Hopefully the students will never get the two confused.

- The students should be reading the changes in velocity and time from the graphs, but some may make the same mistakes as mentioned previously.

PLENARIES

Pendulum bob – Show the students the oscillations of a pendulum and ask them to sketch a displacement–time graph and a matching velocity–time graph. A mass oscillating on a spring could be used instead. (10 minutes)

Dynamic definitions – The students should provide detailed definitions of speed, velocity, distance, displacement and acceleration, including how they are represented on graphs. (10 minutes)

It's all gone wrong – Give the students the work of an imaginary student who has made a number of mistakes when using the graphs. Ask them to correct all of the mistakes. (10–15 minutes)

The students should have found the distance travelled by an object from a velocity–time graph in the last topic, so challenge them with more difficult graphs of motion.

- You may want to see if they can find the distance travelled when the acceleration is not uniform. This would involve square counting techniques (see 'Counting Squares' below).

- For additional challenge, look into graphs showing the object moving back towards the origin. You could try some velocity–time graphs where the velocity becomes negative, and see if the students can calculate the distance the object ends up from the origin.

- **Counting squares** – One common technique for working out the area under a line on a graph is to count the squares on the graph paper. Anything less than half a square doesn't count and anything more than half a square counts as a complete square. This works reasonably well for simple graphs including those with straight gradients. You could discuss how to improve the accuracy of the method by using smaller and smaller squares on the graph paper. Make sure that the students know the distance each square of the graph paper represents.

Answers to in-text questions

a) 15 m/s

b) The speed decreased gradually and became constant.

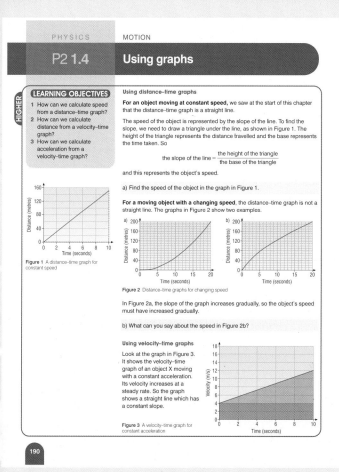

P2 1.4   Using graphs

LEARNING OBJECTIVES

1 How can we calculate speed from a distance–time graph?
2 How can we calculate distance from a velocity–time graph?
3 How can we calculate acceleration from a velocity–time graph?

Using distance–time graphs

For an object moving at constant speed, we saw at the start of this chapter that the distance–time graph is a straight line.

The speed of the object is represented by the slope of the line. To find the slope, we need to draw a triangle under the line, as shown in Figure 1. The height of the triangle represents the distance travelled and the base represents the time taken. So

$$\text{the slope of the line} = \frac{\text{the height of the triangle}}{\text{the base of the triangle}}$$

and this represents the object's speed.

a) Find the speed of the object in the graph in Figure 1.

For a moving object with a changing speed, the distance–time graph is not a straight line. The graphs in Figure 2 show two examples.

Figure 1 A distance–time graph for constant speed

Figure 2 Distance–time graphs for changing speed

In Figure 2a, the slope of the graph increases gradually, so the object's speed must have increased gradually.

b) What can you say about the speed in Figure 2b?

Using velocity–time graphs

Look at the graph in Figure 3. It shows the velocity–time graph of an object X moving with a constant acceleration. Its velocity increases at a steady rate. So the graph shows a straight line which has a constant slope.

Figure 3 A velocity–time graph for constant acceleration

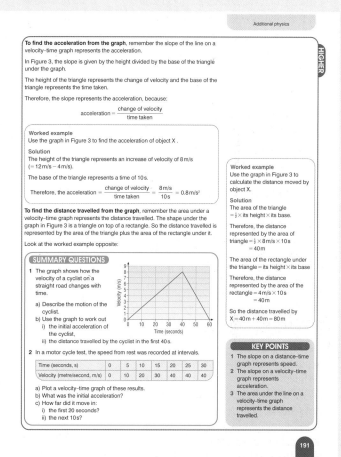

To find the acceleration from the graph, remember the slope of the line on a velocity–time graph represents the acceleration.

In Figure 3, the slope is given by the height divided by the base of the triangle under the graph.

The height of the triangle represents the change of velocity and the base of the triangle represents the time taken.

Therefore, the slope represents the acceleration, because:

$$\text{acceleration} = \frac{\text{change of velocity}}{\text{time taken}}$$

Worked example

Use the graph in Figure 3 to find the acceleration of object X.

Solution

The height of the triangle represents an increase of velocity of 8 m/s (= 12 m/s − 4 m/s).

The base of the triangle represents a time of 10 s.

Therefore, the acceleration $= \dfrac{\text{change of velocity}}{\text{time taken}} = \dfrac{8\,\text{m/s}}{10\,\text{s}} = 0.8\,\text{m/s}^2$

To find the distance travelled from the graph, remember the area under a velocity–time graph represents the distance travelled. The shape under the graph in Figure 3 is a triangle on top of a rectangle. So the distance travelled is represented by the area of the triangle plus the area of the rectangle under it.

Look at the worked example opposite:

SUMMARY QUESTIONS

1 The graph shows how the velocity of a cyclist on a straight road changes with time.

a) Describe the motion of the cyclist.
b) Use the graph to work out
   i) the initial acceleration of the cyclist,
   ii) the distance travelled by the cyclist in the first 40 s.

2 In a motor cycle test, the speed from rest was recorded at intervals.

Time (seconds, s)	0	5	10	15	20	25	30
Velocity (metre/second, m/s)	0	10	20	30	40	40	40

a) Plot a velocity–time graph of these results.
b) What was the initial acceleration?
c) How far did it move in:
   i) the first 20 seconds?
   ii) the next 10 s?

Worked example

Use the graph in Figure 3 to calculate the distance moved by object X.

Solution

The area of the triangle
$= \frac{1}{2} \times$ its height $\times$ its base.

Therefore, the distance represented by the area of triangle $= \frac{1}{2} \times 8\,\text{m/s} \times 10\,\text{s}$
$= 40\,\text{m}$

The area of the rectangle under the triangle = its height $\times$ its base

Therefore, the distance represented by the area of the rectangle $= 4\,\text{m/s} \times 10\,\text{s}$
$= 40\,\text{m}$

So the distance travelled by X $= 40\,\text{m} + 40\,\text{m} = 80\,\text{m}$

KEY POINTS

1 The slope on a distance–time graph represents speed.
2 The slope on a velocity–time graph represents acceleration.
3 The area under the line on a velocity–time graph represents the distance travelled.

SUMMARY ANSWERS

1 a) The cyclist accelerates with a constant acceleration for 40 s, and then decelerates to a standstill in 20 s.

   b) i) 0.2 m/s² ii) 160 m [**HT** only]

2 a) Graph. b) 2 m/s² c) i) 400 m ii) 400 m [**HT** only]

KEY POINTS

- The students should be able to analyse distance–time and velocity–time graphs in detail.

- They should be challenged by asking them to plot a complex graph and calculate both the distance travelled and acceleration of each phase of the motion.

P1a 1.5   Transport issues

This spread can be used to revisit the following aspects covered in this chapter:

Students should use their skills, knowledge and understanding of 'How Science Works':

- to construct distance–time graphs for a body moving in a straight line when the body is stationary or moving with a constant speed.

- to construct velocity–time graphs for a body moving with a constant velocity or constant acceleration.

Teaching suggestions

Activities

- **The Big Fuel protest** –The debate is a good opportunity to develop the students' skills but they will need to find, or be provided with, evidence for their arguments. You could provide the students with details of the price of petrol and the amount of tax placed on it. Information is available on the Internet about the reasons people would reduce their car usage (search for 'petrol use statistics' and you should find information from DEFRA www.defra.gov.uk). The inefficiency of cars in cities can be linked with congestion as described below. If cities were less congested, there would be less stopping and starting and so less pollution.

- **Epic journeys** – Columbus's journey took 34 days and so his velocity was around 6.7 km/h. That isn't particularly fast, but he didn't go in a straight line. The Apollo 11 crew travelled at an average speed of nearly 4000 km/h. A conventional rocket would not have enough fuel to keep up the thrust for a year, but there are alternatives. A 'light sail' uses the thrust provided by photons from the Sun. The acceleration from a large sail would only be 0.5 mm/s², but this acceleration is constant and the probe could reach Pluto in less than 5 years. It's a bit more difficult to come back though.

- **Speed cameras** – For this activity, a template can be used to help the students work on their letter. A collection of letters for and against the issuing of cameras can make an effective display, along with photographs and maps of local camera installations.

P2 1.5   Transport issues

The Big Fuel protest

In 2001, lorry drivers in Britain decided their fuel costs were too high so they blockaded fuel depots. They were angry at the government because most of the cost of the fuel is tax (which raises money for the government).

Garages ran out of petrol and drivers had to queue for hours to fill up. Car drivers were a lot more careful about using their precious fuel.

Car journeys in built-up areas use more fuel per kilometre than 'out of town' journeys at the same average speed. This is because cars slow down and speed up more often in built-up areas. More fuel is used by a car that keeps stopping and starting than one driven at constant speed.

On a motorway journey the faster the speed of a car, the more fuel it uses. Air resistance at high speed is much greater than at low speed, so more fuel is used.

QUESTION

The table shows some information about fuel usage by a petrol-engine car.

	Distance travelled per litre of fuel (km)	
	at 48 kilometres per hour (30 mph)	at 100 kilometres per hour (63 mph)
Driving in town	12	–
On the 'open road'	15	10

1 A driver on the 'open road' would use 6 litres of fuel to drive 60 kilometres at 100 km/h.
   a) How much fuel would the driver use to drive 60 km at 48 km/h:
      i) in town?   ii) on the open road?
   b) The driver pays 85 p per litre for petrol. How much would be saved on a motorway journey of 60 km by driving at 48 km/h instead of 100 km/h?

ACTIVITY

Discuss the issues below in a small group.

What are your views on the different ways that people might protest against the cost of fuel? Would you agree with the protesters? Think about the arguments that might be used by:

- An environmentalist
- A lorry driver
- An oil company
- A government official

Epic journeys

Journey 1: Christopher Columbus and his three ships left the Canary Islands on 8th September 1492. He reached the Bahama Islands on 12th October after a 5500 km journey across the Atlantic Ocean.

Journey 2: Neil Armstrong and Buzz Aldrin were the first astronauts to land on the Moon. They spent 22 hours on the Moon. The 380 000 km journey to the Moon took four days.

Journey 3: If a space rocket accelerated for a year at 2 m/s² (about the same as a car starting from rest), the rocket would reach a speed of 60 000 km/s – about a fifth of the speed of light.

QUESTION

2 Work out the speed, in kilometres per hour, of journeys 1 and 2.

- Students may be aware of devices used to detect speed cameras and they could discuss whether or not these devices should be made illegal. Some people think that a driver following the speed limits wouldn't need to know where the cameras are; others think that knowing where the cameras are helps you to be more aware of dangerous areas.

- **Congestion charges** – Congestion charges have been shown to reduce the number of cars entering the area and have also raised quite a lot of money. Congestion charges on motorways have also been suggested. Satellite technology could be used to track cars and charge people for using the motorways at peak times. Such a system would cost billions of pounds but could raise this money back quite quickly. Ask: 'Is it fair to charge people for using roads? Should they be charged per mile or per journey at peak times?'

- **Green travel** –You might like to provide a survey sheet for the students to use for this activity; it would make a good homework task. Surveys such as this are regularly carried out by local education authorities, in order for them to plan local transport needs; you may be able to get hold of this data. The idea of flexitime for schools is attractive to most students, but what happens if they have brothers or sisters in different year groups? Perhaps different schools could have different start and finish times to spread the rush hour out.

Speed cameras

Speed cameras are very effective in stopping motorists speeding. A speeding motorist caught by a speed camera is fined and can lose his or her driving licence. In some areas, residents are supplied with 'mobile' speed cameras to catch speeding motorists. Some motorists think this is going too far. Lots of motorists say speed cameras are being used by councils to increase their income.

A report from one police force said that where speed cameras had been introduced:

* average speeds fell by 17%,
* deaths and serious injuries had fallen by 55%.

Another police force reported that, in their area, as a result of installing more speed cameras in 2003:

* there were no child deaths in road accidents for the first time since 1927,
* 420 fewer children were involved in road accidents compared with the previous year.

ACTIVITY

Discuss with your friends:

a) Do the bullet-pointed statements opposite prove the argument that speed cameras save lives.
b) In what sort of areas do you think speed cameras should be used?

ACTIVITY

Should more residents be supplied with mobile speed cameras? Write a letter to your local newspaper to argue your case.

ACTIVITY

Do you think congestion charges are a good solution to traffic problems in our cities? Discuss the issue with your friends and take a vote on the question.

Green travel

Travelling to and from school or work can take ages unless you live nearby. Everybody seems to want to travel at the same time. Traffic accidents and rail cancellations in the rush hour cause hours of chaos. Traffic fumes cause pollution and burning fuel produces greenhouse gases.

Green travel means changing the way we travel to improve the environment.

Here are some suggestions about a green travel plan for your school:

* School buses; use school buses instead of cars.
* Car sharing; encourage drivers to share their cars with other drivers.
* Flexitime; finish the school day at different times for each year group.
* Everybody should walk or cycle to school.

ACTIVITY

With the help of your friends, conduct a survey to find out

a) if people in your school and parents think a green travel plan is a good idea,
b) what they think of the suggestions above,
c) if they have any better suggestions.

Write a short report to tell your headteacher about your survey and your findings.

Was your sample large enough to draw any firm conclusions? Explain your answer.

Congestion charges

Travelling across London by road was quicker a hundred years ago than it is today – even though modern cars can travel ten times faster than the horse-drawn carriages that were used then. Congestion charges were introduced in London in 2003 to improve traffic flow. If motorists enter the congestion zone without paying the daily charge, they are likely to be fined heavily.

People in Edinburgh in 2004 voted against proposals for congestion charges. But many people in other cities want to introduce them. However, lots of people who need to travel into cities think they are unfair.

193

ANSWERS TO QUESTIONS

1 a) i) 5 litres.   ii) 4 litres.
   b) £1.70

2 Journey 1: 6.7 km/h; Journey 2: 4000 km/h

Extension or homework

* **Economical cars** – Can the students find the fuel usage of their family's car? Diesel is a more expensive fuel, but many cars have diesel engines; ask: 'why is this?'

* **Around the world in 80 days** – Many people have circumnavigated the world in a variety of different ways. The students can find out the records for different methods (plane, boat, balloon, walking, motorbike, etc.) and calculate the average speeds.

* **Is transport getting better?** – Ask the students to find out the average speed of a car in London. Ask: 'Is this any faster than 30 years ago? What about the journey times from London to Edinburgh; has modern train design improved this significantly and, if not, why not?'

* **Measuring speeds** – The current world record for a 400 m freestyle swim is 220.08 seconds and the 400 m sprint is 43.18 seconds (as of July 2005). Ask: 'Can the speed of a swimmer or runner really be measured this accurately, is the swimming pool or running track built accurately enough to justify this level of precision in speed measurements? What about the 50 km walk record of 3:36.03?'

Special needs

Provide templates for all of the debates with important facts. The students must use this information in their discussions.

Gifted and talented

How would satellite tracking of cars work? The students can write a report on the proposed technology and discuss whether or not they think that this would be a good idea. Ask: 'Should the government be able to track the movement of every car in the country?'

Learning styles

Kinaesthetic: Researching about circumnavigation records.

Visual: Creating a mind map of summary information.

Auditory: Reading aloud information.

Interpersonal: Discussing the developments in pubic and private transport.

Intrapersonal: Considering how people can be discouraged from using their cars.

ICT link-up

Up-to-date information for most of these activities can be found on the Internet with a search. The easiest site to use to find out about human speed is www.olympic.org, which keeps Olympic and World records and is also a good history of how they have changed over the years.

SUMMARY ANSWERS

1 a) 700 m

   b) 40 s

2 a) A to B

   b) i) 2000 m, 100 s

      ii) 20 m/s

3 a) i) 20 m/s

      ii) 2.5 m/s²

   b) −1.2 m/s² i.e. the declaration is 1.2 m/s²

4 a) 3.0 m/s²

   b) 2400 m

Summary teaching suggestions

- The questions here are mostly mathematical in nature and should show if the students are capable of the calculation required by the specification. Use them to check that the students have a solid grasp on the units for velocity and acceleration.

MOTION: P2 1.1 – P2 1.5

SUMMARY QUESTIONS

1 A train travels at a constant speed of 35 m/s. Calculate:
   a) how far it travels in 20 s,
   b) how long it takes to travel a distance of 1400 m.

2 The figure shows the distance–time graph for a car on a motorway.

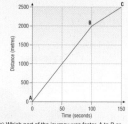

   a) Which part of the journey was faster, A to B or B to C?
   b) i) How far did the car travel from A to B and how long did it take?
      ii) Calculate the speed of the car between A and B?

3 a) A car took 8 s to increase its velocity from 8 m/s to 28 m/s. Calculate
      i) its change of velocity,
      ii) its acceleration.
   b) A vehicle travelling at a velocity of 24 m/s slowed down and stopped in 20 s. Calculate its deceleration.

4 The figure shows the velocity–time graph of a passenger jet before it took off.

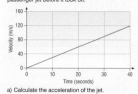

   a) Calculate the acceleration of the jet.
   b) Calculate the distance it travelled before it took off.
   [Higher]

194

EXAM-STYLE QUESTIONS

1 The graph shows how far a marathon runner travels during a race.

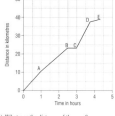

   (a) What was the distance of the race?
   (b) How long did it take the runner to complete the race?
   (c) What distance did the runner travel during the first 2 hours of the race?
   (d) For how long did the runner rest during the race?
   (e) Ignoring the time for which the runner was resting, between which two points was the runner moving the slowest?
       Give a reason for your answer

2 The table gives values of distance and time for a cyclist travelling along a straight road.

Distance in metres	0	20	40	60	80	100
Time in seconds	0	2	4	6	8	1

   (a) Draw a graph of distance against time. Two of the points have been plotted for you.

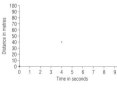

EXAM-STYLE ANSWERS

1 a) 38 km   *(1 mark)*

   b) 4.4 hours (4 hours 24 minutes)   *(1 mark)*

   c) 19 km   *(1 mark)*

   d) 30 minutes   *(1 mark)*

   e) Between D and E   *(1 mark)*
      Because the gradient is least between these points   *(1 mark)*

2 a) All points correctly plotted (lose 1 mark for each incorrect plot)
                                                              (2 marks)
      Drawing line of best fit through the points   *(1 mark)*

   b) Distance travelled = 50 m   *(1 mark)*

   c) Time at 30 m = 3 seconds   *(1 mark)*

   d) Moving at a steady speed   *(1 mark)*

3 a) i) Speed   *(1 mark)*
      ii) Continuous   *(1 mark)*

   b) i) Bar chart   *(1 mark)*
      ii) Control variable   *(1 mark)*

   c) Acceleration = slope   *(1 mark)*
      Acceleration = 40/16   *(1 mark)*
      Acceleration = 2.5 m/s²   *(2 marks)*

   d) Distance = area under graph   *(1 mark)*
      Distance = $\frac{1}{2} \times (32 - 22) \times 40$ *(1 mark)*
      Distance = 200 m   *(1 mark)*

b) Use your graph to find the distance travelled in 5 seconds. (1)

c) Use your graph to find the time at which the distance is 30 metres. (1)

d) Describe the motion of the cyclist. (1)

A van travels on a straight 'test-track' road. The graph shows how the speed of the van changes with time.

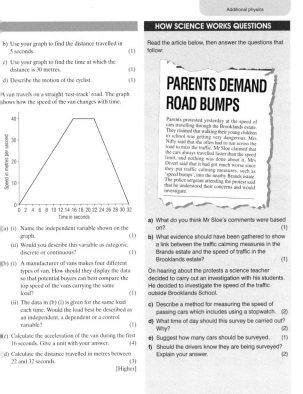

(a) (i) Name the independent variable shown on the graph. (1)

(ii) Would you describe this variable as categoric, discrete or continuous? (1)

(b) (i) A manufacturer of vans makes four different types of van. How should they display the data so that potential buyers can best compare the top speed of the vans carrying the same load? (1)

(ii) The data in (b) (i) is given for the same load each time. Would the load best be described as an independent, a dependent or a control variable? (1)

(c) Calculate the acceleration of the van during the first 16 seconds. Give a unit with your answer. (4)

(d) Calculate the distance travelled in metres between 22 and 32 seconds. (3)
[Higher]

HOW SCIENCE WORKS QUESTIONS

Read the article below, then answer the questions that follow:

PARENTS DEMAND ROAD BUMPS

Parents protested yesterday at the speed of cars travelling through the Brooklands estate. They claimed that walking their young children to school was getting very dangerous. Mrs Nifty said that she often had to run across the road to miss the traffic. Mr Sloe claimed that the cars always travelled faster than the speed limit, and nothing had been done about it. Mrs Divert said that it had got much worse since they put traffic calming measures, such as 'speed bumps', into the nearby Brands estate. The police sergeant attending the protest said that he understood their concerns and would investigate.

a) What do you think Mr Sloe's comments were based on? (1)

b) What evidence should have been gathered to show a link between the traffic calming measures in the Brands estate and the speed of traffic in the Brooklands estate? (1)

On hearing about the protests a science teacher decided to carry out an investigation with his students. He decided to investigate the speed of the traffic outside Brooklands School.

c) Describe a method for measuring the speed of passing cars which includes using a stopwatch. (2)

d) What time of day should this survey be carried out? Why? (2)

e) Suggest how many cars should be surveyed. (1)

f) Should the drivers know they are being surveyed? Explain your answer. (2)

195

HOW SCIENCE WORKS ANSWERS

a) Mr Sloe's comments were based on non-scientific evidence. It could be hearsay or even prejudice. It is unlikely that all cars exceeded the speed limit.

b) It is very difficult to prove a causal relationship in this situation. Evidence from both streets before and after the road bumps would have helped to identify a link.

c) Students could measure a distance on the road and time how long it takes for any car to travel that distance. There are accuracy issues in this that could be discussed.

d) Survey should be carried out at sample times at regular intervals during the day, suggest 10 minutes every hour.

e) As many cars as possible should be surveyed, but at least ten for each sample. A preliminary test could be used to find out how many cars need to be sampled and how often.

f) No, drivers should not know they are being surveyed. It might cause them to behave differently. This is part of a control in such surveys.

How science works teaching suggestions

- **Literacy guidance**
  - Key terms that should be clearly understood: hearsay, prejudice, link, preliminary test.
  - Questions b) and c) expect longer answers, where students can practise their literacy skills.

- **Higher- and lower-level answers.** Question e) is a higher-level question and the answer provided above is also at this level. Question a) is lower level and the answer provided is also lower level.

- **Gifted and talented.** Able students could try to produce a survey technique that would control as many variables as possible and take account of others.

- **How and when to use these questions.** When wishing to develop ideas around non-scientific evidence and survey evidence.
  The questions would best be discussed in small groups.

- **Homework.** Students could gather data concerning people's views on the speed of traffic in their neighbourhood.

- **ICT link-up.** Students might like to develop their ideas in the lab by using light gates as a mock-up of the real situation. (See e.g. www.rogerfrost.com.)

Exam teaching suggestions

- Students often confuse distance–time and velocity–time graphs in examinations. They should practise using and drawing graphs and checking the quantities, units and scales.

- All students should understand that the slope of a distance–time graph represents speed, the slope of a velocity–time graph represents acceleration and the area under a velocity–time graph represents distance travelled.

- Higher-tier students need to know how to calculate speed, acceleration and distance travelled from the appropriate graphs.

- Many students think that they can work out the slopes of graphs by counting the squares on the graph paper, rather than by using the scales provided.

- Students can be assured that they can make marks on graphs provided on the examination paper if it helps their calculation. They should be encouraged to use large triangles when calculating slopes and show clearly where they have taken their readings from.

P2 2.1   Forces between objects

Students should learn that:

- Forces between objects are equal and opposite.
- Fiction is a contact force between surfaces.
- The unit of force is the newton (N).

Most students should be able to:

- State that forces occur in equal and opposite pairs.
- Describe how frictional forces act between objects.

Some students should also be able to:

- Describe examples of equal and opposite forces acting when two objects interact.

Teaching suggestions

- **Gifted and talented.** Ask: 'What is the ideal launch angle of a projectile? Can you discover the ideal angle to fire a projectile and make it travel the furthest distance?' They need to design a launch system to make this investigation work.

- **Learning styles**

  Kinaesthetic: Skating to measure forces involved.

  Visual: Observing the action of forces on people.

  Auditory: Explaining how forces work in pairs.

  Interpersonal: Debating ways of describing energy.

  Intrapersonal: Making deductions about forces operating.

- **Homework.** Have the students describe how forces are used in various simple devices such as doors, tin openers, bicycles etc.

- **Teaching assistant.** Can your teaching assistant skate? Can you?

SPECIFICATION LINK-UP   Unit: Physics 2.13.2

- *Whenever two bodies interact the forces they exert on each other are equal and opposite.*

Lesson structure

STARTER

Picture the force – Show a set of diagrams of objects and ask the students to mark on all of the forces. Alternatively use Animation P2 2.1 'Pulling' from the Additional Science CD ROM. (5–10 minutes)

It's a drag – Show a video clip of a drag racer (search for drag racer at video.google.com) deploying parachutes to assist in braking. Ask the students to explain how the parachutes help to slow it down. (5 minutes)

Friction again – Demonstrate a trolley (or similar) rolling across the floor and ask the students to explain in detail why it stops. (5–10 minutes)

MAIN

- Some of the material here checks the students' understanding of basic forces; they need to be encouraged to draw clear diagrams of the forces acting on objects.

- It will help if the students have a clear understanding of what a one newton force feels like, so pass around a 100 g mass so they can get a feel for it. You could also give examples of very large forces (e.g. the force between the Sun and Earth) and very small forces (e.g. the force of attraction between adjacent students), to show the vast range of forces scientists deal with.

- The idea of equal and opposite forces needs to be reinforced with plenty of examples. Show a range of objects in equilibrium such as a boat, see saw, car rolling and identify the pairs of forces on diagrams. (Search for pictures at images.google.com.)

- The car stuck in mud situation is one where the forces do not appear to be equal and opposite. The force in the rope is clear (you can show this with a model) but this is not the only force at work. To analyse the situation more fully would require including the frictional forces and the forces exerted by the tractor on the Earth. As the car and tractor accelerate, the Earth is accelerated in the opposite direction by a tiny amount.

- You can demonstrate equal and opposite forces using skates (see 'Practical support') or by dragging objects along the floor with a string with newtonmeters at each end.

- It can be difficult to read moving newtonmeters, but the students will get the hang of it with practice. (This relates to 'How Science Works': making measurements and reliability.)

- When discussing the operation of wheels, you might like to go through some of the stages of the force being transferred to the wheel from the engine; especially with those interested in automotive engineering.

- To round off, you could show a car trying to accelerate too rapidly and skidding; this provides a visual answer to in-text question c). (Search for racing or skid at video.google.com.)

PLENARIES

The force is strong in which one? – Give the students a set of cards showing the size of the forces between objects (e.g force on a person due to the gravity of Earth, force produced by a tug of war team) and a description of the objects and ask them to match up the cards. (5–10 minutes)

Pulling power – Give the students cards describing ten (or more) players and ask them to assign them to two tug of war teams, so that the teams are balanced. There may be several solutions. (5 minutes)

Use the force loop – This is a simple loop card game, with questions about forces, friction and movement. (5 minutes)

Practical support

Action and reaction
This makes an interesting demonstration, but skateboards may be more in fashion.

Equipment and materials required
Two sets of roller skates or skateboards, full sets of safety equipment (helmet, pads etc.) a connecting rope, two newtonmeters.

Details
The students should firstly demonstrate the effect of pushing each other. If student A pushes student B forwards gently, then student A should move backwards. If the students are roughly the same size and the skates are similar, then you could show that they both move the same distance before friction stops them. One student can then try to pull the other with a rope; they should both move closer. Measuring the forces to show that they are identical in size is trickier; the rope becomes slack. You might want to pull a skater around instead and take force measurements at both ends of the rope.

P2 2.1 Forces between objects

LEARNING OBJECTIVES
1 When two objects interact, what can we say about the forces acting?
2 What is the unit of force?

Equal and opposite forces
Whenever two objects push or pull on each other, they exert equal and opposite forces on one another. The unit of force is the newton (abbreviated N).

- A boxer who punches an opponent with a force of 100 N experiences a reverse force of 100 N from his opponent.
- Two roller skaters pull on opposite ends of a rope. The skaters move towards each other. This is because they pull on each other with equal and opposite forces. Two newtonmeters could be used to show this.

Figure 1 Equal and opposite forces

FOUL FACTS
Quicksand victims sink because they can't get enough support from the sand. The force of gravity on the victim (acting downwards) is greater than the upwards force of the sand on the victim. Sometimes the incoming tide drowns the victim!

PRACTICAL
Action and reaction
Test this with a friend if you can, using roller skates and two newtonmeters. Don't forget to wear protective head gear!

- What did you find out?
- Comment on the accuracy of your readings.

a) A hammer hits a nail with a downward force of 50 N. What is the size and direction of the force of the nail on the hammer?

In the mud
A car stuck in mud can be difficult to shift. A tractor can be very useful here. Figure 2 shows the idea. At any stage, the force of the rope on the car is equal and opposite to the force of the car on the rope.

To pull the car out of the mud, the force of the ground on the tractor needs to be greater than the force of the mud on the car. These two forces aren't necessarily equal to one another because the objects are not the same.

Pull of rope on car = Pull of car on rope
Force of ground on tractor is greater than force of mud on car
Figure 2 In the mud

b) A lorry tows a broken-down car. When the force of the lorry on the tow rope is 200 N, what is the force of the tow rope on the lorry?

Friction in action
The motive force on a car is the force that makes it move. This force is due to friction between the ground and the tyre of each drive wheel. Friction acts where the tyre is in contact with the ground.

Figure 3 Motive force
Direction of car
Force of tyre on road   Force of road on tyre

When the car moves forwards:
- the force of friction of the ground on the tyre is in the forward direction,
- the force of friction of the tyre on the ground is in the reverse direction.

The two forces are equal and opposite to one another.

c) What happens if there isn't enough friction between the tyre and the ground?

SUMMARY QUESTIONS
1 Complete the sentences below using words from the list.

    downwards   equal   opposite   upwards

a) The force on a ladder resting against a wall is ...... and ...... to the force of the wall on the ladder.
b) A book is at rest on a table. The force of the book on the table is .... The force of the table on the book is ....

2 When a student is standing at rest on bathroom scales, the scales read 500 N.

a) What is the size and direction of the force of the student on the scales?
b) What is the size and direction of the force of the scales on the student?

KEY POINTS
1 When two objects interact, they always exert equal and opposite forces on each other.
2 The unit of force is the newton.

SUMMARY ANSWERS

1 a) Equal, opposite.
  b) Downwards, upwards.

2 a) 500 N downwards.
  b) 500 N upwards.

FOUL FACTS

Quicksand
On average, quicksand is actually more dense than the human body so it is difficult to sink in it further than your chest even if you panic. Survival guides suggest the following method of escape. Stay calm; if you don't struggle you *will* float. Slowly adjust your position so you are lying on your back and then wiggle your legs gently in a circular motion. You will crawl towards the edge. Don't get your friends to pull you out vertically; this apparently takes a very large force. It may be possible to investigate this with a cornflower based practical. (See activity and extension ideas.)

Answers to in-text questions

a) 50 N upwards.
b) 200 N
c) The wheels slip on the ground.

KEY POINTS

Ask the students to complete a range of diagrams demonstrating balanced forces.

P2 2.2

Resultant force

Students should learn:

- How to find the resultant force on an object.
- That a zero resultant force does not cause acceleration.
- That a non-zero resultant force causes acceleration.

LEARNING OUTCOMES

Most students should be able to:

- Find the resultant force acting on an object when there are two forces acting in the same direction or in opposite directions.
- Describe how the resultant force will affect the movement of the object.
- Describe examples where an object acted on by two forces is at rest or in uniform motion.

Some students should be able to:

- Describe examples where the motion of an object acted on by two forces along the same line is changed by the action of the forces.

Teaching suggestions

- **Special needs.** Provide diagrams of objects so that the students can add force arrows and information about how the forces affect movement.
- **Gifted and talented**
  Forces at angles
  Some students may have studied vectors in mathematics and they could be challenged to find the resultant of two forces that are not in line. Start with a pair of perpendicular forces and see if the students can determine the magnitude and direction of the resultant using Pythagoras's theorem. Those talented in mathematics may be able to look into sets of forces that are not perpendicular.
- **Learning styles**
  Kinaesthetic: Making hovercraft and rockets.
  Visual: Observing the movement of objects with and without resultant forces acting on them.
  Auditory: Explaining the actions of forces on objects.
  Interpersonal: Discussing experimental observations.
  Intrapersonal: Evaluating their rocket design.
- **ICT link-up.** Use a distance sensor to monitor the movement of the air track glider.

SPECIFICATION LINK-UP   Unit: Physics 2.13.2

- *A number of forces acting on a body may be replaced by a single force that has the same effect on the body as the original forces all acting together. The force is called the 'resultant force'.*
- *If the resultant force acting on a stationary body is zero, the body will remain stationary.*
- *If the resultant force acting on a stationary body is not zero, the body will accelerate in the direction of the resultant force.*
- *If the resultant force acting on a moving body is zero, the body will continue to move at the same speed and in the same direction.*
- *If the resultant force acting on a moving body is not zero, the body will accelerate in the direction of the resultant force.*

Lesson structure

STARTER

Why do things stop? – Ask the students to explain why they think that a football kicked across a field eventually stops. (10 minutes)

Balanced forces – Show the students a toy boat floating on water and ask them to draw a diagram of all of the forces on the boat. Add small masses, one at a time, until the boat sinks. Ask them to draw a diagram showing the forces at the time when the boat was sinking. (5 minutes)

Mad maths – Give the students an addition sum that includes negative numbers to check their understanding. (5 minutes)

MAIN

- The calculation of resultant forces is generally easy when limited to one direction. The students must take care about the directions of the forces as some can get confused and simply add all of the numbers together.
- It is well worth making the hovercraft, but remember that the glue will take some time to cool so do this bit early.
- Demonstrating a linear air track is a good way of showing motion without friction, and it can help the students get to grips with the idea that objects only slow down because of the friction.
- If you have footage of a jet plane taking off, use it to discuss the forces involved. If it is of an aircraft carrier launch system, you can point out the extra force applied by the steam catapult and ask why this is necessary. (Search for 'jet plane' at video.google.com.)
- An aeroplane cruising is a good example of balanced forces. The students can draw a diagram and discuss the sensations they feel when they are in a plane like this. Because the forces are balanced, the students should feel no acceleration. If they close their eyes they would not be able to tell they were moving at all.
- Be careful that the students do not think that the force applied to the pedal is the actual braking force applied to the wheels. If this were the case, then a car would take a lot longer to stop.
- If the glue is set, then this is a good time to go back to the hovercraft. They should glide well on flat desks. Get the students to explain why they float; perhaps as a diagram.

PLENARIES

It's a tug o' war – Show the students a video of a tug of war (search for 'tug of war' at video.google.com); ask them to work out who will win by calculating the resultant forces. (10 minutes)

An uphill struggle – Ask: 'Why is it harder to push a car uphill rather than on a flat road? Is it easier to drag a piano up a ramp rather than up stairs? Why?' (10 minutes)

Hovercraft acrostic – Students write a short poem about how hovercrafts work based on the letters in the word 'hovercraft' and the ideas they have about forces. (5–10 minutes)

ACTIVITY & EXTENSION IDEAS

Water rockets

These are available as kits or can be improvised from plastic bottles.

Equipment and materials required

Foot pump, 1 litre plastic bottle (screw on top), launch rod, card for fins and possibly nose cone.

Details

- The bottles should be fitted with three equally spaced triangular stabilising fins made from stiff card. They also need a little loop so they can be placed upright from a pole stuck in the ground for launching. The trickiest part is fitting the pump to the cap so that pressure can be built up in the bottle before the connection pops off. You will have to experiment with this to get it just right.
- Fill the bottle about ⅓ full of water and screw on the cap. Stand well back and pump up the pressure until the rocket launches spraying water everywhere. The rockets can reach heights of over 30 m so try to do this well away from roofs, as they seem to have a guidance system targeted on them. If time and several sets of equipment are available, you could let the students build their own (good homework) and have a competition as to which will fly the furthest. The students can change the launch angle (measured with a clinometer) and the amount of water in the rocket to find the optimum combination. This can be used to reinforce ideas from 'How Science Works', particularly the design of investigations.

Linear air track

Equipment and materials required

Linear air track, glider, elastic bands, light gates (optional).

Details

Set the track up so that it is horizontal and has an elastic buffer on both ends. If you are using light gates, set these up so that the glider has to pass through and cut the beam. Position a glider carefully in the middle of the track and turn the air on. If you have balanced the track it should stay still. Nudge it slightly to show that an unbalanced force accelerates it. The collisions with the buffers are nearly elastic and so the glider should stay at the same speed even after bouncing. This can be checked with the light gates or by simply timing the trolley between bumps.

Practical support

Investigating forces

Hovercraft are fun to make. There are various designs but this one uses an old CD.

Equipment and materials required

Balloons and balloon pump, old CD, thick paper, 'sports bottle' top and glue gun.

Details

Glue the sports bottle top onto the centre of the CD with the glue gun so that it covers the hole making sure that the seal around the edge is good. Let this cool for at least ten minutes. Blow up the balloon and carefully pull the end over the bottle top so that the air will be released through the base of the CD. The CD will act like a hovercraft. It is vastly improved by fixing a cylinder of paper around the top edge of the CD so that it holds the balloon vertically and stops it dragging on the desk. You should be able to blow up the balloon while it is still attached to the CD. Searching the Internet will yield a range of designs and pictures to help with this activity.

Answers to in-text questions

a) It stops because friction between the glider and the track is no longer zero.

b) The crate would slide across the floor after being given a brief push.

c) They are equal and opposite to each other.

d) It would have been greater.

SUMMARY ANSWERS

1 a) Less than. b) Greater than. c) Equal to.

2 a) It acts in the opposite direction to the direction in which the plane moves.
   b) It is zero.

PHYSICS   SPEEDING UP AND SLOWING DOWN

P2 2.2   Resultant force

LEARNING OBJECTIVES

1 What is a resultant force?
2 What happens if the resultant force on an object is zero?
3 What happens if the resultant force on an object is not zero?

Most objects around you are acted on by more than one force. We can work out the effect of the forces on an object by replacing them with a single force, the **resultant force**. This is a single force that has the same effect as all the forces acting on the object.

When the resultant force on an object is zero, the object:
- remains stationary if it was at rest, or
- continues to move at the same speed and in the same direction if it was already moving.

PRACTICAL

Investigating forces

Make and test a model hovercraft floating on a cushion of air from a balloon, and/or
Use a glider on an air track to investigate the relationship between force and acceleration.

- What relationship do you find between force and acceleration?
  (See pages 280–1.)

1 **A glider on a linear air track** floats on a cushion of air. Provided the track is level, the glider moves at constant velocity (i.e. with no change of speed or direction) along the track because friction is absent. The resultant force on the glider is zero.

Figure 1 The linear air track

a) What happens to the glider if the air track blower is switched off, and why?

2 **When a heavy crate is pushed across a rough floor at constant velocity,** the resultant force on the crate is zero. The push force on the crate is equal in size but acts in the opposite direction to the force of friction of the floor on the crate.

b) What difference would it make if the floor were smooth?

Figure 2 Overcoming friction

When the resultant force on an object is not zero, the movement of the object depends on the size and direction of the resultant force.

1 **When a jet plane is taking off,** the thrust force of its engines is greater than the force of air resistance on it. The resultant force on it is the difference between the thrust force and the force of air resistance on it. The resultant force is therefore non-zero. The greater the resultant force, the quicker the take-off is.

Figure 3 A passenger jet on take-off

c) What can you say about the thrust force and the force of air resistance when the plane is moving at constant velocity at constant height?

2 **When a car driver applies the brakes,** the braking force is the resultant force on the car. It acts in the opposite direction to that in which the car is moving, so it slows the car down.

d) What can you say about the resultant force if the brakes had been applied harder?

Figure 4 Braking

NEXT TIME YOU...

...are in a plane, think about the forces that are operating when you are taking off. What happens when a plane is taking off into a strong head wind?

KEY POINTS

	Object at the start	Resultant force	Effect on the object
1	at rest	zero	stays at rest
2	moving	zero	velocity stays the same
3	moving	non-zero in the same direction as the direction of motion of the object	accelerates
4	moving	non-zero in the opposite direction to the direction of motion of the object	decelerates

SUMMARY QUESTIONS

1 Complete the following sentences using words from the list.

   greater than   less than   equal to

A car starts from rest and accelerates along a straight flat road.

a) The force of air resistance on it is ...... the motive force of its engine.
b) The resultant force is ...... zero.
c) The downward force of the car on the road is ...... the support force of the road on the car.

2 A jet plane lands on a runway and stops.

a) What can you say about the direction of the resultant force on the plane as it lands?
b) What can you say about the resultant force on the plane when it has stopped?

GET IT RIGHT!

Remember that if a body is accelerating it can be speeding up, slowing down or changing direction. If a body is accelerating there must be a resultant force acting on it.

198

199

P2 2.3 Force and acceleration

Teaching suggestions

- **Gifted and talented**
  - See the more detailed acceleration investigation in the activity box.
  - Ask: 'Why doesn't the snooker table move when a ball hits the cushion?'

- **Learning styles**

  Kinaesthetic: Doing practical tasks.

  Visual: Recording experimental data.

  Auditory: Explaining the cause of friction.

  Interpersonal: Working together in small groups to generate data.

  Intrapersonal: Evaluating experimental technique.

- **ICT link-up.** A range of good simulations of force experiments are available. (See www.sunflowerlearning.com.)

SPECIFICATION LINK-UP   Unit: Physics 2.13.2

- *Force, mass and acceleration are related by the equation:*

  $$\text{resultant force} = \text{mass} \times \text{acceleration}$$
  $$\text{(newton, N)} \quad \text{(kilogram, kg)} \quad \text{(metre/second}^2\text{, m/s}^2\text{)}$$

- *If the resultant force acting on a moving body is zero, the body will continue to move at the same speed and in the same direction.*

- *If the resultant force acting on a moving body is not zero, the body will accelerate in the direction of the resultant force.*

Lesson structure

STARTER

Accelerator – Ask: 'What does the accelerator in a car do? How do you think it works?' (5–10 minutes)

Friction revision – Ask: 'Why do snooker balls stop rolling after being hit?' Ask the students to describe the ways that the initial kinetic energy is lost. (5 minutes)

Lift off – Show the students footage of a chemical rocket launch and ask them to describe as much of what is happening as possible using accurate scientific language. (10 minutes)

MAIN

- A DVD showing a snooker match is a very useful resource (a real table would be great!). You can use it to discuss what is happening to the balls during impact and their movement across the green baize. Remind the students that there are frictional forces at work.

- Pause the play and discuss the forces at work at each stage. With a data projector you can even draw force arrows over the action on your whiteboard. Show clips where the balls are moving in opposite directions and hit each other causing them to recoil. This can be used to illustrate forces in the opposite direction to motion, causing objects to decelerate or even accelerate in the other direction.

- The experiments can be simple or quite detailed depending on the time you have available. They produce quite a bit of data and can produce an excellent analysis task. The students should be encouraged to notice the limitations of the experiments and suggest improvements. As such, there are plenty of opportunities to cover 'How Science Works' concepts.

- As this is another fairly mathematically intensive topic, you will have to spend time on checking the students' ability to use the equation. As usual, encourage a rigorous layout to increase the chances of a correct answer.

- Finally watch out for students thinking that a moving object will always be moving in the direction of the resultant force. They need to understand that the object could be moving in the opposite direction, but slowing down.

PLENARIES

What's wrong? – Ask the students to correct this sentence: 'Objects always move in the direction of the resultant force.' (5 minutes)

I'm snookered – The students must draw a series of diagrams showing the forces involved in getting out of 'a snooker', where the object ball, the blue, is behind the pink. (10 minutes)

The tipping point – Show a diagram of a person trying to push a large box by shoving the top edge. Ask the students to explain why this would not work well and what should be done instead. (5 minutes)

✎ Practical support

Investigating force and acceleration

This is a simple experiment, except for keeping the force constant; the alternative (see activity box) is more accurate but needs more equipment.

Equipment and materials required

For each group: dynamics trolley, string, masses (similar to trolley mass), stopwatch and possibly motion sensor or light gates.

Details

The students pull the trolley along attempting to use a constant force by watching the newtonmeter. They should pull the trolley along a track of known distance so that they can compare the acceleration easily. If insufficient trolleys are available to double up, then just let the students add masses roughly equivalent to that of the trolley.

More investigating force and acceleration

In this experiment, the students can discover the effect of different forces on acceleration or the effect of the objects mass.

Equipment and materials required

For each group: dynamics trolley (or similar), string, pulley, clamp, $10 \times 20\,g$ masses and mass holder, stopwatch and possibly motion sensor or light gates.

Details

- The students mount the pulley over the end of the desks. One end of the string is attached to the mass holder (which hangs down) and the other to the trolley. The mass is released and falls to the floor pulling the trolley with a constant force. With larger masses you will need to protect the floor and students' feet.

- The movement of the trolley can be monitored by a motion sensor, or the time it takes to move between two marked points can be recorded. The students can load the mass holder with different masses to increase the force on the trolley in order to investigate the effect of the size of the force on the acceleration. (This relates to: 'How Science Works': relationships between variables.) Some may even look into the effect of the mass of the trolley by loading it up with increasing mass and accelerating it with a fixed force. By analysing graphs and discovering that a is proportional to F and a is also inversely proportional to m, higher attaining students could link the concepts together to reach $F = ma$.

P2 2.3   Force and acceleration

LEARNING OBJECTIVES

1 How does the acceleration of an object depend on the size of the resultant force?
2 What effect does the mass of the object have on its acceleration?

PRACTICAL

Investigating force and acceleration

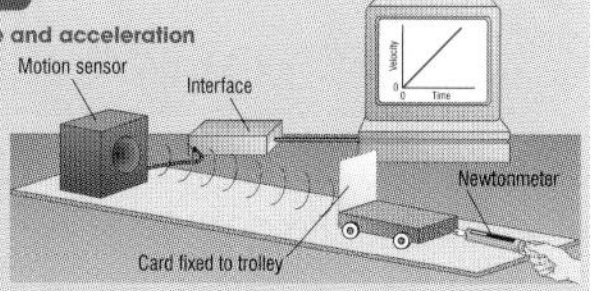

Figure 1 Investigating the link between force and motion

We can use the apparatus above to accelerate a trolley with a constant force. Use the newtonmeter to pull the trolley along with a constant force.

You can double or treble the total moving mass by using double-deck and triple-deck trolleys.

A motion sensor and a computer record the velocity of the trolley as it accelerates.

- What are the advantages of using a data logger and computer in this investigation?

You can display the results as a velocity–time graph on the computer screen.

Figure 2 shows velocity–time graphs for different masses. You can work out the acceleration from the gradient of the line, as explained on page 191.

Look at some typical results in the table below:

Resultant force (newtons)	0.5	1.0	1.5	2.0	4.0	6.0
Mass (kilograms)	1.0	1.0	1.0	2.0	2.0	2.0
Acceleration (m/s²)	0.5	1.0	1.5	1.0	2.0	3.0
Mass × acceleration (kg m/s²)	0.5	1.0	1.5	2.0	4.0	6.0

The results show that the resultant force, the mass and the acceleration are linked by the equation

resultant force = mass × acceleration
(newtons, N)   (kilograms)   (metres/second²)

	Force (N)	Mass (kg)
	1.0	0.5
	1.0	1.0
	1.0	2.0

Figure 2 Velocity–time graph for different combinations of force and masses

Worked example
Calculate the resultant force on an object of mass 6.0 kg when it has an acceleration of 3.0 m/s².

Solution
Resultant force = mass × acceleration = $6.0\,kg \times 3.0\,m/s^2 = 18.0\,N$

a) Calculate the resultant force on a sprinter of mass 50 kg who accelerates at 8 m/s².

Maths notes

We can write the word equation on the previous page as:
Resultant force, $F = ma$,
    where m = mass and a = acceleration.
Rearranging this equation gives $a = \dfrac{F}{m}$ or $m = \dfrac{F}{a}$

Worked example
Calculate the acceleration of an object of mass 5.0 kg acted on by a resultant force of 40 N.

Solution
Rearranging $F = ma$ gives $a = \dfrac{F}{m} = \dfrac{40\,N}{5.0\,kg} = 8.0\,m/s^2$

b) Calculate the acceleration of a car of mass 800 kg acted on by a resultant force of 3200 N.

Speeding up or slowing down

If the velocity of an object changes, it must be acted on by a resultant force. Its acceleration is always in the same direction as the resultant force.

- The velocity of the object increases if the resultant force is in the **same** direction as the velocity. We say its acceleration is positive because it is in the same direction as its velocity.
- The velocity of the object decreases (i.e. it decelerates) if the resultant force is **opposite** in direction. We say its acceleration is negative because it is opposite in direction to its velocity.

KEY POINTS

Resultant force $=$ mass $\times$ acceleration
(newtons, N)   (kilograms)   (metres/second²)

SUMMARY QUESTIONS

1 Complete a) to c) using the words below:

acceleration   resultant force   mass   velocity

a) A moving object decelerates when a ...... acts on it in the opposite direction to its ....
b) The greater the ...... of an object, the less its acceleration when a ...... acts on it.
c) The ...... of a moving object increases when a ...... acts on it in the same direction as it is moving in.

2 Copy and complete the following table:

	a)	b)	c)	d)	e)
Force (newtons, N)	?	200	840	?	5000
Mass (kilograms, kg)	20	?	70	0.40	?
Acceleration (metre/second squared, m/s²)	0.80	5.0	?	6.0	0.20

FOUL FACTS

If you're in a car that suddenly brakes, your neck pulls on your head and slows it down. The equal and opposite force of your head on your neck can injure your neck.

Figure 3 A 'whiplash' injury

GET IT RIGHT!
If an object is accelerating there must be a resultant force acting on it.

SUMMARY ANSWERS

1 a) Resultant force, velocity.

  b) Mass, resultant force.

  c) Acceleration, resultant force.

2 a) 16 N

  b) 40 kg

  c) 12 m/s²

  d) 2.4 N

  e) 25 000 kg

Answers to in-text questions

a) 400 N

b) 4.0 m/s²

KEY POINTS

The students should complete a range of calculations using $F = ma$. This could be as a whole class or a loop game.

P2 2.4

On the road

LEARNING OBJECTIVES

Students should learn:

- That the resultant force on a vehicle travelling at constant velocity is zero.
- About the factors that affect the thinking distance of vehicles.
- About the factors that affect the braking distance of stopping vehicles.

LEARNING OUTCOMES

Most students should be able to:

- Use a chart to find the stopping distance, the braking distance and the thinking distance at a given speed.
- List and describe the factors that affect the stopping distance of a vehicle.
- Explain which are the most important factors for cars moving at a range of speeds.

Some students should also be able to:

- Differentiate between factors that affect the thinking distance, braking distance or both distances.

Teaching suggestions

- **Special needs.** Allow the students to use an experiment template with clear instructions and a results table during the practical task.

- **Learning styles**
  Kinaesthetic: Measuring reaction time.
  Visual: Obtaining accurate measurements.
  Auditory: Listening out for the key word.
  Interpersonal: Collaborating with others in practical work.
  Intrapersonal: Reviewing and evaluating results.

- **Homework.** The students could find out the facts about road deaths in the UK and their local area. Ask: 'What measures have been taken to reduce them?'

- **ICT link-up.** A fairly simple spreadsheet can be used to model stopping distances. This can incorporate speed, reaction times and surface conditions and will quantify how much effect each of these conditions has.

- **Teaching assistant.** Have the teaching assistant help out with the practical and also support those who have difficulty plotting graphs.

SPECIFICATION LINK-UP   Unit: Physics 2.13.2

- *When a vehicle travels at a steady speed the frictional forces balance the driving force.*
- *The greater the speed of a vehicle the greater the braking force needed to stop it in a certain distance.*
- *The stopping distance of a vehicle depends on the distance the vehicle travels during the driver's reaction time and the distance it travels under the braking force.*
- *A driver's reaction time can be affected by tiredness, drugs and alcohol.*
- *A vehicle's braking distance can be affected by adverse road and weather conditions and poor condition of the vehicle.*

Lesson structure

STARTER

Stop! – Ask the students to sort a set of cards about things which may or may not affect stopping distances for cars. (5 minutes)

Chances – Give the students a set of cards describing likely injuries and ask them to match them to car speeds in collisions. (5 minutes)

MAIN

- Video clips of vehicles braking and skidding make this topic more visually stimulating. (Search for video clips at video.google.com.)

- When discussing reaction times, you could try a simple experiment in concentration. At the beginning of the lesson give the students an unusual key word and ask them to put their hands up as quickly as possible whenever they hear it. Early in the lesson they will be quite quick but later, as their concentration flags, they will struggle.

- You could ask the students to evaluate the data used to produce the stopping distance chart. It is based on an alert driver, driving a medium-sized car, but it does not take into account the improved braking systems of modern cars and the increase in the size (mass) of the average car. This can lead to a discussion of whether large cars are safer or more dangerous to passengers and pedestrians.

- The students should understand the factors affecting overall stopping distance, but they need to be clear which affects the thinking distance and which affects the braking distance.

- The braking distance really depends on the kinetic energy of the car and the frictional force between the car and road. You can link these concepts with $F = ma$ from the previous topic and again with kinetic energy in lesson 3.2.

- Note that the speed of the car affects thinking and braking distance so it is the most important factor overall.

- Testing reaction time rounds the lesson off well, you can try the simple or advanced versions or even use driving simulation software. (This relates to 'How Science Works': reliability and validity of evidence.)

PLENARIES

I said stop! – Using the cards from the starter, students have to separate those that were correct into ones that affect thinking distance and ones that affect braking distance. Ask: 'Do some affect both?' Students could put them in order of importance for a car travelling at 30 m.p.h. (5–10 minutes)

Expect the unexpected – Use the unusual key word one more time as the students are packing away. (1 minute)

ACTIVITY & EXTENSION IDEAS

Advanced reaction times

It is possible to try out a more advanced version of the reaction times activity; one more like driving a car. It requires a bit more equipment but is more exciting.

Equipment and materials required

Stopwatch with electronic inputs to start and stop, comfy chair, two pedals, microphone.

Details

You need to make two pedals; the accelerator and the brake. These can be a couple of planks of wood connected with a hinge and then a strong spring to keep them apart. A switch, or micro switch is positioned so that pressing the planks together closes it. You may need to put a block of wood between the planks to ensure that the switch does not get crushed by over-enthusiastic students. The start input of the stopwatch should be connected to a microphone so that the clock starts when you shout. The brake should have a switch that stops the clock when pressed. The 'driver' sits in the comfy chair with his/her foot resting on the accelerator pedal. Stand behind the driver; let them relax for a while and then shout 'boo'. The driver needs to press the stop pedal as fast as possible and the stopwatch should show the reaction time. The switch on the accelerator can be connected to a light to ensure that no cheating goes on. You can also test to see if reactions improve with practice or are better with sound (bangs) than light (flashing bulbs).

Practical support

Testing reaction times

This is a fairly simple activity only requiring a stopwatch with separate start and lap-time buttons.

Equipment and materials required

Stopwatches.

Details

The students can try the simple activity and see the wide range of response times. They should appreciate that the times improve with practice and when they are fully concentrating on the clock. In a real car situation, the driver would not be able to focus on one simple task so the times would be significantly greater. For a more advanced suggestion, see the activity box.

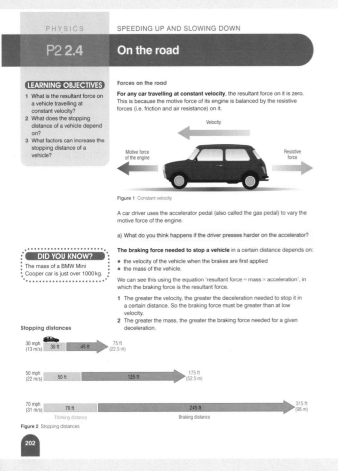

PHYSICS · SPEEDING UP AND SLOWING DOWN

P2 2.4 On the road

LEARNING OBJECTIVES

1 What is the resultant force on a vehicle travelling at constant velocity?
2 What does the stopping distance of a vehicle depend on?
3 What factors can increase the stopping distance of a vehicle?

Forces on the road

For any car travelling at constant velocity, the resultant force on it is zero. This is because the motive force of its engine is balanced by the resistive forces (i.e. friction and air resistance) on it.

Figure 1 Constant velocity

A car driver uses the accelerator pedal (also called the gas pedal) to vary the motive force of the engine.

a) What do you think happens if the driver presses harder on the accelerator?

DID YOU KNOW?

The mass of a BMW Mini Cooper car is just over 1000 kg.

The braking force needed to stop a vehicle in a certain distance depends on:
• the velocity of the vehicle when the brakes are first applied
• the mass of the vehicle.

We can see this using the equation 'resultant force = mass × acceleration', in which the braking force is the resultant force.

1 The greater the velocity, the greater the deceleration needed to stop it in a certain distance. So the braking force must be greater than at low velocity.
2 The greater the mass, the greater the braking force needed for a given deceleration.

Stopping distances

Figure 2 Stopping distances

202

Driving tests always ask about stopping distances. This is the shortest distance a vehicle can safely stop in, and is in two parts:

• **The thinking distance:** the distance travelled by the vehicle in the time it takes the driver to react (i.e. during the driver's reaction time).
• **The braking distance:** the distance travelled by the vehicle during the time the braking force acts.

The stopping distance = the thinking distance + the braking distance.

Figure 2 shows the stopping distance for a vehicle on a dry flat road travelling at different speeds. Check for yourself that the stopping distance at 31 m/s (70 miles per hour) is 96 m.

b) What are the thinking distance, the braking distance and the stopping distance at 13 m/s (30 mph)?

Factors affecting stopping distances

1 **Tiredness, alcohol and drugs** all increase reaction times. So they increase the thinking distance (because thinking distance = speed × reaction time). Therefore, the stopping distance is greater.
2 **The faster a vehicle is travelling**, the further it travels before it stops. This is because the thinking distance and the braking distance both increase with increased speed.
3 **In adverse road conditions**, for example on wet or icy roads, drivers have to brake with less force to avoid skidding. Stopping distances are therefore greater in poor road conditions.
4 **Poorly maintained vehicles**, for example with worn brakes or tyres, take longer to stop because the brakes and tyres are less effective.

c) Why are stopping distances greater in poor visibility?

Figure 3 Stopping distances are further than you might think!

PRACTICAL

Reaction times

Use an electronic stopwatch to test your own reaction time under different conditions in an investigation. Ask a friend to start the stopwatch when you are looking at it with your finger on the stop button. The read-out from the watch will give you your reaction time.

• How can you make your data as reliable as possible?
• What conclusions can you draw?

SUMMARY QUESTIONS

1 Each of the following factors affects the thinking distance or the braking distance of a vehicle. Which of these two distances is affected in each case below?
   a) The road surface condition affects the ...... distance.
   b) The tiredness of a driver increases his or her ...... distance.
   c) Poorly maintained brakes affects the ...... distance.
2 a) Use the chart in Figure 2 to work out, in metres, the increase in i) the thinking distance, ii) the braking distance, iii) the stopping distance from 13 m/s (30 mph) to 22 m/s (50 mph). (1 foot = 0.30 m.)
   b) A driver has a reaction time of 0.8 s. Calculate her thinking distance at a speed of i) 15 m/s, ii) 30 m/s.

KEY POINTS

1 The thinking distance is the distance travelled by the vehicle in the time it takes the driver to react.
2 The braking distance is the distance the vehicle travels under the braking force.
3 The stopping distance = the thinking distance + the braking distance.

203

SUMMARY ANSWERS

1 a) Braking. b) Thinking. c) Braking.

2 a) i) 6 m ii) 24 m iii) 30 m
  b) i) 12 m ii) 24 m

Answers to in-text questions

a) The car speeds up.

b) 9 m, 13.5 m, 22.5 m.

c) The reaction time of the driver is longer because the road ahead is more difficult to see.

KEY POINTS

Can the students make a list of the factors that affect stopping distances and describe the effect of each factor?

P2 2.5

Falling objects

LEARNING OBJECTIVES

Students should learn:

- That the mass of an object is a measure of the material in the object while its weight is the force acting on that object due to its being in a gravitational field.
- The mass of the object is a constant value while the weight depends on the strength of the gravitational field it is in.
- That when an object falls through a fluid, it accelerates until the gravitational force is balanced by frictional forces and this velocity is called the terminal velocity.

LEARNING OUTCOMES

Most students should be able to:

- Explain the difference between mass and weight.
- Calculate the weight of an object of a given mass.
- Describe the forces acting on an object falling through a fluid like air or water, and how these forces affect the acceleration of the object.
- Describe how the velocity of an object released from rest in a fluid changes as it falls.
- Explain why an object reaches a terminal velocity and describe some of the factors that determine this velocity.

Some students should also be able to:

- Explain the motion of an object released from rest falling through a fluid including how the acceleration decreases and becomes zero at terminal velocity.

Teaching suggestions

- **Special needs.** Allow the students to use an experiment template with clear instructions and a results table during the practical task.
- **Learning styles**
  Kinaesthetic: Performing parachute experiments.
  Visual: Obtaining accurate measurements.
  Auditory: Explaining the cause of friction.
  Interpersonal: Collaborating with others in practical work.
  Intrapersonal: Reviewing and evaluating results.

SPECIFICATION LINK-UP   Unit: Physics 2.13.2

Candidates should know and understand:

- *The faster a body moves through a fluid the greater the frictional force that acts on it.*
- *A body falling through a fluid will initially accelerate due to the force of gravity. Eventually the resultant force on the body will be zero and it will fall at its terminal velocity.*

Students should use their skills, knowledge and understanding of 'How Science Works':

- *to calculate the weight of a body using:*

$$\begin{array}{ccc} \text{weight} & = & \text{mass} & \times \text{gravitational field strength} \\ \text{(newton,N)} & & \text{(kilogram, kg)} & \text{(newton/kilogram, N/kg)} \end{array}$$

- *to draw and interpret velocity–time graphs for bodies that reach terminal velocity, including a consideration of the forces acting on the body.*

Lesson structure

STARTER

Air resistance – What causes air or water resistance? The students need to use their understanding of particles and forces to give a description. (5–10 minutes)

Fluid facts – Give the students cards with information about the physical properties and the explanations in terms of particle behaviour for solids, liquids and gases and ask them to match them up. (5 minutes)

Nobody expects the . . . – key word. See if the students have remembered it from the last topic. How are their reactions now? (2 minutes)

MAIN

- Video clips of falling objects are ideal for this topic, in particular clips of parachutists. (Search for video clips of parachutes at video.google.com.)
- Weight and mass are commonly confused. Let the students handle a 1 kg mass and emphasise that the '1 kg' is the material in the block and this will not change just because you take it to the Moon.
- Weigh the mass and explain that the weight is the force that is pulling it towards the centre of the Earth. If there were less gravity then this force would be less.
- There are a couple of phrases used to describe 'the strength of gravity' and these are sometimes interchanged. Try to stick to 'gravitational field strength' and explain that there is a 'field' around the Earth where its gravity affects other objects. The students should accept this field idea after discussing the effect of a magnetic field on magnetic material close by.
- It may have been a while since the students have used the term 'fluid'; remind them that all liquids and gases are fluid so all motion we see on the Earth is motion through fluids.
- Air resistance is easy to show by throwing various sized bits of paper around, some scrunched some not.
- It is very common for students to believe that when the parachute is opened the sky diver 'shoots upwards'. This is an illusion caused by the fact that the cameraman has not opened her parachute and so continues to fall while the skydiver that has opened his parachute slows rapidly. You can compare this to two cars driving side by side when one suddenly brakes.
- When discussing terminal velocity, point out that this depends on the shape, or aerodynamics, of the object falling. A skydiver can adjust his shape and change speeds. Also point out that with the parachute open, there is still a terminal velocity but this is much less than the one without the parachute opened.
- Use Simulation P2 2.5 provided on the Additional Science CD ROM.

PLENARIES

Falling forces – The students should draw a comic strip with stick figures showing the forces at various stages of a parachute jump. (10 minutes)

Charity jump poster – Students can draw a poster encouraging people to jump out of an aeroplane; the poster must explain the science of falling though air. (15–20 minutes)

ACTIVITY & EXTENSION

Falling with style – Skydivers are able to change speed during their flight by altering their body position. The students could put together a brief presentation showing the divers doing this. They could also look at how birds alter their profile while diving for fish.

Practical support

Investigating the motion of a parachutist

This investigation can be trickier than it sounds, mainly because a parachute needs a couple of metres to unfurl and have a significant effect.

Equipment and materials required

For each group: small mass (20 g), string or cotton, scissors, approximately 15 cm by 15 cm square of cloth.

Details

Give the students a few minutes to make a parachute. The higher the parachutes are dropped from, the more effective they are so find somewhere with sufficient height. It is just possible to notice the effect if you drop objects when standing on the desk, but great care must be taken. (This relates to 'How Science Works': designing investigations.)

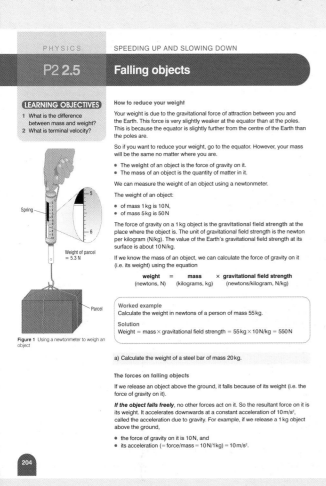

PHYSICS SPEEDING UP AND SLOWING DOWN

P2 2.5 Falling objects

LEARNING OBJECTIVES
1 What is the difference between mass and weight?
2 What is terminal velocity?

How to reduce your weight

Your weight is due to the gravitational force of attraction between you and the Earth. This force is very slightly weaker at the equator than at the poles. This is because the equator is slightly further from the centre of the Earth than the poles are.

So if you want to reduce your weight, go to the equator. However, your mass will be the same no matter where you are.

- The weight of an object is the force of gravity on it.
- The mass of an object is the quantity of matter in it.

We can measure the weight of an object using a newtonmeter.

The weight of an object:
- of mass 1 kg is 10 N,
- of mass 5 kg is 50 N.

The force of gravity on a 1 kg object is the gravitational field strength at the place where the object is. The unit of gravitational field strength is the newton per kilogram (N/kg). The value of the Earth's gravitational field strength at its surface is about 10 N/kg.

If we know the mass of an object, we can calculate the force of gravity on it (i.e. its weight) using the equation

weight = mass × gravitational field strength
(newtons, N) (kilograms, kg) (newtons/kilogram, N/kg)

Worked example
Calculate the weight in newtons of a person of mass 55 kg.

Solution
Weight = mass × gravitational field strength = 55 kg × 10 N/kg = 550 N

a) Calculate the weight of a steel bar of mass 20 kg.

The forces on falling objects

If we release an object above the ground, it falls because of its weight (i.e. the force of gravity on it).

If the object falls freely, no other forces act on it. So the resultant force on it is its weight. It accelerates downwards at a constant acceleration of 10 m/s², called the acceleration due to gravity. For example, if we release a 1 kg object above the ground,
- the force of gravity on it is 10 N, and
- its acceleration (= force/mass = 10 N/1 kg) = 10 m/s².

Figure 1 Using a newtonmeter to weigh an object

Spring

Weight of parcel = 5.3 N

Parcel

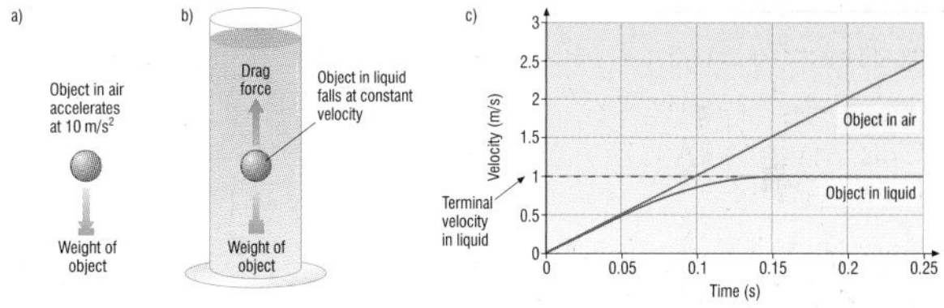

Figure 2 Falling objects. a) Falling in air, b) falling in a liquid, c) velocity–time graph for a) and b).

a) Object in air accelerates at 10 m/s²
Weight of object

b) Drag force — Object in liquid falls at constant velocity
Weight of object

c) Velocity (m/s) vs Time (s)
Object in air
Object in liquid
Terminal velocity in liquid

If the object falls in a fluid, the fluid drags on the object. The drag force increases with speed. At any instant, the resultant force on the object is its weight minus the drag force on it. When an object moves through the air (i.e. the fluid is air) the drag force is called air resistance.

- The acceleration of the object decreases as it falls. This is because the drag force increases as it speeds up. So the resultant force on it decreases.
- The object reaches a constant velocity when the drag force on it is equal and opposite to its weight. We call this velocity its terminal velocity. The resultant force is then zero, so its acceleration is zero.

b) Why does an object released in water eventually reach a constant velocity?

FOUL FACTS

If a parachute *fails* to open, the parachutist could reach a terminal velocity of more than 60 m/s (about 140 miles per hour). The drag force is then equal to his or her weight. The force of the impact on the ground would be equal to *many* times the weight, resulting in almost certain death.

SUMMARY QUESTIONS

1 Complete a) to c) using the words below:

equal to   greater than   less than

When an object is released in a fluid:
a) the drag force on it is …… its weight before it reaches its terminal velocity.
b) its acceleration is …… zero after it reaches its terminal velocity.
c) the resultant force on it is initially …… its weight.

2 A parachutist of mass 70 kg supported by a parachute of mass 20 kg reaches a constant speed.
a) Explain why the parachutist reaches a constant speed.
b) Calculate:
    i) the total weight of the parachutist and the parachute,
    ii) the size and direction of the force of air resistance on the parachute when the parachutist falls at constant speed.

PRACTICAL

Investigating the motion of a parachutist

Release an object with and without a parachute.

Make suitable measurements to compare the two situations.
- Why does the object fall at constant speed when the parachute is open?
- Evaluate the reliability of the data you collected. How could you improve the quality of your data?

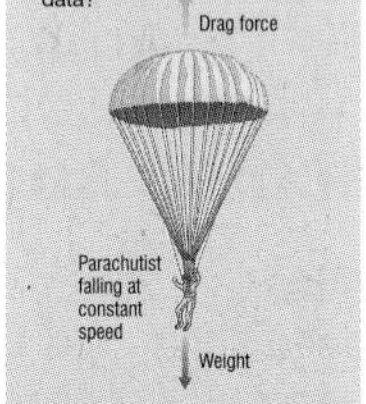

Drag force

Parachutist falling at constant speed

Weight

Figure 3 Using a parachute

KEY POINTS
1 The weight of an object is the force of gravity on it.
2 An object falling freely accelerates at about 10 m/s².
3 An object falling in a fluid reaches a terminal velocity.

204 205

SUMMARY ANSWERS

1 a) Less than. b) Equal to. c) Equal to.

2 a) As the parachutist falls, the drag force increases so the resultant force decreases. The resultant force is zero when the drag force becomes equal and opposite to the weight of the parachutist and the parachute. The speed is then constant.

   b) i) 900 N ii) 900 N upwards

Answers to in-text questions

a) 200 N

b) The drag force on it increases (as its velocity increases) until it is equal and opposite to its weight. The resultant force on it is then zero and its acceleration is zero.

KEY POINTS

Can the students interpret a graph showing the speed of a falling object in terms of the forces acting on the object?

This spread can be used to revisit the following statements covered in this chapter:

- *The factors that affect the stopping distance of a vehicle.*

Candidates should be able, when provided with additional information:

- *To draw and interpret velocity–time graphs for bodies that reach terminal velocity, including a consideration of the forces acting on the body.*

Teaching suggestions

Activities

- **Speed kills!** –You could record this 30-second slot on tape or video. You may also consider uploading it to your school intranet. Media studies students may also have the opportunity to put in a bit of extra work and add a real jingle to the tape.

- **Galileo** – Making a water clock is fiddly but certainly possible; any container with a hole at the bottom should do. Ideally the volume of water in the clock should stay constant, so it has to be continually topped up and allowed to overflow from the top while a constant flow of water is emitted by a hole at the bottom. You should be able to find some basic designs. Ask if the students can come up with any alternative methods of measuring time. One good one is to use a simple pendulum as the oscillations always have the same period as long as it isn't swung too high. The students could verify this.

PHYSICS   SPEEDING UP AND SLOWING DOWN

P2 2.6   Speed limits

Speed kills!

35

At 35mph you are twice as likely to kill someone as you are at 30mph.

kill your speed

- At 20 mph, the stopping distance is 12 metres.
- At 40 mph, the stopping distance is 36 metres.
- At 60 mph, the stopping distance is 72 metres.

ACTIVITY

A local radio station wants your help to make a 30-second road safety 'slot' aimed at car drivers. The idea is to repeat the slot every hour. With the help of your friends, decide what message to put across, then plan and record it. You could put the message across as a 'newsflash' or a catchy jingle.

GALILEO, THE FIRST SCIENTIST OF THE SCIENTIFIC AGE

Galileo was one of the first scientists to test scientific ideas by doing experiments. He realised that if reliable observations don't support a theory, the theory has to be changed. He investigated accelerated motion by timing a ball as it rolled down a slope. He put marks down the slope at equal distances. He lived before the invention of mechanical clocks and watches. So he devised a 'water clock' to time the ball each time it passed a mark.

'Water clock'

Ball released here

Direction of motion

Figure 1 Galileo's water clock experiment

Figure 1 shows the arrangement. The clock was a dripping water vessel. He collected the water from when the ball was released to when it passed each mark. He used the mass of water collected as a measure of time. He repeated the test for each mark in turn. If possible, try this experiment yourself.

QUESTION

1 The table shows some results from Galileo's water clock experiment.

Mark	Start	1	2	3	4	5
Mass of water collected (grams)	0	28	39	48	56	63

a) What can you say about the time taken to pass from one mark to the next as the ball rolled down the slope?

b) Explain why the results show that the ball accelerated as it moved down the slope.

ACTIVITY

Sign Tests

Look at these signs for a second and then write down from memory what the signs were. You and your friends could do a survey to see how the results from females and males compare.

Some road safety campaigners reckon there are too many road signs in some places. Drivers can't read them all as they approach them.

40

- **Sign tests** – You could also use a slideshow of the symbols drivers are supposed to be able to recognise and see how many of them the students can identify. An automatic slideshow of 20 or so can be set up with a timing sequence so that each sign is only on screen for a second. Search the web's pictures for 'road signs'. You could also show the PhotoPLUS P2 2.6 'Speed limits' here.

- **Anti-skid surfaces** – Any letter should contain the scientific arguments about how the material works and economical arguments about how it will save money in the long run. You might also want to discuss other traffic calming measures such as speed bumps.

- **Safer roads** – There are a large range of drugs tests that are available but these take some time to produce results so are unsuitable for on the spot fines. Testing for alertness could be possible; you could link back to the reaction time tests earlier in the chapter. Many drugs suggest that you do not operate heavy machinery (including cars) while using them, including some stronger cough medicines. It is certainly possible to design a car that would not allow the same driver to drive it for more than a few hours without a break. Ask the students if they think that this is a good idea.

QUESTION

2 Athletes are tested routinely to make sure they do not use drugs that boost performance.

a) Why are these tests important?

b) Why do athletes need to be careful about what they eat and drink in the days before a race?

c) Find out how scientific instruments help to fight the battle against drugs in sport.

d) Predict what the men's 100 m record will be in 2050.

SPEED RECORDS

In athletics, the 100 m race is a dramatic event. Electronic timers are used to time it and cameras are used to record the finish in case there is a 'dead heat'. The world record for the time has become shorter and shorter over successive years.

● Jesse Owens	1936	10.2 s
● Jim Hines	1968	9.95 s
● Maurice Green	1999	9.79 s
● Tim Montgomery	2002	9.78 s
● Assafa Powell	2005	9.77 s

Anti-skid surfaces

Have you noticed that road surfaces near road junctions and traffic lights are often different from normal road surfaces?

● The surface is rougher than normal. This gives increased friction between the surface and a vehicle tyre. So it reduces the chance of skidding when a driver brakes.

● The surface is lighter in colour so it is marked out clearly from a normal road surface.

Skidding happens when the brakes are applied too harshly. The wheels lock and the tyres slide on the road as a result. Increased friction between the tyres and the road allows more force to be applied without skidding happening. So the stopping distance is reduced.

ACTIVITY

Discuss the following issues with your friends:

● Should drivers involved in accidents also be tested for tiredness and drugs?

● Would tiredness tests be reliable? Would drivers on medical drugs be caught unfairly?

● Should drivers be pulled over for 'on the spot' tests?

ACTIVITY

Campaigners in the village of Greystoke want the council to resurface the main road at the traffic lights in the village. A child was killed crossing the road at the traffic lights earlier in the year. The council estimates it would cost £45 000. They say they can't afford it. Campaigners have found some more data to support their case.

● There are about 50 000 road accidents each year in the UK.

● The cost of road accidents is over £3000 million per year.

● Anti-skid surfaces have cut accidents by about 5%.

a) Estimate how much each road accident costs.

b) Imagine you are one of the campaigners. Write a letter to your local newspaper to counter the council's response that they can't afford it.

207

ANSWERS TO QUESTIONS

1 a) The time interval is getting smaller.

b) If the marks are equally spaced and the time it takes to move between them is shorter, then the ball must be getting faster; it is accelerating.

2 a) To make sure the athletes do not take drugs that boost performance.

b) Some food and some drinks might contain traces of banned substances.

c) Research.

d) Somewhere between 9.77 and 9.70 s.

Learning styles

Kinaesthetic: Making timepieces.

Visual: Watching video reports.

Auditory: Narrating a radio clip.

Interpersonal: Debating the effectiveness of road safety measures.

Intrapersonal: Writing a report/letter about road junction improvements.

ICT link-up

With digital cameras and basic editing software, the students could make quite an impressive 30-second road safety film. They could even incorporate clips downloaded from the Internet of cars braking.

Teaching assistant

Your teaching assistant can be very helpful in the recording of discussions or helping to generate ideas in group work.

Extension or homework

Is there a limit to human speed? – Using the data presented for the 100 m for men and researching into the same record for women, ask the students to produce a maximum speed limit for humans over 100 m. They could also look at longer distances?

Getting the hump – Where are there speed humps in the local area? Has the speed of the traffic really decreased because of them or have they driven the traffic onto other roads? The students can look at a map of the local area and mark on the areas that have traffic calming measures.

Gifted and talented

These students could try to find out how much a human life is worth. Risk assessors look into various safety measures and decide if the cost is worth the benefits. Billions of pounds are spent on safety features for roads and railways each year, but many billions more could be spent to reduce the risks further but aren't. It should be possible for the students to find out information about this idea and to see if all industries put the same value on a single life.

SUMMARY ANSWERS

1 a) i) In the opposite direction to.

  ii) In the same direction as.

  b) i) Away from the door.

  ii) Away from the door.

2 a) i) 1.6 N/kg

  ii) 1000 N

  b) i) 8 m/s², 640 N

  ii) −0.4 m/s², 28 000 N

3 a) The acceleration of X is constant and equal to 10 m/s².

  b) The object accelerates at first. The drag force on it increases with speed so the resultant force on it and its acceleration decreases. When the drag force is equal to the weight of the object, the resultant force is zero. The acceleration is then zero so the velocity is constant.

Summary teaching suggestions

- Most of these questions check the students' ability to perform important calculations and should yield clear ideas of where the students need more practice.

- Check the answers to question 2 carefully, as they will probably reveal that some students are still struggling to get to grips with mass, gravity and weight.

SPEEDING UP AND SLOWING DOWN: P2 2.1 – P2 2.6

SUMMARY QUESTIONS

1 A student is pushing a box across a rough floor. Friction acts between the box and the floor.

a) Complete the sentences below using words from the list.

> **in the same direction as**
> **in the opposite direction to**

  i) The force of friction of the box on the floor is ...... the force of friction of the floor on the box.

  ii) The force of the student on the box is ...... the force of friction of the box on the floor.

b) The student is pushing the box towards a door. Which direction, towards the door or away from the door, is

  i) the force of the box on the student?

  ii) the force of friction of the student on the floor?

2 a) The weight of an object of mass 100 kg on the Moon is 160 N.

  i) Calculate the gravitational field strength on the Moon.

  ii) Calculate the weight of the object on the Earth's surface.
  The gravitational field strength near the Earth's surface is 10 N/kg.

b) Calculate the acceleration and the resultant force in each of the following situations.

  i) A sprinter of mass 80 kg accelerates from rest to a speed of 9.6 m/s in 1.2 s.

  ii) A train of mass 70 000 kg decelerates from a velocity of 16 m/s to a standstill in 40 s without change of direction.

3 The figure shows the velocity–time graphs for a metal object X dropped in air and a similar object Y dropped in a tank of water.

a) What does the graph for X tell you about its acceleration?

b) In terms of the forces acting on Y, explain why it reached a constant velocity.

208

EXAM-STYLE QUESTIONS

I

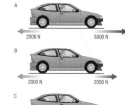

A

2000 N   5000 N

B

2000 N   2000 N

C

5000 N   2000 N

A car travels on a straight, level road. The diagrams show the car at three stages, **A**, **B** and **C** its journey. The arrows show the forward and backward forces acting on the car.

(a) What is happening to the car at:

  (i) Stage A?

  (ii) Stage B?

  (iii) Stage C?

(b) The driver of the car sees some traffic lights ahead change to red. He applies the brakes. Between seeing the lights change and applying the brakes, there is a time delay called the reaction time.

  (i) Suggest two things that would increase the reaction time of the driver.

  (ii) Suggest two things that would increase the braking distance of the car.

(c) The manufacturer of the car makes the same model but with three different engine sizes. The designers wanted to test which model had the highest top speed. They used light gates (sensors) and data loggers to take their measurements. Why didn't they use stopwatches to collect their data?

EXAM-STYLE ANSWERS

1 a) i) Accelerating   *(1 mark*

  ii) Travelling at a steady speed   *(1 mark*

  iii) Decelerating   *(1 mark*

  b) i) Tiredness/taking drugs/drinking alcohol – any two
                                                            (2 marks

  ii) Wet road surface/poor road surface/bald tyres – any two
                                                            (2 marks

  c) The electronic equipment is more sensitive
  or
  The data collected will be more accurate with the electronic equipment
  or
  It is difficult to get accurate readings using a stopwatch when a car is going so fast   *(1 mark*

2 a) Weight = mass × gravitational field strength   *(1 mark*

  b) Air resistance/friction   *(1 mark*

  c) Stays the same   *(1 mark*

  d) i) accelerating downwards   *(2 marks*

  ii) moving at steady speed   *(1 mark*

3 a) Accelerating downwards   *(1 mark*

  b) i) 55 m/s   *(1 mark*

  ii) The drag (air resistance) force on her increases *(1 mark*
  as her velocity increases   *(1 mark*
  when it is equal to her weight she travels at a constant (terminal) velocity   *(1 mark*

  c) Velocity is a continuous variable   *(1 mark*
  Time is also a continuous variable   *(1 mark*

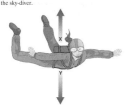

The diagram shows a sky-diver. Two forces, **X** and **Y** act on the sky-diver.

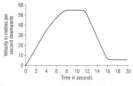

Force **Y** is the weight of the sky-diver.

(a) Write down the equation which links weight, gravitational field strength and mass. (1)

(b) What causes force **X**? (1)

(c) As the sky-diver falls, the size of force **X** increases. What happens to the size of force **Y**? (1)

(d) Describe the motion of the sky-diver when:

  (i) force **X** is smaller than force **Y**.

  (ii) force **X** is equal to force **Y**. (3)

The graph shows how the velocity of a parachutist changes with time during a parachute jump.

(a) Describe the motion of the parachutist during the first 4 seconds of the jump. (1)

(b) (i) What is the terminal velocity of the parachutist before her parachute opens? (1)

  (ii) Explain in terms of the forces acting on the parachutist why she reaches terminal velocity. (3)

(c) Explain why the data shown above can be presented as a line graph. (2)

HOW SCIENCE WORKS QUESTIONS

Weighty problems

Weight is something we are all familiar with and take very much for granted. You now understand that it is about the force of gravity acting on a mass. In the past this realisation had a big impact on science. Sir Isaac Newton attempted to explain why the Earth didn't fall apart as it spun on its own axis. Many people thought the Earth can't be spinning because it would fall apart if it was. Newton worked out that the force of gravity was easily strong enough to stop the Earth falling apart. Newton suggested a way the Earth's spinning motion could be tested: dropping an object from the top of a very tall tower.

The commonly accepted theory was that the object would fall to Earth behind the tower. Newton said that as the top of the tower was travelling much faster than the surface of the Earth, it would fall in front of the tower. Unfortunately there was not a tower tall enough to test the prediction!

Newton even worked out that gravity would eventually take the object to the centre of the Earth if it were able to go through the Earth. Robert Hooke pointed out an error in Newton's thinking and suggested it would follow an ellipse around the centre of the Earth.

Newton worked on this idea and many years later Edmund Halley used Newton's calculations to work out when a comet would return to be seen from the Earth. Halley died aged 85, some 16 years before his prediction about the comet was proved to be correct.

Use this passage to help you to answer these questions.

a) The observation that the Earth did not fall apart as it rotated produced which hypothesis from Newton? (1)

b) What was the prediction that was made from this hypothesis? (1)

c) What was the unscientific expectation for the object falling from the tower? (1)

d) What was the technology that was missing to test this prediction? (1)

Theories are there to be tested. Newton's theories about motion needed to be tested.

e) What was Halley's prediction that had been based on Newton's theories? (1)

f) Did Halley's prediction support Newton's theory? How do you know? (1)

HOW SCIENCE WORKS ANSWERS

a) That the force of gravity was much stronger than the forces that might make it fall apart.

b) That an object falling from a high tower would hit the ground in front of the tower.

c) That the object would fall behind the tower.

d) A very tall tower was missing in the testing.

e) That the comet would reappear at a certain date.

f) Yes, the comet reappeared at the time that Halley predicted from Newton's calculations.

How science works teaching suggestions

- **Literacy guidance**
  - Key terms that should be clearly understood: observation, prediction, hypothesis, theory.
  - Question e) expects a longer answer, where students can practise their literacy skills.

- **Higher- and lower-level answers.** Question e) is a higher-level question and the answers provided above are also at this level. Questions c) and d) are lower level and the answers provided are also lower level.

- **Gifted and talented.** Able students could spend some time discussing e) and perhaps studying the relationship between Hooke and Newton. Able students should appreciate that developments in understanding of space have often used predictions for the occurrence of features that have not been discovered. Their discovery then supports the theory.

- **How and when to use these questions.** When wishing to develop the links between hypothesis, prediction, testing and theory.
  The questions could be used for whole class discussion or for homework with a very able group.

- **Special needs.** Considerable support will be needed to access this topic with less-able students

- **ICT link-up.** Students could carry out research on the Internet into the relationship between Hooke and Newton.

Exam teaching suggestions

- Students should be clear that the term 'steady speed' means a constant speed.

- In everyday language 'mass' and 'weight' are used to mean the same thing. Students must be very clear that in physics they have different meanings, and that weight is a force and always acts vertically downwards.

- A common misconception is that for an object to keep moving at a steady speed there must be a resultant force acting on it. Emphasise to students that a resultant force always causes an acceleration. For an object moving at a steady speed the resultant force must be zero.

- Remind students that frictional forces are always in a direction that opposes motion.

- In questions about 'changes', such as changing forces, students must state whether quantities increase or decrease in order to gain all the marks.

P2 3.1

Energy and work

LEARNING OBJECTIVES

Students should learn that:

- The term 'work' means the amount of energy transferred to a body.
- When a force is used to move an object, work is done against friction and this is transferred as thermal energy.

LEARNING OUTCOMES

Most students should be able to:

- State that the 'work done' is the amount of energy transferred.
- Calculate the work done when a force moves an object through a distance.

Some students should also be able to:

- Perform calculations including the rearrangement of the work done equation.

Teaching suggestions

- **Gifted and talented.** These students could look into the more formal definition of work done. This is 'that the work done is equal to the force required multiplied by the distance travelled **in the direction** of the force'. This can lead to analysis of an object moving up slopes, where the direction travelled and direction of the force are not the same.

- **Learning styles**

  Kinaesthetic: Carrying out practical tasks.

  Visual: Displaying and presenting results of the activity.

  Auditory: Discussing the effect of friction on movement.

  Interpersonal: Discussing and evaluating the experiments.

  Intrapersonal: Reflecting on the limitation of results.

- **Homework.** The frictional forces on rapidly moving objects are very high. The SR-71 'Blackbird' spy plane used to leak quite a bit of fuel when on the ground, but when it was at full speed it became hotter and the metal expanded and sealed up the gaps. Ask: 'What colour was the plane and why?'

SPECIFICATION LINK-UP   Unit: Physics 2.13.3

- *When a force causes a body to move through a distance, energy is transferred and work is done.*
- *Work done = energy transferred*
- *The amount of work done, force and distance are related by the equation:*

$$\text{work done} = \text{force applied} \times \text{distance moved in direction of force}$$
$$\text{(joule, J)} \quad \text{(newton, N)} \qquad\qquad \text{(metre, m)}$$

- *Work done against frictional forces is mainly transformed into heat.*

Lesson structure

STARTER

Hard at work – Give the students a list of activities and ask them to put them in order of the amount of energy transferred. (5 minutes)

Energy transfer – The students should draw energy transfer diagrams for a range of machines and identify useful energy output. (5–10 minutes)

Energy recap – Ask the students to draw a mind map or concept map showing what they remember about energy and energy transfer. (10 minutes)

MAIN

- The term 'work done' has a very particular meaning in physics and the students will have to accept that it does not mean the same as its everyday usage.
- Two main types of work can be done: work done against a force (as covered in this topic) and work done heating. The examples when people are holding up a heavy object but are doing no mechanical work, should be discussed in terms of energy being transferred to heat by the muscles.
- The calculation is relatively straightforward, but check that the students are confident with it and that they remember to use the correct units.
- In the main practical activity, the students should quickly realise the limitations of the experiments; it is easy to measure the amount of useful work done but very difficult to even estimate how much energy is being wasted.
- They might like to think about ways in which the energy wasted as heat could be measured using their understanding of how the body removes excess heat energy. They should eventually reach, or be lead to, the conclusion that the experiment would have to be carried out in an enclosed room where all of the energy radiated away or carried by evaporating sweat could be accounted for.
- Students could be reminded of the importance of maintaining the correct body temperature and of the ways the body manages this, even when larger amounts of heat are being produced by the muscles.
- The heating effect due to friction should be demonstrated in some way, even if it is simple hand rubbing. You may be able to find footage of Formula One cars braking, where the brake disks literally glow red hot.
- This can lead to a discussion about how frictional forces can be reduced, and how thermal energy can be removed; touching on earlier work.

PLENARIES

Work or not? – Give the students a set of statements about activities and ask them to put them into two piles: 'work is done' and 'no work done'. (5 minutes)

Demonstrating friction – The students design their own demonstration to show that doing work against friction has a heating effect. (10 minutes)

Human efficiency – Ask the students to outline how they would perform an experiment to measure the energy output of a human being over a period of one day, so that they could estimate the efficiency of the human. (10–15 minutes)

ACTIVITY & EXTENSION IDEAS

Work done against friction

To show that the work done against frictional force causes heating you can use a bicycle.

Equipment and materials required

A bicycle that will stand upside down, gloves.

Details

Turn the bike upside down and get the wheel spinning by turning the pedal by hand. Don't go too fast because you now need to stop the wheel by slowing it down with the palm of your gloved hand against the tyre. Once you know the right speed to cause a noticeable heating effect but no hand damage, you can get a volunteer to have a go. As an alternative you could lift the rear wheel and drive it very quickly before applying the brakes gently. Repeat this until the smell of burning rubber is obvious.

Practical support

Work done during tasks

Any tasks preformed should be relatively simple and non-strenuous. Make sure that the students have no medical conditions that could be triggered by the activities.

Equipment and materials needed

This depends on the exact activity but typically a bench, lots of 1 kg masses, a range of newtonmeters and stopwatches.

Details

- There are many suitable tasks such as standing on and off benches, lifting a set of objects onto shelves or dragging objects or such like. The students will need to know the weight of the objects moved (newtonmeters or bathroom scales) and the heights lifted to (metre rules or tape measures).

- You might like to link back to power, getting the students to measure the time it takes to do the task and sort out the power output, using power = work done/energy transferred.

P2 3.1 — Energy and work

LEARNING OBJECTIVES

1. What do we mean by 'work' in science?
2. What is the relationship between work and energy?
3. What happens to the work done against frictional forces?

Working out

Figure 1 Working out

In a fitness centre or a gym, you have to work hard to keep fit. Raising weights and pedalling on an exercise bike are just two ways to keep fit. Whichever way you choose to keep fit, you have to apply a force to move something. So the work you do causes transfer of energy.

a) When you pedal on an exercise bike, where does the energy transferred go to?

When an object is moved by a force, we say **work** is done on the object by the force. The force transfers energy to the object. So we say the work done on the object is the energy transferred. For example, if you raise an object and increase its gravitational potential energy by 20 J, the work you do on the object is 20 J.

Work done = energy transferred

The work done by a force depends on the force and the distance moved. We use the following equation to calculate the work done by a force when it moves an object:

work done = force × distance moved in the direction of the force
(joules, J)   (newtons, N)   (metres, m)

DID YOU KNOW?

You use energy when you hold an object stationary in your outstretched hand. The biceps muscle of your arm is in a state of contraction. Energy must be supplied to keep the muscles contracted. No work is done on the object. All the energy transferred to the muscle is transformed to heat energy.

Note

Change of gravitational potential energy (in J) =
weight × change of height
(in N)   (in m)

Worked example

A 20 N weight is raised through a height of 0.4 m. Calculate i) the work done, ii) the gain of gravitational potential energy of the object.

Solution
i) The force needed to lift the weight = 20 N
Work done = force × distance moved in the direction of the force
force = 20 N × 0.4 m
= 8.0 J
ii) Gain of gravitational potential energy = work done = 8.0 J

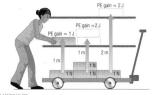

Figure 2 Using joules

b) A weightlifter raises a 200 N metal bar through a height of 1.5 m. Calculate the gain of gravitational potential energy.

PRACTICAL

Doing work

Carry out a series of experiments to calculate the work done in performing some simple tasks.

- Comment on the accuracy of your measurements. How sensitive are your measuring instruments? How accurately can you read them in your experiments?

Friction at work

Work done to overcome friction is mainly transformed into heat energy.

1. If you rub your hands together vigorously, they become warm. Your muscles do work to overcome the friction between your hands. The work you do is transformed into heat energy.

2. Brake pads become hot if the brakes are applied for too long. Friction between the brake pads and the wheel discs opposes the motion of the wheel. The kinetic energy of the vehicle is transformed into heat energy. A small proportion of the energy may be transformed into sound if the brakes 'squeal'.

SUMMARY QUESTIONS

1. Calculate the work done when:
   a) a force of 20 N makes an object move 4.8 m in the direction of the force,
   b) an object of weight 80 N is raised through a height of 1.2 m.

2. a) A student of weight 450 N steps on a box of height 0.20 m.
   i) Calculate the gain of gravitational potential energy of the student.
   ii) Calculate the work done by the student if she steps on and off the box fifty times.
   b) The student steps off the floor onto a platform and gains 270 J of gravitational potential energy. Calculate the height of the platform.

NEXT TIME YOU...

... step on a box, calculate your increase of gravitational potential energy. Your muscles push you up with a force equal and opposite to your weight. So your gain of gravitational potential energy is equal to your weight × the height of the step.

Figure 3 Steps

KEY POINTS

1. Work done = energy transferred.
2. Work done (joules) = force (newtons) × distance moved in the direction of the force (metres).

SUMMARY ANSWERS

1. a) 96 J
   b) 96 J

2. a) i) 90 J
   ii) 4500 J
   b) 0.60 m

Answers to in-text questions

a) To the surroundings as heat energy and sound energy.
b) 300 J

KEY POINTS

The students should be able to complete a worksheet of calculations about work done.

P2 3.2 Kinetic energy

Students should learn:

- That kinetic energy is the energy a moving object has.

- That the kinetic energy of an object increases when the object is travelling faster or is more massive.

- That elastic potential energy is energy stored in an object when work is done to change the shape of the object.

- How to calculate the kinetic energy of a moving object. [**HT** only]

LEARNING OUTCOMES

Most students should be able to:

- Explain how the kinetic energy of an object depends on the speed and mass of the object.

- Describe situations where elastic potential energy is stored.

Some students should also be able to:

- Perform calculations using the kinetic energy equation including those that involve rearrangement of the equation. [**HT** only]

Teaching suggestions

- **Gifted and talented.** Students talented in design could build their own elastic powered vehicles and hold a competition on whose can go furthest. The vehicles should all have identical elastic bands and could be cars, boats or aeroplanes. The results can lead to a discussion about which mode of transport is the most efficient.

- **Learning styles**

  Kinaesthetic: Building models.

  Visual: Making detailed observations of moving objects.

  Auditory: Defining key words and units.

  Interpersonal: Reporting and discussing results of experiments.

- **Homework**
  - Students could build their elastic vehicles at home for a future lesson.
  - They could find out the record distance/flight times for these toys.

SPECIFICATION LINK-UP   Unit: Physics 2.13.3

- *For an object that is able to recover its original shape, elastic potential is the energy stored in an object when work is done on the object to change its shape.*

- *The kinetic energy of a body depends on its mass and its speed.*

- *Calculate the kinetic energy of a body using the equation:*

$$\text{kinetic energy} = \tfrac{1}{2} \times \quad mass \quad \times \quad speed^2$$
$$\text{(joule, J)} \qquad \text{(kilogram, kg)} \qquad \text{((metre/second)}^2, \text{(m/s)}^2) \quad [\textbf{HT only}]$$

Students should use their skills, knowledge and understanding of 'How Science Works':

- *to discuss the transformation of kinetic energy to other forms of energy in particular situations.*

Lesson structure

STARTER

Kinetic cards – Give the students a set of cards with various moving objects on. Each card shows the mass and the velocity; the students have to put them into order with least kinetic energy to most. (5 minutes)

Mass and velocity – Using mini-whiteboards, the students must give accurate definitions of mass and velocity. Ask: 'What are the units of each?' (5 minutes)

MAIN

- The students should remember that moving objects have energy and this is called 'kinetic energy'. Some will still be using the term 'movement energy', but it is time to leave this behind and get them to use the correct term.

- The 'investigating kinetic energy' practical task works well with light gates. If you don't have them then the modified version is a reasonable alternative.

- There are a few sources of error in the results and this would be a good opportunity to look into the nature of taking measurements ('How Science Works') and how repeating readings can improve the quality of the data.

- You could have a set of results in a spreadsheet table so that you can show the relationship graphically, or let the students enter data as they go along. (This relates to 'How Science Works': relationships between variables.)

- Clearly many students will not come up with the relationship themselves, although most will see that the relationship is not a simple linear one. It is more important to show that the data fits a pattern that we already know.

- Some of the students will have a problem with the '$\frac{1}{2}$' in the kinetic energy equation and ask you: 'half of what?' This is tricky to explain without going into the derivation, so tell the students that they will find out if they go on to study A level Physics.

- The kinetic energy equation is the most difficult one that the higher attaining students need to rearrange, and you should lead them through this carefully.

- The elastic potential ideas are a bit simpler, but the students will need to be able to give a reasonable definition like the one in their textbook.

- It is important that the students realise that it is not only elastic bands that are elastic. Show them some springs and sponge, or even a football, and explain how energy is stored in these when they are distorted.

- Making elastic band toys is a good endpoint and shows another important energy transfer. The models can also be tested applying concepts from 'How Science Works' in another lesson.

PLENARIES

Kinetic cards revisited – Try the same activity as in the starter, but the students now have to calculate the energy to check their order. (5–10 minutes)

Higher/lower – Go through a series of objects with different masses and velocities and ask the students to say (or calculate) if the kinetic energy is higher or lower than the previous one. Include a trick one that's exactly the same. (5 minutes)

Practical support

Investigating kinetic energy

This experiment can be demonstrated with a ball and motion sensor or with a dynamics trolley and light gates.

Equipment and materials required (Ball)

A ramp (or drainpipe), tennis ball, velocity or distance sensor, balance to measure mass of object.

Details

If you don't have a velocity sensor then the software may be able to convert the distance measurements into speed measurements. Some velocity sensors have two parts; one of which needs to be mounted on the moving object. Clearly a ball won't do so a trolley can be used.

Equipment and materials required (Trolley)

Long ramp, dynamics trolley, card of known length, light gate, balance to measure mass of object.

Details

Mount the card on the trolley so that it interrupts the light gate when it passes through. Position the trolley at various measured heights on the track so that it rolls down the track and its speed is measured at the bottom. The ramp works well at an angle of around 30°.

Alternative equipment

It is possible to measure the speed of the object by letting it pass through a measured distance and timing it with a stopwatch. For this you will need to ensure that the object isn't travelling very fast, so shallow launch angles will be needed. To improve the results, the students will have to repeat each roll several times; this can lead to a discussion about the accuracy of the measurements and the value of repeat readings.

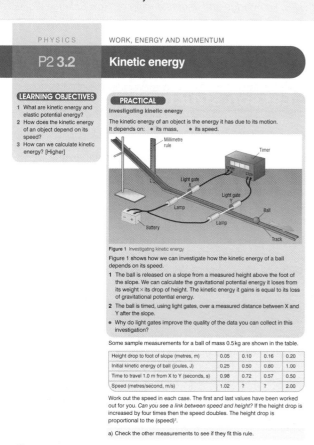

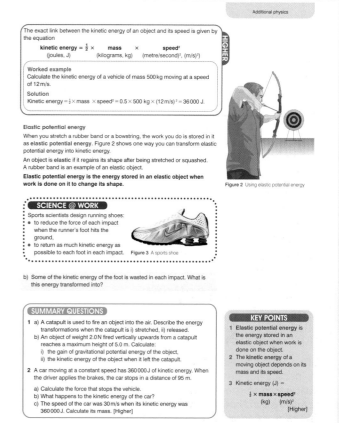

SUMMARY ANSWERS

1 a) i) Chemical energy from the loader is transferred into elastic potential energy of the catapult and some is wasted as heat energy.

ii) Elastic potential energy in the catapult is transformed into kinetic energy of the object and the rubber band and heat energy (plus a little sound energy).

b) i) 10 J **ii)** 10 J

2 a) 3800 N

b) Friction due to the brakes transforms it from kinetic energy of the car to heat energy in the brakes.

c) 800 kg.

Answers to in-text questions

a) 1.38 m/s gives 0.5 J of kinetic energy, 1.75 m/s gives 0.8 J of kinetic energy.

b) Heat energy transferred to the surroundings, the foot and the shoe; also sound energy.

KEY POINTS

The students should be able to calculate the kinetic energy of a moving object.

P2 3.3

Momentum

LEARNING OBJECTIVES

Students should learn:

- That the momentum of an object is the product of the mass and velocity of the object.
- The unit of momentum is the kilogram metre/second (kg m/s).
- That momentum is conserved in any collision provided no external forces act on the colliding bodies.

LEARNING OUTCOMES

Most students should be able to:

- Calculate the momentum of an object of known mass and velocity.
- State that momentum is conserved in any collision provided no external forces act on the colliding bodies.

Some students should also be able to:

- Apply and rearrange the appropriate equations to two bodies that collide in a straight line.

Teaching suggestions

- **Special needs.** As before, a layout template for calculations will help a great deal.
- **Gifted and talented.** Who came up with the ideas about forces and momentum? What is inertia? The students can look up and explain Newton's laws of motion. Ask: 'Why is conservation of momentum considered a very important part of physics?'
- **Learning styles**
  Kinaesthetic: Playing a game of real or virtual snooker.
  Visual: Observing collisions between objects.
  Auditory: Listening to the concept of momentum.
  Interpersonal: Discussing and evaluating the collision demonstrations.
  Intrapersonal: Making deductions about momentum being conserved from experimental evidence.
- **ICT link-up.** Detailed models are available to simulate these collisions. These can be used as a demonstration for individual student use. Snooker or pool games can also be used. See examples at www.fable.co.uk or www.sunflowerlearning.com.

SPECIFICATION LINK-UP   Unit: Physics 2.13.4

- *Momentum has both magnitude and direction.*
- *Momentum, mass and velocity are related by the equation:*

$$\underset{\text{(kilogram metre/second, kg m/s)}}{\text{momentum}} = \underset{\text{(kilogram, m)}}{\text{mass}} \times \underset{\text{(metre/second, m/s)}}{\text{velocity}}$$

- *When a force acts on a body that is moving, or able to move, a change in momentum occurs.*
- *Momentum is conserved in any collision/explosion provided no external forces act on the colliding/exploding bodies.*

Students should use their skills, knowledge and understanding of 'How Science Works':

- *to use the conservation of momentum (in one dimension) to calculate the mass, velocity or momentum of a body involved in a collision or explosion.*

Lesson structure

STARTER

Trying to stop – The students should explain why it takes an oil tanker several kilometres to stop, but a bicycle can stop in only a few metres. (5–10 minutes)

Stopping power – Give the students a set of cards with various sports balls on them. Ask the students to put them in order of difficulty to stop, and then explain what properties make the balls more difficult. (5–10 minutes)

Who is toughest? – The students must design a simple test to determine who is the most difficult person in a rugby team to stop. The test must be a fair one and produce measurable results. (This relates to 'How Science Works': designing a fair test.) (10 minutes)

MAIN

- It is best to begin with a discussion about trying to stop something moving or start something off. Trains are a good example of something with a large mass that can travel quickly. The students will know how long it takes a train to get up to speed and how long it takes it to stop, even in an emergency.
- The demonstration will take a little time to explain, but should give good results. Any discrepancies should be accounted for using the idea that external forces (frictional) have changed the momentum.
- Conservation of momentum is a fundamental concept in physics; just as important as conservation of energy.
- You could talk about the famous jumping 'everybody in China jumping at the same time' idea. It is a scientific myth that this would cause an earthquake or even change the orbit of the Earth. This would actually have no real effect on the Earth at all.
- The shunting affect can be demonstrated by a Newton's Cradle. This can be improvised from a set of ping-pong balls on wire, or similar, if a real one is not available.
- The calculation is a multi-stage one and these often confuse students. Make sure they have plenty of practice calculating the momentum of objects before they try to work out velocities after collisions.
- To extend students, you can look at collisions where both of the trolleys are moving before the collision or collisions where the trolleys 'bounce off' and end up travelling in opposite directions.

PLENARIES

The skate escape – Two people are trapped on a **perfectly** friction-free circular surface just out of reach of each other. They are both 10 m from the edge and all that they have to help them escape is a tennis ball. Ask: 'How do they escape?' (10 minutes)

Impossibly super – In several films, super heroes stop cars or trains by standing in front of them and letting them crash into them. The cars stop dead and the costumed hero doesn't move an inch. Ask: 'What's wrong with the science here?' (10 minutes)

Calculation dominoes – Give groups of students a set of domino cards with questions and numerical answers. Let them play dominoes with them. (5–10 minutes)

Practical support

Investigating collisions

This activity can be carried out with dynamics trolleys or a linear air track. Two light gates are required.

Equipment and materials required

Two or three dynamics trolleys or gliders on a linear air track, card of known length, two light gates.

Details

Mount the card on the first trolley so that it passes through a light gate before the collision. The trolleys can be made to stick together using Velcro or a pin and bit of cork. After the collision, they should pass through the second light gate to measure the new velocity. Keep the light gates close to the collision point so that the trolleys do not slow down too much. If the trolleys have the same mass then the velocity should simply half after the collision. If frictional forces are affecting the result, it is possible to tilt the track slightly, so that the frictional force is balanced by a small component of the weight of the trolleys. It is important to try this if a detailed investigation is taking place.

ACTIVITY & EXTENSION IDEAS

Snooker loopy

Real snooker balls or a computer game can help to show the idea of momentum.

Equipment and materials required

Mini snooker game (bigger is better though) or computer snooker game.

Details

Play the game but use it to show that the balls keep on rolling unless there is a force acting on them. A ball that is hit hard has a lot of momentum and is difficult to stop, but if it hits a group of balls the momentum is quickly transferred to them (smash the white into the pack). The car shunting idea can also be demonstrated using the balls, and you could even line them up so that the last one goes in.

Answers to in-text questions

a) 240 kg m/s

b) 0.48 m/s

PHYSICS   WORK, ENERGY AND MOMENTUM

P2 3.3 Momentum

LEARNING OBJECTIVES

1 How can we calculate momentum?
2 What is its unit?
3 What happens to the total momentum of two objects when they collide?

Momentum is important to anyone who plays a contact sport. In a game of rugby, a player with a lot of momentum is very difficult to stop.

The momentum of a moving object = its mass × its velocity.

The unit of momentum is the kilogram metre/second (kg m/s).

a) Calculate the momentum of a 40 kg person running at 6 m/s.

Figure 1 A contact sport

PRACTICAL

Investigating collisions

When two objects collide, the momentum of each object changes. Figure 2 shows how to use a computer and a motion sensor to investigate a collision between two trolleys.

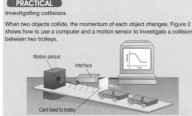

Figure 2 Investigating collisions

Trolley A is given a push so it collides with a stationary trolley B. The two trolleys stick together after the collision. The computer gives the velocity of A before the collision and the velocity of both trolleys afterwards.

● What does each section of the velocity–time graph show?

1 **For two trolleys of the same mass**, the velocity of trolley A is halved by the impact. The combined mass after the collision is twice the moving mass before the collision. So the momentum (= mass × velocity) after the collision is the same as before the collision.

2 **For a single trolley pushed into a double trolley**, the velocity of A is reduced to one-third. The combined mass after the collision is three times the initial mass. So once again, the momentum after the collision is the same as the momentum before the collision.

In both tests, the total momentum is unchanged (i.e. is conserved) by the collision. We can use this rule to predict what happens whenever objects collide or push each other apart in an 'explosion'.

Momentum is conserved in any collision or explosion provided no external forces act on the objects that collide or explode.

If a vehicle crashes into the back of a line of cars, each car in turn is 'shunted' into the one in front. Momentum is transferred along the line of cars to the one at the front.

Figure 3 A 'shunt' collision

Worked example

A 0.5 kg trolley A is pushed at a velocity of 1.2 m/s into a stationary trolley B of mass 1.5 kg. The two trolleys stick to each other after the impact.

Calculate:
a) the momentum of the 0.5 kg trolley before the collision,
b) the velocity of the two trolleys straight after the impact.

Solution

a) Momentum = mass × velocity = 0.5 kg × 1.2 m/s = 0.6 kg m/s.
b) The momentum after the impact = the momentum before the impact = 0.6 kg m/s
(1.5 kg + 0.5 kg) × velocity after the impact = 0.6 kg m/s

the velocity after the impact = $\frac{0.6 \text{ kg m/s}}{2 \text{ kg}}$ = 0.3 m/s

b) Calculate the speed after the collision if trolley A had a mass of 1.0 kg.

GET IT RIGHT!

The unit of momentum is kg m/s (or N s). In calculations always give a unit with your answer. Remember that momentum has a size and direction.

SUMMARY QUESTIONS

1 Complete a) and b) using the words below:

force   mass   momentum   velocity

a) The momentum of a moving object is its ...... × its ....
b) ...... is conserved when objects collide, provided no external ...... acts.

2 A 1000 kg rail wagon moving at a velocity of 5.0 m/s on a level track collides with a stationary 1500 kg wagon. The two wagons move together after the collision.

a) Calculate the momentum of the 1000 kg wagon before the collision.
b) Show that the two wagons move at a velocity of 2.0 m/s after the collision.

KEY POINTS

1 Momentum (kg m/s) ≈ mass (kg) × velocity (m/s).
2 Momentum is conserved whenever objects interact, provided no external forces act on them.

214

215

SUMMARY ANSWERS

1 a) Mass, velocity.
  b) Momentum, force.

2 a) 5000 kg m/s
  b) velocity = $\frac{\text{momentum}}{\text{mass}} = \frac{5000}{2500} = 2.0$ m/s

KEY POINTS

The students should be able to calculate the momentum of an object.

P2 3.4

More on collisions and explosions

LEARNING OBJECTIVES

Students should learn that:

- Momentum is a vector quantity and the direction of travel is important in collisions.
- There is no change in momentum in an explosion.

LEARNING OUTCOMES

Students should be able to:

- State that the total momentum before and after an explosion is the same, provided no external forces act.
- Describe how the launching of a bullet causes recoil.

Some students should also be able to:

- Explain that momentum is conserved in all interactions that do not include external forces.
- Apply the conservation of momentum to perform calculations where an explosion occurs causing two objects to recoil from each other.

Teaching suggestions

- **Special needs.** Momentum conservation questions are best posed as a set of diagrams showing the situation before and after the collisions. The students can be led through the calculations with a calculation template until they are more comfortable with the technique.

- **Gifted and talented.**
  - Ask: 'Why doesn't momentum change?' The students could try to link the idea of conservation of momentum to equal and opposite forces. Ask: 'What exactly is a force? What is the scientific definition?'
  - Mathematically skilled students could look at collisions in two dimensions and calculate the resulting velocities.

- **Learning styles**
  Kinaesthetic: Recording results from experiments.
  Visual: Watching demonstration of explosions.
  Auditory: Discussing limitations in the explosion model.
  Interpersonal: Discussing and evaluating the suitability of crash test dummies to model collisions.

SPECIFICATION LINK-UP   Unit: Physics 2.13.4

- *Momentum has both magnitude and direction.*
- *Momentum, mass and velocity are related by the equation:*

$$\text{momentum} = \text{mass} \times \text{velocity}$$
(kilogram metre/second, kg m/s)   (kilogram, m)   (metre/second, m/s)

- *When a force acts on a body that is moving, or able to move, a change in momentum occurs.*
- *Momentum is conserved in any collision/explosion provided no external forces act on the colliding/exploding bodies.*

Students should use their skills, knowledge and understanding of 'How Science Works':

- *to use the conservation of momentum (in one dimension) to calculate the mass, velocity or momentum of a body involved in a collision or explosion.*

Lesson structure

STARTER

Explaining explosions – Give the students a set of cards explaining how a chemical explosion causes a projectile to be fired from a cannon. They must sort them into order. (5–10 minutes)

Slow motion – Show a video of a simple explosion frame by frame and ask the students to explain what is happening. (Search for explosion at video.google.com.) (5–10 minutes)

Jumping frogs – Position a few spring-loaded jumping frog toys on the desk and set them off. The students have to explain the energy transfers before they all go off. (5–10 minutes)

MAIN

- Students may only think of explosions as chemical explosions instead of simple spring ones. Talk about an explosion being caused when some kind of stored energy (chemical or elastic) is suddenly transferred into kinetic.

- The explosion experiment usually works well, but you might want to repeat it a couple of times and analyse the mean results. This gives an opportunity for the students to consider the errors inherent in these measurements and why repeat readings are so important. This is an excellent opportunity to explore concepts in 'How Science Works'.

- Show the students some footage of crash test dummies search the web for 'crash test dummy video'.

- A good way of showing the recoil effect of firing a shell from a gun is to show a field gun in operation. These are really quite large and are knocked backwards significantly. When firing a 'twenty-one gun salute', there is little backwards movement because no shell is fired.

- The calculation can be very difficult for many students so lead them through it carefully.

- You can discuss the energy transfers involved with the damping spring and perhaps link this to the suspension on cars.

- The students should be made to realise that the gun has to have much more mass that the projectile, otherwise it would recoil at very high velocities. A modern shell is fired at velocities of up to 1000 m/s and may have a mass of 100 kg.

PLENARIES

Boating – Discuss what happens when somebody steps onto a boat but falls in the water because the boat moves away. Ask the students to explain what happened, perhaps with diagrams. (5 minutes)

Practical support

Investigating a controlled explosion

This demonstration can be used to show that momentum is conserved in explosions.

Equipment and materials required

Four dynamics trolleys, two light gates or velocity sensors or wooden blocks.

Details

- This experiment can be carried out with wooden blocks as shown in the Student Book or with light gates or velocity sensors to measure the speed. If the sensors are used then use interrupter cards as in previous experiments. The momentum of the objects can be calculated using the equation.

- You should make sure that the sensors are positioned close to the explosion point so that not too much energy is lost due to friction. The same kind of experiment can be carried out with a linear air track.

PHYSICS   WORK, ENERGY AND MOMENTUM

P2 3.4 More on collisions and explosions

LEARNING OBJECTIVES

1 Why does momentum have a direction as well as size?
2 When two objects fly apart, why is their total momentum zero?

PRACTICAL

Investigating a controlled explosion

When a bomb explodes, fragments of metal fly off in all directions. The fragments fly off with enormous momentum in different directions. Figure 1 shows a more controlled explosion using trolleys. When the trigger rod is tapped, a bolt springs out and the trolleys recoil from each other.

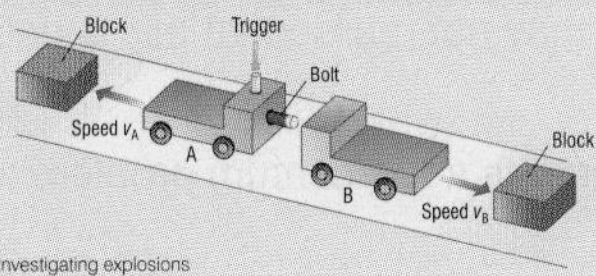

Figure 1 Investigating explosions

Using trial and error, we can place blocks on the runway so the trolleys reach them at the same time. This allows us to compare the speeds of the trolleys. Some results are shown in Figure 2.

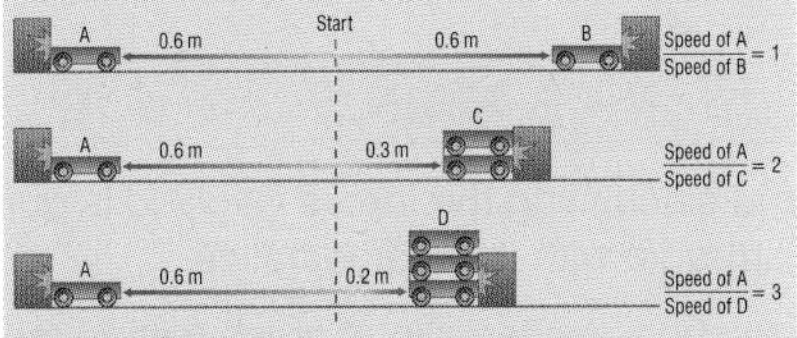

Figure 2 Using different masses

- Did your results agree exactly with the ones above? If not, try to explain why.
- Two single trolleys travel equal distances in the same time. This shows that they recoil at equal speeds.
- A double trolley only travels half the distance that a single trolley does. Its speed is half that of the single trolley.

In each test,

1 the mass of the trolley × the speed of the trolley is the same, and
2 they recoil in opposite directions.

So momentum has size and direction. The results show that the trolleys recoil with equal and opposite momentum.

a) Why does a stationary rowing boat recoil when someone jumps off it?

DID YOU KNOW?

Crash tests with dummies in cars are used to test car safety features such as seat belts. In a 'head-on' crash test between two cars, if the cars have equal and opposite momentum before the collision, they have no momentum afterwards. All their kinetic energy is transformed into heat, sound and work done deforming the cars.

Conservation of momentum in an explosion

In the trolley examples:

- momentum of A after the explosion = (mass of A × velocity of A)
- momentum of B after the explosion = (mass of B × velocity of B)
- total momentum before the explosion = 0 (because both trolleys were at rest).

Using conservation of momentum gives:

(mass of A × velocity of A) + (mass of B × velocity of B) = 0

Therefore

(mass of A × velocity of A) = −(mass of B × velocity of B)

This tells us that A and B move apart with equal and opposite amounts of momentum.

Momentum in action

When a shell is fired from an artillery gun, the gun barrel recoils backwards. The recoil of the gun barrel is slowed down by a spring. This lessens the backwards motion of the gun.

> **Worked example**
>
> An artillery gun of mass 2000 kg fires a shell of mass 20 kg at a velocity of 120 m/s. Calculate the recoil velocity of the gun.
>
> **Solution**
>
> Applying the conservation of momentum gives:
>
> mass of gun × recoil velocity of gun = −(mass of shell × velocity of shell)
>
> If we let V represent the recoil velocity of the gun,
>
> $$2000 \text{ kg} \times V = -(20 \text{ kg} \times 120 \text{ m/s})$$
>
> $$V = \frac{-2400 \text{ kg m/s}}{2000 \text{ kg}} = -1.2 \text{ m/s}$$

Figure 3 An artillery gun in action

b) A 600 kg cannon recoils at a speed of 0.5 m/s when a 12 kg cannon ball is fired from it.
   Calculate the velocity of the cannon ball when it leaves the cannon.

SUMMARY QUESTIONS

1 A 30 kg skater and a 40 kg skater standing in the middle of an ice rink push each other away. Complete the following sentences using words from the list.

   force   momentum   velocity

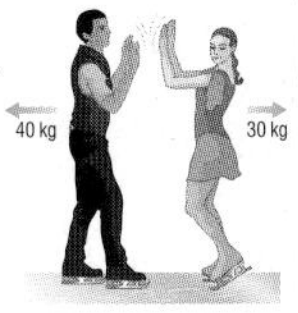

   a) They move apart with equal and opposite ……. .
   b) The 30 kg skater moves away with a bigger …… than the other skater.
   c) They push each other with equal and opposite ……. .

2 In question 1, the 30 kg skater moves away at 2.0 m/s. Calculate:

   a) her momentum,
   b) the velocity of the other skater.

KEY POINTS

1 Momentum has size and direction.
2 When two objects push each other apart, they move apart with equal and opposite momentum.

216

217

SUMMARY ANSWERS

1 a) Momentum.   b) Velocity.   c) Force.

2 a) 60 kg m/s   b) 1.5 m/s

Answers to in-text questions

a) The boat and the person who jumps off move away with equal and opposite amounts of momentum.

b) 25 m/s

KEY POINTS

The students should calculate the velocity of objects moving apart from an 'explosion'.

P2 3.5   Changing momentum

LEARNING OBJECTIVES

Students should learn that:

- A resultant force applied to an object will change its momentum.

- The change in momentum can be found by multiplying the force by the time it acts on the object. [**HT** only]

LEARNING OUTCOMES

Most students should be able to:

- State that a resultant force will change the momentum of an object.

- Explain that the longer the force is applied for, and the larger it is, the greater the change in momentum.

Some students should also be able to:

- Calculate the change in momentum of an object from the resultant force and the time it acts. [**HT** only]

- Perform calculations involving the rearrangement of the equation: force = change of momentum/time taken. [**HT** only]

Teaching suggestions

- **Learning styles**

  Kinaesthetic: Hurling of eggs!

  Visual: Observing different types of impact.

  Auditory: Listening to 'thuds'.

  Interpersonal: Working together on practicals.

  Intrapersonal: Solving problems.

- **Special needs**

  Provide a set of layout templates to guide the students through the calculations until they get in to the habit of laying out their work correctly.

- **Homework**

  - If there is no time in the lesson, the students could construct their egg safety capsule at home for testing next lesson.

  - Additional questions on collisions and calculating the velocity of objects before and after collisions will reinforce the students' skills.

- **Teaching assistant.** A brave teaching assistant can measure out the distances the eggs are thrown in the Olympic style.

SPECIFICATION LINK-UP   Unit: Physics 2.13.4

- *Momentum is conserved in any collision/explosion provided no external forces act on the colliding/exploding bodies.*

- *Force, change in momentum and time taken for the change are related by the equation:*

$$\text{force (newton, N)} = \frac{\text{change in momentum (kilogram metre/second, kg(m/s))}}{\text{time taken for the change (second, s)}} \qquad \textbf{[HT only]}$$

Students should use their skills, knowledge and understanding of 'How Science Works':

- *to use the conservation of momentum (in one dimension) to calculate the mass, velocity or momentum of a body involved in a collision or explosion.*

Lesson structure

STARTER

Crumpled cars – Show the students selected photographs of crashed cars (search the web's images at www.google.com) and ask them to describe the damage. They should notice the crumpling effect, but may not realise that this is deliberate design. (5–10 minutes)

Crash flashback – Give the students a momentum problem to solve to refresh the ideas from the last topic. (5 minutes)

'It's not the fall that kills you' – Ask the students to explain what they think this phrase is supposed to mean. Ask: 'What is it that kills you?' (5 minutes)

MAIN

- Changing momentum and calculating the forces involved is quite a tricky concept, and some students will struggle with the mathematics.

- A good starting point is to show a video clip of crash testing (search the web for 'crash testing' video); there are a few available. You should emphasise the large amount of energy that is transferred during the collision and ask the students where they think it is transferred to.

- The 'Investigating impacts' practical clearly shows that the forces involved in impact are reduced by using a material that distorts. These plastic materials absorb some of the energy of the impact. You might like to show what happens if a spring (an elastic material) is used instead.

- The calculations will take a bit of explaining and the students will most likely need to go through the ideas a couple of times. Use plenty of examples including ones involving the trolleys or toys that you have been using.

- Impact times tend to be very short, so you may like to start with longer lasting collisions before moving on to the bullet example.

- After the maths, either demonstrate the egg throwing or let the students have a go at the egg hurling competition (see activity box). This will make the lesson more memorable!

PLENARIES

Bouncy castles – Small children often cry when they fall over, but not on bouncy castles. The students should draw a diagram showing why not. (5 minutes)

Armoured pedestrians – Can pedestrians protect themselves from car impact by wearing soft or hard materials? The students could design a system and, more importantly, point out problems with each other's designs. (10 minutes)

'Owwzatt!' – How should cricketers catch fast moving cricket balls? The students should write out instructions explaining the science behind their ideas. (5–10 minutes)

Practical support

Investigating impacts
The impacts can be investigated on a simple or more detailed level depending on time available.

Equipment and materials required
Dynamics trolley, Plasticine, motion sensor, launch ramp.

Details
- You can compare the two impacts just by observing them or by monitoring the movement with a distance sensor. The trolleys should be launched from the same height on the ramp; firstly onto the brick directly and then with a round blob of Plasticine. With the motion sensor you can then compare the two impacts, and you should be able to show that the second impact took place over a longer time. The first impact should make a nice thud, and this helps you to discuss what happened to the kinetic energy.

- You may like to see if the students can design a crumple zone for the trolley out of paper. Give each student a small amount of sticky tape and a single sheet of A4 paper, and ask them to try to make a crumple zone that they can attach to the front of a trolley to absorb the kinetic energy. The trolley can be rolled from a fixed height on a ramp to make the test fair, and the collisions observed or even measured with a motion sensor. This should give an indication of the effectiveness.

Teaching suggestions – continued

- **Science @ work.** Bullet-proof vests are remarkably complex. It isn't easy making one that is effective against all types of bullets or even knives. The art of designing armour is thousands of years old and its history can be seen as a battle between weapon-smiths and armour designers each trying to outdo each other. Currently weapons designers are a long way ahead, and even the best body armour is of little use against a high powered battlefield rifle. Search online for details of spider silk and bullet-proof vests. Strangely bullet-proof vests are illegal to wear in Australia; perhaps this is something to do with an historical incident?

Answers to in-text questions

a) If a child falls off the swing, the rubber mat reduces the impact force by increasing the impact time when the child hits the ground.

b) The force is bigger.

c) 1800 N

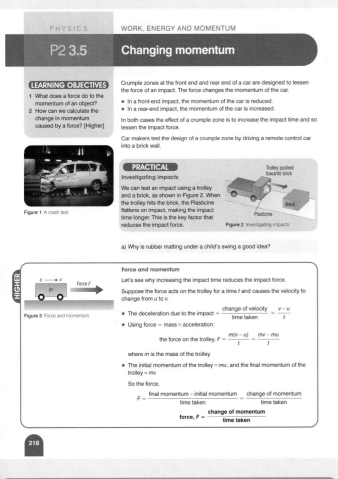

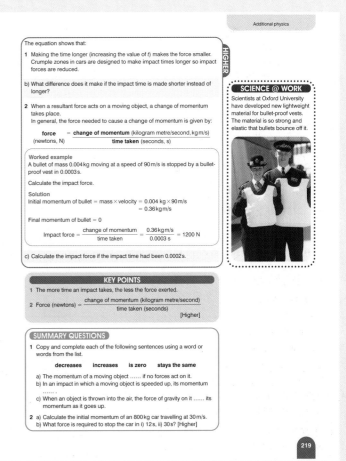

PHYSICS   WORK, ENERGY AND MOMENTUM

P2 3.5 Changing momentum

LEARNING OBJECTIVES
1 What does a force do to the momentum of an object?
2 How can we calculate the change in momentum caused by a force? [Higher]

Figure 1 A crash test

Crumple zones at the front end and rear end of a car are designed to lessen the force of an impact. The force changes the momentum of the car.

- In a front-end impact, the momentum of the car is reduced.
- In a rear-end impact, the momentum of the car is increased.

In both cases the effect of a crumple zone is to increase the impact time and so lessen the impact force.

Car makers test the design of a crumple zone by driving a remote control car into a brick wall.

PRACTICAL
Investigating impacts
We can test an impact using a trolley and a brick, as shown in Figure 2. When the trolley hits the brick, the Plasticine flattens on impact, making the impact time longer. This is the key factor that reduces the impact force.

Figure 2 Investigating impacts

a) Why is rubber matting under a child's swing a good idea?

Figure 3 Force and momentum

Force and momentum
Let's see why increasing the impact time reduces the impact force.

Suppose the force acts on the trolley for a time t and causes the velocity to change from u to v.

- The deceleration due to the impact $= \dfrac{\text{change of velocity}}{\text{time taken}} = \dfrac{v - u}{t}$
- Using force = mass × acceleration:

  the force on the trolley, $F = \dfrac{m(v - u)}{t} = \dfrac{mv - mu}{t}$

  where m is the mass of the trolley
- The initial momentum of the trolley $= mu$, and the final momentum of the trolley $= mv$,

So the force,

$$F = \frac{\text{final momentum} - \text{initial momentum}}{\text{time taken}} = \frac{\text{change of momentum}}{\text{time taken}}$$

$$\text{force, } F = \frac{\text{change of momentum}}{\text{time taken}}$$

The equation shows that:

1 Making the time longer (increasing the value of t) makes the force smaller. Crumple zones in cars are designed to make impact times longer so impact forces are reduced.

b) What difference does it make if the impact time is made shorter instead of longer?

2 When a resultant force acts on a moving object, a change of momentum takes place.
In general, the force needed to cause a change of momentum is given by:

$$\text{force} \ (\text{newtons, N}) = \frac{\text{change of momentum (kilogram metre/second, kg m/s)}}{\text{time taken (seconds, s)}}$$

Worked example
A bullet of mass 0.004 kg moving at a speed of 90 m/s is stopped by a bullet-proof vest in 0.0003 s.

Calculate the impact force.

Solution
Initial momentum of bullet = mass × velocity = 0.004 kg × 90 m/s
= 0.36 kg m/s

Final momentum of bullet = 0

$$\text{Impact force} = \frac{\text{change of momentum}}{\text{time taken}} = \frac{0.36 \text{ kg m/s}}{0.0003 \text{ s}} = 1200 \text{ N}$$

c) Calculate the impact force if the impact time had been 0.0002 s.

SCIENCE @ WORK
Scientists at Oxford University have developed new lightweight material for bullet-proof vests. The material is so strong and elastic that bullets bounce off it.

KEY POINTS
1 The more time an impact takes, the less the force exerted.
2 Force (newtons) = $\dfrac{\text{change of momentum (kilogram metre/second)}}{\text{time taken (seconds)}}$
[Higher]

SUMMARY QUESTIONS
1 Copy and complete each of the following sentences using a word or words from the list.

decreases   increases   is zero   stays the same

a) The momentum of a moving object ...... if no forces act on it.
b) In an impact in which a moving object is speeded up, its momentum ....
c) When an object is thrown into the air, the force of gravity on it ...... its momentum as it goes up.

2 a) Calculate the initial momentum of an 800 kg car travelling at 30 m/s.
b) What force is required to stop the car in i) 12 s, ii) 30 s? [Higher]

SUMMARY ANSWERS

1 a) Stays the same. b) Increases. c) Decreases.

2 a) 24 000 kg m/s

  b) i) 2000 N ii) 800 N [HT only]

KEY POINTS

The students should be able to design measures to reduce the forces involved in a range of impacts. These could be on cars or sports equipment, for example in American football.

PHYSICS WORK, ENERGY AND MOMENTUM

P2 3.6 Forces for safety

SPECIFICATION LINK-UP

Unit: Physics 2.13.3 and 4

This spread helps students to apply the principles covered in this chapter (as described by the contexts taken from the specification below):

- *When a body speeds up or slows down, its kinetic energy increases or decreases. The forces that cause the change in speed do so by transferring energy to, or from, the body.*

- *The faster a body is moving the more kinetic energy it has. It also has momentum. When working out what happens to bodies as a result of explosions or collisions, it is more useful to think in terms of momentum than in terms of energy.*

Teaching suggestions

Activities

- **'Clunk click'** – There is always an active campaign for road safety and you should be able to find information from the Royal Society for the Prevention of Accidents web site www.rospa.com. With a search for 'public information film' or 'road safety film', you should be able to find a wide range of films from the 1970s and later, that include road safety measures including some really dated ones. The web site www.thinkseatbelts.com has a road crash simulator and a wide variety of facts about the law and safety; it is well worth a visit.

- **Analysing a road crash** – This is an interesting problem for analysis. The students might like to look at the assumptions made about the crash (the direction of the lorry, that the braking distance chart applies to lorries moving sideways etc.). They could look at impact analysis like this in more detail, including finding out about simulation software.

Motor News

CLUNK CLICK!

When seat belts were first introduced, some car users claimed that they should not be forced by law to wear them. A very successful campaign was launched to convince car users to 'belt up'. It included the catchy phrase 'Clunk click every trip'. As a result, deaths and injuries in road accidents fell significantly. A seat belt stops its wearer from continuing forwards when the car stops suddenly. Someone without a seat belt would hit the windscreen in a 'short sharp' impact and suffer major injury.

- The time taken to stop someone in a car is longer with a seat belt than without it. So the decelerating force is reduced by wearing a seat belt.

- The seat belt acts across the chest so it spreads the force out. Without the seat belt, the force would act on the head when it hits the windscreen.

QUESTION

1 Explain why an inflated air bag in front of a car user reduces the force on a user of a 'head-on' crash.

ACTIVITY

'Clunk click every trip' is a positive message. Sometimes a negative message has bigger effect. Come up with your own short message to remind parents to check that children in cars must always wear seat belts.

NEWS

Air bags

An airbag in action

A crazy motorist was sent to prison for three years yesterday at Newtown County Court. He drove for twenty miles at top speed down the wrong side of a motorway. He was stopped when he drove into a police car blocking his route. One of the police officers said, 'We braced ourselves for the impact when he didn't stop. The airbags in our car inflated and took the force of the impact.' The bravery of the police officers was commended by the judge.

G-FORCES

We sometimes express the effect of an impact on an object or person as a force-to-weight ratio. We call this the 'g-force'. For example, a g-force of 2g means the force on an object is twice its weight. You would experience a g-force of

- about 3–4g on a fairground ride that whirls you round,
- about 10g in a low-speed car crash,
- more than 50g in a high-speed car crash-force. You would be lucky to survive though!

220

- **Air bags** – Air bags are quite a cunning device and have to be very rapid in operation to inflate the bag, but allow it to start to deflate before your head hits it too hard. They use the explosive decomposition of sodium azide (NaN_3) into sodium metal and nitrogen gas that inflates the bag in around 50 milliseconds. The head is in contact with the bag for a much longer time than it would be with the dashboard, and so a smaller force is exerted on the head to change its momentum.

- The students might like to consider why you should not mount a child safety seat in a front seat that has an airbag fitted. You should be able to find video clips demonstrating how air bags operate. Download these before the lesson as searches for videos of 'air bags' can give undesired results.

- **g-forces** – The term 'g-force' is very commonly used in relation to aeroplanes. A normal human can withstand around 5g without passing out, while trained pilots in pressured suits can make it up to 9g for a few seconds. Negative, −g, where the blood if forced to the head instead of away from it, is much more difficult to handle. At only −3g so much blood is forced to the head that the capillaries in the eyes burst – nasty.

Analysing a road crash

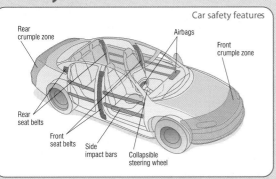

A car crashed into a lorry that was crossing a busy road. Was the car travelling faster than the speed limit of 70 miles per hour (31 m/s)?

6 m

Measurements made by police officers at the scene of the road crash:

- The car and the lorry ended up 6 metres from the point of impact
- The car's mass was 750 kg and the lorry's mass was 2150 kg.

QUESTION

2 The speed of a vehicle for a braking distance of 6 m is 9 m/s.
   a) Use this speed to calculate the momentum of the car and the lorry immediately after the impact.
   b) Use conservation of momentum to calculate the velocity of the car immediately before the collision.
   c) Was the car travelling over the speed limit before the crash?

Safety costs

Car safety features

Rear crumple zone
Airbags
Front crumple zone
Rear seat belts
Front seat belts
Side impact bars
Collapsible steering wheel

Car makers need to sell cars. If their cars are too expensive, people won't buy them. Safety features add to the cost of a new car. Some safety features (e.g. seat belts) are required by law and some (e.g. side impact bars) are optional. The table shows the main safety features in a new car.

ACTIVITY

a) With the help of your friends, find out what safety features are in some other new cars. Find out if they are compulsory or optional. List the price (including tax) of each car.
b) Use your information to say if cheaper cars have fewer safety features than more expensive cars.
c) What do you think could be done to make more cars safer?

Car make and price Nippy, £6500		
Front seat belts	✓
Rear seat belts	✓
Airbags	
Front crumple zone	✓
Rear crumple zone	
Side impact bars	
Collapsible steering wheel	✓

ACTIVITY

Do you think all cars should have the best safety features money can buy? Or should owners choose these as options? What are the points for and against these views?

Which do you support?

221

ANSWERS TO QUESTIONS

1 The air bag increases the time taken to stop the person it acts on. This reduces the force of the impact. Also, the force is spread out across the chest by the air bag so its effect is lessened again.

2 a) 26 100 kg m/s
   b) 34.8 m/s
   c) Yes.

Safety costs – The costs of cars and optional extras are readily available on manufacturers and dealers web sites, though the students may have to go through some of the pre-ordering stages to get all the information they need. Make sure nobody has a credit card. Adding all of the possible options would make most cars far too expensive, but the students may like to prioritise the features and list which ones should be made mandatory. They could also look into the European Safety feature rating; see www.euroncap.com for a detailed guide.

xtension or homework

he students can find out how pilots are trained and what equipment assists them in esisting high *g*-forces. Ask: 'What physical type of person would make the best fighter ilot?'

Learning styles

Kinaesthetic: Designing safety campaigns.

Visual: Visualising collisions.

Auditory: Reading information aloud.

Interpersonal: Discussing road safety.

Intrapersonal: Deducing the elements involved in a crash investigation.

ICT link-up

The Internet offers up a host of research possibilities for all of these activities. Simulation software also allows the students to look at collisions in more detail and can incorporate impacts at an angle and frictional forces. E.g. look at www.fable.com and www.crocodile-clips.com.

SUMMARY ANSWERS

1 a) i) Equal to.
   ii) Less than.

  b) i) 180 J
    ii) 11 N × 20 m = 220 Nm = 220 J
   iii) Friction between the trolley and the slope causes some of the energy from the student to be transformed to heat energy of the surroundings.

2 a) $\dfrac{700\,\text{kg} \times (20\,\text{m/s})^2}{2} = 140\,000\,\text{J}$

  b) 1750 N

3 a) i) 12 kg m/s
   ii) 6 m/s

  b) i) 1.8 J
    ii) 36 J

4 a) 2000 N

Summary teaching suggestions

- This chapter has been, by necessity, quite mathematically intensive and several of the questions test the students' skills to deal with the equations.

- The second part of question 1 should show you if the students have a good grasp of work done and understanding that energy is wasted when objects are moved.

- Question 2 links a kinetic energy calculation to acceleration and force calculations; this is a good indicator of thorough understanding.

- Questions 3 and 4 are further calculations and will probably throw-up a wide range of mistakes or weaknesses. Use them to find out the weak spots for revision.

SUMMARY QUESTIONS

1 a) Copy and complete the following sentences using words from the list.

> **equal to   greater than   less than**

When a braking force acts on a vehicle and slows it down,
i) the work done by the force is …… the energy transferred from the object,
ii) the kinetic energy after the brakes have been applied is …… the kinetic energy before they were applied.

b) A student pushes a trolley of weight 150 N up a slope of length 20 m. The slope is 1.2 m high.

i) Calculate the gravitational potential energy gained by the trolley.
ii) The student pushed the trolley up the slope with a force of 11 N. Show that the work done by the student was 220 J.
iii) Give one reason why all the work done by the student was not transferred to the trolley as gravitational potential energy.

2 A 700 kg car moving at 20 m/s is stopped in a distance of 80 m when the brakes are applied.
a) Show that the kinetic energy of the car at 20 m/s is 140 000 J.
b) Calculate the braking force on the car.   [Higher]

3 A student of mass 40 kg standing at rest on a skateboard of mass 2.0 kg jumps off the skateboard at a speed of 0.30 m/s. Calculate:
a) i) the momentum of the student,
  ii) the recoil velocity of the skateboard,
b) the kinetic energy of i) the student, ii) the skateboard, after they move apart.   [b] – Higher]

4 A car bumper is designed not to bend in impacts at less than 4 m/s. It was fitted to a car of mass 900 kg and tested by driving the car into a wall at 4 m/s. The time of impact was measured and found to be 1.8 s. Work out the impact force.   [Higher]

EXAM-STYLE QUESTIONS

1 The picture shows a catapult.

Stone   Elastic   Catapult

(a) When a force is applied to the stone, work is do stretching the elastic and the stone moves backw

  (i) Write down the equation you could use to calculate the work done.

  (ii) The average force applied to the stone is 20 This moves it backwards 0.15 m. Calculate the work done and give its unit.

(b) The work done is stored as energy.

  (i) What type of energy is stored in the stretche elastic?

  (ii) What type of energy does the stone have wf is released?

2 (a) The diagram shows three cars, **A**, **B** and **C**, trave along a straight, level road at 25 m/s.

A

1000 kg

B

1250 kg

C

1500 kg

  (i) Explain which vehicle, **A**, **B** or **C** has the gre momentum.

  (ii) Would you need a more sensitive weighing device to be more certain of your answer to part (i)? Give your reasoning.

EXAM-STYLE ANSWERS

1 a) i) Work done = force × distance moved in direction of the force   *(1 mark)*
   ii) Work done = 20 N × 0.15 m   *(1 mark)*
    work done = 3 J   *(2 marks)*

  b) i) elastic potential energy   *(1 mark)*
    ii) kinetic energy   *(1 mark)*

2 a) i) All travelling at same velocity, so car with greatest mass has greatest momentum.   *(1 mark)*
    Car C has greatest momentum.   *(1 mark)*
   ii) No, as there are large differences in the masses   *(1 mark)*
    so there is no need to read values with a sensitive instrumen
         (1 mark)

  b) All have same mass, so car with greatest velocity has greatest momentum.   *(1 mark)*
    Car F has greatest momentum.   *(1 mark)*

  c) Momentum = mass × velocity   *(1 mark)*
    Momentum = 1500 kg × 25 m/s   *(1 mark)*
    Momentum = 37 500 kg m/s   *(2 marks)*

3 a) *Total* momentum after a collision equals *total* momentum before the collision.   *(2 marks)*
    (momentum before equals momentum after = 1 mark)

  b) Explosions   *(1 mark)*

  c) 0.2 kg × 1.5 m/s + 0 = (0.2 + 0.3) kg × v m/s   *(1 mark)*
    0.3 kg m/s = 0.5 kg × v m/s   *(1 mark)*
    0.6 m/s   *(1 mark)*
    to the right   *(1 mark)*

b) The diagram shows three identical cars, **D**, **E** and **F**, all of mass 1500 kg, travelling along a straight, level road at different speeds.

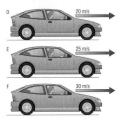

Explain which vehicle, **D**, **E** or **F** has the greatest momentum. (2)

c) Calculate the momentum of car **E**, include the unit with your answer. (4)

A student is doing an investigation of the conservation of momentum with a horizontal air track and two 'gliders'.

a) Explain what is meant by conservation of momentum. (2)

b) Apart from collisions, give another type of event in which conservation of momentum applies. (1)

c) The diagram shows the air track and the two 'gliders', **X** and **Y**.

The mass of **X** is 0.2 kg and its velocity is 1.5 m/s to the right.

The mass of **Y** is 0.3 kg and it is stationary. When 'glider' **X** collides with trolley **Y** they move off together.

Calculate the velocity of the 'gliders' after the collision and give their direction. (4)

HOW SCIENCE WORKS QUESTIONS

Claire was interested in how ancient catapults were used to fire rocks at the enemy. She designed a catapult that was similar to one she found in a history book. She couldn't work out the angle at which to fire the catapult, so she used 'stoppers' to test three different positions. Her catapult looked like this:

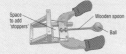

As the ball was fired the spoon was pulled by the force of the elastic bands. The spoon hit the wooden support and the ball was fired into the distance. The three positions in which the wooden spoon was stopped are shown in the diagram opposite.

Here are Claire's results:

	Distance travelled (cm)		
	Front	Upright	Back
1st go	110	114	110
2nd go	117	116	112
3rd go	109	121	108
Mean	112	117	110

a) Claire made a prediction that the backward position would make the ball travel the furthest. Do the results support her prediction? Explain your answer. (1)

b) If you had to have a new prediction, what might it be? (1)

c) Do the results show precision? Explain your answer. (1)

d) What is the independent variable in Claire's investigation? (1)

e) Would you describe this as a discrete, categoric or ordered variable? (1)

f) How could it be changed into a continuous variable? (1)

g) What would be the advantage of using a continuous independent variable? (3)

223

Exam teaching suggestions

- Remind students to always show their working in calculations so that they can gain credit even if their final answer is wrong.

- Students do not have to use quantity algebra, but they should be familiar with units and always give a unit for their final answer if this is not given in the answer line on the examination paper.

- Emphasise that work done is the same as energy transferred.

- Emphasise that force, acceleration and momentum have direction.

HOW SCIENCE WORKS ANSWERS

a) No, there appears to be no real difference between the three sets of data or the upright position makes the ball travel furthest.

b) From these observations it might be that the upright position is able to propel the ball the furthest. If the datum from '2nd go/front' was considered an anomaly then this prediction would be more likely.

c) No, results do not show precision because they have a wide range within each set of results. The results for one actually overlap the other.

d) Position of the release point is the independent variable.

e) Categoric variable.

f) By measuring the angle of the spoon to the upright it could be changed to a continuous variable.

g) Advantage of using continuous independent variables is that you can gain more information from them than categoric variables. A graph could be drawn and a pattern discerned (or not).

How science works teaching suggestions

- **Literacy guidance.** Key terms that should be clearly understood: prediction, precision, independent variable, categoric, continuous variables.

- **Higher- and lower-level answers.** Questions b) and f) are higher-level questions. The answers for these have been provided at this level. Question e) is lower level and the answer provided is also lower level.

- **Gifted and talented.** Able students could suggest how a continuous variable might be used. Also, how the dependent variable might have been measured.

- **How and when to use these questions.** When wishing to develop ideas around detailed experimental design. The questions could be used in small group discussion.

- **Homework.** The data could be presented as a bar chart. Individual plots could be drawn on the same bar to illustrate the difficulty in establishing a clear pattern.

- **Special needs.** A pre-prepared bar chart could aid in an appreciation of the difficulty in establishing patterns with some data.

- **ICT link-up.** Spreadsheet software such as Excel could be used to enter the data and create the bar chart.

P2 4.1

Electrical charges

LEARNING OBJECTIVES

Students should learn that:

- When certain insulating materials are rubbed together, they become electrically charged.

- Objects can become charged when electrons are transferred from one to another.

- Similarly charged objects repel each other, while oppositely charged ones attract each other.

LEARNING OUTCOMES

Most students should be able to:

- Describe the process of electrical charging by friction in terms of transfer of electrons.

- State the directions of the forces between charged objects.

Some students should also be able to:

- Work out the type of charge on a charged object from the force on it due to another charged object.

Teaching suggestions

- **Gifted and talented.** Ask: 'Is it actually friction that charges up objects?' Apparently objects of different materials can become charged up just by being left in contact with each other, and rubbing objects together just increases the area of contact. The students can find out about this explanation.

- **Learning styles**

  Kinaesthetic: Charging up objects in practical activities.

  Visual: Imagining the movement of electrons / drawing diagrams to represent forces of attraction/repulsion.

  Auditory: Explaining how objects are becoming charged.

  Interpersonal: Working in pairs to report the results of practical investigations.

  Intrapersonal: Making deductions about the type of charge a material has.

SPECIFICATION LINK-UP   Unit: Physics 2.13.5

- *When certain insulating materials are rubbed against each other they become electrically charged. Negatively charged electrons are rubbed off one material onto the other.*
- *The material that gains electrons becomes negatively charged. The material that loses electrons is left with an equal positive charge.*
- *When two electrically charged bodies are brought together they exert a force on each other.*
- *Two bodies that carry the same type of charge repel. Two bodies that carry different types of charge attract.*

Lesson structure

STARTER

Laws of attraction – Give the students a set of three cards with pictures of bar magnets on them and ask them to arrange them so that they all attract each other or all repel each other. Use real magnets to check the answers. (5 minutes)

Invisible force fields – Give the students two bar magnets and ask them to balance them so that the end of one is floating above the end of the other. Ask: 'Can they balance two magnets above one another?' (5 minutes)

Attractive or repulsive – The students must give definitions of these two words. (5 minutes)

MAIN

- Start by demonstrating the balloon sticking effect; it should be fairly easy to get the balloon to stick to a wall or to your own body. You may also be able to show that two charged balloons repel each other.
- You can discuss the static build up on a TV screen by talking about the amount of dust that builds up on it.
- The use of a Van de Graaff generator is fairly essential. Students tend to get excited and some volunteer to receive a shock. Try some of the demonstrations in 'Practical support'. Make sure that you do not shock any students with any medical problems.
- The students should be familiar with the structure of the atom by now and you should be able to go through this part quickly.
- Emphasis needs to be placed on the idea that it is only the electrons that are free to move. When electrons leave an object it becomes positively charged and when they enter a neutral object it becomes negatively charged.
- Some students struggle with the idea that adding electrons makes something negative. They need to grasp that the electron has a negative charge and so if you have more electrons you have more negative charge.
- To demonstrate the effect that charged objects have on each other, the students can carry out the simple practical activity 'The force between two charged objects' from the students' book. They should have no trouble finding that like charges repel and opposite attract.
- At the end, the students should be able to tell you the simple attraction/repulsion rules.

PLENARIES

Static force – Give the students a set of diagrams with charged objects on them, two or more on each card, and ask them to draw force arrows. Some students can try to draw the direction of the resultant force. (5–10 minutes)

Forever amber – The students should write a newspaper report for the ancient Greek Newspaper νέα, ειδήσεις announcing the discovery and properties of static electricity. It was first discovered using amber or 'electrum' as they called it. (10–15 minutes)

That's magic! – Ask the students to try to design a magic trick based around static electricity. (5–10 minutes)

ractical support

he Van de Graaff generator

his is an impressive and fun piece of equipment that can be used to demonstrate many of ie aspects of static electricity. It's not just for giving shocks!

quipment and materials required

VDG and accessory kit.

etails

- A VDG is a very temperamental device. Some days it will work very well but on others you will barely get a crackle. Dry days are best, and it is advisable to polish the dome to make it shiny. Keep computer (and mobile phones) away from the VDG
- It is traditional to start by showing the sparks that the VDG can produce. Connect the discharging wand (or discharging dome) to Earth and switch on the generator. Give the dome a couple of minutes to build up charge while you explain what the VDG is doing. Bring the wand close to the dome and with luck you will get reasonably big sparks.
- Hair standing on end can be demonstrated easily, and works best if the student stands on an insulating box. Make sure that the dome is discharged before the student steps off the insulator. If you don't want to use a student, then you may have a hair sample that can be attached to the top of the dome or use a set of polystyrene balls in a container.
- Other demonstrations can include bringing a fluorescent tube close to the dome or demonstrating a current as a flow of charge.

he force between two charged objects

Vith this simple experiment, the students should be able to find that there are two types of harge and investigate how they affect each other.

quipment and materials required

or each group: retort stand with boss and clamp, cotton, two perspex rods, two polythene ods and a dry cloth.

etails

he students first need to make a 'hammock' from the cotton to be able to suspend one of ie rods from the retort stand; they might find this easier if they use some light card as a ase. They then rub one of the rods vigorously with the dry cloth and place it in the ammock. Next they rub one of the other rods and bring it close to the suspended one and ote the interaction; the suspended rod should rotate towards or away. They continue this rocedure for all of the combinations of rods. If there seems to be little movement, it is robably because the cloth is not dry enough.

DID YOU KNOW?

Some people become charged up when travelling in cars. When they get out they feel a shock as they become discharged. There are even discharging strips you can buy to fit on the back of cars that are supposed to discharge it as it travels so you don't get a shock. The shocks are becoming less common now as the compounds used in tyres change.

SUMMARY ANSWERS

1 a) Gains, to, from.
  b) Loses, from, to.

2 a) Attraction.
  b) Attraction.
  c) Repulsion.

Answers to in-text questions

a) Static electricity builds up on the screen.

b) It loses electrons.

c) The electron is negative. The nucleus is positive. So there is a force of (electrostatic) attraction between them.

KEY POINTS

- Can the students state the laws of attraction/repulsion for charges?
- Can they explain how objects become negatively or positively charged?

PHYSICS — STATIC ELECTRICITY

P2 4.1 Electrical charges

LEARNING OBJECTIVES
1 What happens when insulating materials are rubbed together?
2 What is transferred when objects become charged?
3 What happens when charges are brought together?

Have you ever stuck a balloon on a ceiling? All you need to do is to rub the balloon on your clothing before you touch it on the ceiling. The rubbing action charges the balloon with **static electricity**. The charge on the balloon attracts it to the ceiling.

a) Why does a TV screen crackle when you switch it on?

NEXT TIME YOU...
. . . take off a woolly jumper, listen out! You can hear it crackle as tiny sparks from static electricity are created. If the room is dark, you can even see the sparks.

DEMONSTRATION
The Van de Graaff generator
A Van de Graaff generator can make your hair stand on end. The dome charges up when the generator is switched on. Massive sparks are produced if the charge on the dome builds up too much.

Metal dome — Rubber belt — Earth — Felt pad (in metal holder)

Figure 1 The Van de Graaff generator

The Van de Graaff generator charges up because:
– the belt rubs against a felt pad and becomes charged,
– the belt carries the charge onto an insulated metal dome,
– sparks are produced when the dome can no longer hold any more charge.
• Why should you keep away from a Van de Graaff generator?

DID YOU KNOW?
You can get charged up just by sitting in a plastic chair. If this happens, you may feel a slight shock from static electricity when you stand up.

Inside the atom
The protons and neutrons make up the nucleus of the atom. Electrons move about in the space round the nucleus.
• A proton has a positive charge.
• An electron has an equal negative charge.
• A neutron is uncharged.
An uncharged atom has equal numbers of electrons and protons. Only electrons can be transferred to or from an atom.
1 Adding electrons to an uncharged atom makes it negative (because the atom then has more electrons than protons).
2 Removing electrons from an uncharged atom makes it positive (because the atom has fewer electrons than protons).

Electron — Proton — Neutron

Figure 2 Inside an atom

224

Additional physics

Charging by friction
Some insulators become charged by rubbing them with a dry cloth.
• Rubbing a polythene rod with a dry cloth transfers electrons to the surface atoms of the rod from the cloth. So the polythene rod becomes negatively charged.
• Rubbing a perspex rod with a dry cloth transfers electrons from the surface atoms of the rod onto the cloth. So the perspex rod becomes positively charged.

b) Glass is charged positively when it is rubbed with a cloth. Does glass gain or lose electrons when it is charged?

Electrons gained by rod — Polythene rod — Atoms become positive as a result of losing electrons — Dry cloth
Atoms become positive as a result of losing electrons — Perspex rod — Electrons gained by cloth — Dry cloth

Figure 3 Charging by friction

PRACTICAL
The force between two charged objects
Two charged objects exert a force on each other. Figure 4 shows how you can investigate this force.
• What happens?

Thread

Figure 4 The law of force for charges

Your results in the experiment above should show that:
• two objects with the same type of charge (i.e. like charges) repel each other.
• two objects with opposite types of charge (i.e. unlike charges) attract each other.

Like charges repel. Unlike charges attract.

c) What force keeps the electrons inside an atom?

SUMMARY QUESTIONS
1 Choose words from the list to complete a) and b) below:
to from loses gains
a) When a polythene rod is charged using a dry cloth, it becomes negative because it ...... electrons that transfer ...... it ...... the cloth.
b) When a perspex rod is charged using a dry cloth, it becomes positive because it ...... electrons that transfer ...... it ...... the cloth.
2 When rubbed with a dry cloth, perspex becomes positively charged. Polythene and ebonite become negatively charged. State whether or not attraction or repulsion takes place when:
a) a perspex rod is held near a polythene rod,
b) a perspex rod is held near an ebonite rod,
c) a polythene rod is held near an ebonite rod.

KEY POINTS
1 Like charges repel; unlike charges attract.
2 Insulating materials that lose electrons when rubbed become positively charged.
3 Insulating materials that gain electrons when rubbed become negatively charged.

225

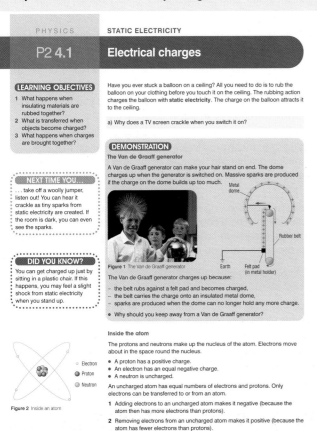

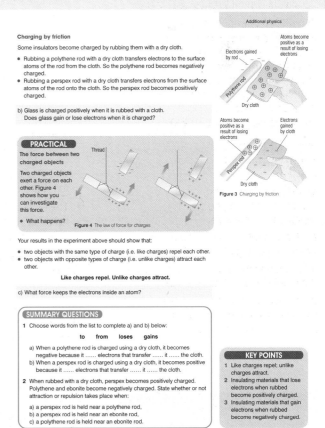

P2 4.2

Charge on the move

STATIC ELECTRICITY

LEARNING OBJECTIVES

Students should learn that:

- Conductors cannot become charged when the electrons are free to move to and from earth.
- Charge is carried by electrons moving through conducting materials and this flow of charge is called an electric current.
- A build-up of charge on an isolated body can result in the production of sparks. [**HT** only]

LEARNING OUTCOMES

Most students should be able to:

- Describe the flow of charge in a metal in terms of electron movement.
- Describe how an insulated conductor becomes charged by direct contact with a charged body.
- Explain why metals become discharged when they are connected to the earth.

Some students should also be able to:

- Explain why an earthed metal object cannot be charged.
- Explain loss of charge from a conductor due to a sharp point on the conductor.
- Explain why sparks are produced between an isolated body and an earthed conductor. [**HT** only]

Teaching suggestions

- **Gifted and talented.** Ask: 'Why does chewing metal foil on your fillings really hurt?'
- **Learning styles**
  Kinaesthetic: Using an electroscope.
  Visual: Observing the behaviour of charged objects.
  Auditory: Explaining the behaviour of an electroscope.
  Intrapersonal: Making deductions about the flow of electrons.
- **ICT link-up.** There are several pieces of software that help show that a current in a wire is a flow of electrons. These can really help with the students' visualisation of what is happening.

KEY POINTS

The students should draw a set of diagrams showing how objects become positively and negatively charged.

SPECIFICATION LINK-UP   Unit: Physics 2.13.5

- *Electrical charges can move easily through some substances, e.g. metals.*
- *The rate of flow of electrical charge is called the current.*
- *A charged body can be discharged by connecting it to earth with a conductor, charge then flows through the conductor.*
- *The greater the charge on an isolated body the greater the potential difference between the body and Earth. If the potential difference becomes high enough, a spark may jump across the gap between the body and any earthed conductor that is brought near it.* [**HT** only]

Lesson structure

STARTER

Energy transfer diagram – The students should draw a complete energy transfer diagram for a torch and an electric motor. (5 minutes)

Twenty questions – The students have twenty 'yes/no' questions to find the secret word 'current'. (5 minutes)

Current – Ask the students to describe what a 'water current' is; try to get them to realise that it is the **flow** of tiny particles of water from one place to another. (5 minutes)

MAIN

- Start by demonstrating a basic torch and discussing with the students:
  - what energy transfers are taking place
  - where the energy is coming from, and
  - where it ends up.
- This leads onto a discussion about what is carrying the energy around the circuit and why we cannot see the electrons doing this.
- Using the gold leaf electroscopes you can demonstrate, or let the class discover, that charge will escape to Earth unless the conductor is insulated.
- You can use a Van de Graaff generator to demonstrate a current is a flow of charge; see the activity box.
- The VDG can also be used to explain the idea of discharging and you should focus on the idea that electrons are moving into or out of charged objects.
- It should be relatively easy to find images or video of lightning strikes (search for 'lightning' at video.google.com); these are always impressive. Explain that the charged clouds are becoming discharged because of the flow of charge from one place to another. A large flow of charge produces a large electric current, so large that the air glows white-hot.
- There is some fairly famous footage showing that cars actually do protect you from lightning strikes. It is worth trying to find a copy of this to show the students as it makes a good end point for discussion. (Search for 'car struck by lightning video'.) The metal frame of the car conducts the current around the occupants and leaves them unharmed.

PLENARIES

Traffic lights – Give the students a set of 'facts' about static electricity and electrical current and ask them to hold up a red card for false, amber for not sure and green for true. (5–10 minutes)

Dangerous sports – The students should discuss which sports are the most dangerous with respect to lightning strikes and why. [They are actually golfing, fishing, camping and hiking.] (5–10 minutes)

'By Thor's mighty hammer!' – There are a lot of legends about the origin of lightning. Ask the students to make up a new one. (5–10 minutes)

Demonstrating a current

It is possible to show that an electric current is a flow of charge using a VDG. Higher attaining students should understand the concepts quite well.

Equipment and materials required

VDG, two tall retort stands, polystyrene ball coated in conducting paint and attached to a length of thin cotton, leads, metal plate, crocodile clips and a sensitive galvanometer.

Details

Set up the VDG and a retort stand so that the polystyrene ball rests against the dome and is free to swing on a length of cotton. Place the metal plate nearby so that when the ball swings it can easily reach the plate. Connect the plate through the galvanometer to the Earth connection on the VDG. When the VDG is switched on, the ball should charge up and be repelled by the dome. It will swing towards the metal plate and discharge to Earth, producing a brief current that the galvanometer will register. Test this out first, as it is fiddly to get just right.

Making a gold leaf electroscope

Gold leaf electroscopes have become strangely rare, but you can improvise a basic one or get your students to make a set. You can actually make quite a big one for demonstrations if you have a large conical flask.

Equipment and materials required

A conical flask (250 cm³ or larger), a cork bung to fit, longish nail to go through the cork, flat metal plate, sheet of Dutch metal foil and some sticky tape. You can use real gold if you have it!

FOUL FACTS

Standing near a tree in a thunderstorm is never a good idea. The lightning may hit the tree, but as the wood isn't a good conductor the tree is superheated and explodes sending splinters in all directions. So, if the current doesn't kill you, the flying wood might. There are many ways to avoid being killed, but the best is to get inside a building or metal car. The current will pass through the easiest path and hopefully you will be fine.

Answers to in-text questions

a) The positive end.

b) Electrons transferred to the can pass through it to the ground.

c) It gains electrons.

Practical support

Charging a conductor

This demonstration requires a gold leaf electroscope. If you don't have one, then a basic one can be made; see activity box.

Equipment and materials required

A gold leaf electroscope, crocodile clips, a lead, cloth and polythene rod.

Details

- To demonstrate that a metal object cannot be charged if it is earthed, set up the gold leaf electroscope and then attach the top plate to a pipe or other earthed object though a lead. Rub the rod vigorously and then bring it near to the top plate, finally touching it. The gold leaf should not move.

- To demonstrate that an insulated metal object can be charged, repeat the same process without the earthing lead. The gold leaf should lift, showing that the top plate becomes charged by induction as the rod approaches. When touching the rod against the plate, it works best if you just touch it with the very corner of the rod and then move it away quickly.

SUMMARY ANSWERS

1 **a)** The rate of flow of charge.

   b) Electrons that move about freely.

   c) Negatively charged.

2 **a)** Any charge supplied to it flows to Earth.

   b) Charge leaks off the dome from the tip of the pin into the air. [**HT** only]

PHYSICS   STATIC ELECTRICITY

P2 4.2   Charge on the move

LEARNING OBJECTIVES

1 Why can't we charge metals by rubbing them?
2 How is charge transferred through conducting materials?
3 What happens when a charged conductor is connected to Earth?
4 Why do charged objects sometimes produce sparks? [Higher]

Charge and current

Figure 1 Electrons on the move

When a torch lamp is on, millions of electrons pass through it every second. The electric current through the lamp is due to electrons passing through it. Each electron carries a tiny negative charge.

The rate of flow of electrical charge is called the *current*.

The filament of the torch lamp is a fine metal wire. Metals conduct electricity because they contain conduction (or delocalised) electrons. These electrons move about freely inside the metal. They are not confined to a single atom. When the torch is switched on, the battery pushes electrons through the filament.

Insulators can't conduct electricity because all the electrons are held in atoms.

a) When electrons pass through a wire in a circuit, do they move towards the positive or the negative end of the wire?

Charging a conductor

A conductor can only hold charge if it is insulated from the ground. If it isn't insulated, it won't hold any charge because electrons transfer between the conductor and the ground.

To charge an insulated conductor, it needs to be brought into contact with a charged object.

- If the object is positively charged, electrons transfer from the conductor to the object. So the conductor becomes positive because it loses electrons.

- If the object is negatively charged, electrons transfer to the conductor from the object. So the conductor becomes negative because it gains electrons.

b) A negatively charged rod is touched against a metal can on the ground. Why *doesn't* the can become negatively charged?

PRACTICAL

Using an electroscope

Figure 2 shows an electroscope, a device that detects charge, being charged. The charged rod makes direct contact with the cap. The leaf of the electroscope is repelled by the metal plate when the electroscope is charged. This happens because they both gain the same type of charge.

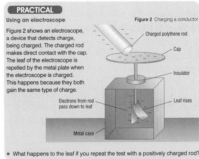

Figure 2 Charging a conductor

- What happens to the leaf if you repeat the test with a positively charged rod?

Discharging

To discharge a charged conductor safely, a conducting path (e.g. a wire) needs to be provided between the object and the ground. The conducting path allows electrons to transfer between the object and the ground. Then we say that the object is **earthed**. (See Figure 3.)

c) A positively charged metal can is discharged by earthing it. Does the can gain or lose electrons?

Sparks and strikes

If we supply a conductor with more and more charge, its **electric potential energy** increases. The **potential difference** (i.e. voltage) between the conductor and the ground increases.

If the potential difference becomes high enough, a **spark** may jump between the conductor and any nearby earthed object. A lightning strike is a dramatic example of what happens when a charged thundercloud can hold no more charge. (See Figure 4.)

SUMMARY QUESTIONS

1 Complete the following sentences:

   a) An electric current is ....
   b) A metal is a conductor because it contains ....
   c) A ...... metal object loses electrons when it is connected to the ground.

2 a) Why can't we charge a metal object if it is earthed?
   b) A drawing pin is fixed to the dome of a Van de Graaff machine with its point in the air. Explain why this stops the dome charging up when the machine is switched on. [Higher]

Figure 3 Earthing a negatively charged conductor

DID YOU KNOW?

A lightning strike is a massive flow of charge between a thundercloud and the ground. A lightning conductor on a tall building prevents lightning strikes by allowing the thundercloud to discharge gradually. The conductor is joined to the ground by a thick copper strip. This allows charge to flow safely between the conductor tip and the ground.

Figure 4 A lightning conductor

KEY POINTS

1 Electrical current is the rate of flow of charge.
2 A metal object can only hold charge if it is isolated from the ground.
3 A metal object is earthed by connecting it to the ground.
4 If a metal object gains too much charge, it will produce sparks. [Higher]

P2 4.3

Uses and dangers of static electricity

LEARNING OBJECTIVES

Students should learn:

- How static electricity is used in paint spraying, electrostatic precipitators and photocopiers.
- That static electricity can cause explosions when charge builds up and produces sparks.

LEARNING OUTCOMES

Most students should be able to:

- Describe the role that static electricity plays in paint spraying, smoke precipitation and the photocopier.
- Explain how sparks are caused by the build up of static electricity and why this is dangerous.
- Describe precautions taken to prevent static electricity and to ensure it is discharged safely.

Some students should also be able to:

- Explain safety measures to reduce or remove hazards due to static electricity.

Teaching suggestions

- **Special needs.** It is best to give the students a set of diagrams showing the equipment. They can then add flow charts to the diagrams explaining what is happening in terms of static charge.

- **Learning styles**

  Visual: Observing experiments.

  Auditory: Listening to explanations of explosions.

  Interpersonal: Discussing and evaluating anti-static measures.

  Intrapersonal: Considering the uses of static electricity.

- **ICT link-up.** The original development of the photocopier (from electro-photography through to fully working Xerox machine) is quite a tale of perseverance. The students should find out about this and see some animation of how a photocopier works by searching for 'photocopier history'.

- **Homework.** Several cleaning sprays make the claim that they prevent static build-up. Can the students design a fair experiment to test this claim?

SPECIFICATION LINK-UP   Unit: Physics 2.13.5

- *Electrostatic charges can be useful, for example in photocopiers and smoke precipitators and the basic operation of these devices.*

Students should use their skills, knowledge and understanding of 'How Science Works':

- *to explain why static electricity is dangerous in some situations and how precautions can be taken to ensure that the electrostatic charge is discharged safely.*
- *to explain how static electricity can be useful.*

Lesson structure

STARTER

The wrong carpet – Ask: 'Do some carpets cause more static build up than others?' The students should design a scientific test to find out. (10 minutes)

Shocked – Ask: 'Do you ever get shocked by static electricity?' Have them explain where and why this happens. (5–10 minutes)

It makes your hair stand on end – Static electricity can make your hair stand on end, but what else can? Discuss. (5 minutes)

MAIN

- There are lots of little bits to this lesson because static electricity has a range of uses and dangers.
- Tiny pieces of paper sticking to a charged rod can be used to give the idea of paint droplets being drawn to a charged surface.
- You can show the deflection of a stream of water from a tap by a charged polythene rod to show how charge can be used to direct flow.
- Your ICT department may have an old laser printer. With care (take off the mains lead), this can be dismantled to show the drum, toner cartridge and heating element. Emphasise that the drum contains a material that is not conductive when it is left in the dark, but it is conductive when light is shone onto it. This is what allows the image to be formed.
- The students may be familiar with the ozone smell from these printers. This is caused by the charge ionising oxygen molecules, O_2, and forming ozone, O_3, molecules.
- Demonstrating the dangers of sparks near flammable liquids is worthwhile.
- If you have made a large electroscope you might be able to demonstrate the build up of charge when a powder flows through a pipe. Set a large metal cup onto the electroscope and let cornflower flow down a plastic hosepipe into the cup. You should see some movement of the leaf. This can be saved for the next topic, where it can be studied in more detail.
- You may like to let the students explore discharging with the electroscopes; a fairly brief practical.
- Some students may not believe that things like custard powder can explode. Try the demonstration in the activity box to show their mistake. It makes a memorable end to the lesson!

PLENARIES

Sum it up – The students draw a spider diagram containing information about the uses and dangers of static electricity. They should draw it large enough so that they can add more information next lesson. (10 minutes)

Trouble at mill! – Students to write a police investigation report explaining why the local flourmill blew up last week. (10–15 minutes)

Do you smell gas? – Read out this scenario: 'You come home late at night, open your front door and smell gas! Should you turn on the light to have a look? Pick up the phone to dial for help? Get out your mobile?' The students explain why not. (5–10 minutes)

ACTIVITY & EXTENSION IDEAS

Exploding powder

A very fine powder, like custard powder or cornflower, can explode fairly readily. This demonstration uses a naked flame but sparks can do the same. Test the experiment out before demonstrating it, as it can be difficult to judge the amount of powder required. Use a safety screen and keep your head away from the flying lid.

Equipment and materials required

Metal tin with push-on metal lid (a metal coffee tin works well), candle, small bung with glass pipe through it to blow through, rubber tube and pipette bulb, safety screen, safety glasses.

Details

Drill a hole in the side of the can about half-way up and fit the bung into it. Set up the can with a candle fitted inside to the base so that the flame is about the same height as the hole. Place a small stand between the hole and the candle inside the tin. Set the can up behind a safety screen and place a **small** amount of custard powder onto the stand. Fit a rubber tube to the glass pipe and a pipette bulb on the far end, long enough so that you can be out of the way. Finally light the candle, place the lid on firmly and step back. Press the bulb so that fine powder is blown into the flame. You should get a decent bang.

Practical support

Get rid of the charge

This is simple reinforcement of the discharging ideas from the last topic.

Equipment and materials required

For each group: electroscope, polythene and perspex rods, cloths, metal wires.

Details

The students charge up the electroscopes with the rods and then try to think of ways to discharge them. They should be explaining what is happening to the electrons – are they entering or leaving the electroscope?

P2 4.3   Uses and dangers of static electricity

LEARNING OBJECTIVES

1 In what ways is static electricity useful?
2 In what ways is static electricity dangerous?
3 How can we get rid of static electricity where it is dangerous?

Using electrostatics

The electrostatic paint sprayer

Automatic paint sprayers are used to paint metal panels. The spray nozzle is connected to the positive terminal of an electrostatic generator. The negative terminal is connected to the metal panel. The panel attracts paint droplets from the spray. The droplets of paint all pick up the same charge and repel each other, so they spread out to form a fine cloud of paint.

a) Why are the spray nozzle and the panel oppositely charged?

Figure 1 An electrostatic paint sprayer

The electrostatic precipitator

Coal-fired power stations produce vast quantities of ash and dust. Electrostatic precipitators remove this material from the flue gases before they get into the atmosphere.

The particles of ash and dust pass through a grid of wires in the precipitator. Look at Figure 2. The grid wires are negative so the particles become negatively charged when they touch it. The charged particles are attracted onto the positively charged metal plates. The plates are shaken at intervals so the ash and dust that build up on them drop to the floor of the precipitator. They are then removed.

b) What difference would it make if the grid was not charged?

Ash and dust collect on plates
Grid of charged wires
Metal plates charged oppositely to the grid wires
Waste gases carrying ash and dust
Figure 2 An electrostatic precipitator

The photocopier

The key part of a photocopier is a charged drum or plate. This loses charge from the parts of its surface exposed to light. Figure 3 shows how a photocopier works.

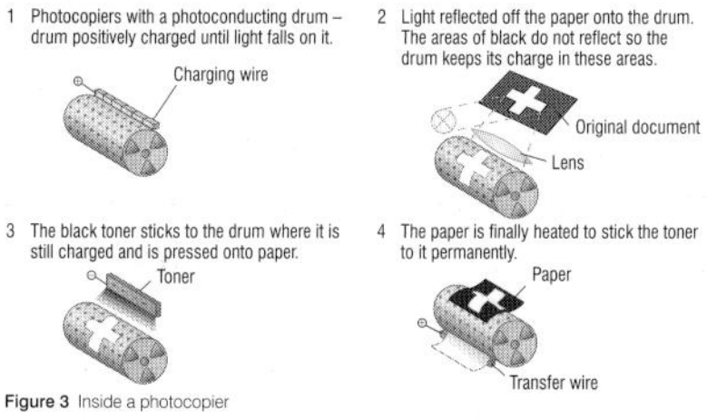

1 Photocopiers with a photoconducting drum – drum positively charged until light falls on it.
Charging wire

2 Light reflected off the paper onto the drum. The areas of black do not reflect so the drum keeps its charge in these areas.
Original document
Lens

3 The black toner sticks to the drum where it is still charged and is pressed onto paper.
Toner

4 The paper is finally heated to stick the toner to it permanently.
Paper
Transfer wire

Figure 3 Inside a photocopier

c) Why are photocopies sometimes charged when they come out of the photocopier?

Electrostatics hazards

Pipe problems

When a road tanker pumps oil or petrol into a storage tank, the connecting pipe must be earthed. If it isn't, the pipe could become charged. A build-up of charge would cause a spark. This could cause an explosion as the fuel vapour reacts with oxygen in the air.

Static electricity is also generated when grains of powder are pumped through pipes. Friction between the grains and the pipe charges them. An explosion could happen due to a spark igniting the powder.

d) Why is the rubber hose of a petrol pump made of special conducting rubber?

Antistatic floors

In a hospital, doctors use anaesthetic gases during operations. Some of these gases are explosive. If the gas escapes into the air, a tiny spark could make it explode. To eliminate static charge in operating theatres, an **antistatic material** is used for the floor surface. This material is a poor electrical insulator so it conducts charge to Earth.

e) Why do the doctors and nurses wear antistatic clothes in an operating theatre?

Figure 4 Operating theatres have antistatic floors

PRACTICAL

Getting rid of the charge

Charge up an electroscope.

● How do you discharge it? Explain what happens.

SUMMARY QUESTIONS

1 Complete a) and b) using the words below:

attracted   gain   lose   repelled

a) Positively charged paint droplets from a paint spray are ...... by the spray nozzle. The droplets ...... electrons when they reach the negatively charged metal panel.

b) Dust particles in an electrostatic precipitator touch a positively charged wire. The particles ...... electrons to the wire and are then ...... by a negatively charged metal plate.

2 a) The delivery pipe between the road tanker and the storage tank must be earthed before any petrol is pumped from the tanker. Why is this an important safety measure?

b) Why does an operating theatre in a hospital have antistatic floor covering?

GET IT RIGHT!

Remember that electrostatic charge has its uses as well as its dangers.

KEY POINTS

1 A spark from a charged object can make powder grains or certain gases explode.
2 To eliminate static electricity,
a) use antistatic materials, and
b) earth metal pipes and objects.

SUMMARY ANSWERS

1 a) Repelled, gain.

b) Lose, attracted.

2 a) To conduct any charge on the pipe nozzle to the ground, so it can't cause sparks which would ignite the fuel.

b) To conduct any charge to the ground so it can't cause sparks, which would cause gases used in the theatre to explode.

Answers to in-text questions

a) So that droplets are charged as they leave the spray nozzle and attracted to the panel.

b) Most of the particles would pass straight through it.

c) The powder transfers charge onto the paper from the photocopier drum. The charge stays on the paper sometimes.

d) So that it conducts charge away from the pump nozzle to Earth.

e) So their clothing doesn't become charged and produce sparks.

KEY POINTS

Can the students describe two ways in which sparks can be prevented in industry?

P2 4.4 Static issues

SPECIFICATION LINK-UP
Unit: Physics 2.13.5

Students should use their skills, knowledge and understanding of 'How Science Works':

- *to explain why static electricity is dangerous in some situations and how precautions can be taken to ensure that the electrostatic charge is discharged safely.*

- *to explain how static electricity can be useful.*

An electric discovery

What does the word 'charge' mean? Someone who runs at top speed 'charges along' filled with adrenalin. An electrically charged object is filled with static electricity. The term 'electric charge' was first used over 300 years ago when scientists discovered that certain materials such as ebonite, glass and resin attracted bits of paper when they are rubbed. They knew this effect had been discovered by the ancient Greeks using amber, a naturally occurring fossil resin. So they used the word 'electric', from the Greek word for 'amber', to describe the attractive power of these materials. The action of rubbing a suitable material was said to *charge* it with electricity.

Further experiments showed that:

- identical charged materials always repel each other,
- ebonite and glass attract,
- ebonite and resin repel,
- glass and resin attract.

More tests showed that there are two types of charge and they cancel each other out. So the two types of charge were called 'positive' and 'negative'.

QUESTION

1 a) Why did scientists conclude from these results that there are only two types of charge?

b) In terms of electrons, explain why equal and opposite amounts of charge cancel each other out.

Powder tests

The diagram shows how to test the charging of powder grains. The powder is poured through a pipe into a metal can on an electroscope.

If the powder is charged, the metal plate of the electroscope and the gold leaf attached to it both become charged. As a result, the leaf is repelled by the plate.

To find out if the powder charge is positive or negative, a negatively charged rod (e.g. polythene) held near the can will make the leaf rise further if the charge on the electroscope is negative.

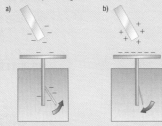

Using an electroscope to show that a powder gets charged when it flows through a pipe

Powder in beaker — Funnel — Pipe — Metal can — Leaf rises as powder is poured into the can — Metal plate

a) b)

An electroscope test. a) The leaf rises when a negative rod is brought near. b) The leaf falls when a positive rod is brought near.

QUESTION

2 An electroscope is charged negatively by touching the cap with a negatively charged rod. Explain, in terms of electrons, why this makes the leaf go up and stay up.

Teaching suggestions

Activities

- **An electric discovery** – The first writings on electrical charge are thought to be those of Thales of Miletus. He is considered, by some, to be the first recorded scientist because of his belief that the world could be explained without reference to gods or supernatural forces. Ask: 'Why are the two types of charge called positive and negative? Scientists could have chosen any words that indicated some kind of 'oppositeness'.'

- **Powder tests** – This test can be carried out using very fine powder, e.g. cornflower powder, and letting it roll along different tubes into a metal cup of a gold leaf electroscope. It can be difficult to get the powder charged up enough to detect without a long tube. The best way to get a long tube is to use a **dry** hosepipe and make the powder go through by rippling it along the length and finally into the can.

- **The ink jet printer** – To demonstrate the spitting action of an ink jet you can use melting point tubes. Dip the tube in ink at one end, so that a tiny drop moves into the tube. Seal the far end with a Plasticine blob or push it into a bit of cork. If you heat the middle of the tube strongly with a Bunsen, the ink should spit out. It won't be a very accurate method and you can't direct the ink. You could show the deflection of flowing water, again to show how charge can be used to change the path of the liquid.
  You can use Animation P2 4.3 'Photocopier' from the Additional Science CD ROM at this point.

- **A chip problem** – The vast majority of microprocessors use CMOS technology, as it needs less power to operate and so produces less heat. This means that computer systems are very vulnerable to static electricity until they are earthed in a circuit board. You should be able to find an anti-static wrist strap used by installers and the anti-static bag and foam that the chips are kept in prior to installation. Can the students design an experiment to see how effective the anti-static strap and packaging are?

The ink jet printer

An ink jet printer has an 'ink gun' inside that directs a jet of charged ink droplets at the paper. The ink droplets pass between two metal 'deflecting' plates before reaching the paper.

- By making one plate positive and the other negative, the droplets can be deflected as they pass between the plates. This happens because the droplets are attracted to the oppositely charged plate.
- The plates are made positive and negative by applying a potential difference to them. The potential difference is controlled by signals from the computer. The computer is programmed to make the inkjet print characters and graphics on the paper at high speed.

An ink jet printer

QUESTION

3 What do you think would happen if the ink droplets are too big?

A chip problem

Computer chips can be damaged by static electricity. Most microcomputers contain *CMOS* chips. Tiny amounts of charge on the pins of a CMOS chip can destroy its electrical properties. To prevent chips being damaged by static electricity, manufacturers insert them into antistatic foam sheets before packaging them.

Special tools are available to transfer chips to and from circuits to prevent them becoming charged in the transfer. Touching the chip briefly when a charged object is nearby would cause it to become charged. The figure shows how this can happen.

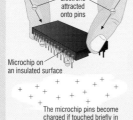

Electrons attracted onto pins

Microchip on an insulated surface

The microchip pins become charged if touched briefly in the presence of a charged object

Microchip damage

ACTIVITY

A company that makes computers has found that some of its chips don't work. The supplier says the company must be more careful when the chips are used. Imagine you work in the company. You think the problem is at the supplier. Send an e-mail to the supplier to find out.

Global junk

Computers sooner or later become out of date. But what happens to them then? At the present time, thousands of old or damaged computers are shipped out every year to junkyards in poor countries. People survive there by taking valuable material out of these computers and selling it. However, this is often dangerous work and chemicals from the junk get into local water supplies. Most of the junk is not biodegradable. It's mounting up all the time.

Computer junk

ACTIVITY

What can we do to stop this problem?
a) Discuss ways to tackle the problem.
b) Present a five-minute radio slot to raise awareness of the issue and to suggest some solutions.

231

Special needs

If the students are to research any of the above topics, they should be provided with a template to collect information on. This should include a list of suitable web sites to look at and enough space for the students to make relevant notes. See for example, www.howstuffworks.com.

ICT link-up

Ideally any research templates should be in electronic form so that the students can paste the images into it. A word processor or presentation package can be used to make a file with headings and questions that students can use as a template. With this they can assemble notes and images.

Teaching assistant

The assistant should help with the research to make sure that the students are focused on the tasks and not having any IT difficulties.

Learning styles

Kinaesthetic: Researching into history of electricity.

Auditory: Explaining how static electricity can damage computers.

Interpersonal: Debating ways to reduce computer waste.

Intrapersonal: Writing a report of computer waste/static damage.

- **Global junk** – The ecological damage due to the computer industry is quite large as many resources are used in the manufacture, and some heavy metals are incorporated in the machines. A typical computer accounts for 6000 MJ of energy during its construction, use and disposal. Even though computers are becoming more efficient and using less energy each, more and more people are using them so the cost to the environment increases. Do the students think that computers are benefiting society enough to justify their costs?

Extension or homework

Printer history – Printer technology has evolved rapidly over the last 20 years. Ink jet printers are now so cheap that they are given away free with computers – but it wasn't always this way. The first low-resolution black and white ink jet was released in 1988 and cost £1000. Usable laser printers were developed by Hewlett-Packard and Apple in 1984, again the prices were well above £1000. The students can look into the development of these two static-based devices.

SUMMARY ANSWERS

1 a) i) When she moved on the chair, her clothing rubbed against the chair and charged her.

    ii) The charge on her discharged to the door handle as a spark.

  b) i) Negatively charged.   ii) It would attract it.

2 a) i) From, to. ii) On.

  b) i) From, to. ii) To, from.

3 a) Negative.

  b) To attract the droplets on to it.

  c) Electrons flow along the wires to the spray nozzle, are carried by the charged paint droplets, and return to the voltage supply from the metal panel.

4 a) i) They would go in the same direction onto the paper, so there would be a straight line on the paper as it moves past the jet.

    ii) By contact with the grid wires.

  b) To stop the fuel becoming charged or charging the fuel nozzle as it flows out of the nozzle. To stop the aircraft fuel tank becoming charged so no sparks are produced.

Summary teaching suggestions

• The students should be able to come up with a complete explanation of charging and discharging and the forces between objects. The answers to questions 1 and 2 should show this clearly.

• The remaining two questions test the applications and dangers of static electricity; again the students should be clearly describing the movement of charge and the attraction and repulsion effects.

SUMMARY QUESTIONS

1 a) Helen has just had a shock. She got up from a plastic chair to open the door and got an electric shock when she touched the door handle.
  i) How did she become charged?
  ii) Why did she feel a shock when she touched the door handle?

  b) An object was charged by rubbing it with a dry cloth. When it was held near a negatively charged rod, it repelled the rod.
  i) State if the object was charged positively or negatively.
  ii) Would the object attract or repel a positively charged rod?

2 Complete the sentences below using words from the list.

from   on   to

a) A polythene rod is charged negatively by rubbing it with a cloth.
  i) Electrons transfer …… the cloth …… the rod.
  ii) The electrons …… the rod cannot move about freely.

b) A positively charged rod is touched on an insulated metal object.
  i) Electrons transfer …… the metal object …… the rod.
  ii) If the metal object is then 'earthed', electrons transfer …… it …… the ground.

3 A paint sprayer in a car factory is used to paint a metal panel. The spray nozzle is connected to the negative terminal of a voltage supply unit. The metal panel is connected to the positive terminal of the voltage supply unit.
a) What type of charge is gained by the paint droplets when they leave the spray nozzle?
b) Why is the metal panel made positive?
c) Why is there an electric current along the wires joining the metal panel and the paint spray nozzle to the voltage supply unit?

4 a) i) In an ink jet printer, what difference would it make if the droplets were not charged?
  ii) In an electrostatic precipitator, how are the dust particles charged?
  b) When an airplane is being refuelled, explain why a wire is connected between the aircraft and the fuel tanker?

EXAM-STYLE QUESTIONS

1 A plastic rod is rubbed with a dry cloth.

(a) The rod becomes negatively charged. Explain how this happens.

(b) What charge is left on the cloth?

(c) What happens if the negatively charged rod is brought close to another negatively charged rod.

2 The picture shows an electrostatic paint spray being used to apply paint to a sheet of metal.

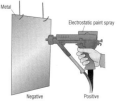

Metal

Electrostatic paint spray

Negative   Positive

(a) The paint droplets are given a positive charge as they leave the nozzle. Explain why.

(b) The sheet of metal is given a negative charge. Explain why.

(c) (i) A painter wanted to find out the best distance between the nozzle of the paint spray and the sheet of metal to be painted. What could the painter use to measure the independent variable in this investigation?

  (ii) Why would it be a good idea for the painter to carry out some trials before deciding upon the range of the independent variable?

EXAM-STYLE ANSWERS

1 a) Electrons are rubbed off the cloth *(1 mark)*
and are transferred onto the rod. *(1 mark)*
Electrons have a negative charge, so rod gains a negative charge. *(1 mark)*

  b) Positive *(1 mark)*

  c) They repel each other *(1 mark)*

2 a) Drops all have same charge so they repel each other *(1 mark)*
so paint spreads out to give a fine spray. *(1 mark)*

  b) Opposite charge to paint spray *(1 mark)*
so paint is attracted to metal *(1 mark)*
and less paint is needed. *(1 mark)*

  c) i) Ruler or any instrument that measures distance. *(1 mark)*
    ii) If the distance is too small there will be splashing of paint off the metal. *(1 mark)*
    If the distance is too great no paint will reach the metal. *(1 mark)*

3 The waste gases and smoke particles pass through the negatively charged metal grid. *(1 mark)*
The smoke particles gain negative charge *(1 mark)*
so they are repelled from the grid. *(1 mark)*
They are attracted to the positively charged collecting plates. *(1 mark)*

The smoke particles stick to the plates. *(1 mark)*
The collecting plates are periodically knocked so the smoke particles fall off and are taken away. *(1 mark)*

4 **G E A F B** *(4 marks)*
(minus 1 for each letter not in correct order)

The picture shows an electrostatic smoke precipitator. This is used to separate smoke particles from waste gases in a chimney.

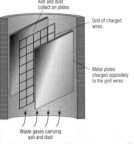

Explain how the smoke precipitator works. (6)

A photocopier uses static electricity to make photocopies.

The following sentences describe how the photocopier works.

The sentences are in the wrong order.

A Black ink powder is attracted to the charged parts of the plate.
B The paper is heated so the powder melts and sticks to the paper.
C The copying plate is given a charge.
D This is now a photocopy of the original page.
E Where light hits the plate the charge leaks away, leaving a pattern of the page.
F Black ink powder is transferred onto a piece of paper.
G An image of the page to be copied is projected onto the charged copying plate.

Arrange the sentences in the right order. Start with sentence **C** and finish with sentence **D**.

(4)

HOW SCIENCE WORKS QUESTIONS

Lightning conductors are very important in protecting buildings from lightning strikes. New designs must be thoroughly tested. They must work first time and every time. They have to be tested in a standard way. This method is described in the diagram below.

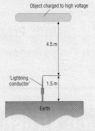

Object charged to high voltage

4.5 m

'Lightning conductor'   1.5 m

Earth

The conditions must be followed strictly. This includes the temperature of the room and the humidity. The charge is built up on the object above the lightning conductor and photographs are taken of the 'lightning' as it forms. This allows accurate measurements to be made of the time taken for the lightning conductor to respond. The measurements are made in microseconds.

a) Explain why it is important that the testing is carried out in exactly the same way each time. (1)
b) To find the correct temperature for these tests, the scientists carried out surveys.
   Suggest when they carried out the surveys. (1)
c) What do you think they were measuring? (1)
d) How many sets of data do you think they collected? (1)
e) What is the sensitivity of the equipment used to time the response of the lightning conductor? (1)
f) Explain why repeat tests on the same lightning conductor might give different results. (1)
g) Should this testing be carried out by the company manufacturing the lightning conductors or by an independent company? Explain your answer. (1)

233

HOW SCIENCE WORKS ANSWERS

a) To ensure that the results are valid, i.e. it is a type of control for different people carrying out the testing.

b) When lightning was striking.

c) The air temperature.

d) As many as possible (e.g. a minimum of 50 as there is likely to be a wide range of temperatures.)

e) Microseconds are used to time the response of the lightning conductor.

f) The lightning conductor may have been damaged.

g) It could be done by both. However, a potential buyer would want to be assured of its reliability and therefore an independent company would be better. The testing will probably be monitored by an independent company.

How science works teaching suggestions

- **Literacy guidance**
  - Key terms that should be clearly understood: control, reliability, sensitivity, bias.
  - Question d) expects a longer answer, where students can practise their literacy skills.

- **Higher- and lower-level answers.** Question d) is a higher level question and the answer provided above is also at this level. Question b) is lower level and the answer provided is also lower level.

- **Gifted and talented.** Able students could consider how the speed of the conduction of the charge is measured. It is not as simple as it sounds here. The charge is built up and it is this relationship to the discharge through the lightning conductor that has to be measured.

- **How and when to use these questions.** When wishing to develop idea of controls in developing testing regimes and the potential for bias.
  The questions could be prepared for homework and then used in class in a plenary.

- **Homework.** Prepare questions at home. Consider the testing regime needed for other equipment such as trip switches or transformers.

- **Special needs.** Some students will need a more visual representation of the testing apparatus to appreciate what is happening.

Exam teaching suggestions

- Weaker students often think that for an object to be positively charged it has gained protons. Emphasise that it is only electrons that move during the transfer of charge.

- This section of the specification is very qualitative. To gain full marks in questions such as question 3, students must write their explanations clearly and in a logical sequence.
  Encourage them to plan their answer before putting pen to paper.

- In question 4 students are given the statements that form a description to put in the correct order. They should read through all the statements first, before attempting to order them.

- Students must be able to describe both uses and dangers of static electricity.

P2 5.1

Electric circuits

LEARNING OBJECTIVES

Students should learn:

- That electrical circuits are drawn using standard symbols.
- The symbols used to represent common circuit components.

LEARNING OUTCOMES

Most students should be able to:

- Recognise and draw the circuit symbols for a cell, a battery, a switch, a lamp, a resistor, a variable resistor, a diode, a fuse, a voltmeter, an ammeter, a thermistor and an LDR.
- Describe the function of each of the above components.

Some students should also be able to:

- Draw circuit diagrams using the above symbols.

Teaching suggestions

- **Special needs.** Some students have particular difficulties with connecting up electronic circuits correctly, because they cannot match the neat circuit diagrams with the jumble of wires they are given. With these students it is best to use fixed boards, like the Locktronic ones. It is a good idea to write the names of the component on them until the students connect the symbol and name correctly.
- **Gifted and talented.** For the circuit building exercise, these students should be asked to look at the currents through the different branches of the circuit and find any relationships. They could even look into the potential differences and see if they can come up with the relationship before you discuss it in future lessons.
- **Learning styles**
  Kinaesthetic: Doing circuit building activities.
  Visual: Recognising symbols.
  Auditory: Listening to explanations of circuit behaviour.
  Interpersonal: Discussing and collaborating on circuit building.
- **Teaching assistant.** Your teaching assistant will be quite busy helping the students assemble the circuits. Make sure that you both describe how to construct the circuit in exactly the same way, so that you do not confuse the students.
- **Homework.** Get the students to memorise the symbols and have a quick test at the beginning of the next lesson.

SPECIFICATION LINK-UP   Unit: Physics 2.13.6

- *To interpret and draw circuit diagrams using standard symbols.*
  (See Student Book page 234 for symbols)

Lesson structure

STARTER

It's symbolic – Show a set of slides/diagrams to the students containing common symbols and ask them to say what they mean. Use road signs, hazard signs, washing symbols, etc. (5–10 minutes)

Describe the circuit – Give the students diagrams of two circuits containing cells, switches and lamps, one series and one parallel, and ask them to describe them both in a paragraph. (5–10 minutes)

Shoddy diagrams – Show the students a set of poorly draw circuit diagrams and ask them to explain how they could be improved or draw corrected circuits. (10 minutes)

MAIN

- Much of this topic will be revision. The students should be familiar with the basic ideas of circuits and circuit symbols from Key Stage 3.
- It is best to use this topic to check the students' circuit building skills, so that you can be sure that they can carry out the investigations later.
- Ask: 'Do symbols have to look like what they represent?' When introducing each symbol, show the students a real device represented by that symbol.
- You could show them that there are several physically different looking devices that match each symbol. For example, there are a range of different ammeters represented by the same symbol.
- Most students cope well with the basic symbols for lamps, switches and batteries. You will probably find that they struggle more with the various resistors.
- Point out the difference between a cell and a battery. Many students still do not understand that a battery is a series of cells. It helps to physically show a 1.5 V cell and then put two or more together to produce a battery. You can point out that the word 'battery' means 'a collection put close together' as in 'battery hens' and a 'battery of guns'.
- The best way to describe resistors is by discussing what is added to the basic resistor symbol:
  - The variable resistor has an arrow through it showing that you can adjust it.
  - The LDR has arrows going towards it representing light.
  - The fuse has a thin line representing the thin wire that runs inside it.
- With the remaining time, you should let the students build a couple of circuits. Those in the 'Circuits tests' activity are fine, or you could challenge higher attaining students further (see 'Gifted and talented').

PLENARIES

Match them up – Show the students a set of pictures/photographs of circuits and a set of circuit diagrams. They have to match them up. (5 minutes)

Symbol domino loop – Give the students a set of cards showing circuit symbols and descriptions of their functions. They have to place these cards in a complete loop, matching the symbol to the function. Can they name them all? (5–10 minutes)

Circuit problems – The students have to spot problems with diagrams of simple circuits, marking errors and suggesting corrections. (5 minutes)

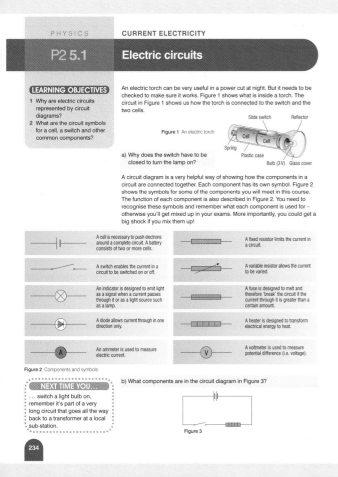

ACTIVITY & EXTENSION IDEAS

Circuit building equipment
There are several schools of thought on which circuit building equipment is best. I have assumed that you are building circuits from separate components and simple leads, so you may have to modify the equipment lists for this chapter to suit your preferences. Using battery packs is not very economic when compared to low voltage power supplies, unless your students are careless and destroy a lot of bulbs.

Circuit building
This is more of a support activity to help students remember how to build basic circuits.

Equipment and materials required
Battery pack (3 V), three torch bulbs (3 V), leads, ammeter.

Details
Ask the students to set up a simple series circuit with two bulbs, and then a parallel one with a bulb on each branch. Can they make a parallel circuit with one bulb on one branch and two on the other? What can they say about the brightness of the bulbs? They should draw circuit diagrams of all these circuits before they construct them.

Practical support

Circuit tests
This is a simple introduction to building circuits allowing the students to refresh their skills.

Equipment and materials required
Cells (1.5 V), torch bulb (1.5 V), leads, diode, variable resistor.

Details
The students set up a simple circuit with the variable resistor and the bulb. They should find that the variable resistor can be used to alter the brightness of the bulb and be told that this is due to the current being changed. The students then include a diode in the circuit. They should then reverse the diode. This will show that the diode only allows the current in one direction.

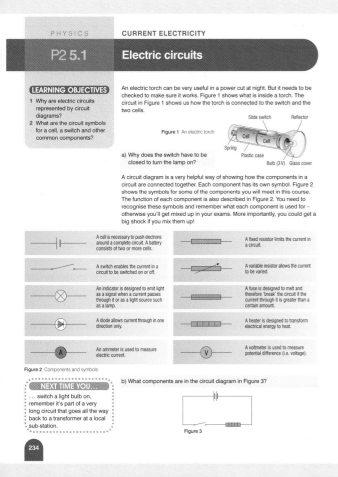

The following is the textbook spread (pages 234–235):

PHYSICS **CURRENT ELECTRICITY**

P2 5.1 Electric circuits

LEARNING OBJECTIVES
1 Why are electric circuits represented by circuit diagrams?
2 What are the circuit symbols for a cell, a switch and other common components?

An electric torch can be very useful in a power cut at night. But it needs to be checked to make sure it works. Figure 1 shows what is inside a torch. The circuit in Figure 1 shows us how the torch is connected to the switch and the two cells.

Figure 1 An electric torch

a) Why does the switch have to be closed to turn the lamp on?

A circuit diagram is a very helpful way of showing how the components in a circuit are connected together. Each component has its own symbol. Figure 2 shows the symbols for some of the components you will meet in this course. The function of each component is also described in Figure 2. You need to recognise these symbols and remember what each component is used for – otherwise you'll get mixed up in your exams. More importantly, you could get a big shock if you mix them up!

A cell is necessary to push electrons around a complete circuit. A battery consists of two or more cells.

A switch enables the current in a circuit to be switched on or off.

An indicator is designed to emit light as a signal when a current passes through it or as a light source such as a lamp.

A diode allows current through in one direction only.

An ammeter is used to measure electric current.

A fixed resistor limits the current in a circuit.

A variable resistor allows the current to be varied.

A fuse is designed to melt and therefore 'break' the circuit if the current through it is greater than a certain amount.

A heater is designed to transform electrical energy to heat.

A voltmeter is used to measure potential difference (i.e. voltage).

Figure 2 Components and symbols

NEXT TIME YOU...
... switch a light bulb on, remember it's part of a very long circuit that goes all the way back to a transformer at a local sub-station.

b) What components are in the circuit diagram in Figure 3?

Figure 3

PRACTICAL
Circuit tests

Connect a variable resistor in series with the torch lamp and a battery, as shown in Figure 4. Adjusting the slider of the variable resistor alters the amount of current flowing through the bulb and therefore affects its brightness.

Figure 4 Using a variable resistor

• In Figure 4, the torch lamp goes dim when the slider is moved one way. What happens if the slider is moved back again?
• What happens if you include a diode in the circuit?

DID YOU KNOW...
You would damage a portable radio if you put the batteries in the wrong way round unless a diode is in series with the battery. The diode only allows current through when it is connected as shown in Figure 5. If the battery is reversed in the circuit, the diode stops electrons passing round the circuit.

Figure 5 Using a diode

c) Would the radio in Figure 5 work if the diode was 'turned round' in the circuit?

SCIENCE @ WORK
Drivers need to know what road signs mean, otherwise there would be chaos on our roads. Electricians and circuit designers need to know what circuit signs and symbols mean for the same reason. We mark the direction of the current in a 'direct current' circuit from + to – round the circuit. This convention was agreed long before electrons were discovered.

SUMMARY QUESTIONS
1 Name the numbered components in the circuit diagram.
2 a) Redraw the circuit diagram in question 1 with a diode in place of the switch so it allows current through.
   b) What further component would you need in this circuit to alter the current in it?

KEY POINTS
1 Every component has its own agreed symbol.
2 A circuit diagram shows how components are connected together.
3 A battery consists of two or more cells connected together.

234 · 235

SUMMARY ANSWERS

1 Cell, switch, indicator, fuse.

2 a)

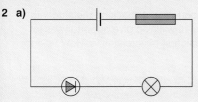

b) A variable resistor.

Answers to in-text questions

a) So current passes through it and through the lamp bulb.

b) Two cells, a switch and a heater.

c) No.

KEY POINTS

The students should be able to identify and draw circuit symbols (matching exercise).

DID YOU KNOW?

Diodes have limitations; if too high a voltage is placed on them in the wrong direction they 'break down' and allow a current to flow. This breakdown voltage is different for different types of diode, but it means that we cannot always rely on a diode to prevent the current flowing the wrong way. It's best to put the batteries in the right-way round.

P2 5.2   Resistance

LEARNING OBJECTIVES

Students should learn:

- How to use an ammeter and voltmeter.
- How to measure the resistance of a component.
- That a wire at a constant temperature obeys Ohm's law.
- That the resistance of a metal wire does not depend on the direction of the current.

LEARNING OUTCOMES

Most students should be able to:

- Measure the resistance of a resistor using an ammeter and voltmeter.
- Calculate the resistance of a device from the current through it and the potential difference across it.
- State Ohm's law for a metal wire.

Some students should also be able to:

- Perform calculations that involve rearrangement of the resistance equation.

Teaching suggestions

- **Special needs.** For resistance calculations, provide the students with a question sheet that has templates for the layout for equations so that they go through the process step by step.

- **Gifted and talented.** The students can find out about resistor coding bands used on simple resistors. Give them one each to take home, and ask them to come back with the resistance and tolerance.

- **Learning styles**
  Kinaesthetic: Building a range of circuits.
  Visual: Obtaining and presenting resistance information.
  Auditory: Explaining the pattern of the results.
  Interpersonal: Discussing and evaluating results.
  Intrapersonal: Making deductions about the behaviour of devices.

- **Homework.** Give the students a set of current–potential difference data for three different diameters of wire of the same length, and ask them to plot the three on the same set of axes. Ask: 'What can you say about the relationship between the diameter and the resistance?'

SPECIFICATION LINK-UP   Unit: Physics 2.13.6

- *Current–potential difference graphs are used to show how the current through a component varies with the potential difference across it.*
- *The current through a resistor (at a constant temperature) is directly proportional to the potential difference across the resistor.*
- *Potential difference, current and resistance are related by the equation:*

$$\text{potential difference} = \text{current} \times \text{resistance}$$
$$\text{(volt, V)} \qquad \text{(ampere, A)} \qquad \text{(ohm, }\Omega\text{)}$$

- *The resistance of a component can be found by measuring the current through and potential difference across the component.*

Students should use their skills, knowledge and understanding of 'How Science Works':

- *to apply the principles of basic electrical circuits to practical situations.*

Lesson structure

STARTER

Resistors – Show the students the circuit symbols for all of the different types of resistor and ask them to describe the similarities in the symbols. Ask: 'What do they think the other parts of the symbols mean?' (5 minutes)

Reading the meter – Show the students some pictures of analogue meters and ask them to read off the value shown. Use a variety of different scales for the meters. (5 minutes)

MAIN

- It is very important that the students understand how to use an ammeter and voltmeter, and they have a good opportunity to do that in this lesson.

- Currents through components are often less than one ampere, so the students will have to get used to using 'milliamperes' (most people just use 'milliamps') in a lot of their work.

- A simple analogy explaining resistance is a student moving along a packed corridor with his eyes closed. Other students in the corridor will get in the way, resisting his progress. If all of the other students are moving about a lot, the resistance will be higher – a bit like the wire heating up.

- During the movement, the electrons will lose energy as they collide with the ions in the metal. Link this idea to earlier energy transformation work. It is always important to check that the students do not think that electrons are used up as they move. They just lose (transfer) energy.

- Some computer simulations of electron movement show that the electrons are losing energy as they move through the potential difference. These are very useful.

- There will be a few students who will find it strange that the letter 'I' is used to represent current in equations. It is surprisingly difficult to find out why. The students may be more comfortable just using word equations. The Greek letter omega is chosen to represent ohms, because it sounds the same (as good a reason as any).

- The practical activity in the Student Book is a good way of checking the students' skills in using the meters and using the equation. It will also give opportunities for students to manipulate variables and design a fair test (this relates to 'How Science Works').

PLENARIES

An electron's tale – Students write a paragraph about the journey of an electron around a circuit containing a lamp and resistor. They should write about the energy changes that are going on in the circuit. (10 minutes)

ACTIVITY & EXTENSION IDEAS

Resistance and length of a wire

This traditional experiment works very well and has often been a source of centre-assessed practical work in the past. Most students find the experiment easier if they use high resistivity wire, such as constantan, as this produces resistances that are easy to understand (1 Ω), as opposed to copper wires which have very low resistances and can make the graphs harder to draw for some.

Equipment and materials required

Ammeter, voltmeter, metre ruler, 3 V battery pack (or power supply), leads, switch, two crocodile clips, test wire, heatproof mat.

Details

The students set up the circuit used for the measurement of resistance of a wire, but they connect the crocodile clips to the test wire at measured lengths. This allows them to find out how resistance varies with length. There are many ways to improve the accuracy and precision of this experiment (this relates to 'How Science Works'). The experiment should be carried out on a heatproof mat as short lengths can get hot.

Teaching suggestions – continued

ICT link-up. If you get different groups to investigate the current–potential difference characteristics of different lengths (or diameters) of wire, then the data can be collected in a spreadsheet. This can be used to calculate the mean resistance of the wire from the data, and then to check for a relationship between the length (or diameter) and the resistance by quickly plotting a graph.

Teaching assistant. As in the previous lesson, the assistant will be best employed in helping the students construct their circuits. They can also help some students with the plotting of graphs.

SUMMARY ANSWERS

1 a)
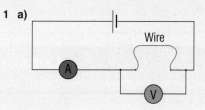
Wire

b) 6.0 Ω

2 W: 6.0 Ω; X: 80 V; Y: 2.0 A; Z: 24 Ω

KEY POINTS

The students should plot a graph of the results of their investigations to find the relationship between current and potential difference.

Practical support

Investigating the resistance of a wire

The students can investigate if the resistance of a wire depends on the current flowing through it. Constantan wires works well, as these do not change resistance as much when they heat up. It is also advisable to use battery packs or power packs with lockable voltage outputs, as the wires can heat up and cause burns if high currents are used.

Equipment and materials required

For each group: a power supply or battery pack, connecting leads, switch, crocodile clips, variable resistor, length of wire (30–50 cm), heatproof mat, ammeter and voltmeter.

Details

The students connect up the circuit with the variable resistor and test wire in series. The ammeter is also placed in series and the voltmeter in parallel across the test wire. Some students will struggle to set this up, so check the circuits before they are switched on. Using the variable resistor, the students can control the current through the test wire and measure both the current and the potential difference. In general, they should find that the resistance stays constant unless the wire heats up too much. The experiment shouldn't get too hot if low p.d.s are used but use a heatproof mat anyway.

Answers to in-text questions

a) 8.0 Ω

b) 10 Ω

P2 5.2 Resistance

LEARNING OBJECTIVES

1 Where should you put an ammeter and a voltmeter in a circuit?
2 What is resistance and what is its unit?
3 What is Ohm's law?
4 What happens if you reverse the current in a resistor?

Ammeters and voltmeters

Figure 1 Using an ammeter and a voltmeter

Look at the ammeter and the voltmeter in the circuit in Figure 1.

- The ammeter measures the current through the torch lamp. It is connected in series with the lamp so the current through them is the same. The ammeter reading gives the current in amperes (A) (or milliamperes, (mA) for small currents, where 1 mA = 0.001 A).
- The voltmeter measures the potential difference (p.d.) across the torch lamp. It is connected in parallel with the torch lamp so it measures the pd across it. The voltmeter reading gives the p.d. in volts (V).

Electrons passing through a torch lamp have to push their way through lots of vibrating atoms. The atoms resist the passage of electrons through the torch lamp.

We define the **resistance** of an electrical component as:

$$\text{Resistance (ohms)} = \frac{\text{potential difference (volts)}}{\text{current (amperes)}}$$

The unit of resistance is the *ohm*. The symbol for the ohm is the Greek letter Ω.

We can write the definition above as:

$$R = \frac{V}{I}$$

where V = potential difference (volts)
I = current (amperes)
R = resistance (ohms).

Worked example

The current through a wire is 2.0 A when the potential difference across it is 12 V.

Calculate the resistance of the wire.

Solution

$$R = \frac{12V}{2.0A} = 6.0\,\Omega$$

GET IT RIGHT!

Ammeters are always connected in series and voltmeters are always connected in parallel.

a) The current through a wire is 0.5 A when the current through it is 4.0 V. Calculate the resistance of the wire.

PRACTICAL

Investigating the resistance of a wire

Does the resistance of a wire change when the current through it is changed? Figure 2 shows how we can use a variable resistor to change the current through a wire. Make your own measurements and use them to plot a current–potential difference graph like the one in Figure 2.

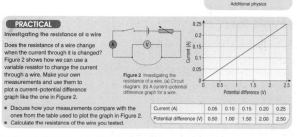

Figure 2 Investigating the resistance of a wire. (a) Circuit diagram. (b) A current–potential difference graph for a wire.

- Discuss how your measurements compare with the ones from the table used to plot the graph in Figure 2.
- Calculate the resistance of the wire you tested.

Current (A)	0.05	0.10	0.15	0.20	0.25
Potential difference (V)	0.50	1.00	1.50	2.00	2.50

b) Calculate the resistance of the wire that gave the results in the table.

Current–potential difference graphs

The graph in Figure 2 and your own graph should show:

- a straight line through the origin,
- that the current is directly proportional to the potential difference.

Reversing the potential difference makes no difference to the shape of the line. The resistance is the same whichever direction the current is in.

The graph shows that the resistance (= potential difference/current) is constant. This was first discovered for a wire at constant temperature by Georg Ohm and is known as Ohm's law:

The current through a resistor at constant temperature is directly proportional to the potential difference across the resistor.

We say a wire is an ohmic conductor because its resistance is constant.

SUMMARY QUESTIONS

1 a) Draw a circuit diagram to show how you would use an ammeter and a voltmeter to measure the current and potential difference across a wire.
b) The potential difference across a resistor was 3.0 V when the current through it was 0.5 A. Calculate the resistance of the resistor.

2 Rearranging the equation $R = \frac{V}{I}$ gives $V = IR$ or $I = \frac{V}{R}$

Use these equations to calculate the missing values in each line of the table.

Resistor	Current (A)	Potential difference (V)	Resistance (Ω)
W	2.0	12.0	?
X	4.0	?	20
Y	?	6.0	3.0
Z	0.5	12.0	?

KEY POINTS

1 Resistance (ohms) =
$$\frac{\text{potential difference (volts)}}{\text{current (amperes)}}$$

2 The current through a resistor at constant temperature is directly proportional to the potential difference across the resistor.

P2 5.3

More current–potential difference graphs

LEARNING OBJECTIVES

Students should learn:

- That the resistance of a filament lamp increases as the temperature rises.
- How the resistance of a diode depends on the p.d. applied across it.
- How the resistance of a thermistor decreases when its temperature increases.
- How the resistance of an LDR decreases when the light level increases.

LEARNING OUTCOMES

Most students should be able to:

- Draw current–p.d. graphs for a resistor, a filament lamp and a diode.
- Describe how the resistance of a filament lamp changes depending on the current through it.
- Describe how the resistance of a diode depends on which way round it is connected in a circuit.
- Describe how the resistance of a thermistor and light dependent resistor depend on the temperature and light level respectively.

Some students should also be able to:

- Explain the changes that take place in a series circuit including a thermistor or a LDR when the temperature or the light level changes.

Teaching suggestions

- **Gifted and talented.** Ask; 'How does a diode work?' This simple semiconductor is quite difficult to explain, but these students can try to find out how they operate.
- **Learning styles**
  Kinaesthetic: More building of circuits.
  Visual: Presenting data graphically.
  Auditory: Discussing patterns in results.
  Interpersonal: Reporting on behaviour of components.
  Intrapersonal: Evaluating investigations.
- **ICT link-up.** Using data logging equipment is a very good way of collecting data for current–potential difference graphs. Once set up, the students just have to adjust the variable resistor, press the space bar to take readings and then repeat until all the data is collected. The graphs can be displayed in seconds.

SPECIFICATION LINK-UP   Unit: Physics 2.13.6

- *Current–potential difference graphs are used to show how the current through a component varies with the potential difference across it.* (See Student Book page 238 for graphs.)
- *The resistance of a filament lamp increases as the temperature of the filament increases.*
- *The current through a diode flows in one direction only. The diode has a very high resistance in the reverse direction.*
- *The resistance of a light-dependent resistor (LDR) decreases as light intensity increases.*
- *The resistance of a thermistor decreases as the temperature increases (i.e. knowledge of negative temperature coefficient thermistor only is required).*
- *The current through a component depends on its resistance. The greater the resistance the smaller the current for a given potential difference across the component.*

Students should use their skills, knowledge and understanding of 'How Science Works':

- *to apply the principles of basic electrical circuits to practical situations.*

Lesson structure

STARTER

Pop! – Set up a circuit with a filament bulb that will have too high a current. Switch it on when the room is silent (so that they can hear the 'tink' sound) and ask the students to explain what happened. (5–10 minutes)

Three switches – Ask: 'You are outside a room with three switches that control three light bulbs inside the room; one switch for each light. How can you work out which switch controls which light if you are only allowed to open the door and go into the room once?' (5 minutes)

MAIN

- Start this topic with a reminder of the practical work from last lesson.
- The initial practical activities can take up a lot of time if the students wish to take plenty of measurements. You may like to let some groups do one of the experiments while the rest do the other, and then get them to share the results.
- The results should show that the filament lamp does not have a straight line on its current–potential difference graph. This is because it is heating up and the resistance is increasing, the greater the current in the wire. (This relates to 'How Science Works': identifying relationships between variables.)
- Link this back to the students' ideas about what happens to a material when it gets hotter. The ions are vibrating more and the electrons are having more collisions with them. This increases the resistance.
- A diode is a more complex device. It behaves in a non-ohmic way. The reasons for its behaviour are beyond Key Stage 4, but you might like to ask the gifted and talented group to look into it.
- Some students will have heard of light emitting diodes and think that all diodes give out light. You could demonstrate one of these in a circuit, showing that it only lights up if it is placed in the circuit the right way. The arrow on the symbol shows the direction of the current.
- As with the initial practical task, you might like to set different groups different tasks for the thermistor and LDR.
- These two devices can be investigated to cover many of the investigative aspects of 'How Science Works'.

PLENARIES

Inside the black box – An electrical component has been placed inside a black box with only the two connections visible. The students should design an experiment to find out what it is. (5 minutes)

ractical support

nvestigating different components

he students can investigate how the resistance of a filament lamp and a diode change
hen the p.d. across them is changed.

quipment and materials required

or each group: a power supply or battery pack, connecting leads, variable resistor,
mmeter, voltmeter, filament lamp, fixed resistor and diode.

etails

he students connect up the circuit with the component under test in series with the variable
esistor. The ammeter is also placed in series and the voltmeter is placed in parallel with the
est component. Using the variable resistor, the students change the p.d. across the
omponent and record the current and p.d. From the results, the students produce a
urrent–potential difference graph. They should also try the circuit with the current flowing in
e opposite direction, to show that this does not affect the lamp but is very important for the
iode.

hermistors and light-dependent resistors (LDRs)

he students can investigate a LDR by finding out how its resistance is related to the
istance it is from a bright light. Sensitive thermistors can have a significant change in
esistance from just placing them between finger and thumb to warm them up.

Answers to in-text questions

a) i) 5 Ω **ii)** 10 Ω

b) It decreases.

c) The resistance is constant.

d) The resistance decreases.

DID YOU KNOW?

The longest lasting light bulb has been on for more than 100 years. It's in a fire station in Livermore, USA, and was installed in 1901. It is never off, except in power cuts and when it was moved to the new fire station. You might like to check if it's still going!

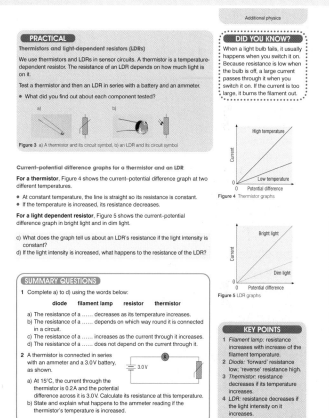

PHYSICS

CURRENT ELECTRICITY

P2 5.3 More current–potential difference graphs

LEARNING OBJECTIVES

1 What happens to the resistance of a filament lamp as its temperature increases?
2 How does the current through a diode depend on the potential difference across it?
3 What happens to the resistance of a thermistor as its temperature increases and of an LDR as the light level increases?

Have you ever switched a light bulb on only to hear it 'pop' and fail? Electrical appliances can fail at very inconvenient times. Most electrical failures are because too much current passes through a component in the appliance.

PRACTICAL

Investigating different components

The current through a component in a circuit depends on its resistance. We can use the circuit in Figure 2 on the previous page to find out what affects the resistance of a component. We can also see if reversing the component in the circuit has any effect.

Make your own measurements using a filament lamp and a diode.

Plot your measurements on a current–potential difference graph.

- Why can you use a line graph to display your data? (See page 280.)

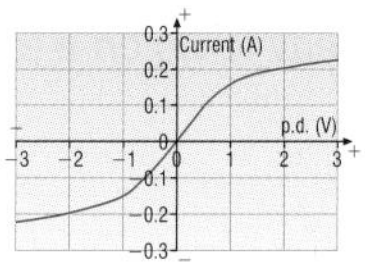

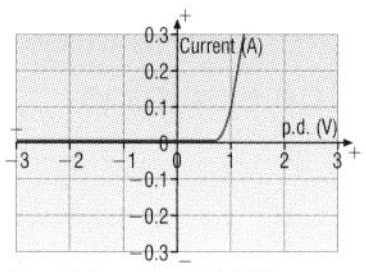

Figure 1 A current–potential difference graph for a filament lamp

Using current–potential difference graphs

A filament lamp

Figure 1 shows the current–potential difference graph for a torch lamp (i.e. a low-voltage filament lamp). The 'reverse' measurements are plotted on the negative sections of each axis.

- The line ***curves*** away from the current axis. So the current is ***not*** directly proportional to the potential difference. The filament lamp is a non-ohmic conductor.
- The resistance (= potential difference/current) increases as the current increases. So the resistance of a filament lamp increases as the filament temperature increases.
- Reversing the potential difference makes no difference to the shape of the curve. The resistance is the same for the same current, regardless of its direction.

a) Calculate the resistance of the lamp at i) 0.1 A, ii) 0.2 A.

Figure 2 A current–potential difference graph for a diode

The diode

Look at Figure 2 for a diode:
- In the 'forward' direction, the line curves towards the current axis. So the current is not directly proportional to the potential difference. A diode is not an ohmic conductor.
- In the reverse direction, the current is negligible. So its resistance in the reverse direction is much higher than in the forward direction.

b) What can we say about the forward resistance as the current increases?

238

Additional physics

PRACTICAL

Thermistors and light-dependent resistors (LDRs)

We use thermistors and LDRs in sensor circuits. A thermistor is a temperature-dependent resistor. The resistance of an LDR depends on how much light is on it.

Test a thermistor and then an LDR in series with a battery and an ammeter.

- What did you find out about each component tested?

Figure 3 a) A thermistor and its circuit symbol, b) an LDR and its circuit symbol

DID YOU KNOW?

When a light bulb fails, it usually happens when you switch it on. Because resistance is low when the bulb is off, a large current passes through it when you switch it on. If the current is too large, it burns the filament out.

Current–potential difference graphs for a thermistor and an LDR

For a thermistor, Figure 4 shows the current–potential difference graph at two different temperatures.

- At constant temperature, the line is straight so its resistance is constant.
- If the temperature is increased, its resistance decreases.

Figure 4 Thermistor graphs

For a light dependent resistor, Figure 5 shows the current–potential difference graph in bright light and in dim light.

c) What does the graph tell us about an LDR's resistance if the light intensity is constant?
d) If the light intensity is increased, what happens to the resistance of the LDR?

Figure 5 LDR graphs

SUMMARY QUESTIONS

1 Complete a) to d) using the words below:

diode filament lamp resistor thermistor

a) The resistance of a ...... decreases as its temperature increases.
b) The resistance of a ...... depends on which way round it is connected in a circuit.
c) The resistance of a ...... increases as the current through it increases.
d) The resistance of a ...... does not depend on the current through it.

2 A thermistor is connected in series with an ammeter and a 3.0 V battery, as shown.

a) At 15°C, the current through the thermistor is 0.2 A and the potential difference across it is 3.0 V. Calculate its resistance at this temperature.
b) State and explain what happens to the ammeter reading if the thermistor's temperature is increased.

KEY POINTS

1 *Filament lamp:* resistance increases with increase of the filament temperature.
2 *Diode:* 'forward' resistance low; 'reverse' resistance high.
3 *Thermistor:* resistance decreases if its temperature increases.
4 *LDR:* resistance decreases if the light intensity on it increases.

239

SUMMARY ANSWERS

1 **a)** Thermistor. **b)** Diode. **c)** Filament lamp. **d)** Resistor.

2 **a)** 15 Ω

b) The ammeter reading increases because the resistance of the thermistor decreases.

KEY POINTS

Get the students to construct a sentence describing how the resistance of a filament lamp, diode, thermistor and light dependent resistor change.

P2 5.4

Series circuits

LEARNING OBJECTIVES

Students should learn that:

- In a series circuit the same current passes through all components.

- The p.d. of the voltage supply is shared across the components in a series circuit.

- Cells in series add their potentials to give a higher voltage.

- The total resistance in a series circuit is the sum of the component resistances.

LEARNING OUTCOMES

Most students should be able to:

- State that the current through components in series is the same.

- Find the total potential difference across several components in series, given the potential difference across each component.

- Find the total potential difference of a group of cells connected in series.

- Calculate the total resistance in a series circuit.

Some students should also be able to:

- Analyse a simple series circuit to find the current and p.d. across components.

Teaching suggestions

- **Special needs.** Provide the students with a printed set of circuit rules containing the ones from this topic and the next, to help them remember them all.

- **Gifted and talented.** There are a set of rules about the current and potentials in a circuit called Kirchhoff's laws. These are basically an electrical statement of the laws of conservation of energy, and the students should be able to find out what they are.

- **Learning styles**
  Kinaesthetic: Carrying out practical activities with series circuits.
  Visual: Obtaining data from meter readings.
  Auditory: Discussing results.
  Interpersonal: Collaborating on experiments.
  Intrapersonal: Evaluating results, including the accuracy of measuring instruments.

SPECIFICATION LINK-UP   Unit: Physics 2.13.6

- *The potential difference provided by cells connected in series is the sum of the potential difference of each cell (depending on the direction in which they are connected).*

- *For components connected in series:*
  - *The total resistance is the sum of the resistance of each component.*
  - *There is the same current through each component.*
  - *The total potential difference of the supply is shared between the components.*

Students should use their skills, knowledge and understanding of 'How Science Works':

- *to apply the principles of basic electrical circuits to practical situations.*

Lesson structure

STARTER

Duff battery – Ask the students to correct this information: 'A chemical reaction in a battery makes electrons. These move quickly around a circuit and go through the components until there are no electrons left. The battery 'runs out' when there are no chemicals left in it to make electrons from.' [e.g. 'A chemical reaction in the battery provides electrons with energy. These electrons move slowly around the circuit and push other electrons through it. As the electrons move through the components of the circuit they lose energy until they reach the cell again when they have transferred all of the energy they were provided with. The battery 'runs out' when all of the chemicals in it have reacted together and it cannot provide the electrons with any more energy.'] (5 minutes)

Series – Ask: 'What is the meaning of the word 'series'?' The students have to give as many examples of its use as possible. (5 minutes)

One way only – Ask: 'In what situation are we allowed only one way through something?' Let the students think of a few. Ask: 'If there is only one way to go on a tour, do the same number of people come out as go in?' (5 minutes)

MAIN

- When discussing series and parallel circuits, many teachers use the analogy of a central heating system with the water representing the electrons, a pump representing the battery etc. There are limitations with this concept, but it can help lower ability students.

- The students need to be reminded that the current is a flow of electrons. The larger the current, the more electrons are passing a point each second. The electrons cannot be destroyed and they do not escape from the circuit.

- The students tend to understand the current rules quite well, but struggle more with the idea that the potential difference is shared. They should test this out in the practical task.

- Generally, try to move students from using 'voltage' to 'potential difference', as reflected in the specification.

- As noted in the practical, there can be some minor errors produced by the meters so you will have to explain them to the students. This is a useful opportunity to consider 'How Science Works': accuracy/precision/reliability.

- Simulation software can be used to show the measurement of the p.d. across many lamps connected in series. It is also easy to add more cells to show that the total p.d. drop across the components always matches the p.d. of the battery.

- Many students will simply accept that the total resistance of a set of components in series is just the same as the individual resistances without the need for calculations.

- Test their understanding by showing them a set of resistors in series, and asking for the total resistance. Students should have no problems with this.

- You might like to show some more difficult resistors such as 1.5 MΩ or 33 mΩ to get the students used to them.

Practical support

Investigating potential differences in a series circuit

This experiment helps to verify the rule about potential differences in series circuits.

Equipment and materials required

For each group: a power supply or battery pack (1.5 V), connecting leads, variable resistor, 1.5 V lamp and three voltmeters.

Details

The students connect up a lamp and variable resistor in series. Connect up one voltmeter across the cell (with voltage, V_{tot}), one across the lamp (with voltage, V_1) and one across the variable resistor (with voltage, V_2). When the circuit is switched on the students should find that $V_1 + V_2 = V_{tot}$ when the variable resistor is set to any position. You may find that the voltmeters don't quite show this, and so it is a good time to discuss errors and the limitation of the equipment (this relates to 'How Science Works').

Teaching suggestions – continued

- **ICT link-up.** If at all possible, show a simulation of electron movement through the circuit to show that the electrons pass all the way around the circuit and are not used up. The simulation should also have some way of showing that the electrons are transferring energy as they go.

- **Homework.** Give the students some series circuit diagrams with missing voltages, currents or resistances. Ask them to find the missing values. This should test their knowledge of the current–p.d.–resistance relationship and the total resistance rule.

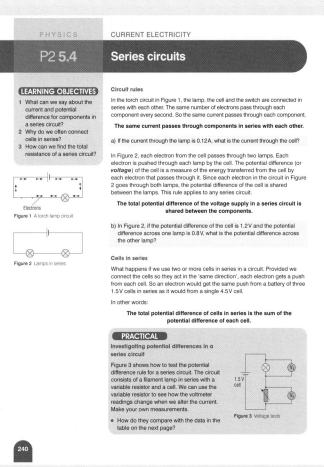

P2 5.4   Series circuits

LEARNING OBJECTIVES

1 What can we say about the current and potential difference for components in a series circuit?
2 Why do we often connect cells in series?
3 How can we find the total resistance of a series circuit?

Figure 1 A torch lamp circuit

Figure 2 Lamps in series

Circuit rules

In the torch circuit in Figure 1, the lamp, the cell and the switch are connected in series with each other. The same number of electrons pass through each component every second. So the same current passes through each component.

The same current passes through components in series with each other.

a) If the current through the lamp is 0.12 A, what is the current through the cell?

In Figure 2, each electron from the cell passes through two lamps. Each electron is pushed through each lamp by the cell. The potential difference (or **voltage**) of the cell is a measure of the energy transferred from the cell by each electron that passes through it. Since each electron in the circuit in Figure 2 goes through both lamps, the potential difference of the cell is shared between the lamps. This rule applies to any series circuit.

The total potential difference of the voltage supply in a series circuit is shared between the components.

b) In Figure 2, if the potential difference of the cell is 1.2 V and the potential difference across one lamp is 0.8 V, what is the potential difference across the other lamp?

Cells in series

What happens if we use two or more cells in series in a circuit. Provided we connect the cells so they act in the 'same direction', each electron gets a push from each cell. So an electron would get the same push from a battery of three 1.5 V cells in series as it would from a single 4.5 V cell.

In other words:

The total potential difference of cells in series is the sum of the potential difference of each cell.

PRACTICAL

Investigating potential differences in a series circuit

Figure 3 shows how to test the potential difference rule for a series circuit. The circuit consists of a filament lamp in series with a variable resistor and a cell. We can use the variable resistor to see how the voltmeter readings change when we alter the current. Make your own measurements.

- How do they compare with the data in the table on the next page?

Figure 3 Voltage tests

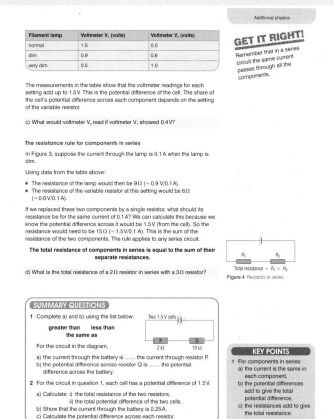

Filament lamp	Voltmeter V_1 (volts)	Voltmeter V_2 (volts)
normal	1.5	0.0
dim	0.9	0.6
very dim	0.5	1.0

The measurements in the table show that the voltmeter readings for each setting add up to 1.5 V. This is the potential difference of the cell. The share of the cell's potential difference across each component depends on the setting of the variable resistor.

c) What would voltmeter V_2 read if voltmeter V_1 showed 0.4 V?

The resistance rule for components in series

In Figure 3, suppose the current through the lamp is 0.1 A when the lamp is dim.

Using data from the table above:

- The resistance of the lamp would then be 9 Ω (= 0.9 V/0.1 A).
- The resistance of the variable resistor at this setting would be 6 Ω (= 0.6 V/0.1 A).

If we replaced these two components by a single resistor, what should its resistance be for the same current of 0.1 A? We can calculate this because we know the potential difference across it would be 1.5 V (from the cell). So the resistance would need to be 15 Ω (= 1.5 V/0.1 A). This is the sum of the resistance of the two components. The rule applies to any series circuit.

The total resistance of components in series is equal to the sum of their separate resistances.

d) What is the total resistance of a 2 Ω resistor in series with a 3 Ω resistor?

Figure 4 Resistors in series

Total resistance = $R_1 + R_2$

GET IT RIGHT!

Remember that in a series circuit the same current passes through all the components.

SUMMARY QUESTIONS

1 Complete a) and b) using the list below:

> greater than   less than
> the same as

For the circuit in the diagram,

Two 1.5 V cells   P   2 Ω   Q   10 Ω

a) the current through the battery is ...... the current through resistor P.
b) the potential difference across resistor Q is ...... the potential difference across the battery.

2 For the circuit in question 1, each cell has a potential difference of 1.5 V.

a) Calculate: i) the total resistance of the two resistors,
     ii) the total potential difference of the two cells.
b) Show that the current through the battery is 0.25 A.
c) Calculate the potential difference across each resistor.

KEY POINTS

1 For components in series:
a) the current is the same in each component,
b) the potential differences add to give the total potential difference,
c) the resistances add to give the total resistance.

PLENARIES

Current loop – Let the students play a looped question game with questions based on electrical circuits; no branches allowed. (5 minutes)

Controlling current – Give the students a set of cards representing cells (1.5 V) and resistors (1 Ω, 2 Ω, 5 Ω etc.) and ask them to put some of them together to produce a current of 1 A, then a current of 0.5 A. (5 minutes)

Circuit rules – The students should start making a list of circuit rules that help them work out the currents, potential differences and resistances in series and parallel circuits. (5–10 minutes)

KEY POINTS

The students should fill in the missing values from a set of circuit diagrams to show that they understand current and potential difference.

Answers to in-text questions

a) 0.12 A
b) 0.4 V
c) 1.1 V
d) 5 Ω

SUMMARY ANSWERS

1 a) The same as.   b) Less than.

2 a) i) 12 Ω   ii) 3.0 V
b) $\dfrac{3\,V}{12\,\Omega} = 0.25\,a$
c) P = 0.5 V, Q = 2.5 V

P2 5.5

Parallel circuits

LEARNING OBJECTIVES

Students should learn:

- That the potential difference across components in parallel is the same.
- That the total current in a parallel circuit is the sum of the currents in the individual branches.

LEARNING OUTCOMES

Most students should be able to:

- Recognise components in parallel with each other.
- Calculate the current in a branch of a parallel circuit, given the total current and the current in the other branches.
- Identify, for resistors of known resistance in parallel, which resistor has the most current passing through it and which has the least.

Some students should also be able to:

- Analyse simple parallel circuits to find the current through branches and the p.d. across components.

Teaching suggestions

- **Special needs.** There are some more tricky circuits here and the students may need a step-by-step guide to assemble them: 'connect the positive end of the battery to the ammeter', etc. You might also think about attaching labels A_1, A_2 to the ammeters to reduce confusion.
- **Learning styles**
  Kinaesthetic: Carrying out practical tests involving parallel circuits.
  Visual: Recording and presenting data.
  Auditory: Explaining the observations.
  Interpersonal: Working in small groups in practical work.
  Intrapersonal: Making deductions about current and p.d. in circuits.
- **ICT link-up.** A range of software is available to simulate circuit construction and measure current and voltages. This can be much easier to use than assembling larger parallel circuits with a number of voltmeters and ammeters.
- **Homework.** Give the students some series and parallel circuits to analyse. They should find the missing currents, potential differences and resistances.
- **Teaching assistant.** The students will have much more difficulty connecting devices up in parallel than they did in series, so your teaching assistant will again have to help out with construction of these circuits.

SPECIFICATION LINK-UP   Unit: Physics 2.13.6

- *For components connected in parallel:*
  - *The potential difference across each component is the same.*
  - *The total current through the whole circuit is the sum of the currents through the separate components.*

Students should use their skills, knowledge and understanding of 'How Science Works':

- *to apply the principles of basic electrical circuits to practical situations.*

Lesson structure

STARTER

Circuit jumble – Show the students a diagram of a parallel circuit with three branches and several components on each branch. The wires and components are jumbled up and the students have to redraw the circuit properly. (5–10 minutes)

The river – Show the students a picture of a river that branches and rejoins. Ask then to explain what happens to the current in the river before, during and after the split. (5–10 minutes)

Parallel – Ask: 'What does the word 'parallel' mean?' The students can give as many uses as possible. (5 minutes)

MAIN

- The initial investigation is straightforward and the students should be able to find the rule easily. A discussion of errors involved in the ammeter readings helps to get across concepts involving single measurements from 'How Science Works'.
- A simulation can be used if there are not enough ammeters, but you should show the results in a real circuit too.
- Spend a bit of time explaining that at the junction of a branch some of the electrons go one way while the rest go the other way, but they all come from and go back to the battery.
- The bypass idea helps some students realise that because there are more paths for the current a larger current can flow.
- The second simple circuit should confirm that the p.d. is the same across both of the resistors. If the resistors are the same size then the currents should also be the same through each branch.
- To stretch higher attaining students, ask them to investigate a circuit that has two resistors on one branch and one on the other. Ask: 'Does the p.d. across the first branch match that across the second?'
- The circuit analysis will show if the students have got a firm grip of the equations. You may have to lead them through the analysis one step at a time. Try a couple more circuits if time permits.

PLENARIES

The light that shines twice as bright lasts half as long – If two lamps are connected to a battery in parallel, they will shine more brightly than if they were connected in series but they will only last half as long. Can the students explain why? (5–10 minutes)

Stair lights – Can the students design a simple circuit that can be used to turn the lights on and off from the top and bottom of a set of stairs. If time permits, they could build one. (10–15 minutes)

Parallel analogies – Can the students come up with any more analogies for a parallel circuit besides the ones from the 'Did you know' box? They should explain them to each other to decide which is best. (5–10 minutes)

Practical support

Investigating parallel circuits

This experiment shows that that the current is divided through parallel branches.

Equipment and materials required

For each group: a power supply or battery pack (1.5 V), connecting leads, variable resistor, two 1.5 V lamps and three ammeters.

Details

The students set up the circuit with two parallel branches, each with an ammeter. The third ammeter is placed in series with the power supply or battery to measure total current, and the variable resistor is used in series with the battery to control the current. The readings from the two ammeters on the branches (A_2 and A_3) should be equal to the total current from the battery (A_1). As in the experiment from the last lesson, there can be inaccuracies in the readings so go through the results with the students and discuss the reasons for these errors (this relates to 'How Science Works').

Potential difference in a parallel circuit

This is another simple circuit used to verify that the potential difference across parallel components is the same.

Equipment and materials required

For each group: a power supply or battery pack (1.5 V), connecting leads, a 2 Ω resistor and a 5 Ω resistor, a variable resistor, and two voltmeters.

Details

The students connect up the circuit as shown and measure the p.d. across the two resistors. This should be the same. To show that this fact does not change, replace one of the resistors with a variable one and alter its resistance.

Answers to in-text questions

a) 0.30 A

b) The 3 Ω resistor.

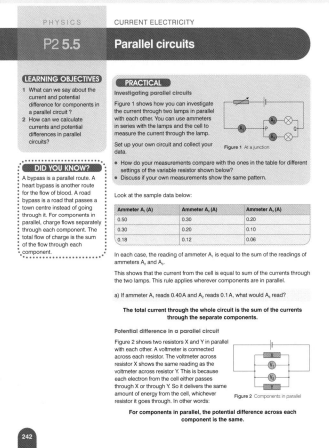

P2 5.5 Parallel circuits

LEARNING OBJECTIVES

1 What can we say about the current and potential difference for components in a parallel circuit?
2 How can we calculate currents and potential differences in parallel circuits?

DID YOU KNOW?

A bypass is a parallel route. A heart bypass is another route for the flow of blood. A road bypass is a road that passes a town centre instead of going through it. For components in parallel, charge flows separately through each component. The total flow of charge is the sum of the flow through each component.

PRACTICAL

Investigating parallel circuits

Figure 1 shows how you can investigate the current through two lamps in parallel with each other. You can use ammeters in series with the lamps and the cell to measure the current through the lamp.

Set up your own circuit and collect your data.

Figure 1 At a junction

- How do your measurements compare with the ones in the table for different settings of the variable resistor shown below?
- Discuss if your own measurements show the same pattern.

Look at the sample data below:

Ammeter A₁ (A)	Ammeter A₂ (A)	Ammeter A₃ (A)
0.50	0.30	0.20
0.30	0.20	0.10
0.18	0.12	0.06

In each case, the reading of ammeter A_1 is equal to the sum of the readings of ammeters A_2 and A_3.

This shows that the current from the cell is equal to sum of the currents through the two lamps. This rule applies wherever components are in parallel.

a) If ammeter A_1 reads 0.40 A and A_2 reads 0.1 A, what would A_3 read?

The total current through the whole circuit is the sum of the currents through the separate components.

Potential difference in a parallel circuit

Figure 2 shows two resistors X and Y in parallel with each other. A voltmeter is connected across each resistor. The voltmeter across resistor X shows the same reading as the voltmeter across resistor Y. This is because each electron from the cell either passes through X or through Y. So it delivers the same amount of energy from the cell, whichever resistor it goes through. In other words:

Figure 2 Components in parallel

For components in parallel, the potential difference across each component is the same.

Calculations on parallel circuits

Components in parallel have the same potential difference across them. The current through each component depends on the resistance of the component.

- The bigger the resistance of the component, the smaller the current through it. The resistor which has the largest resistance passes the smallest current.
- We can calculate the current using the equation:

$$\text{current (amperes)} = \frac{\text{potential difference (volts)}}{\text{resistance (ohms)}}$$

b) A 3 Ω resistor and a 6 Ω resistor are connected in parallel in a circuit. Which resistor passes the most current?

Worked example

The circuit diagram shows three resistors $R_1 = 1\,\Omega$, $R_2 = 2\,\Omega$ and $R_3 = 6\,\Omega$ connected in parallel to a 6 V battery.

Calculate:

i) the current through each resistor,
ii) the current through the battery.

Solution

i) $I_1 = \dfrac{V_1}{R_1} = \dfrac{6}{1} = 6\,\text{A}$

$I_2 = \dfrac{V_2}{R_2} = \dfrac{6}{2} = 3\,\text{A}$

$I_3 = \dfrac{V_3}{R_3} = \dfrac{6}{6} = 1\,\text{A}$

ii) The total current from the battery $= I_1 + I_2 + I_3 = 6\,\text{A} + 3\,\text{A} + 1\,\text{A} = 10\,\text{A}$

SUMMARY QUESTIONS

1 Choose words from the list to complete a) and b):

current   potential difference

a) Components in parallel with each other have the same ....
b) For components in parallel, each component has a different ....

2 The circuit diagram shows three resistors $R_1 = 2\,\Omega$, $R_2 = 3\,\Omega$ and $R_3 = 6\,\Omega$ connected to each other in parallel and to a 6 V battery.

Calculate:

a) the current through each resistor,
b) the current through the battery.

KEY POINTS

1 For components in parallel,
a) the potential difference is the same across each component,
b) the total current is the sum of the currents through each component,
c) the bigger the resistance of a component, the smaller its current is.

SUMMARY ANSWERS

1 a) Potential difference. **b)** Current.

2 a) R_1: 3 A; R_2: 2 A; R_3: 1 A

  b) 6 A

KEY POINTS

Can the students find the current through the branches of a parallel circuit when given the resistances and battery voltage? Give the students some parallel circuits to analyse. They should be able to fill in missing values.

P2 5.6 Circuits in control

SPECIFICATION LINK-UP

Unit: Physics 2.13.6

This spread can be used to revisit:

Students should use their skills, knowledge and understanding of 'How Science Works':

* *to apply the principles of basic electrical circuits to practical situations.*

Teaching suggestions

Activities

* **A magic eye** – The magic eye circuit is not too difficult to build, so show one to the students. In reality these circuits often have transistors or relays to switch on the second circuit containing the motor or fan, but for the students' designs this is not necessary.

* **The development of microelectronics** The computing power available on a microchip has followed a pattern first described by Gordon E Moore (founder of Intel) in 1965. He suggested that the available computing power on a microchip would double every year. This hasn't quite happened; it seems to have doubled every two years from 1965 to the current day. A high power computer chip has close to one billion transistors on it (although many of these are from on chip memory); though, according to Moore's law, this information will be out of date by the time you read it!

* Connecting 'control chips' to human brains is the topic of many stories, generally about how this would be a bad idea. There are alternative views presented in a few stories and the students should be encouraged to look into both sides of the issue. Imagine being able to instantly remember anything or reach out to a billion people at once and ask them a question. Imagine being able to upload knowledge directly into your brain without having to go to lessons. This leads us to . . .

* **No more school!** – It has always been assumed that using computers helps learning, but does it? There is very little research and what there is seems to show that this assumption is wrong. Ask: 'Do students with computers learn more just because they are wealthier?' In the poem or discussion, the students not only need to consider if the learning

PHYSICS   CURRENT ELECTRICITY

P2 5.6 Circuits in control

A magic eye

When you go shopping, doors often open automatically in front of you. An automatic door has a sensor that detects anyone who approaches it. Children think there's a magic eye. But Figure 1 shows you it's no more than an electric circuit.

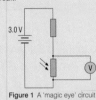

3.0 V

Figure 1 A 'magic eye' circuit

The 'light beam' sensor in Figure 1 is a light-dependent resistor (LDR) in series with a resistor and a battery. A voltmeter is connected across the LDR to show what happens when the LDR is covered. If you make and test this circuit, you should find the voltmeter reading goes up when the LDR is covered. This can be used to switch an electric motor or an alarm circuit on.

> **ACTIVITIES**
>
> a) Use your knowledge of electric circuits to discuss why the voltmeter reading in Figure 1 goes up when you cover the LDR?
>
> b) Design a circuit using a thermistor instead of an LDR to switch an electric fan on if the room gets too hot.

The development of microelectronics

* The first amplifier, the electronic valve, was invented in the 1920s.
* The first electronic switch, the transistor, was invented in the 1940s.
* The microchip was invented in the 1970s.
* The World Wide Web was invented in the 1990s.

The latest computers contain microchips which each contain millions of tiny electronic switches. We measure the capacity of a chip in *bytes*, where a byte is a sequence of bits of data (0's and 1's).

> **ACTIVITY**
>
> Imagine a microchip that could be inserted into the human brain to control your actions and thoughts. Would this be good or bad? Discuss with your friends why it could be good and why it might be bad.

Figure 2 Chip capacity

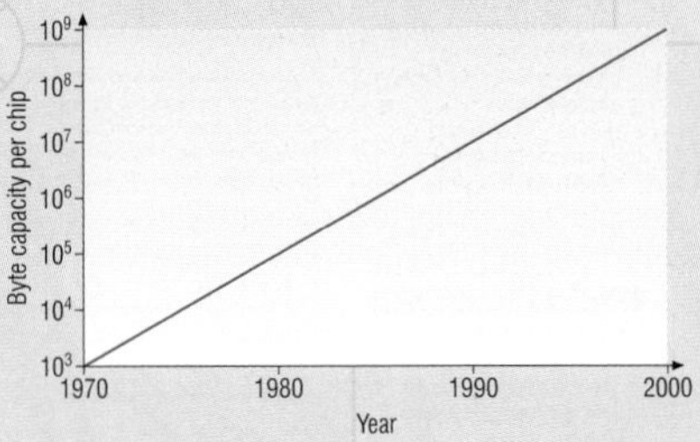

[Graph: Byte capacity per chip (10^3 to 10^9) vs Year (1970 to 2000)]

Figure 2 shows the growth in the capacity of chips since the first one was invented. As chip capacity has increased, electronic devices have become smaller and smaller, as well as more and more sophisticated. They have also become cheaper and cheaper. If cars had changed in the same way, everyone in the world could have a car for less than £1 that would travel 10 000 kilometres on a litre of petrol.

244

experience will be as good but also the lack of social interactions. Ask: 'Would we end up as a society of people who never go out of the house? Would teachers be forced to become comedians in the amusement camps?' You could try out some jokes to see how you would get on.

* **Robots in charge** – When using the word 'robot', students often just think of the human-shaped robots in films and TV. Show them the wide range of real machines, very few of which are humanoid.

* There are many films, TV shows and books with robots in them to discuss, and there is no space to list them here; but at some point, one of the students may bring up the three laws of robotics: a set of rules that are meant to protect humans from their machines. These were formulated by Isaac Asimov and are:

    – A robot may not harm a human being, or, through inaction, allow a human being to come to harm.

    – A robot must obey the orders given to it by human beings, except where such orders would conflict with the First Law.

    – A robot must protect its own existence, as long as such protection does not conflict with the First or Second Law.

ANSWERS TO QUESTIONS

1 A daytime fire alarm.

2 A greenhouse alarm if the sunlight is too strong or the temperature is too high.

No more school!

The Government today announced that children will not have to go to school for lessons any more. Instead, each child will sit in front of a home computer every day. Children who do not go on-line for their lessons will be sent to 'boot camps' to learn. The schools will reopen as amusement arcades with entertainers instead of teachers.

ACTIVITY

Do you think this government policy is a good or a bad idea?

Either: Write a poem about it

or hold a discussion about the issue.

Robots in charge

Robots took over the world in the last century – but only in a play by the Czech writer, Karel Čapek. He used the word 'robot' for machine 'slaves'. Real robots were not invented until many years later. Now we use robotic machines for:

- *routine jobs, such as on assembly lines in factories,*
- *dangerous jobs, such as bomb disposal,*
- *space exploration, such as the two Rover robots which landed on Mars in 2004.*

ACTIVITY

Science fiction writers often write far-fetched stories about robots.

a) Robots are only automated machines programmed to do certain tasks. So why does the word 'robot' catch everyone's attention?

b) Use a science-fiction story to discuss the boundary between science fiction and science.

Electronic logic

We use logic circuits in lots of electronic devices, including computers. A logic circuit has an output that depends on the inputs. Figure 3 shows the symbols for two simple logic circuits, an AND gate and an OR gate. Figure 3 shows an AND gate with a temperature sensor and a light sensor connected to its inputs. If the temperature AND the light intensity are too high, the output of the AND gate is high and it switches an alarm circuit on.

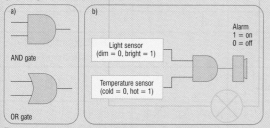

a) AND gate, OR gate

b) Light sensor (dim = 0, bright = 1), Temperature sensor (cold = 0, hot = 1), Alarm 1 = on 0 = off

Figure 3 Logic gates. a) Symbols for an AND gate and an OR gate. b) An alarming circuit.

QUESTIONS

1 What could you use the circuit for in Figure 3b)?

2 If the AND gate was replaced by an OR gate, the alarm would switch on if the temperature OR the light intensity is too high. What could you use this circuit for?

245

without seeing the real world at all. Let the students design a complete personal isolation system that cuts them off from the outside, when they want to live in the unreal world.

Learning styles

Kinaesthetic: Researching into the development of microelectronics.

Visual: Imagining future technology.

Auditory: Reading short science fiction stories out loud.

Interpersonal: Debating robotic technology.

Intrapersonal: Writing a poem about new school policy.

Gifted and talented

Those talented in literature or language could write their own robot-based short story, perhaps in collaboration with the English department.

Special needs

For the 'No more school!' discussion, provide the students with some scripts for each role. Print them out double-spaced, or give them in electronic form, so that the students can modify them easily.

Homework

The students will have to read the science fiction stories at home and report on them in the next lesson.

ICT link-up

- Show some clips from films featuring robots. How realistic do the students feel they are?

- Robotic toy dogs (and other pets) are available. They show some of the features of possible future technology.

- Can the students find any problems with these laws? For example, I could tell my neighbour's robot to self destruct just for fun. Asimov wrote a number of stories about getting around these rules and the eventual consequences of them.

- **Electronic logic** – Logic circuits can be very complex and the students can come up with a range of designs. Ask: 'Can you design an alarm that only goes off when these conditions are met: There is a loud sound at night, or the back door is opened and the alarm switch is on.'

  – You could introduce the NOT gate that converts a high signal to a low one and vice versa.

Extension or homework

- **Rise of the robots** – Ask the students to read a short science fiction story with robots in it, and write a review of the science. Ask: 'Are the things in the story possible?'

- **Living in your own world** – Ask: 'Are people becoming more isolated from each other even when they are crowded together?' Passengers on trains often listen to music through a personal stereo while reading a book and avoiding all contact with other people, except through text messaging. Soon we will be able to project video onto the inside of glasses or directly into the eye with tiny lasers; we could be walking around

SUMMARY ANSWERS

1 a)

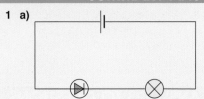

b)

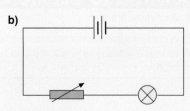

2 a) Filament lamp.

b) Resistor.

c) Thermistor.

d) Diode.

3 a)

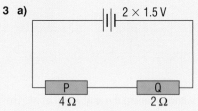

2 × 1.5 V

P   4 Ω   Q   2 Ω

b) i) 3.0 V   **ii)** 6 Ω   **iii)** 0.5 A   **iv)** P: 2.0 V; Q: 1.0 V

4 a)

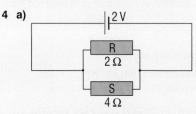

2 V

R   2 Ω

S   4 Ω

b) i) 1.0 A   **ii)** 0.5 A   **iii)** 1.5 A

5 a) Different from.

b) The same as.

Summary teaching suggestions

- When the students answer these questions they should be drawing accurate circuit diagrams. They should not be leaving gaps of any kind or using the wrong symbols.

- The students should easily be able to match up the devices with their description; if not, then play the domino game mentioned in the plenary in lesson 5.1 again.

- Questions 3 and 4 should be used to compare series and parallel circuits. Higher attaining students should be getting quite competent at circuit analysis by now.

SUMMARY QUESTIONS

1 Sketch a circuit diagram to show:
a) a torch bulb, a cell and a diode connected in series so that the torch bulb is on,
b) a variable resistor, two cells in series and a torch bulb whose brightness can be varied by adjusting the variable resistor.

2 Match each component in the list to each statement a) to d) that describes it.

    diode   **filament lamp**   **resistor**   **thermistor**

a) Its resistance increases if the current through it increases.
b) The current through it is proportional to the potential difference across it.
c) Its resistance decreases if its temperature is increased.
d) Its resistance depends on which way round it is connected in a circuit.

3 a) Sketch a circuit diagram to show two resistors P and Q connected in series to a battery of two cells in series with each other.
b) In the circuit in a), resistor P has a resistance of 4 Ω, resistor Q has a resistance of 2 Ω and each cell has a potential difference of 1.5 V. Calculate
i) the total potential difference of the two cells,
ii) the total resistance of the two resistors,
iii) the current in the circuit,
iv) the potential difference across each resistor.

4 a) Sketch a circuit diagram to show two resistors R and S in parallel with each other connected to a single cell.
b) In the circuit in a), resistor R has a resistance of 2 Ω, resistor S has a resistance of 4 Ω and the cell has a potential difference of 2 V. Calculate
i) the current through resistor R,
ii) the current through resistor S,
iii) the current through the cell, in the circuit.

5 Complete the following sentences using words from the list below:

    different from   **equal to**   **the same as**

a) For two components X and Y in series, the potential difference across X is ...... the potential difference across Y.
b) For two components X and Y in parallel, the potential difference across X is ...... the potential difference across Y.

EXAM-STYLE QUESTIONS

1 In a circuit diagram, symbols are used to represent different components.

Complete the table below. The first line has been do for you.

Symbol	Component	What the component does
 ammeter	ammeter	Measures the current in a circuit
	voltmeter	a)
	b)	Supplies energy to a circui
c)	diode	d)
e)	f)	Varies resistance as the temperature varies
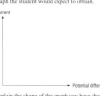	g)	h)

2 A student sets up a circuit to investigate how the potential difference across a filament lamp varies wit the current through it.

(a) How can the student vary the current through the lamp?

(b) (i) Copy the axes below and sketch the shape of graph the student would expect to obtain.

Current

          Potential differen

(ii) Explain the shape of the graph you have draw

(iii) What do we call the line drawn through point on a graph plotted from experimental data wh smooths out variations in measurements?

EXAM-STYLE ANSWERS

1

Symbol	Component	What the component does
		Measure the potential difference across a component
	Cell	
(diode symbol)		Allows current flow in one direction only
(thermistor symbol)	Thermistor	
	Light dependent resistor	Resistance varies with light intensity

(1 mark for each correct cell

2 a) By changing the setting on the variable resistor.   *(1 mark*

b) i) curve drawn   *(1 mark*
     shape correct   *(1 mark*
   ii) as more current flows the lamp gets hotter   *(1 mark*
     so its resistance increases.   *(1 mark*
   iii) A line of best fit.   *(1 mark*

3 a) 9 Ω   *(1 mark*

b) $Current = \dfrac{potential\ difference}{resistance}$ *(1 mark*

     $current = \dfrac{4.5}{9}$ *(1 mark*

     Current = 0.5 A   *(1 mark*

c) Potential difference = current × resistance
     Potential difference = 0.5 × 4   *(1 mark*
     Potential difference = 2 V   *(1 mark*

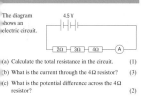

The diagram shows an electric circuit.

4.5 V

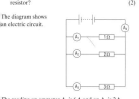

| 2Ω | 3Ω | 4Ω | (A) |

(a) Calculate the total resistance in the circuit. (1)

(b) What is the current through the 4Ω resistor? (3)

(c) What is the potential difference across the 4Ω resistor? (2)

The diagram shows an electric circuit.

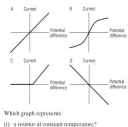

The reading on ammeter A_1 is 6 A and on A_3 is 2 A.

(a) (i) What is the reading on ammeter A_2? (4)

(ii) What is the reading on ammeter A_4? (1)

(b) The graphs **A, B, C** and **D** show how the current through a component varies with the potential difference across it.

A Current
Potential difference

B Current
Potential difference

C Current
Potential difference

D Current
Potential difference

Which graph represents

(i) a resistor at constant temperature?

(ii) a diode? (2)

(c) Why can't the data in part (b) be presented as bar charts? (2)

HOW SCIENCE WORKS QUESTIONS

The laboratory has just bought a new digital thermometer. It uses a thermistor to measure the temperature. It costs £35 because it is accurate and sensitive. The chief technician is very anxious to know if the thermometer works properly. She read all of the data that came with it. It claims that the thermometer will be accurate to ±0.3°C over a range of −50°C to 150°C and it will read to 0.1°C.

a) What is the range over which this instrument should work accurately? (1)

b) What might happen if you used the instrument to read temperatures below −50°C? (1)

c) What is the sensitivity of the thermometer? (1)

d) What is meant by 'the thermometer will be accurate to ±0.3°C'? (1)

The chief technician wanted to check the claims made by the company selling the thermometer. She decided to test its accuracy for herself. She set up some water baths at different temperatures. She used a £400 thermometer that measured to 0.01°C. A company specialising in testing thermometers had independently calibrated this instrument. She compared the readings given by the two thermometers. These are her results.

Thermistor	Temperature of water bath (°C)		
£400	20.15	26.78	65.43
£35	19.9	26.6	65.6

e) Why did the technician doubt the claims made by the company selling the thermometer? (1)

f) Why was the technician more confident in the expensive thermometer? (1)

g) Find the mean for each of the two sets of data? (2)

h) Suggest how the technician might have ensured that her results were valid. (1)

i) Did she choose a range of temperatures that fully tested the new thermometer? Explain your answer. (1)

j) Were her doubts about the £35 thermometer correct? Explain your answer. (1)

247

HOW SCIENCE WORKS ANSWERS

a) The range over which this instrument should work accurately is −50°C to 150°C.

b) It might work, but it would not be accurate.

c) 0.1°C is the sensitivity of the thermometer.

d) It cannot be relied on to be giving a more accurate temperature than 0.3°C above or below that recorded.

e) The company could be biased.

f) It had been independently calibrated.

g) 37.45°C and 37.4°C.

h) e.g. checked the temperature of the water with the two thermometers at the same time.

i) No. The new thermometer had a range of −50°C to +150°C.

j) No, because all are within the ±0.3°C.

How science works teaching suggestions

- **Literacy guidance**
  - Key terms that should be understood: accuracy, sensitivity, calibrated, bias, range.
  - Question d) expects a longer answer, where students can practise their literacy skills.

- **Higher- and lower-level answers.** Questions d) and g) are higher-level questions. The answers for these have been provided at this level. Question a) is lower level and the answer provided is also lower level.

- **Gifted and talented.** Able students could be asked to provide a protocol for testing these thermometers over the full range.

- **How and when to use these questions.** When wishing to develop ideas around accuracy and sensitivity. The questions could be used for homework.

- **Homework.** Questions could be done for homework.

- **Special needs.** The questions could be adapted for thermometers in the lab and they could be checked for accuracy.

- **ICT link-up.** Researching of the many different thermometers and how their accuracy and range are related to their task.

a) i) p.d. across 2Ω resistor is same as p.d across 1Ω resistor because they are in parallel. *(1 mark)*

p.d. across 1Ω resistor = current × resistance

p.d. $= 6 A \times 1 Ω$ *(1 mark)*

p.d. $= 6 V$

Current in 2Ω resistor $= \dfrac{6\,V}{2\,Ω}$ *(1 mark)*

Current $= 3 A$ *(1 mark)*

ii) Reading on $A_4 = 6\,A + 3\,A + 2\,A = 11\,A$ *(1 mark)*

b) i) Graph A *(1 mark)*

ii) Graph C *(1 mark)*

c) The independent variable has to be categoric/ordered/not continuous for a bar chart. *(1 mark)*

The independent variable in this case – potential difference – is a continuous variable. *(1 mark)*

Exam teaching suggestions

- Students must know all the circuit symbols given in the specification.

- Students should practise drawing circuits carefully with a ruler. It helps many pupils to have components in front of them and connect up circuits that they draw.

- Emphasise that ammeters go in series and voltmeters go in parallel.

- Students should be clear about the differences between series and parallel circuits. They should practise doing calculations on both types of circuit. Emphasise that in parallel circuits the potential difference is the same across each of the parallel components in the circuit.

P2 6.1

Alternating current

Students should learn that:

- Direct current involves the flow of electrons in one direction and can be provided by cells or batteries.

- Alternating current involves the rapid change in direction of the current and it can be provided by generators.

- UK mains electricity is alternating current with a frequency of 50 Hz.

LEARNING OUTCOMES

Most students should be able to:

- Distinguish between alternating and direct current.

- State the frequency of UK mains electricity.

- Describe how the potential of the live wires varies each cycle.

- State that the potential of the neutral wire is approximately zero.

- Use oscilloscope traces to compare direct and alternating potential differences.

Some students should also be able to:

- Measure the peak voltage, period and frequency of an a.c. source using an oscilloscope or diagrams of oscilloscope traces. [**HT** only]

Teaching suggestions

- **Gifted and talented.** Ask: 'Why is our mains electricity frequency 50 Hz? What is the physical reason for this and is it the same in all countries? How was this frequency and voltage decided on and why?'

- **Learning styles**

  Kinaesthetic: Operating the CRO.

  Visual: Observing a.c. wave traces.

  Auditory: Listening to descriptions of mains electricity.

  Intrapersonal: Interpreting the information from a CRO trace.

- **ICT link-up.** There are computer-based oscilloscopes that can display traces. These are very useful for demonstrations, because the display can be projected so that everybody can see at once. (Search the web for 'oscilloscope' simulation.) It's still worth showing the students an old-fashioned one too.

SPECIFICATION LINK-UP   Unit: Physics 2.13.7

- *Cell and batteries supply current that always passes in the same direction. This is called direct current (d.c.).*

- *An alternating current (a.c.) is one that is constantly changing direction. Mains electricity is an a.c. supply. In the UK it has a frequency of 50 cycles per second (50 Hz).*

- *UK mains supply is about 230 volts.*

- *The live terminal of the mains supply alternates between positive and negative potential with respect to the neutral terminal. [**HT** only]*

- *The neutral terminal stays at a potential close to zero with respect to Earth. [**HT** only]*

Students should use their skills, knowledge and understanding of 'How Science Works':

- *to compare potential differences of d.c. supplies and the peak potential differences of a.c. supplies from diagrams of oscilloscope traces.*

- *to determine the period, and hence the frequency of a supply, from diagrams of oscilloscope traces. [**HT** only]*

Lesson structure

STARTER

Mains facts – Ask the students a set of true/false questions about mains electricity to see what they already know. (5–10 minutes)

Wave forms – Show the students a wave diagram (e.g. picture from Student Book on Additional Science CD ROM) and ask them to discuss it. (5 minutes)

Electricity dominoes – The students connect question/answer dominoes on basic electrical terms like current, potential difference, cell etc. (5 minutes)

MAIN

- Many of the students will have been wondering what the other two outputs on a power supply are for. Show them that a bulb will light up from a d.c. source and also from the a.c. source.

- The d.c. outputs are colour coded for positive and negative, but the a.c. ones aren't: ask the students why they think this is.

- In a d.c. circuit the electrons eventually make it around the complete circuit. In an a.c circuit they just oscillate back and forth a few centimetres. Describe this to the students pointing out that the electrons are still transferring energy.

- Make sure that the students know that mains is 230 V a.c. at 50 Hz. This is frequently asked for in examination papers. Don't use these high voltages in demonstrations.

- Higher-tier students really need to be aware that the neutral wire oscillates slightly around the Earth potential.

- Some students may know that fluorescent lamps in some buildings flicker or buzz. Let them hear a 50 Hz signal using a signal generator and loudspeaker, and they will probably recognise the noise.

- The oscilloscope is a complex device, but the students only need to know about the time base and the Y-gain. (See 'Practical support'.)

- Higher-tier students will need to be able to take measurements from CRO traces. Make sure that they are only using the controls that they need. You can explain what some of the other buttons do, but make sure that the students know that they only have to be able to read the traces.

- If you have a computer-based oscilloscope, it is much better to use this for demonstrations rather than a small CRO. Connect it up to a signal generator or a.c. power supply to show the traces. The whole class should be able to see it at once if you use a data projector too.

Practical support

The oscilloscope

Oscilloscopes can be fiddly to use and are expensive, but they are essential to understanding alternating current. If not enough equipment is available, let the students use what there is, one group at a time.

Equipment and materials required

Per group: cathode ray oscilloscope, low voltage a.c. source, battery and leads.

Details

The greatest problem the students will have with this experiment is setting the time base and volts per centimetre (Y-gain) dials on the CRO. If these are incorrectly set, then the students will not get a useful trace. To make things easier for them, put small blobs of paint on the scale around the dials showing the correct setting to show a 2 V, 50 Hz trace clearly. This will be a common function, so don't worry too much about defacing the scopes. If you want to show what would happen to the trace if the frequency of p.d. is changed, you can set up a signal generator instead of the a.c. source.

Answers to in-text questions

a) The bulb would flicker continuously.

b) 325 V

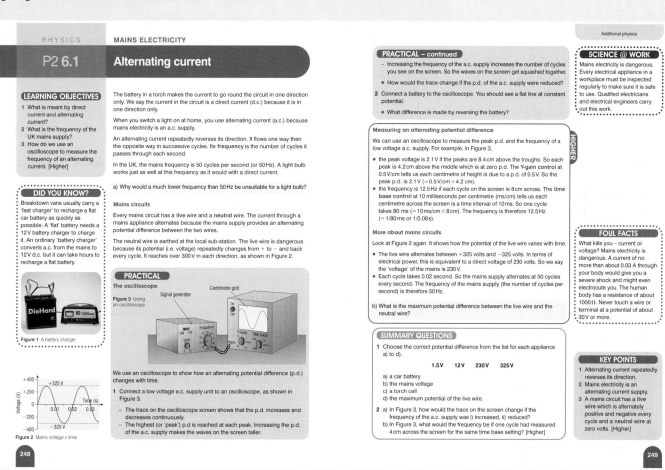

(Reproduced student textbook pages 248–249: P2 6.1 Alternating current)

PLENARIES

a.c./d.c.? – Give the students a set of electrical devices and ask them to stack them in two piles: a.c. operation and d.c. operation. Ask: 'What about devices like laptops that have transformers and rectifiers to convert?' (5 minutes)

Traces – Show the students a series of oscilloscope traces and ask them to say if the peak p.d. is higher or lower, and the frequency higher or lower, than the previous one. (5 minutes)

Making connections – Ask the students to complete the sentence 'Electrical energy is a very convenient form of energy because . . .' including these words 'energy', 'transfer' and 'current'. (5 minutes)

SUMMARY ANSWERS

1 a) 12 V   **b)** 230 V
   c) 1.5 V   **d)** 325 V

2 a) The number of cycles on the screen would:
   i) Increase.   **ii)** Decrease.

   b) 25 Hz [**HT** only]

KEY POINTS

The students should be asked to draw traces showing the difference between a.c. and d.c.

P2 6.2

Cables and plugs

LEARNING OBJECTIVES

Students should learn:

- That mains plugs and sockets are made from robust insulating materials.
- The names and colours of the wires in a three-pin plug.
- The structure of an electrical and a three-pin plug.
- About the function of the live wire, the neutral wire and the earth wire.

LEARNING OUTCOMES

Most students should be able to:

- Describe the design and function of a three-pin mains plug, including the choice of materials and the colours of the wires.
- Recognise errors in the wiring of a three-pin plug.
- Explain why it is necessary to connect some devices to the earth via the earth wire.
- Explain, in terms of safety, why the fuse in the plug of an appliance and the switch of an appliance are on the live side of the appliance.

Some students should also be able to:

- Explain the choice of materials used for the mains parts of a three-pin main plug.

Teaching suggestions

- **Special needs.** Provide the students with a large diagram of plug wiring. They should then label the parts, colour the wires and describe the materials uses for each part.
- **Gifted and talented.** Get the students to write a 'How to wire a plug' guide as found in some DIY stores. The guide should contain idiot-proof step by step instructions of what equipment you need and what you should do.
- **Learning styles**
  Kinaesthetic: Wiring or handling mains plugs.
  Visual: Making observations about faults.
  Auditory: Explaining the dangers of faulty wiring.
  Interpersonal: Discussing and evaluating the materials used in plugs and cables.
  Intrapersonal: Appreciating the dangers associated with high voltage electricity.
- **Homework**
  Safety in the home: The students should make a safety poster to be sent to every house in the country encouraging electrical safety.

SPECIFICATION LINK-UP   Unit: Physics 2.13.7

- *Most electrical appliances are connected to the mains using cable and a three-pin plug.*
- *The structure of electrical cable.*
- *The structure of a three-pin plug.*
- *Correct wiring of a three-pin plug.*

Lesson structure

STARTER

Mystery object – Put a mains plug in a bag and ask one student to describe it to the rest of the class, but only using shape and texture. This can be made more difficult by using a continental plug. (5 minutes)

Material sorting – Give each group of students a bag containing a range of materials and ask them to sort the materials in any way they wish. They must explain how they sorted them to other groups. (10 minutes)

Colour coding – Ask: 'How many different types of thing are colour coded?' The students should make a list of things that are organised by putting colours on them. (10 minutes)

MAIN

- If you have a metal electric heater then use it to introduce the idea of earthing a device.
- Discuss the materials used in a plug and cable by actually showing them. If you have very old devices you might like to show how these have improved over the years. The students need to be able to explain why each material has been chosen.
- The colour coding is usually well understood, but some students will know that black and red wires are used in mains circuits in houses – this can lead to some confusion.
- If you choose to let the students wire plugs, then make sure that there is no chance of the plugs being plugged in.
- The activity can take quite a bit of time, but some students turn out to be exceptionally good. Get these students to help other groups when they are finished.
- Afterwards, or as an alternative, show the students some badly wired plugs. This works best if the plugs are real, but use diagrams if necessary. Make sure these can't be plugged in by using a plug wiring board.
- Some of the faults should be hard to spot. One commonly missed mistake is the cable grip gripping the wires instead of the larger cable.
- You may have plugs for different countries electrical systems or adapters for them. Showing them to students will emphasise that each country has its own designs for plugs.
- A tip for wiring a plug is: When looking down onto a plug as it is being wired the **BR**own wire connects to the **B**ottom **R**ight, the **BL**ue wire connects to the **B**ottom **L**eft. The other wire goes to the other pin!

PLENARIES

Plug poetry – Ask the students to write a plug-wiring rhyme of their own. (5 minutes)

Materials summary – The students should make a table listing the parts of a plug and cable, the materials used and the reasons for those choices. (5–10 minutes)

Wonky wiring – Show the students incorrectly wired plugs and ask them to describe the problems. (5–10 minutes)

ACTIVITY & EXTENSION IDEAS

Wiring a three-pin plug
- Wiring a three-pin plug is a handy skill, and most students enjoy the challenge, but you must be very conscious of the safety concerns. Most appliances come with a pre-fitted moulded plug anyway, so it is becoming less common to have to wire your own.
- **Safety:** Most importantly turn off the mains electricity to the laboratory and never allow the students to plug in their plugs. Even if they are wired correctly, the exposed end of the cable will be live. You should check that no sockets remain live when the main electricity supply is turned off. There are usually some wall sockets that are not connected to the lab circuit breakers. You can also put bolts/screws through the Earth pin to prevent them being plugged in.

Equipment and materials required
For each student: a plug, wire strippers, suitable screwdriver, and 50 cm length of three-core mains cable.

Details
There are many different designs of plugs, some are easier to wire than others. The students will need to be shown how to strip the cable and then the wires without cutting into the core. They will also need help with deciding how much of the metal to expose and how long the wires should be, as most plugs require the Earth wire to be longer than the other two. Make sure that the mains cables are at least 30 cm long, otherwise the students will end up pulling out the wires when they try to strip them. You also need to make sure that all of the bits go back in the right plug, otherwise next time there will be bits missing.

Plug wiring board
If you have concerns about the safety of plug wiring in your laboratory, then you can pass around a plug board for the students to see faulty wiring.

Equipment and materials required
A plank of wood with six incorrectly wired plugs mounted on it.

Details
All that is involved is mounting six plugs onto a board with the pins sticking through it so that they cannot be plugged in. Drill or chisel out the board, stick the cases down and wire up the six plugs in incorrect ways so that the students can try to explain what has been done wrong. You might like to glue the pins into the wood to make sure that they don't fall out. Here are some examples of problems: wires stripped all the way back to the cable grip so that they short, live and neutral wire swapped, wires not tightened at the pins, fuse replaced with metal pin or similar, cable gripping wires not cable, cracked case (glue it down then whack it with a screwdriver). If you have a bigger board then add others.

Answers to in-text questions
a) So each one can be switched on or off without affecting the others.
b) Brass is harder than copper or zinc.
c) The live wire could be exposed where the cable is worn away or damaged.

PHYSICS — MAINS ELECTRICITY

P2 6.2 — Cables and plugs

LEARNING OBJECTIVES
1 What is the casing of a mains plug made from and why?
2 What colour are the live, neutral and earth wires?
3 Which wire is connected to the longest pin in a three-pin plug?

When you plug in a heater with a metal case into a wall socket, you 'earth' the metal case automatically. This stops the metal case becoming 'live' if the live wire breaks and touches it. If the case did become 'live' and you touched it, you would be electrocuted.

Plugs, sockets and cables
The outer casings of plugs, sockets and cables of all mains circuits and appliances are made of hard-wearing electrical insulators. That's because plugs, sockets and cables contain 'live' wires.

Sockets are made of stiff plastic materials with the wires inside. Figure 1 shows part of a wall socket circuit. It has an 'earth' wire as well as a live wire and a neutral wire.

FOUL FACTS
Mains electricity is dangerous. Mains wiring must by law be done by properly qualified electricians.

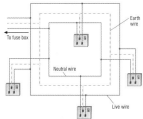

Figure 1 A 'wall socket' circuit

- The 'earth wire' of this circuit is connected to the ground at your home.
- The longest pin of a three-pin plug is designed to make contact with the 'earth wire' of a wall socket circuit. So when you plug an appliance with a metal case to a wall socket, the case is automatically earthed.

a) Why are sockets wired in parallel with each other?

Plugs have cases made of stiff plastic materials. The live pin, the neutral pin and the earth pin, stick out through the plug case. Figure 2 shows inside a three-pin plug.

- The pins are made of brass because brass is a good conductor and does not rust or oxidise. Copper isn't as hard as brass even though it conducts better.
- The case material is an electrical insulator. The inside of the case is shaped so the wires and the pins cannot touch each other when the plug is sealed.

- The plug contains a fuse between the live pin and the live wire. The fuse melts and cuts the live wire off if too much current passes through it.

b) Why is brass, an alloy of copper and zinc, better than copper or zinc for the pins of a three-pin plug?

Cables used for mains appliances (and for mains circuits) consist of two or three insulated copper wires surrounded by an outer layer of rubber or flexible plastic material.

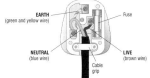

Figure 2 Inside a three-pin plug.
- The brown wire is connected to the live pin.
- The blue wire is connected to the neutral pin.
- The green-yellow wire (of a three-core cable) is connected to the earth pin. A two-core cable does not have an earth wire.

- Copper is used for the wires because it is a good electrical conductor.
- Plastic is a good electrical insulator and therefore prevents anyone touching the cable from receiving an electric shock.
- Two-core cables are used for appliances which have plastic cases (e.g. hairdryers, radios).

Figure 3 Mains cable

c) Why are cables that are worn away or damaged dangerous?

SUMMARY QUESTIONS
1 Choose words from the list to complete the sentences a) to e):

    earth   live   neutral   series   parallel

a) The ...... wire in a mains plug is blue.
b) If too much current passes through the fuse, it blows and cuts the ...... wire off.
c) Appliances plugged into the same mains circuit are in ...... with each other.
d) The metal frame of an appliance is connected to the ...... wire of a mains circuit when it is plugged in.
e) The fuse in a plug is in ...... with the live wire.

2 a) Match the list of parts 1–4 in a three-pin plug with the list of materials A–D.
    1 cable insulation   2 case   3 pin   4 wire
    A brass   B copper   C rubber   D stiff plastic
b) Explain your choice of material for each part in a).

KEY POINTS
1 Cables consist of two or three insulated copper wires surrounded by an outer layer of flexible plastic material.
2 Sockets and plugs are made of stiff plastic which enclose the electrical connections.
3 In a three-pin plug or a three-core cable, the live wire is brown, the neutral wire is blue, the earth wire is yellow/green. The earth wire is used to earth the metal case of a mains appliance.

SUMMARY ANSWERS

1 a) Neutral. b) Live. c) Parallel. d) Earth. e) Series.

2 a) 1C; 2D; 3A; 4B
  b) 1 rubber is flexible and is an insulator.
     2 stiff plastic is an insulator, it doesn't wear and it can't be squashed.
     3 brass is a good conductor and doesn't deteriorate.
     4 copper is an excellent conductor and copper wires bend easily.

KEY POINTS

The students should be able to draw up a table showing how the parts of a mains plug are connected and the correct materials.

P2 6.3

Fuses

LEARNING OBJECTIVES

Students should learn:

- That fuses and circuit breakers are devices that cut off electrical circuits when too large a current flows.
- About the advantages of using circuit breakers to cut off circuits instead of fuses.
- How to choose the correct rating of fuse for a device.
- That double insulated devices have a shell made of insulating materials and so do not need to be earthed.

LEARNING OUTCOMES

Most students should be able to:

- Explain how and why a fuse cuts off an electrical circuit.
- Explain why the fuse in the plug of an appliance protects the appliance.
- List the advantages of a circuit breaker over a fuse.
- Explain why it is important that devices are earthed or are double insulated.

Some students should also be able to:

- Explain why earthing the metal case of an appliance protects the user.

Teaching suggestions

- **Special needs.** For the 'Electromagnets' starter, give the students a set of cards to put in order.
- **Learning styles**
  Visual: Observing the melting of fuses and switching off of current by circuit breakers.
  Auditory: Listening to explanations of how fuses work.
  Interpersonal: Discussing the hazards of mains electricity.
  Intrapersonal: Appreciating the importance of earthing and fuses.
- **ICT link-up.** The students could find out about the numbers of fires and deaths caused by faulty wiring each year using the Internet.
- **Homework.** This is a good opportunity to get the students to make a poster about mains electricity and safety. The poster should be targeted at reducing deaths and injury from shocks and house fires.

SPECIFICATION LINK-UP   Unit: Physics 2.13.7

- *If an electrical fault causes too great a current, the circuit should be switched off by a fuse or a circuit breaker.*
- *When the current in a fuse wire exceeds the rating of the fuse it will melt, breaking the circuit.*
- *Appliances with metal cases are usually earthed.*
- *The Earth wire and fuse together protect the appliance and the user.*

Students should use their skills, knowledge and understanding of 'How Science Works':

- *to recognise dangerous practice in the use of mains electricity.*

Lesson structure

STARTER

Heating effect – Ask: 'Why do wires get hot when a current passes through them?' The students should explain. (5 minutes)

Electromagnets – Demonstrate an electromagnetic switch or relay and get the students to draw a flow chart of what is happening. (10 minutes)

MAIN

- Fuses are a bit dull without demonstrations, so try to fit in a few of the ones in the activity box.
- If you are showing a fuse melting, use one with a glass casing so that the students can see the wire becoming hot and then melt. This will disappoint some students that think a fuse actually explodes in some way.
- You can show the students the differences between fuses, by showing them the fuse wire that is found in them. Connect up some 1 A, 3 A and 5 A fuse wire together in series with an ammeter and variable resistor, and pass an increasing current through it to show that the 1 A fuse wire melts first. Hopefully this will be when a current of 1 A passes through it, but just how accurately is fuse wire manufactured? This would give a good opportunity to discuss aspects of 'How Science Works' on making measurements.
- Many students will think that the fuse is a device that protects the user of a device. It is important to point out that the fuse really prevents a device from catching fire through overheating. Emphasise that it only takes a small current to kill and a 3.5 A device with a 5 A fuse in it can provide a current of 1.5 A without troubling the fuse.
- Earthing confuses some, but just point out that the basic idea is to give an easy path for the current to take if there is a fault. Usually if the device is earthed, then a large current would flow if the live wire touched the case and the fuse should melt and cut off the device. This is the common reason why a device keeps melting fuses and so, if the students see this happen, they should realise that the live wire is loose.
- Even if the fuse does not melt (usually because of putting 13 A fuses in everything), the Earth wire provides a low resistance path for the current and the user would not be electrocuted by touching the case.
- You can demonstrate the use of circuit breakers as outlined in the activity box. The students should realise the advantages fairly quickly. If you want to go into extra detail, then you can show a large model circuit breaker and refer back to the work on electromagnets from earlier in the course.

PLENARIES

Dump your fuses – The students can produce an outline of an advertisement from a company that manufactures circuit breakers that is trying to convince householders to swap their fuse boxes for breaker boxes. (10–15 minutes)

Mains safety – The students produce a catchphrase or slogan to encourage people to use mains electricity safely. (5–10 minutes)

ACTIVITY & EXTENSION IDEAS

Demonstrating circuit breakers

Most power supplies come with a built in circuit breaker so it is simple to demonstrate one.

Equipment and materials required

Low voltage power supply with circuit breaker and a lead.

Details

- Connect up the power supply so that the positive and negative d.c. outputs are shorted by the lead. Turn up the voltage to maximum and then switch on the supply. It will hum for a few seconds and the lead will get warm before the breaker cuts the current off.

- Your laboratory should also have a main circuit breaker with a test switch that will cut off the supply to the benches and you can demonstrate this. Don't make the mistake of testing it if your computer or projector is plugged into the circuit.

Electrical fires

With this you can demonstrate what could happen if no fuse was present.

Equipment and materials required

Power supply, two crocodile clips, heat resistant mat, safety screen and 20 cm length of thin constantan or nichrome wire, variable resistor, safety glasses.

Details

Simply connect the wire up behind the screen and pass a current through it. Turn the current up slowly using the variable resistor so that the students can see that the wire starts to glow red-hot and then white-hot before melting. If you wish you can place some paper on the wire and show it catching fire. Try exactly the same with a 1 A fuse in the circuit and the fuse should melt safely first and cut off the circuit. If you want to show that even low voltages can cause a fire, then try using wire wool and a 1.5 V cell.

PHYSICS   MAINS ELECTRICITY

P2 6.3 Fuses

LEARNING OBJECTIVES

1 What do we use fuses and circuit breakers for?
2 Why is it important to use a fuse with the correct rating?
3 Why don't appliances with plastic cases need to be earthed?

DID YOU KNOW?

If a live wire inside the appliance touches a neutral wire, a very large current passes between the two wires at the point of contact. We call this a **short-circuit**. If the fuse blows, it cuts the current off.

Fuses are included in vehicle circuits too. This is because the current from a 12 V vehicle battery can cause a fire if a short-circuit happens in the circuit.

If you need to buy a fuse for a mains appliance, make sure you know the fuse rating. Otherwise, the new fuse might 'blow' as soon as it is used or, even worse, it might let too much current through and cause a fire.

- A fuse contains a thin wire that heats up and melts if too much current passes through it. If this happens, we say the fuse 'blows'.
- The rating of a fuse is the maximum current that can pass through it without melting the fuse wire.

A fuse in a mains plug must always have the correct rating for the appliance.

If the rating is too large, the fuse will not blow when it should. The heating effect of the current could set the appliance on fire.

a) What would happen if the rating of the fuse was too small?

Figure 1 a) Cartridge fuses, b) a rewireable fuse

The importance of earthing

Figure 2 shows why an electric heater is made safer by earthing its frame.

In Figure 2a), the heater works normally and its frame is earthed. The frame is safe to touch.

In Figure 2b), the earth wire is broken. The frame would become live if the live wire touched it.

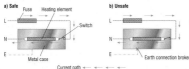

Figure 2 Earthing an electric heater

In Figure 2c), the heater element has touched the unearthed frame so the frame is live. Anyone touching it would be electrocuted. The fuse provides no protection to the user because a current of no more than 20 mA can be lethal.

In Figure 2d), the earth wire has been repaired but the heater element still touches the frame. The current is greater than normal and passes through part of the heater element via the live and the earth wires. Because the frame is earthed, anyone touching it would not be electrocuted. But Figure 2d) is still dangerous because the current might not be enough to blow the fuse and the appliance might overheat.

b) Why is the current in Figure 2d) greater than normal?

Circuit breakers

Figure 3 A circuit breaker

A circuit breaker is an electromagnetic switch that opens (i.e. 'trips') and cuts the current off if the current is greater than a certain value. It can then be reset once the fault that made it trip has been put right.

Circuit breakers are sometimes fitted in 'fuse boxes' in place of fuses. They work faster than fuses and can be reset quicker.

c) What should you do if a circuit breaker trips again after being reset?

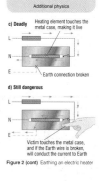

c) **Deadly**

d) **Still dangerous**

Victim touches the metal case, and if the Earth wire is broken, will conduct the current to Earth

Figure 2 (cont) Earthing an electric heater

SUMMARY QUESTIONS

1 a) What is the purpose of a fuse in a mains circuit?
  b) Why is the fuse of an appliance always on the live side?
  c) What advantages does a circuit breaker have compared with a fuse?

2 The diagram shows the circuit of an electric heater that has been wired incorrectly.
  a) Does the heater work when the switch is closed?
  b) When the switch is open, why is it dangerous to touch the element?
  c) Redraw the circuit correctly wired.

KEY POINTS

1 A fuse contains a thin wire that heats up and melts, cutting the current off, if too much current passes through it.
2 A circuit breaker is an electromagnetic switch that opens (i.e. 'trips') and cuts the current off if too much current passes through it.

SUMMARY ANSWERS

a) A fuse protects an appliance or a circuit.

b) So it cuts off the live wire if too much current passes through it.

c) It is faster than a fuse and doesn't need to be replaced after it 'trips'.

2 a) Yes. b) The element is live.

c)

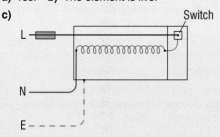

Answers to in-text questions

a) The fuse wire would melt.

b) The mains voltage is across less resistance because only part of the element is between the live and the neutral wire. So the current is bigger.

c) The fault has not been put right so consult an electrician.

KEY POINTS

The students should make a comparison of how fuses and circuit breakers operate.

P2 6.4

Electrical power and potential difference

LEARNING OBJECTIVES

Students should learn:

- That the power of an electrical device is the rate at which it transfers energy.

- How to calculate the electrical power of a device using the current and potential difference.

LEARNING OUTCOMES

Most students should be able to:

- State that the power of a device is the amount of energy it transfers each second.

- Calculate the power of an electrical device from the current and the potential difference.

Some students should also be able to:

- Perform calculations involving the rearrangement of the electrical power equation.

Teaching suggestions

- **Special needs.** The calculations here can be very confusing to some students, and they should be provided with a template to encourage them to lay them out correctly; this is especially important in the rearrangement of the equations.

- **Gifted and talented.** Can the students produce a comparison between electrical potential difference and gravitational potential difference? This is a trick task, but one that can cement understanding of what a potential difference represents.

- **Learning styles**

  Visual: Making observations about the energy-use of lamps.

  Auditory: Explaining how energy is transferred in electrical circuits.

  Intrapersonal: Making deductions about the relationship between power current and potential difference.

- **Homework.** Give the students a worksheet with questions based on the electrical power equation and choice of fuses.

SPECIFICATION LINK-UP   Unit: Physics 2.13.8

- *Electric current is the rate of flow of charge.*

- *When an electrical charge flows through a resistor, electrical energy is transformed into heat energy.*

- *The rate at which energy is transformed in a device is called the power.*

$$\frac{power}{(watt,\ W)} = \frac{energy\ transformed\ (joule,\ J)}{time\ (second,\ s)}$$

- *Power, potential difference and current are related by the equation:*

$$\underset{(watt,\ W)}{power} = \underset{(ampere,\ A)}{current} \times \underset{(volt,\ V)}{potential\ difference}$$

Students should use their skills, knowledge and understanding of 'How Science Works':

- *to calculate the current through an appliance from its power and the potential difference of the supply, and from this determine the size of fuse needed.*

Lesson structure

STARTER

Power – Can the students give a scientific definition of the word power? Can they remember any equations? You could even set them a mechanical power question. (5 minutes)

Electrical units – The students match up electrical quantities, with their definitions, abbreviations and units. (5–10 minutes)

Key words – Students quickly scan the double page spread and write out all of the key words. (5–10 minutes)

MAIN

- Start with a brief recap about power; the students should remember how to calculate the power of a mechanical device.

- Point out that if energy is being transferred by a device, then some form of work must be being done so there is a power output. With electricity there is no force or distance moved, so there must be another way of finding the power output.

- The next section involves a derivation of an equation; higher attaining groups should be fine with this, but lower ability students will probably struggle to grasp this section fully.

- Take some time to go through what each of the phrases means and to come up with the final equation; some students will find this difficult. The definition of potential difference as 'electrical energy per unit charge' is one that many students will find particularly hard to understand.

- In the end, most students will happily accept that the power is the current times the potential difference even if they don't thoroughly understand why. For most this is fine, but it may be worth persisting with those you want to move on to the higher level.

- The calculations are not difficult but the students should have quite a bit of practice. Get them to work out the power of several devices before moving on to rearrangement.

- Sometimes examiners ask the students to work out the power of a mains device without giving the voltage. They expect them to remember that mains is 230 V so make sure that they do.

- Show the students real fuses to point out that they are all the same size, so it is easy to use the wrong one without thinking. They might like to see the 30 A fuses used for cookers. Ask: 'Why are these physically larger?'

- When choosing a fuse, always choose one that is slightly higher than the operating current otherwise it will melt during normal operation. For example, if the device needs exactly 3 A, then a 5 A fuse should be used.

Enlightenment

This is a simple way to show that the higher the power rating of a device the more energy it transfers.

Equipment and materials required

Three identical lamps except that one has a 40 W bulb, the others have 60 W and 100 W. As with all mains devices these should have passed safety tests.

Details

Just plug all of the lamps in and turn them on. The students should easily see the difference in brightness and relate this to the amount of energy being transferred. Explain that all are operating at 230 V; the students should then calculate the current in each lamp. [0.17 A, 0.26 A, 0.43 A] Ask: 'What fuse should each of the lamps have?'

Answers to in-text questions

a) About 1 W
b) 1150 W
c) The normal current through the lamp is much less than 13 A. A 13 A fuse may not blow if there is a fault in the lamp.

SUMMARY ANSWERS

1 a) Power, current.
  b) Potential difference, current.

2 a) i) 36 W   ii) 460 W
  b) i) 3 A   ii) 5 A

P2 6.4 — Electrical power and potential difference

LEARNING OBJECTIVES

1 What is the relationship between power and energy?
2 How can we calculate electrical power?
3 What is the unit of electrical power?

SCIENCE @ WORK

A surgeon fitting an artificial heart in a patient needs to make sure the battery will last a long time. Even so, the battery may have to be replaced every few years.

When you use an electrical appliance, it transforms electrical energy into other forms of energy. The power of the appliance, in watts, is the energy it transforms, in joules, per second. We can show this as the following equation:

$$\text{Power (watts, W)} = \frac{\text{energy transformed (joules, J)}}{\text{time (seconds, s)}}$$

Worked example

A lamp bulb transforms 30 000 J of electrical energy when it is on for 300 s. Calculate its power.

Solution

$$\text{Power} = \frac{\text{energy transformed}}{\text{time}} = \frac{30\,000\,J}{300\,s} = 100\,W$$

a) The human heart transforms about 30 000 J of energy in a school day of about 8 hours. Calculate an estimate of the power of the human heart.

Figure 1 An artificial heart

Calculating power

Millions of millions of electrons pass through the circuit of an artificial heart every second. Each electron transfers a small amount of energy to it from the battery. So the total energy transferred to it each second is large enough to enable the device to work.

For any electrical appliance:

- the current through it is a measure of the number of electrons passing through it each second (i.e. the charge flow per second),
- the potential difference across it is a measure of how much energy each electron passing through it transfers to it (i.e. the electrical energy transferred per unit charge),
- the power supplied to it is the energy transferred to it each second. This is the electrical energy it transforms every second.

Therefore:

$$\frac{\text{the energy transfer to}}{\text{the device each second}} = \frac{\text{the charge flow}}{\text{per second}} \times \frac{\text{the energy transfer}}{\text{per unit charge}}$$

In other words:

power supplied = current × potential difference
(watts, W)   (amperes, A)   (volts, V)

For example, the power supplied to

- a 4 A, 12 V electric motor is 48 W (= 4 A × 12 V),
- a 0.1 A, 3 V torch lamp is 0.3 W (= 0.1 A × 3.0 V).

b) Calculate the power supplied to a 5 A, 230 V electric heater.

Maths note

The equation can written as:

electrical power, $P = I \times V$ where I = current, and
V = potential difference

Rearranging this equation gives:

potential difference, $V = \dfrac{P}{I}$ or

current, $I = \dfrac{P}{V}$

Choosing a fuse

Domestic appliances are often fitted with a 3 A, or a 5 A or a 13 A fuse. If you don't know which one to use for an appliance, you can work it out from the power rating of the appliance and its potential difference (voltage).

Worked example

i) Calculate the normal current through a 500 W, 230 V heater.
ii) Which fuse, a 3 A, or a 5 A or a 13 A, would you use for the appliance?

Solution

i) Current $= \dfrac{500\,W}{230\,V} = 2.2\,A$

ii) A 3 A fuse would be needed.

c) Why would a 13 A fuse be unsuitable for a 230 V, 100 W table lamp?

SUMMARY QUESTIONS

1 Choose words from the list to complete sentences a) and b):

current   potential difference   power

a) When an electrical appliance is on, ... is supplied to it as a result of ...... passing through it.
b) When an electrical appliance is on, a ...... is applied to it which causes ...... to pass through it.

2 a) Calculate the power supplied to each of the following devices in normal use.
  i) a 12 V, 3 A light bulb,   ii) a 230 V, 2 A heater,
  b) Which type of fuse, 3 A or 5 A or 13 A, would you select for:
  i) a 24 W, 12 V heater?   ii) a 230 V, 800 W microwave oven?

Figure 2 Power rating

1650 – 1960 W
220 – 230 V ~
50 – 60 Hz

NEXT TIME YOU...

... change a fuse, do a quick calculation to make sure its rating is correct for the appliance.

Figure 3 Changing a fuse

KEY POINTS

1 The power supplied to a device is the energy transfer to it each second.
2 Electrical power supplied (watts) = current (amperes) × potential difference (volts)

PLENARIES

Match the fuse – The students need to match the fuse with an electrical device after being told the power rating. Use 3 A, 5 A, 13 A and 30 A fuses. (5–10 minutes)

Electrical error – 'I'm sick of all my stuff fusing; I'm going to put a 13 amp fuse in all of my things so that they'll all keep working.' Ask: ' Is this a good plan or not?' Discuss. (5 minutes)

Motor question – Get the students to calculate how high an electric motor operating at 230 V and 2 A can lift a 100 N weight in 10 seconds. (5 minutes)

SCIENCE @ WORK

The batteries used in artificial hearts and pacemakers contain explosive materials (as do the pacemakers themselves). If a body is cremated and the pacemaker hasn't been removed, then the pacemaker will explode in the incinerator and cause quite a bit of damage and a really loud bang. This does not help the grieving relatives.

KEY POINTS

Get the students to match up fuses with devices by using the power equation. What size fuses would be needed for the same devices in the USA with a mains voltage of 110 V?

P2 6.5

Electrical energy and charge

LEARNING OBJECTIVES

Students should learn:

- That an electric current is a flow of charge; in metal wires this charge is carried by electrons.

- That the unit of charge is the coulomb where one ampere represents a flow of charge of one coulomb per second.

- That charge transferred is current × time.

- That potential difference is energy transferred per unit charge.

- That a resistor transfers electrical energy into thermal energy.

LEARNING OUTCOMES

Most students should be able to:

- State that an electrical current is a flow of charge.

- Calculate the charge transferred by a current in a specified time.

- Calculate the energy transferred using the p.d. and the charge transferred.

Some students should also be able to:

- Perform calculations involving rearrangement of the charge = current × time equation and the potential difference = energy transferred per unit charge equation.

Teaching suggestions

- **Special needs.** Use calculation templates to help the students through the equations and to make sure that they are laying out their calculations clearly.

- **Gifted and talented.** Ask: 'How many electrons are passing each second at a point, if there is a current of 1 A and each electron carries a charge of 1.6×10^{-19} C?' [The students should be able to figure out that 1 C of charge passes each second, so the number of electrons is given by $1 \text{C}/1.6 \times 10^{-19}$ C which is 6.25×10^{18} electrons. This shows just how small the charge on a single electron is.] These numbers are impossible for a calculator to handle without using scientific notation, so it's a good opportunity to improve these skills.

SPECIFICATION LINK-UP   Unit: Physics 2.13.8

- *Electric current is the rate of flow of charge.*

- *Energy transformed, potential difference and charge are related by the equation:*

  energy transformed = potential difference × charge
  (joule, J)   (volt, V)   (coulomb, C)   **[HT** only]

- *The amount of electrical charge that flows is related to current and time by the equation:*

  charge   =   current   ×   time
  (coulomb, C)   (ampere, A)   (second, s)   **[HT** only]

Lesson structure

STARTER

Stuck for words? – Pair up the students and give one of them cards with electrical words including charge, current etc. Ask them to mime the words to the other students. (5 minutes)

Electrical transformation – How many electrical devices can the students draw energy transfer diagrams for? (10 minutes)

Charge! – How many meanings of the word 'charge' can the students come up with? (5 minutes)

MAIN

- This is another fairly mathematically intense topic with two important equations; keep the emphasis on the electrons carrying charge from place to place and so carrying energy. The spread is only needed for students taking the Higher Tier exam.

- The first equation comes from the definition of current and charge. The size of the electric current is just how much charge passes each second (just as the size of a water current is how many litres of water pass each second). Use water flowing down a tube into a big measuring cylinder if you want a visual illustration.

- It is probably best to avoid using the symbols for current '*I*' and charge '*Q*' in equations, as these lead to more confusion. If the students are confident enough, they can use $Q = It$ to save a bit of writing, but don't let it confuse them.

- The derivation of the energy-transferred equation will again be confusing for some. For these students just concentrate on the end equation.

- Using the equation is fairly straightforward – the most difficult part is remembering it.

- Check that the students are using the correct units. With so many equations it's easy for them to pick the wrong one. A reference wall display is very handy.

- There may be situations on higher level examination papers where the students are expected to combine the equations, so give these students some examples, e.g. 'How much energy is transferred when a current of 2 A passes through a potential difference of 4 V for 1 minute'?

- The last section deals with energy transfer. You should go through the description of the energy being provided to the electrons, then carried by them and transferred to the lamp and resistor, carefully. The students should be picturing electrons as energy carriers by now, and then thinking of a coulomb as the charge carried by a big bunch of electrons.

- Try more examples of this, making sure that the students are picking up the idea that **each** coulomb of charge (bunch of electrons) is getting the same number of joules as the battery provides volts.

- It's actually the changes in the electric field that the charge produces that transfers the energy, but the students need not worry about this.

PLENARIES

Electrical spelling – Hold a spelling competition about electrical words using mini-whiteboards. If a student gets a word wrong, they get knocked out. The last one in wins 'coulomb eliminates a fair few'. (5 minutes)

Map it out – The students should produce a summary or mind map of the information about mains electricity and electrical energy calculations. (15 minutes)

Electric crossword – The students have finished this look into current and mains electricity, so let them have a go at a crossword with answers based on this chapter. (10 minutes)

Teaching suggestions – continued

- **Learning styles**

  Visual: Imagining the movement of electrons in a wire carrying charge and energy.

  Auditory: Listening to detailed explanations of charge and energy.

  Interpersonal: Working in pairs, discussing answers to problems.

  Intrapersonal: Working individually to answer calaculations.

- **Homework.** Use this opportunity to give the students some additional calculations to check their understanding and ability.

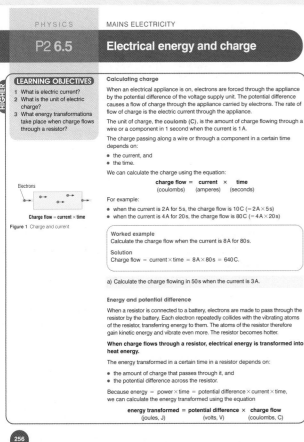

PHYSICS   MAINS ELECTRICITY

HIGHER

P2 6.5 — Electrical energy and charge

LEARNING OBJECTIVES

1 What is electric current?
2 What is the unit of electric charge?
3 What energy transformations take place when charge flows through a resistor?

Calculating charge

When an electrical appliance is on, electrons are forced through the appliance by the potential difference of the voltage supply unit. The potential difference causes a flow of charge through the appliance carried by electrons. The rate of flow of charge is the electric current through the appliance.

The unit of charge, the **coulomb (C)**, is the amount of charge flowing through a wire or a component in 1 second when the current is 1 A.

The charge passing along a wire or through a component in a certain time depends on:

- the current, and
- the time.

We can calculate the charge using the equation:

$$\text{charge flow} = \text{current} \times \text{time}$$
$$\text{(coulombs)} \quad \text{(amperes)} \quad \text{(seconds)}$$

Electrons

Charge flow = current × time

Figure 1 Charge and current

For example:

- when the current is 2 A for 5 s, the charge flow is 10 C (= 2 A × 5 s)
- when the current is 4 A for 20 s, the charge flow is 80 C (= 4 A × 20 s)

Worked example
Calculate the charge flow when the current is 8 A for 80 s.

Solution
Charge flow = current × time = 8 A × 80 s = 640 C.

a) Calculate the charge flowing in 50 s when the current is 3 A.

Energy and potential difference

When a resistor is connected to a battery, electrons are made to pass through the resistor by the battery. Each electron repeatedly collides with the vibrating atoms of the resistor, transferring energy to them. The atoms of the resistor therefore gain kinetic energy and vibrate even more. The resistor becomes hotter.

When charge flows through a resistor, electrical energy is transformed into heat energy.

The energy transformed in a certain time in a resistor depends on:

- the amount of charge that passes through it, and
- the potential difference across the resistor.

Because energy = power × time = potential difference × current × time, we can calculate the energy transformed using the equation

$$\text{energy transformed} = \text{potential difference} \times \text{charge flow}$$
$$\text{(joules, J)} \quad \text{(volts, V)} \quad \text{(coulombs, C)}$$

256

For example:

- when the charge flow is 10 C and the potential difference is 10 V, the energy transformed = 100 J (= 10 V × 10 C),
- when the charge flow is 20 C and the potential difference is 10 V, the energy transformed = 200 J (= 10 V × 20 C)

Worked example
Calculate the energy transformed in a component when the charge flow is 30 C and the potential difference is 20 V.

Solution
Energy transformed = 20 V × 30 C = 600 J.

b) Calculate the energy transformed when the charge flow is 30 C and the p.d. is 4 V.

Energy transformations in a circuit

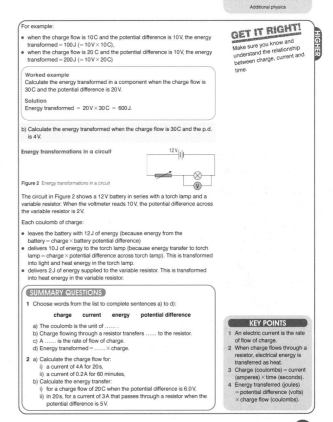

Figure 2 Energy transformations in a circuit

The circuit in Figure 2 shows a 12 V battery in series with a torch lamp and a variable resistor. When the voltmeter reads 10 V, the potential difference across the variable resistor is 2 V.

Each coulomb of charge:

- leaves the battery with 12 J of energy (because energy from the battery = charge × battery potential difference)
- delivers 10 J of energy to the torch lamp (because energy transfer to torch lamp = charge × potential difference across torch lamp). This is transformed into light and heat energy in the torch lamp.
- delivers 2 J of energy supplied to the variable resistor. This is transformed into heat energy in the variable resistor.

SUMMARY QUESTIONS

1 Choose words from the list to complete sentences a) to d):

   charge   current   energy   potential difference

   a) The coulomb is the unit of ....
   b) Charge flowing through a resistor transfers ...... to the resistor.
   c) A ...... is the rate of flow of charge.
   d) Energy transformed = ... × charge.

2 a) Calculate the charge flow for:
      i) a current of 4 A for 20 s,
      ii) a current of 0.2 A for 60 minutes,
   b) Calculate the energy transfer:
      i) for a charge flow of 20 C when the potential difference is 6.0 V,
      ii) in 20 s, for a current of 3 A that passes through a resistor when the potential difference is 5 V.

GET IT RIGHT!
Make sure you know and understand the relationship between charge, current and time.

KEY POINTS

1 An electric current is the rate of flow of charge.
2 When charge flows through a resistor, electrical energy is transferred as heat.
3 Charge (coulombs) = current (amperes) × time (seconds).
4 Energy transferred (joules) = potential difference (volts) × charge flow (coulombs).

257

SUMMARY ANSWERS

1 a) Charge.
   b) Energy.
   c) Current.
   d) Potential difference. [**HT** only]

2 a) i) 80 C
      ii) 720 C

   b) i) 120 J
      ii) 300 J [**HT** only]

Answers to in-text questions

a) 150 C
b) 120 J

KEY POINTS

The students should be able to answer a range of questions using the two equations so a worksheet based task is appropriate.

SPECIFICATION LINK-UP

Unit: Physics 2.13.7

Students should use their skills, knowledge and understanding of 'How Science Works':

- to recognise errors in the wiring of a three-pin plug.
- to recognise dangerous practice in the use of mains electricity.

Teaching suggestions

Activities

- **Spot the hazards!** – In addition to spotting the hazards in the stately manor, you can get the students to perform a safety check of the laboratory or any other classrooms they visit during the school day. Ask: 'How safe is your school and what can be done about it?' This would also be a good time to explain why it is not wise to poke pencils into the bench sockets or try to unscrew the covers with coins.

- **Circuit breakers for safety** – A four-star skull rating may be suitable for the table if the students can't think of any.

- A common TV murder technique is to throw a live hairdryer into a bathtub of water. Would a RCCB prevent this? If so, why aren't all fuses replaced with this technology?

- **Cutting out the cowboys** – It took a great deal of time for the government to come to the decision to regulate electrical work in the home in the same way as they regulated work on gas pipes. All work on the ring main should now be performed or checked by a qualified electrician. This has made quite a few home DIYers unhappy. Do the students think that it is unfair that they cannot wire their own house? What would happen if there were a fire after they had sold the house?

- **Electrical jargon** – 'There was serious trouble in a physics lesson today; two students were charged.'

ACTIVITY

Spot the hazards!

Imagine you are a safety inspector who has been asked to check the electrics in Shockem Hall. How many electrical faults and hazards can you find just by looking around the main hall?

Circuit breakers for safety

A special 'RCCB' socket should be used for outdoor appliances such as lawnmowers. These sockets each contain a residual current circuit breaker instead of a fuse. This type of circuit breaker switches the current off if the live current and the neutral current differ by more than 30 mA. This can happen, for example, if the insulation of the live wire becomes worn and current 'leaks' from the live wire to 'earth'.

A residual current circuit breaker

QUESTIONS

1 What other appliances would you use an RCCB for besides a lawn mower?

List them in the table like the one below.

Appliance	Hazard	Rating
Lawnmower	The blades might cut the cable	
Electric drill		

2 Design a hazard rating icon like a star rating but use something different to stars. A '4-star hazard' doesn't sound right.

258

The Evening Post

Family rescued in house fire!

The Fire Service rescued two children and their parents from the upper floor of a burning house in Lower Town last night. Fortunately, all family members were safe and well. The fire spread to two neighbouring properties before being brought under control. A fire service spokesperson said the fire was caused by an electrical fault.

- **Holiday time** – You should be able to find a range of adapters for different purposes to show the students. Spanish mains supply is at 220 V and 50 Hz, so most devices are compatible (but kettles take a bit longer to boil apparently and you ask the students why this is). The sockets only have holes for two pins and simple adapters can be used. Many sockets also have an Earth connection at the edge.

Extension or homework

- **Sparky.** Some of the students may be interested in becoming an electrician or an electrical engineer. They should find out about what qualification and training they will need for this career.

- **Special needs.** You could provide the students with separate cards with the appliance and hazard information for the circuit breakers activity. They can match them up and add the danger rating.

- **Gifted and talented.** The students are familiar with the colour coding or wires in electrical devices; they could try to find out about the wiring used in mains circuits. They should research this and the nature of ring mains.

Cutting out the cowboys

The UK government has passed a law to stop unqualified people doing electrical work. This is because many accidents have happened due to shoddy electrical work, not just by unqualified 'cowboy' electricians but also by householders in their own homes. If you want to be an electrician, you have to train for several years as an apprentice and study for exams. When you qualify, you can register as an approved electrician.

ACTIVITY

The new law is intended to reduce accidents due to unsafe electrical work. But what other effects will it have? It might make rewiring jobs by qualified electricians too expensive and create more work for the cowboys.

Discuss whether this new law is a good law and if there are other ways of regulating electrical work.

ACTIVITY

a) What do these expressions mean? See if you and your friends can add more electrical examples.

b) Use the jargon in a discussion with your friends about something that happened in your favourite TV soap. Award one point each time jargon is used and see who wins.

c) Is jargon unsafe? Can it be misunderstood? Think of a situation where jargon is dangerous.

Electrical jargon

People often complain about jargon – the words that experts use. But sometimes, we use jargon without realising it, especially electrical jargon because we all use electricity. Sometimes, we even use it in our everyday conversations.

Here are some examples:

'Don't blow a fuse.'

'She's a sparky character.'

'Can't you short-circuit the usual procedure?'

Holiday time!

ACTIVITY

Find out what type of adaptor you would need if you go on holiday to Spain.

Holiday Essentials

When you go abroad... be careful if you intend to take mains appliances with you.

☀ If the voltage is not 230 V (as in the UK and Europe), the appliance must have a 'dual voltage' switch that can be changed from 230 V to the new voltage. You **must** change the switch back when you return.

☀ If the voltage is 230 V, you may need to take a suitable plug adaptor with you for each appliance. This is because sockets abroad may be different to those at home.

☀ Only use one appliance per socket or you might blow a fuse!

Learning styles

Kinaesthetic: Researching into alternative electrical mains systems.

Visual: Observing safety hazards.

Auditory: Reading information aloud.

Interpersonal: Discussing different mains systems.

Intrapersonal: Writing a report on house fires.

Teaching assistants

During any research task, the assistant should be making sure that the students are using the appropriate web sites.

ICT link-up

There are plenty of opportunities here for ICT based research; as usual a list of suitable web sites should be provided along with a template of some kind if possible.

ANSWERS TO QUESTIONS

1 **a)** Examples: an electric drill, a hedge trimmer, a power washer, outdoor lights, an electric water pump.

   b) Own hazard rating icon.

SUMMARY ANSWERS

1 a) i) The neutral wire.

   ii) The live wire.

   b) i) The waves on the screen would be taller.

   ii) There would be more waves on the screen.

2 a) Live, neutral.

   b) i) Neutral.

   ii) Live.

   iii) Earth.

3 a) i) Parallel.

   ii) Series, live.

   b) i) A fuse has a wire that melts if too much current passes through it. A circuit breaker has a switch that is pulled open if too much current passes through it.

   ii) A circuit breaker is faster. Also a circuit breaker does not need to need to be replaced, but a fuse does.

4 a) i) 10.8 A

   ii) 13 A

   b) 920 W

5 1200 C [**HT** only]

6 a)

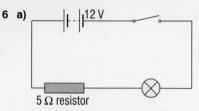

   5 Ω resistor

   b) i) 432 J

   ii) 108 J

   iii) 324 J [**HT** only]

Summary teaching suggestions

- Make sure that the students can interpret an oscilloscope trace with question 1; a few extra traces should help.

- Wiring plug questions are quite common and you need to make sure that the students know the positions and colours of the wires and the role of fuses using the next two questions.

- Question 4 checks the students' calculations skills; they should cope well with these and you might want to stretch higher attaining students with a few more taxing questions if they find these too easily.

- The last question should stretch all of the students; be on the lookout for the students tackling the question in clear logical steps.

MAINS ELECTRICITY: P2 6.1 – P2 6.6

SUMMARY QUESTIONS

1 a) In a mains circuit, which wire:
   i) is earthed at the local sub-station,
   ii) alternates in potential?
   b) An oscilloscope is used to display the potential difference of an alternating voltage supply unit. How would the trace change if:
   i) the p.d. is increased,
   ii) the frequency is increased?

2 Complete a) and b) using words below:

   earth   live   neutral

   a) When a mains appliance is switched on, current passes through it via the ...... wire and the ...... wire.
   b) In a mains circuit:
   i) the ...... wire is blue,
   ii) the ...... wire is brown,
   iii) the ...... wire is green yellow.

3 a) Complete the sentences:
   i) Wall sockets are connected in ...... with each other.
   ii) A fuse in a mains plug is in ...... with the appliance and cuts off the ...... wire if too much current passes through the appliance.
   b) i) What is the main difference between a fuse and a circuit breaker?
   ii) Give two reasons why a circuit breaker is safer than a fuse.

4 a) i) Calculate the current in a 230 V, 2.5 kW electric kettle.
   ii) Which fuse, 3 A or 5 A or 13 A, would you fit in the kettle plug?
   b) Calculate the power supplied to a 230 V electric toaster when the current through it is 4.0 A.

5 Calculate the charge flow through a resistor when the current is 6 A for 200 s. [Higher]

6 A 5 Ω resistor is in series with a lamp, a switch and a 12 V battery.
   a) Draw the circuit diagram.
   b) When the switch is closed for 60 seconds, a direct current of 0.6 A passes through the resistor. Calculate:
   i) the energy supplied by the battery,
   ii) the energy transformed in the resistor,
   iii) the energy transformed in the lamp. [Higher]

EXAM-STYLE QUESTIONS

1 An electric heater is connected to a 230 V mains su... The current flowing through the heater is 12 A.

   (a) What is the power of the heater?

   (b) The heater is switched on for 30 minutes. Calculate how much charge flows through the heater during this time and give the unit.

2 The diagram shows a three-pin plug.

   (a) State the colour of each wire.

   Live .... Neutral .... Earth ....

   (b) State and explain which parts of the plug are m... out of . . .
   (i) plastic   (ii) brass

3 Explain:
   (a) why appliances with metal cases need to be ear... but appliances with plastic cases do not.
   (b) which wire in a circuit should contain the fuse.
   (c) why the rating of the fuse in an appliance shoul... slightly higher than the normal working current through the appliance.

4 Cells and the electrical mains are both sources of electrical energy. Describe the currents and potential differences from each of these types of supply.

5 Most domestic appliances are connected to the 230 V mains supply with a 3-pin plug containing a fuse. 3 A, 5 A and 13 A fuses are available.

   (a) A food mixer has a normal current of 2 A. What is the power of the mixer?

   (b) What fuse should be used in the plug for a 2.8 k... kettle?

EXAM-STYLE ANSWERS

1 a) Power = current × potential difference   (1 mark)
     Power = 12 A × 230 V   (1 mark)
     Power = 2760 W

  b) Charge = current × time   (1 mark)
     Time = 30 × 60 s   (1 mark)
     Charge = 12 A × 1800 s   (1 mark)
     Charge = 21 600 coulombs   (1 mark)

2 a) Live – brown   (1 mark)
     Neutral – blue   (1 mark)
     Earth – green/yellow   (1 mark)

  b) i) Cable grip and plug cover are plastic   (1 mark)
        because plastic does not conduct.   (1 mark)
     ii) Pins of the plug are brass   (1 mark)
        Because brass is a good conductor
        and the pins will not bend.   (1 mark)

3 a) If the live wire touches the metal case of an appliance   (1 mark)
     the case will become live   (1 mark)
     current will flow through anyone who touches the case   (1 mark)
     if the case is plastic it does not conduct.   (1 mark)

  b) The live wire   (1 mark)
     or current could still flow if the fuse blows. (1 mark)

  c) Fuse value needs to be higher or it would melt during normal use.   (1 mark)
     Should only be slightly higher or it will take too long to melt.   (1 mark)

4 Cells provide direct current.   (1 mark)
  Direct current always passes in the same direction. (1 mark)
  Mains supplies alternating current.   (1 mark)
  Alternating current is constantly changing direction.   (1 mark)
  Frequency of the mains supply is 50 Hz.   (1 mark)
  Potential difference from a cell is approximately 1.5 V.   (1 mark)
  Potential difference from the mains is about 230 V. (1 mark)

(c) (i) A 9kW shower is wired directly to the mains. It has a separate fuse in the household fuse box. Explain why? (3)

(ii) The fuse for the shower keeps melting. The householder replaces it with a nail. Why is this dangerous? (2)

The pictures show situations in which electricity is not being used safely.

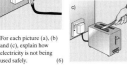
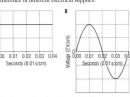

For each picture (a), (b) and (c), explain how electricity is not being used safely. (6)

An oscilloscope can be used to measure the potential difference of different electrical supplies.

The diagrams show the traces produced on a centimetre grid by two different supplies.

(a) What is the potential difference of supply A? (3)

(b) (i) What type of supply is supply B? (1)

(ii) What is the peak potential difference of supply B? (1)

(iii) What is the frequency of supply B? (3)

[Higher]

HOW SCIENCE WORKS QUESTIONS

'There I was watching Rovers beat United, when it blew a fuse. No, it wasn't the United manager, it was the box. I reckon it was down to the United fans switching off their tellies when we scored that second goal. It must have been some sort of surge. Anyway, I fixed it before the end of the game. I put a bit of wire into where the fuse had burned and the telly worked perfectly. Unfortunately the house burned down! Anyway Rovers won and that's the important thing . . .'

a) Would you say that putting a piece of wire to replace a fuse was based on good science? Explain your answer. (1)

b) Do you think there was a link between Rovers scoring a second goal and the television fuse blowing? Was it causal, due to association or due to chance? Explain your answer. (1)

The fire brigade did a thorough investigation into the cause of the fire. They recovered a reel of the wire used in place of the 3A fuse that should have been used. Their scientists at the Fire Service laboratory found that six equal lengths of this wire fused at currents of 6.5A, 6.1A, 6.2A, 5.8A, 6.0A and 6.1A. They also discovered a fault in the television had caused it to overheat. This had caused the curtains to catch fire and burn the house down.

c) i) Calculate the mean value of the measurements above. (1)

ii) Comment of the precision of the results. (1)

iii) Why did they test equal lengths? (1)

d) Is it likely that there was a causal link between the 'repair' of the fuse and the house burning down? Explain your answer. (1)

e) Why can you trust this investigation? (1)

261

Exam teaching suggestions

- Students must be familiar with S.I. units. They need to remember to convert time into seconds for most calculations.

- The best way for students to learn about wiring a plug is to actually do it. Most enjoy this activity. If possible show students some incorrectly wired plugs and get them to 'spot the mistakes'.

- Questions 3 and 4 require students to 'explain' and 'describe'. You should remind students that these words mean they must give detail in their answers in order to gain all the available marks. Expect weaker students to score around half marks for each question.

HOW SCIENCE WORKS ANSWERS

a) No! It is based on a whim!!

b) No, there was no relationship between Rovers scoring a second goal and the television fuse blowing. It would not have blown the fuse. The result of the subsequent experiment was that the house burned down, so it clearly wasn't!

c) i) 6.1A

ii) Not very precise as the current ranged from 5.8A to 6.5A.

iii) Different lengths would heat up by different amounts and would fuse at different currents.

d) Yes. The only difference between the television before and after the 'repair' of the fuse was the bit of wire.

e) It would have been carried out in a scientific way, i.e. the tests would have been valid and reliable and reported without bias.

How science works teaching suggestions

- **Literacy guidance.** Key terms that should be understood: causal links, good and poor science based on a whim.

- **Higher- and lower-level answers.** Question d) is a higher-level question and the answer provided above is also at this level. Question a) is lower level and the answer provided is also lower level.

- **Gifted and talented.** Able students could learn about how such forensic investigations can detect the source of a fire after a house has burned down.

- **How and when to use these questions.** When wishing to develop ideas around good and poor science. The questions could be done for homework or in small group discussions.

- **Special needs.** Identify to these students where a fuse is and how dangerous it is to tamper with fuses, once they have blown. Remind these students that all electrical work needs to be carried out by a qualified electrician and show how most modern appliances have non-changeable fuses.

---

5 a) P = IV, P = 2A × 230V *(1 mark)*
P = 460W *(1 mark)*

b) 2.8kW = 2800W *(1 mark)*
I = P/V
I = 2800W/230V *(1 mark)*
I = 12.2A *(1 mark)*
Hence use 13A fuse *(1 mark)*

c) i) I = 9000W/230V *(1 mark)*
I = 39A *(1 mark)*
Current too large to be safe in a plug *(1 mark)*

ii) Nail will allow very large currents to flow *(1 mark)*
This will cause heating and possibly a fire *(1 mark)*

6 a) Too many appliances plugged into one socket will cause too much current *(1 mark)*
which may overheat/be a fire risk *(1 mark)*

b) plastic insulation on wire is broken *(1 mark)*
risk of electric shock to anyone touching wire *(1 mark)*

c) toaster is switched on *(1 mark)*
knife could conduct giving an electric shock *(1 mark)*

7 a) line is at 2cm *(1 mark)*
peak p.d. = 2cm × 2V/cm *(1 mark)*
peak p.d. = 4V *(1 mark)*

b) i) a.c. supply *(1 mark)*
ii) peak p.d. is 4V *(1 mark)*
iii) one cycle is 4cm
Time period = 4cm × 0.01 s/cm *(1 mark)*
Time period = 0.04s
Frequency = 1/time = 1/0.04 *(1 mark)*
Frequency = 25Hz *(1 mark)*

P2 7.1   Nuclear reactions

LEARNING OBJECTIVES

Students should learn that:

- When a nucleus emits an alpha particle, its mass number is reduced by 4 and its proton number by 2.

- When a nucleus decays by beta emission, its mass number stays the same but its proton number increases by 1.

- Background radiation is present everywhere due to cosmic rays and decay of unstable isotopes in rocks.

LEARNING OUTCOMES

Most students should be able to:

- State the relative charge and mass of the constituents of an atom.

- State how many protons and neutrons are in a nucleus, given its mass number and its atomic number.

- Describe the origins of background radiation.

Some students should also be able to:

- Describe what happens to an isotope when it undergoes alpha or beta decay.

Teaching suggestions

- **Special needs.** It is probably best to provide the students with a list of the terms and symbols used in this topic, along with diagrams representing the basic decays for them to label.

- **Gifted and talented.** Alchemists dreamed for thousands of years that lead could be transformed into gold. With nuclear physics this can now actually be achieved. The students should find out who has done this and why the market has not been flooded with this artificial gold.

- **Learning styles**

  Kinaesthetic: Modelling the changes during nuclear decay.

  Visual: Imagining the structure of an atom.

  Auditory: Explaining how a nucleus changes during nuclear decay.

  Intrapersonal: Making deductions about the nature of the nucleus.

SPECIFICATION LINK-UP   Unit: Physics 2.13.9

- *The relative masses and relative electric charges of protons, neutrons and electrons.*

- *In an atom the number of electrons is equal to the number of protons in the nucleus. The atom has no net electrical charge.*

- *Atoms may lose or gain electrons to form charged particles called 'ions'.*

- *All atoms of a particular element have the same number of protons.*

- *Atoms of different elements have different numbers of protons.*

- *Atoms of the same element that have different numbers of neutrons are called isotopes.*

- *The total number of protons in an atom is called its atomic number.*

- *The total number of protons and neutrons in an atom is called its mass number.*

Lesson structure

STARTER

Fact or fiction – The students use red, amber and green cards to decide if a series of statements about radioactivity are false, they don't know, or true. (5–10 minutes)

Nuclear action – The students should produce a mind map showing what they remember about radioactivity and nuclear power. (15 minutes)

Radiation danger – Can the students remember why radioactivity is so dangerous? They should explain the damage it can do to humans. (5–10 minutes)

MAIN

- There is quite a lot of information in this topic and students are likely to become confused if they move too quickly through it. The main source of confusion is often with the large number of scientific terms.

- Start with a reminder of the structure of an atom, but do not dwell on it too long because this will be the fifth or sixth time they have been through it.

- The terms 'proton number' and 'atomic number' are often interchanged.

- Similarly you may find references to 'nucleon number' instead of 'mass number' in some textbooks.

- Watch out for students getting confused about finding the number of neutrons. Some think that there is always the same number of neutrons as protons.

- Some students find it very difficult to write out the superscript and subscripts on the isotopes in the correct positions. Try to encourage them to be precise.

- You may find animations of nuclear decays helpful, as the students can see the alpha or beta particle leave the nucleus and how it is changed by the process. (See Simulation P2 7.1 'Nuclear reaction' on the Additional Science CD ROM.)

- Somebody might ask where the electron comes from in beta decay. They may think that a neutron is an electron and a proton stuck together, and it just splits.

- Gamma ray emission is really just the dumping of excess energy by the nucleus after another form of decay leaves it with a bit too much energy. As there are no particles emitted there is no change to the nucleus.

- The background radiation section is a basic recap of information the students should have studied before. It should be pointed out that almost all of our exposure is from natural sources.

- **ICT link-up.** Use Simulation P2 7.1 'Nuclear reaction' from the Additional Science CD ROM to show the changes in the nucleus during decays. This helps the students imagine what is going on a lot better.

- **Homework.** Give the students some additional questions on the constituents of different isotopes, and ask them to determine what new isotopes are formed following certain decays. You might like to stretch some students by giving them some decay sequences. The students will need a periodic table.

PLENARIES

Definitions – The students must give accurate definitions of the terms: 'ion, mass number, atomic number, isotope, alpha particle, beta particle and gamma ray.' (10 minutes)

Name that isotope – Provide the students with a table describing different isotopes with gaps in and ask them to complete the table. They may need a periodic table to help. (5–10 minutes)

Say it with words – Give the students a couple of nuclear decay equations and ask them to describe what the equations show in words. (5–10 minutes)

ACTIVITY & EXTENSION IDEAS

Nuclear reminders – It's worthwhile reminding students of the nature and properties of the three radiations. Have a look back to the demonstrations in P1.

NUCLEAR PHYSICS

P2 7.1 Nuclear reactions

LEARNING OBJECTIVES

1 How does the nucleus of an atom change when it emits an alpha particle or a beta particle?

2 How can we represent a nuclear reaction?

3 Where does background radiation come from?

The atom has a nucleus composed of protons and neutrons surrounded by electrons. In a nuclear reaction, neutrons and protons crash into each other and get rearranged. At speeds approaching the cosmic speed limit, the speed of light, they can even annihilate each other or create new particles.

The table gives the relative masses and the relative electric charges of a proton, a neutron and an electron.

	Relative mass	Relative charge
proton	1	+1
neutron	1	0
electron	0.0005	−1

An uncharged atom has equal numbers of protons and electrons. A charged atom, an **ion**, has unequal numbers of protons and electrons.

The atoms of the same element each have the same number of protons. The number of protons in a nucleus is denoted by **Z**. It is called the **atomic number** (or proton number).

Isotopes are atoms of the same element with different numbers of neutrons.

The number of protons and neutrons in a nucleus is called its **mass number**, denoted by **A**.

An isotope of an element X, which has Z protons and A protons and neutrons, is represented by the symbol $^{A}_{Z}X$. For example, the uranium isotope $^{238}_{92}U$ contains 92 protons and 146 neutrons (= 238 − 92) in each nucleus. So its relative mass is 238 and its relative charge is 92.

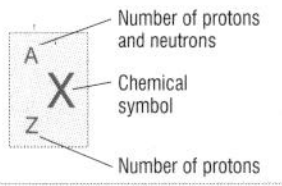

a) How many protons and how many neutrons are in the nucleus of the uranium isotope $^{235}_{92}U$?

A
X
Z

Number of protons and neutrons
Chemical symbol
Number of protons

Example: the symbol for the uranium isotope with 92 protons and 146 neutrons is

$^{238}_{92}U$ (or sometimes U-238)

Figure 1 Representing an isotope

Radioactive decay

An unstable nucleus becomes more stable by emitting an α (alpha) or a β (beta) particle or by emitting γ (gamma) radiation.

α emission

● An α particle consists of two protons and two neutrons. Its relative mass is 4 and its relative charge is 2. So we can represent it by the symbol $^{4}_{2}α$.

● When an unstable nucleus emits an α particle, its atomic number goes down by 2 and its mass number goes down by 4.

For example, the thorium isotope $^{228}_{90}Th$ decays by emitting an α particle. So it forms the radium isotope $^{224}_{88}Ra$.

b) How many protons and how many neutrons are in $^{228}_{90}Th$ and $^{224}_{88}Ra$?

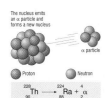

The nucleus emits an α particle and forms a new nucleus

α particle

Proton   Neutron

$^{228}_{90}Th \longrightarrow {}^{224}_{88}Ra + {}^{4}_{2}α$

Figure 2 α emission

β emission

● A β particle is an electron created and emitted by a nucleus which has too many neutrons compared with protons. A neutron in its nucleus changes into a proton and a β particle. This is instantly emitted at high speed by the nucleus.

● The relative mass of a β particle is effectively zero and its relative charge is −1. So we can represent a β particle by the symbol $^{0}_{-1}β$.

● When an unstable nucleus emits a β particle, its atomic number goes up by 1 but its mass number stays the same (because the neutron changes into a proton).

For example, the potassium isotope $^{40}_{19}K$ decays by emitting a β particle. So it forms a nucleus of the calcium isotope $^{40}_{20}Ca$.

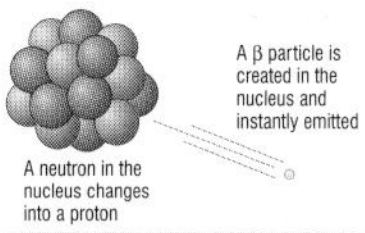

c) How many protons and how many neutrons are in $^{40}_{19}K$ and $^{40}_{20}Ca$?

A β particle is created in the nucleus and instantly emitted

A neutron in the nucleus changes into a proton

$^{40}_{19}K \longrightarrow {}^{40}_{20}Ca + {}^{0}_{-1}β$

Figure 3 β emission

γ emission

γ radiation is emitted by some unstable nuclei after an α particle or a β particle has been emitted. γ radiation is uncharged and has no mass. So it does not change the number of protons or the number of neutrons in a nucleus.

The origins of background radiation

Background radiation is ionising radiation from space (cosmic rays), from devices such as X-ray tubes and from radioactive isotopes in the environment. Some of these isotopes are present because of nuclear weapons testing and nuclear power stations. But most of it is from substances in the Earth. For example, radon gas is radioactive and is a product of the decay of uranium in rocks found in certain areas.

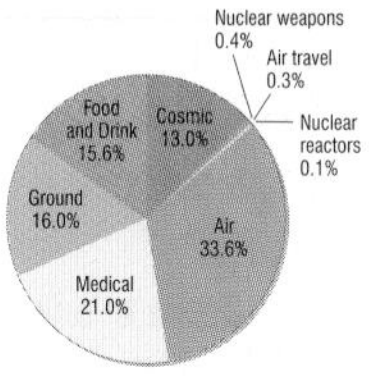

Figure 4 The origins of background radioactivity

Nuclear weapons 0.4%
Air travel 0.3%
Nuclear reactors 0.1%
Food and Drink 15.6%
Cosmic 13.0%
Ground 16.0%
Air 33.6%
Medical 21.0%

KEY POINTS

		Change in the nucleus	Particle emitted
1	α decay	Nucleus loses 2 protons and 2 neutrons	2 protons and 2 neutrons emitted as an α particle
2	β decay	A neutron in the nucleus changes into a proton	An electron is created in the nucleus and instantly emitted

SUMMARY QUESTIONS

1 How many protons and how many neutrons are there in the nucleus of each of the following isotopes?

a) $^{12}_{6}C$
b) $^{60}_{27}Co$
c) $^{235}_{92}U$

2 A substance contains the radioactive isotope $^{238}_{92}U$, which emits alpha radiation. The product nucleus X emits beta radiation and forms a nucleus Y. How many protons and how many neutrons are present in:

a) a nucleus of $^{238}_{92}U$,
b) a nucleus of X,
c) a nucleus of Y?

SUMMARY ANSWERS

1 a) 6p + 6n

b) 27p + 33n

c) 92p + 143n

2 a) 92p + 146n

b) 90p + 144n

c) 91p + 143n

Answers to in-text questions

a) 92p, 143n

b) $^{228}_{90}Th$ = 90p + 138n; $^{224}_{88}Ra$ = 88p + 136n

c) $^{40}_{19}K$ = 19p + 21n; $^{40}_{20}Ca$ = 20p + 20n

KEY POINTS

The students should complete decay equations showing alpha, beta and gamma decay. This could be in the form of a card game.

P2 7.2

The discovery of the nucleus

LEARNING OBJECTIVES

Students should learn:

- That the alpha-scattering experiments carried out by Rutherford and his research team led Rutherford to deduce the nuclear model of the atom. [**HT** only]
- About such experiments, the results they produced and why these results led Rutherford to deduce the nuclear model of the atom. [**HT** only]
- That the nuclear model of the atom was accepted because it explained alpha scattering much better than the previous models could. [**HT** only]
- That the 'plum pudding' model of the atom was replaced by the nuclear model. [**HT** only]

LEARNING OUTCOMES

Most students should be able to:

- Describe the Rutherford scattering experiment and the evidence it produced. [**HT** only]
- Explain how this evidence leads to the nuclear model of the atom. [**HT** only]
- Describe the 'plum pudding' model and explain why this model proved to be inadequate. [**HT** only]

Some students should also be able to:

- Draw and explain the paths of alpha particles scattered by a nucleus.

Teaching suggestions

- **Special needs.** Provide a diagram of the experiment so that the students can add the conclusions to the evidence presented.
- **Gifted and talented.** Ask: 'How was the neutron discovered?' Because it has no electrical charge, it is much more difficult to detect than the electron or proton. The students should find out who discovered it and how.
- **Learning styles**
  Kinaesthetic: Modelling scattering experiment.
  Visual: Imagining the behaviour of alpha particles in the scattering experiment.
  Auditory: Explaining how the conclusions match the evidence.
  Interpersonal: Discussing and evaluating the experiment.
  Intrapersonal: Appreciating the techniques and difficulties involved.

SPECIFICATION LINK-UP   Unit: Physics 2.13.9

Students should use their skills, knowledge and understanding of 'How Science Works':

- to explain how the Rutherford and Marsden scattering experiment led to the plum pudding model of the atom being replaced by the nuclear model. [**HT** only]

Lesson structure

STARTER

Believe it or not? – What does it take to change the students' minds about something? How much evidence would be needed to convince them that NASA have really sent men to the Moon? (5–10 minutes)

What's in the tin? – Peel the label off a tin of sponge pudding (spotted dick is best). Show the unmarked tin to the students and ask then to describe ways they could find out about what's inside without opening it. (5–10 minutes)

Who's the boss? – Give the students a set of cards with academic job titles and ask them to rank them in order of seniority. Use 'dean, professor, lecturer, fellow, research assistant, postgraduate and undergraduate'. (5 minutes)

MAIN

- This topic is all about a famous experiment and it should be built up as such. Through hard work and brilliant ideas, our idea of 'what an atom is' was developed.
- You might want to establish the context; electrons (cathode rays) had not long been discovered and Rutherford had discovered that one element could change into another when it emitted an 'alpha particle'.
- The actual experiment took weeks in a very dark laboratory where Geiger or Marsden had to count tiny flashes of light through a microscope. Each flash was one alpha particle hitting the fluorescent screen.
- If you have electron tubes, you can show a little bit of what this would be like (see activity box).
- The most important result of the experiment was the few particles that bounced back. These showed that there was something massive at the centre of the atom.
- One possible analogy would be to spread a large sheet of paper out vertically and behind it fix a small metal disc held firmly by a stand. If you threw darts at it, most would go straight through but one in a thousand may hit the metal disc and bounce back.
- It will be impossibly difficult for the students to imagine the size of an atom and then the relative size of the nucleus. You might like to point out that 99.99% of the chair they are sitting on is just empty space; then again so is 99.99% of their bodies!
- The problem with plum puddings is that nobody eats them any more, so many students don't understand what you are on about. Try illustrating with a real plum (or spotted dick) pudding. They are cheap and you can always eat it afterwards.

PLENARIES

It's not like a solar system – Some people think of an atom as being a bit like a solar system. The students should make a list of similarities but, more importantly, the differences. (5–10 minutes)

New improved recipe! – The term 'plum pudding' is out of date. Can the students come up with another material/object/whatever that would be a bit more modern? (5 minutes)

I don't believe it – Can the students write a letter to an unconvinced scientist that wants to hold on to the plum pudding model? (10–15 minutes)

ACTIVITY & EXTENSION IDEAS

A scattering experiment

It is possible to model the scattering experiment of Rutherford using a hidden cone and marbles. The marbles are rolled at the cone and scatter in directions similar to those in the original experiment. You should find a kit available in a good science equipment catalogue. This is really only suitable for small groups though. More useful animations can be found at various web sites on the Internet.

Electron tubes

These are generally only used at A-level, but you could use them here with higher attaining groups.

Details

Use the manual for the tube to set it up. It will require an extremely high-tension power supply and some proper connecting leads. These shouldn't be able to provide a dangerous current but take care with any high voltages. With the tube you should be able to show the phosphorescence effect of a charged particle and some magnetic deflection if you wish.

Teaching suggestions – continued

- **Homework.** Whatever happened to Ernest Marsden? Hans Geiger will always be famous for the co-invention of the Geiger-Muller tube, but what did Marsden do? The students can compare the fates of these two nuclear physicists for homework.

- **ICT link-up.** Use Animation P2 7.2 'Nucleus' to help students understand the nature of the nucleus.

Practical support

Lucky strike

This practical really needs no additional explanation. A more advanced version is outlined in the activity box.

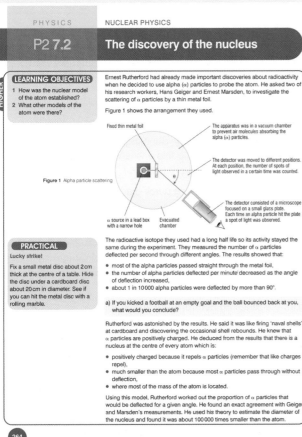

PHYSICS   NUCLEAR PHYSICS

P2 7.2   The discovery of the nucleus

LEARNING OBJECTIVES

1 How was the nuclear model of the atom established?
2 What other models of the atom were there?

Ernest Rutherford had already made important discoveries about radioactivity when he decided to use alpha (α) particles to probe the atom. He asked two of his research workers, Hans Geiger and Ernest Marsden, to investigate the scattering of α particles by a thin metal foil.

Figure 1 shows the arrangement they used.

Figure 1 Alpha particle scattering

The radioactive isotope they used had a long half life so its activity stayed the same during the experiment. They measured the number of α particles deflected per second through different angles. The results showed that:

- most of the alpha particles passed straight through the metal foil,
- the number of alpha particles deflected per minute decreased as the angle of deflection increased,
- about 1 in 10000 alpha particles were deflected by more than 90°.

a) If you kicked a football at an empty goal and the ball bounced back at you, what would you conclude?

Rutherford was astonished by the results. He said it was like firing 'naval shells' at cardboard and discovering the occasional shell rebounds. He knew that α particles are positively charged. He deduced from the results that there is a nucleus at the centre of every atom which is:

- positively charged because it repels α particles (remember that like charges repel),
- much smaller than the atom because most α particles pass through without deflection,
- where most of the mass of the atom is located.

Using this model, Rutherford worked out the proportion of α particles that would be deflected for a given angle. He found an exact agreement with Geiger and Marsden's measurements. He used his theory to estimate the diameter of the nucleus and found it was about 100 000 times smaller than the atom.

PRACTICAL

Lucky strike!

Fix a small metal disc about 2 cm thick at the centre of a table. Hide the disc under a cardboard disc about 20 cm in diameter. See if you can hit the metal disc with a rolling marble.

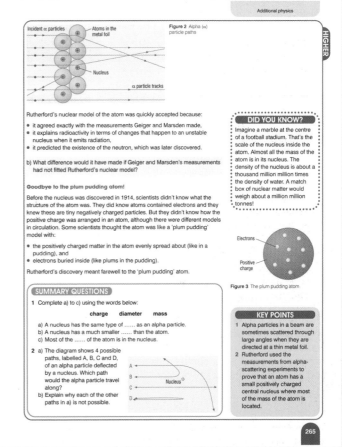

Rutherford's nuclear model of the atom was quickly accepted because:

- it agreed exactly with the measurements Geiger and Marsden made,
- it explains radioactivity in terms of changes that happen to an unstable nucleus when it emits radiation,
- it predicted the existence of the neutron, which was later discovered.

b) What difference would it have made if Geiger and Marsden's measurements had not fitted Rutherford's nuclear model?

Goodbye to the plum pudding atom!

Before the nucleus was discovered in 1914, scientists didn't know what the structure of the atom was. They did know atoms contained electrons and they knew these are tiny negatively charged particles. But they didn't know how the positive charge was arranged in an atom, although there were different models in circulation. Some scientists thought the atom was like a 'plum pudding' model with:

- the positively charged matter in the atom evenly spread about (like in a pudding), and
- electrons buried inside (like plums in the pudding).

Rutherford's discovery meant farewell to the 'plum pudding' atom.

SUMMARY QUESTIONS

1 Complete a) to c) using the words below:

charge   diameter   mass

a) A nucleus has the same type of ...... as an alpha particle.
b) A nucleus has a much smaller ...... than the atom.
c) Most of the ...... of the atom is in the nucleus.

2 a) The diagram shows 4 possible paths, labelled A, B, C and D, of an alpha particle deflected by a nucleus. Which path would the alpha particle travel along?
b) Explain why each of the other paths in a) is not possible.

DID YOU KNOW?

Imagine a marble at the centre of a football stadium. That's the scale of the nucleus inside the atom. Almost all the mass of the atom is in its nucleus. The density of the nucleus is about a thousand million million times the density of water. A match box of nuclear matter would weigh about a million million tonnes!

Figure 3 The plum pudding atom

KEY POINTS

1 Alpha particles in a beam are sometimes scattered through large angles when they are directed at a thin metal foil.
2 Rutherford used the measurements from alpha-scattering experiments to prove that an atom has a small positively charged central nucleus where most of the mass of the atom is located.

264

265

SUMMARY ANSWERS

1 a) Charge.
  b) Diameter.
  c) Mass. [**HT** only]

2 a) Path B.
  b) A is wrong because it is attracted by the nucleus; C is wrong because it is unaffected by the nucleus; D is wrong because it is repelled by the nucleus through too great an angle. [**HT** only]

Answers to in-text questions

a) It had hit something much heavier.
b) Rutherford's model would have been incorrect.

DID YOU KNOW?

There are objects made up of purely nuclear material. A neutron star is made up of neutrons packed together as tightly as the protons and neutrons in a nucleus.

KEY POINTS

The students should link the observations of Rutherford to the conclusions he made about atomic structure.

P2 7.3   Nuclear fission

LEARNING OBJECTIVES

Students should learn:

- That uranium and plutonium isotopes are used in nuclear fission reactors as fuel.
- That nuclear fission is the splitting of large nuclei into small ones; a process that releases energy.
- How a fission reactor operates.

LEARNING OUTCOMES

Most students should be able to:

- List the isotopes used as fuel in nuclear fission reactors.
- Describe what happens in a fission event.
- Sketch a labelled diagram to show how a chain reaction may occur.

Some students should also be able to:

- Explain how a chain reaction in a nuclear reactor can take place.

Teaching suggestions

- **Special needs.** Give the students a large diagram of the reactor, so that they can label the parts and write their notes around it.
- **Gifted and talented.** The students can find out about the choice of materials used for the moderator, control rods and coolant in different types of reactor.
- **Learning styles**
  Visual: Drawing and labelling the components of the power station.
  Auditory: Discussing the safety of fission.
  Interpersonal: Discussing and evaluating the safety features of the power station.
  Intrapersonal: Appreciating the rapid build up in a chain reaction.
- **Homework.** The emergency shutting down of a reactor is called 'scramming'. Where does this term come from. There are a couple of possibilities.
- **ICT link-up.** Animations and simulations showing chain reactions are available in commercial software. There are also some simple animations available freely on the Internet. Search for 'chain reaction simulation'.

SPECIFICATION LINK-UP   Unit: Physics 2.13.10

- *There are two fissionable substances in common use in nuclear reactors, uranium-235 and plutonium-239.*
- *Nuclear fission is the splitting of an atomic nucleus.*
- *For fission to occur the uranium-235 or plutonium-239 nucleus must first absorb a neutron.*
- *The nucleus undergoing fission splits into two smaller nuclei, and 2 or 3 neutrons and energy is released.*
- *The neutrons may go on to start a chain reaction.*

Students should use their skills, knowledge and understanding of 'How Science Works':

- *to sketch a labelled diagram to illustrate how a chain reaction may occur.*

Lesson structure

STARTER

Protection from radiation – Can the students describe the penetrating powers of the three radiations and explain how we can be protected from them? (5–10 minutes)

Lucky lady – A woman bets £1 on roulette and wins, doubling her money. Then she bets the winnings and wins again. She keeps doing this until she has won 20 times in a row. Ask: 'How much has she won?' [£1,048,575] (10 minutes)

Power station basics – The students should draw a quick diagram showing how a fossil fuel power station operates. (10 minutes)

MAIN

- You can show an example of a chain reaction with dominoes. Set them up so that one knocks over two more, and these two knock over four, etc. After only a few steps, you could have hundreds and then thousands falling.
- In a nuclear chain reaction, the released neutrons are important.
- In a nuclear reactor core, it is important to keep the reaction critical. If it becomes 'super critical', the reactor will heat up but not like a nuclear explosion. More likely the reaction becomes 'sub-critical' and slows down.
- Good moderators slow down the fast neutrons without absorbing them. If the moderator absorbs too many neutrons, then the chain reaction cannot continue. In some reactors, graphite is used instead of water.
- The control rods have to be good at absorbing neutrons. When they are inserted the number of available neutrons is decreased, and the reaction becomes sub-critical, cooling the core down. Cadmium and boron are common materials for this job.
- In an emergency, the rods are dropped completely into the core, rapidly reducing the reaction to almost zero. The reactor still produces some heat through natural (non-induced) decay of the radioactive materials. This means that it still has to be cooled or it will meltdown.
- The coolant may be water or some more exotic material such as liquid sodium. It has to be able to rapidly carry thermal energy from the core, but in doing this it becomes radioactive.
- The core itself is very heavily shielded and only a few gamma rays can escape.

PLENARIES

Flow – The students should draw a flow chart and energy transfer diagram showing what happens in a nuclear fission reactor. (10 minutes)

The China syndrome – If a nuclear core melts down, it gets so hot that it can melt the rock beneath it and start sinking into the Earth. If an American reactor melts down, ask 'What's to stop it melting all the way through to China?' (5–10 minutes)

Let's split – The word 'fission' means 'to break into parts'. How many other words can the students think of that mean roughly the same thing? How many words can they think of that mean the opposite? (5 minutes)

FOUL FACTS

The 'critical mass' of pure U-235 is 50 kg. The first nuclear weapon had 60 kg in three pieces and most of the material did not undergo fission. A more efficient design has a 'neutron reflector' material around it that will go supercritical and explode with only 15 kg of material.

P2 7.3 — Nuclear fission

LEARNING OBJECTIVES

1 What radioactive isotopes are used in nuclear power stations?
2 What is nuclear fission?
3 How is heat produced in a nuclear power station?
4 What are fission neutrons?

Chain reactions

Energy is released in a nuclear reactor as a result of a process called **nuclear fission**. In this process, the nucleus of an atom of a fissionable substance splits into two smaller 'fragment' nuclei. This event can cause other fissionable nuclei to split, so producing a **chain reaction** of fission events.

Fission neutrons

When a nucleus undergoes fission, it releases

• two or three neutrons (referred to as 'fission' neutrons) at high speeds,
• energy in the form of radiation and kinetic energy of the fission neutrons and the fragment nuclei.

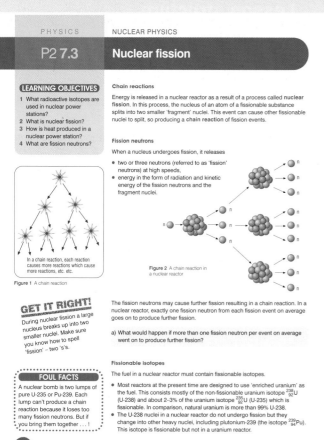

In a chain reaction, each reaction causes more reactions which cause more reactions, etc. etc.

Figure 1 A chain reaction

Figure 2 A chain reaction in a nuclear reactor

GET IT RIGHT!

During nuclear fission a large nucleus breaks up into two smaller nuclei. Make sure you know how to spell 'fission' – two 's's.

FOUL FACTS

A nuclear bomb is two lumps of pure U-235 or Pu-239. Each lump can't produce a chain reaction because it loses too many fission neutrons. But if you bring them together . . . !

The fission neutrons may cause further fission resulting in a chain reaction. In a nuclear reactor, exactly one fission neutron from each fission event on average goes on to produce further fission.

a) What would happen if more than one fission neutron per event on average went on to produce further fission?

Fissionable isotopes

The fuel in a nuclear reactor must contain fissionable isotopes.

• Most reactors at the present time are designed to use 'enriched uranium' as the fuel. This consists mostly of the non-fissionable uranium isotope $^{238}_{92}$U (U-238) and about 2–3% of the uranium isotope $^{235}_{92}$U (U-235) which is fissionable. In comparison, natural uranium is more than 99% U-238.
• The U-238 nuclei in a nuclear reactor do not undergo fission but they change into other heavy nuclei, including plutonium-239 (the isotope $^{239}_{94}$Pu). This isotope is fissionable but not in a uranium reactor.

Inside a nuclear reactor

A nuclear reactor consists of uranium fuel rods spaced evenly in the reactor core. Figure 3 shows a cross-section of a Pressurised Water Reactor (PWR).

• The reactor core is a thick steel vessel containing the fuel rods, control rods and water at high pressure. The fission neutrons are slowed down by collisions with the atoms in the water molecules. This is necessary as fast neutrons do not cause further fission of U-235. We say the water acts as a **moderator** as it slows the fission neutrons down.
• **Control rods** in the core absorb surplus neutrons. This keeps the chain reaction under control. The depth of the rods in the core is adjusted to maintain a steady chain reaction.
• The water acts as a **coolant**. Its molecules gain kinetic energy from the neutrons and the fuel rods. The water is pumped through the core and through sealed pipes to and from a heat exchanger outside the core. The water transfers thermal energy to the heat exchanger from the core.
• The reactor core is a thick steel vessel, designed to withstand the very high temperature and pressure in the core. The core is enclosed by thick concrete walls which absorb radiation that escapes through the walls of the steel vessel.

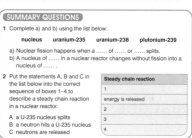

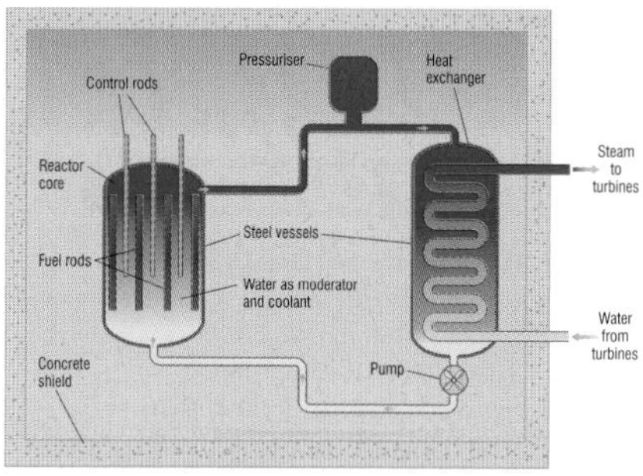

Figure 3 A nuclear reactor

b) What would happen if the control rods were removed from the core?

SUMMARY QUESTIONS

1 Complete a) and b) using the list below:

nucleus   uranium-235   uranium-238   plutonium-239

a) Nuclear fission happens when a ...... of ...... or ...... splits.
b) A nucleus of ...... in a nuclear reactor changes without fission into a nucleus of ....

2 Put the statements A, B and C in the list below into the correct sequence of boxes 1–4 to describe a steady chain reaction in a nuclear reactor.

A a U-235 nucleus splits
B a neutron hits a U-235 nucleus
C neutrons are released

Steady chain reaction
1
energy is released
2
3
4

KEY POINTS

1 Nuclear fission occurs when a uranium-235 nucleus or a plutonium-239 nucleus splits.
2 A chain reaction occurs in a nuclear reactor when each fission event causes further fission events.
3 In a *nuclear reactor*, one neutron per fission on average goes on to produce further fission.

SUMMARY ANSWERS

1 a) Nucleus, uranium-235, plutonium-239.

 b) Uranium-238, plutonium-239.

2 1A, 2C, 3B, 4A.

Answers to in-text questions

a) The chain reaction would go out of control and the reactor would explode.

b) The chain reaction would go out of control and the reactor would explode.

KEY POINTS

The students should be able to draw a chain reaction diagram.

P2 7.4

Nuclear fusion

LEARNING OBJECTIVES

Students should learn that:

- The Sun releases energy due to nuclear fusion of hydrogen isotopes in its core.

- Nuclear fusion is the joining of two small nuclei and this process releases energy.

- Nuclear fusion reactors are difficult to build mainly due to the difficulty of reaching sufficiently high temperatures and pressures.

LEARNING OUTCOMES

Most students should be able to:

- Describe the nuclear fusion process happening in the Sun.

- Outline how experimental nuclear fusion reactors work on Earth.

Some students should also be able to:

- Describe some of the problems associated with nuclear fusion reactors.

Teaching suggestions

- **Gifted and talented**
  - Ask: 'What's so special about iron?' The students can find out more detail about nuclear energy release by researching binding energy. It is this energy that is released by fusion and fission processes when the nucleons rearrange. If they go on to look at stars and supernovae they will discover the importance of iron in these explosions.
  - Alternatively, students could find out about the claims made by Pons and Fleischmann in the late 1980s regarding 'cold fusion'.

- **Learning styles**
  Visual: Following the sequence of a nuclear fusion diagram.

  Auditory: Discussing advantages of fusion over fission.

  Interpersonal: Debating the possibility of fusion power.

  Intrapersonal: Evaluating the difficulties of making progress with the research.

- **Homework.** The poster comparing the two types of nuclear power could be a homework task, as could research into the latest developments.

SPECIFICATION LINK-UP   Unit: Physics 2.13.10

- *Nuclear fusion is the joining of two atomic nuclei to form a larger one.*
- *Nuclear fusion is the process by which energy is released in stars.*

Lesson structure

STARTER

Star One – Ask: 'Where does the Sun get its energy?' The students brainstorm their ideas and then discuss possible problems with them. (5–10 minutes)

A Sun myth – The Sun has a lot of mythology based on it. What stories do the students know? (5–10 minutes)

Solar fact or solar fiction? – Give the students a set of statements about the Sun and ask them to separate fact from fiction. (5–10 minutes)

MAIN

- Students may confuse the words 'fission' and 'fusion' in general conversation, but should be able to remember the difference when writing answers.

- The reactions in the Sun are hugely powerful. Its power output is around 4×10^{26} watts. The students might like to imagine how many light bulbs' worth that represents.

- The students might want to know what you mean by 'the antimatter counterpart of the electron'. This is a topic for A-level study really, so just say that it is exactly the same size as an electron but all of its other properties are opposite.

- If you like, you can act out the reaction process in the Sun with marbles or with molecular modelling kits. The balls should be close together though. Alternatively, show the Animation P2 7.4 'Nuclear fusion' from the Additional Science CD ROM.

- The overall process shown is four protons (hydrogen nuclei) converting into one helium nucleus, and so the Sun is generally said to be converting hydrogen into helium. This means that the percentages of hydrogen and helium are slowly changing.

- The reactions also produce a lot of positrons and neutrinos.

- The main difficulty to overcome is the fact that the protons strongly repel each other. In the Sun, the gravitational forces are strong enough to keep the very high temperature protons close enough together so that they will collide and fuse. It is this process that is proving very difficult to replicate on Earth.

- Some of the students will have heard the term 'plasma' before and when you tell them that it is at a temperature of several thousand degrees, they will assume it has a lot of thermal energy and will be very dangerous. The plasma is actually of very low density and so hasn't got that much thermal energy.

- When discussing the promising future of fusion-produced energy, remind the students that we have been working on the project for a long time and it has proven very difficult to achieve. There is a lot of work yet to be done and opportunities for great scientists to make a difference.

- Fusion-reactor research continues with the construction of the latest testing facility in France. This International Thermonuclear Experimental Reactor (Iter) may actually be able to sustain a reaction long enough for it to be useful. It will cost over 10 billion euros though.

- There are possible hazards associated with a fusion reactor: free neutrons are produced and could be absorbed by the materials in the reactor. This would produce dangerous radioactive isotopes. However, there would be much less radiation released than in the nuclear fission reaction.

- **ICT link-up.** The latest state of nuclear fusion research is available online. The students should be able to find news articles about the new and previous research centres. (Search for 'nuclear fusion breakthrough'.)

PLENARIES

Bring it together – The word 'fusion' means 'to combine together'. How many examples of fusion can the students think of, and how many words that mean the same thing? (5 minutes)

A bright future – A company claims to have developed a working nuclear fusion plant and wants to build one in the local area. Do the students object or rejoice? They should have a quick discussion and vote. (5 minutes)

Compare and contrast – The students should make a poster, comparing and contrasting the processes of nuclear fission and nuclear fusion. (20 minutes)

PHYSICS   NUCLEAR PHYSICS

Additional physics

P2 7.4 Nuclear fusion

LEARNING OBJECTIVES

1 Where does the Sun's energy come from?
2 What happens during nuclear fusion?
3 Why is it difficult to make a nuclear fusion reactor?

Imagine if we could get energy from water. Stars release energy as a result of fusing small nuclei like hydrogen to form larger nuclei. Water contains lots of hydrogen atoms. A glass of water could provide the same amount of energy as a tanker full of petrol – if we could make a fusion reactor here on the Earth.

Fusion reactions

Two small nuclei release energy when they are fused together to form a single larger nucleus. The process releases energy only if the relative mass of the product nucleus is no more than about 55 (about the same as an iron nucleus). Energy must be supplied to create bigger nuclei.

Figure 1 A fusion reaction

The Sun is mostly 75% hydrogen and about 25% helium. The core is so hot that it consists of a 'plasma' of bare nuclei with no electrons. These nuclei move about and fuse together when they collide. When they fuse, they release energy. Figure 2 shows how protons fuse together to form a $^4_2$He nucleus. Energy is released at each stage.

Figure 2 Fusion reactions in the Sun

○ Proton
● Neutron

FOUL FACTS

A hydrogen bomb is a uranium bomb surrounded by the hydrogen isotope, $^2_1$H. When the uranium bomb explodes, it makes the surrounding hydrogen fuse and release even more energy. A single hydrogen bomb would completely destroy London!

• When two protons (i.e. hydrogen nuclei) fuse, they form a 'heavy hydrogen' nucleus, $^2_1$H. A positron, the antimatter counterpart of the electron, is created and emitted at the same time.
• Two more protons collide separately with two $^2_1$H nuclei and turn them into heavier nuclei.
• The two heavier nuclei collide to form the helium nucleus $^4_2$He.
• The energy released at each stage is carried away as kinetic energy of the product nucleus and other particles emitted.

a) Look at Figure 2 and work out what is formed when a proton collides with a $^2_1$H nucleus.

Fusion reactors

There are enormous technical difficulties with fusion. The 'plasma' of light nuclei must be heated to very high temperatures before the nuclei will fuse. This is because two nuclei approaching each other will repel each other due to their positive charge. If the nuclei are moving fast enough, they can overcome the force of repulsion and fuse together.

In a fusion reactor:

• the plasma is heated by passing a very large electric current through it,
• the plasma is contained by a magnetic field so it doesn't touch the reactor walls. If it did, it would go cold and fusion would stop.

Figure 3 An experimental fusion reactor

Scientists have been working on these problems since the 1950s. A successful fusion reactor would release more energy than it uses to heat the plasma. At the present time, scientists working on experimental fusion reactors are able to do this by fusing 'heavy hydrogen' nuclei to form helium nuclei – but only for a few minutes!

b) Why is a fusion reactor unlikely to explode?

A promising future

Practical fusion reactors could meet all our energy needs.

• The fuel for fusion reactors is readily available as 'heavy hydrogen' and is present in sea water.
• The reaction product, helium, is a non-radioactive inert gas so is harmless.
• The energy released could be used to generate electricity.

SUMMARY QUESTIONS

1 Complete a) and b) using the words below:

        larger   small   stable

a) When two ...... nuclei moving at high speed collide, they form a ...... nucleus.
b) Energy is released in nuclear fusion if the product nucleus is not as ...... as an iron nucleus.

2 a) Why does the plasma of light nuclei in a fusion reactor need to be very hot?
  b) Why would a fusion reactor that needs more energy than it produces not be much use?

KEY POINTS

1 Nuclear fusion occurs when two nuclei are forced close enough together so they form a single larger nucleus.
2 Energy is released when two light nuclei are fused together.
3 A fusion reactor needs to be at a very high temperature before nuclear fusion can take place.

268   269

SUMMARY ANSWERS

1 a) Small, larger.
  b) Stable.

2 a) So the nuclei have enough kinetic energy to overcome the force of repulsion between them and fuse.

  b) The energy output would be less than the energy input so it would not produce any energy overall.

Answers to in-text questions

a) $^3_2$He nucleus.

b) If it goes out of control, the plasma would touch the walls and go cold.

KEY POINTS

Can the students outline the nuclear fusion processes in the Sun and the problems we have copying them on Earth?

P2 7.5   Nuclear energy issues

PHYSICS   NUCLEAR PHYSICS

P2 7.5   Nuclear energy issues

The Manhattan project

In the Second World War, scientists in Britain and America were recruited to work in Arizona on the Manhattan project, the project to build the first atomic bomb. They knew they would be in deadly competition with scientists in Nazi Germany. They also knew that if they lost the race, the war would be lost.

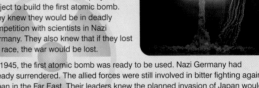

By 1945, the first atomic bomb was ready to be used. Nazi Germany had already surrendered. The allied forces were still involved in bitter fighting against Japan in the Far East. Their leaders knew the planned invasion of Japan would claim the lives of many allied troops. An atomic bomb was dropped on the Japanese city of Hiroshima to force Japan to surrender. The explosion killed 140 000 people. The Japanese government did not give in until after a second atomic bomb was dropped on the Japanese city of Nagasaki a week later.

ACTIVITY

Discuss these questions as a small group:

a) Most people think the British and American governments were right to build an atomic bomb. But do you think scientists should continue to work on deadly weapons?

b) Many people think the power of the atomic bomb should have been demonstrated to Japan by dropping it on an uninhabited island. What do you think?

Cold fusion

a star in a jar, a claim too far!

- scientists at local uni claim they can fuse hydrogen in a beaker of water
- energy from the sun due to it fusion
- say they have detected nuclear radiation from the beaker – tell tale signs of fusion
- could mean cheaper electricity
- claim not yet confirmed by other scientists

ACTIVITY

Imagine you're a journalist and you've got a 'scoop' on cold fusion. Your editor wants you to write it up for the front page – nothing too complicated. Prepare a front-page feature on your scoop. Remember the claims have not been confirmed yet.

The fast-breeder reactor

This fast-breeder reactor uses plutonium-239 as its fuel. It can 'breed' its own plutonium by fusion from uranium-238. Present and planned uranium reactors will use up the world's supply of uranium within about 200 years. Fast-breeder reactors would extend that to thousands of years. As in the uranium reactor, control rods in the reactor core are used to keep the rate of fission events constant. This ensures energy is released at a constant rate. **But** if somehow, plutonium got stuck in a pipe . . . !

ACTIVITY

a) Finish the sentence at the end of the paragraph.

b) The UK government built and tested an experimental fast-breeder reactor on the coast of Northern Scotland at Dounreay. It has now been closed. So why are many people still worried about it? Imagine you are one of them. Write a letter to your local newspaper about your concerns.

SPECIFICATION LINK-UP

Unit: Physics 2.13.10

This spread can be used to revisit substantive content covered in this chapter:

- *There are two fissionable substances in common use in nuclear reactors uranium-235 and plutonium-239.*

- *Nuclear fusion is the joining of two atomic nuclei to form a larger one.*

- *Nuclear fusion is the process by which energy is released in stars.*

Students should use their skills, knowledge and understanding of 'How Science Works':

- *to sketch a labelled diagram to illustrate how a chain reaction may occur.*

Teaching suggestions

Activities

The Manhattan project

The use of nuclear bombs on Japan at the end of World War II is obviously a contentious matter. Issues to discuss include:

- The lack of warning or demonstration to Japan – the first bomb was dropped on Hiroshima without any form of warning. This was to prevent the remaining Japanese forces from trying to intercept the mission. After this bombing leaflets were dropped on Japanese cities to say that more bombs would come if there were no surrender. Three days later the warning was fulfilled at Nagasaki.

- The two nuclear weapons used in the bombings were of very different designs. On Hiroshima the 'little boy' uranium bomb was dropped, while three days later the 'fat man' plutonium bomb was dropped. Ask: 'Was the second bomb dropped to test this different technology?'

- Ask: 'Were the Americans demonstrating their technology to the Russians to warn them about future gains in Europe?'

- Ask: 'How many civilians in Japanese-controlled China and prisoner camps were dying every month? How many were saved by a quick end to the war?'

- Ask: 'What did the scientists that made the bombs think about their use? What did they do after the war?'

Nuclear reprocessing – a hot problem!

The students may have debated this issue before, but they could look at the reprocessing techniques in more detail. Ask: 'What happens to the chemicals used in the reprocessing? If they become radioactive where are they stored?'

The fast-breeder reactor

- You could use this activity to discuss the fail-safe designs of nuclear reactors. Ask: 'What is the likelihood of the control rods not working? The reactor was cooled by liquid sodium metal; what would happen if this leaked?'

- All of the reactors at Dounreay have now been shut down, except for some experimental nuclear submarine reactors. The process of decommissioning has begun and the government hopes to have the site back to 'green field' status by 2047!

Nuclear reprocessing – a hot problem!

Used fuel rods contain uranium-238 and plutonium-239. After removal from a reactor, a used fuel rod is left to cool in a large tank of water for up to a year. Then the fuel in it is removed and the uranium and plutonium content is taken out chemically. This process is called reprocessing. The rest of the fuel is stored in sealed containers at secure sites. Reprocessed uranium and plutonium can be used in fast-breeder reactors to generate electricity. Plutonium can also be used to make nuclear bombs.

The UKs THORP reprocessing plant in Cumbria reprocesses waste from other countries as well as from the UK. Lots of scientists are employed there. It generates income but it also generates lots of controversy. Many people think it should be closed.

ACTIVITY

Should we reprocess nuclear waste for other countries? Should we reprocess our own nuclear waste or just store it? Discuss the issue as a group. Send an e-mail to your MP to tell him/her what you think.

Atom smashers

Here's something you don't need to know for your GCSE exam – yet! We now know that neutrons and protons are made of smaller particles called **quarks**. Physicists use big machines (like the one in the picture) called accelerators to make charged particles travel extremely fast. They discovered that a beam of fast-moving electrons is scattered by three small particles inside each neutron and proton. They worked out that

- a proton is made of two 'up' quarks and a 'down' quark,
- a neutron is made of two 'down' quarks and an 'up' quark.

You'll learn more about the quark family at AS level!

ACTIVITY

What conclusions can you make about the charge of an 'up' quark and the charge of a 'down' quark?

New improved nuclear reactors

Most of the world's nuclear reactors presently in use will need to be replaced in the next 20 years. They were built to last for no more than about 30 to 40 years. We all want electricity and we want it without burning fossil fuel. Reactor companies have been developing new improved 'third-generation' nuclear reactors to replace existing nuclear reactors when they are taken out of use.

These new types of reactors have:

- a standard design to cut down capital costs and construction time,
- a longer operating life – typically 60 years,
- improved safety features,
- much less effect on the environment.

Some of the new reactors are designed with 'passive' safety features, where natural processes (for example, convection of outside air through cooling panels along the reactor walls) are used to prevent accidents. Such features are additional to 'active' safety controls, such as the use of control rods and safety valves. Some scientists claim these 'new' features are about giving nuclear power a more 'positive image'.

ACTIVITY

New reactors are being built in many countries. Should new reactors be built in the UK? Discuss the benefits and the drawbacks of such a programme.

271

Atom smashers

The quark forms part of the standard model in particle physics. The charges of the quarks are $+\frac{2}{3}e$ for an 'up' quark and $-\frac{1}{3}e$ for a 'down' quark (where e is the charge of a proton). If you put the right combinations together you should find a neutron ends up with zero charge, while a proton ends up with $+1e$ charge. For more fun, the students can find out about leptons and mesons: the other fundamental particles.

New improved nuclear reactors

Public opposition to new nuclear reactors is still very strong. The students are better informed than most about the technology, so what do they think? No matter how many safety features are employed, the damage caused by a single reactor melting down can be so devastating that student fears can never be soothed.

However, the long-term damage from a coal power station could be just as great, but because the damage is caused over a period of 50 or more years it is not easily noticed.

Gifted and talented

Antimatter – Scientists have recently manufactured a few atoms of anti-hydrogen. Ask them to find out what this is and how it was made. Can they find out anything else about antimatter?

Learning styles

Kinaesthetic: Researching into the history of nuclear weapons.

Visual: Obtaining more information on particle physics.

Auditory: Discussing the use of nuclear weapons.

Interpersonal: Discussing the operation and evolution of fast-breeder reactors.

Intrapersonal: Writing a report on cold fusion or reprocessing.

ICT link-up

To find out more about particle physics visit the web site of 'The Particle Adventure'. There are several copies of the site online, so you should find it easily.

SUMMARY ANSWERS

1 a) i) 6 p + 8 n

    ii) 90 p + 138 n

  b) i) 7 p + 7 n

    ii) $^{14}_{7}$N

  c) i) 88 p + 136 n

    ii) $^{224}_{88}$Ra

2 a) i) Stays the same.

    ii) Decreases.

    iii) Increases.

  b) i) The reactor would overheat and the materials in it might melt. In the meltdown the reactor pressure might be high enough to cause an explosion releasing radioactive material into the atmosphere.

    ii) The excess neutrons would be absorbed and the reaction would slow down releasing less energy.

3 a) i) The process where two small nuclei fuse together to form a single larger nucleus.

    ii) Because they are both positively charged.

    iii) To overcome the force of repulsion between them due to their charge.

  b) The plasma needs to be very hot. The plasma is difficult to control.

4 a) i) Fusion.

    ii) Fission.

    iii) Fission.

  b) The fuel is readily available. The products of fusion are not radioactive.

Summary teaching suggestions

- Question 1 checks the understanding of isotopes, nuclear change and nuclear nomenclature. Watch out for the students putting the mass and proton numbers in the wrong place.

- The last three questions are about reactors. There may still be some students confusing fission and fusion. Get them to do a table comparing the two techniques.

NUCLEAR PHYSICS: P2 7.1 – P2 7.5

SUMMARY QUESTIONS

1 a) How many protons and how many neutrons are in a nucleus of each of the following isotopes?
  i) $^{14}_{6}$C,   ii) $^{228}_{90}$Th

  b) $^{14}_{6}$C emits a β particle and becomes an isotope of nitrogen (N).
    i) How many protons and how many neutrons are in this nitrogen isotope?
    ii) Write down the symbol for this isotope.

  c) $^{228}_{90}$Th emits an α particle and becomes an isotope of radium (Ra).
    i) How many protons and how many neutrons are in this isotope of radium?
    ii) Write down the symbol for this isotope.

2 a) Complete the sentences using words from the list.

    decreases   increases   stays the same

  When energy is released at a steady rate in a nuclear reactor,
    i) the number of fission events each second in the core ....
    ii) the amount of uranium-235 in the core ....
    iii) the number of radioactive isotopes in the fuel rods ....

  b) Explain what would happen in a nuclear reactor if:
    i) the coolant fluid leaked out of the core,
    ii) the control rods were pushed further into the reactor core.

3 a) i) What do we mean by nuclear fusion?
    ii) Why do two nuclei repel each other when they get close?
    iii) Why do they need to collide at high speed in order to fuse together?

  b) Give two reasons why nuclear fusion is difficult to achieve in a reactor.

4 a) Complete the sentences using words from the list.

    fission   fusion

    i) In a ...... reactor, two small nuclei join together and release energy.
    ii) In a ...... reactor, a large nucleus splits and releases energy.
    iii) The fuel in a ...... reactor contains uranium-235.

  b) State two advantages that nuclear fusion reactors would have in comparison with nuclear fission reactors.

EXAM-STYLE QUESTIONS

1 The diagram shows two isotopes of the element carbon

    ● Proton
    ○ Neutron
    × Electron

  (a) What are isotopes of an element?

  (b) (i) What is the atomic number of carbon?
    (ii) What are the mass numbers of the two isotopes of carbon shown in the diagram?

  (c) Which of the particles ●, ○ and ×, shown in the diagram:
    (i) has a negative charge?
    (ii) has no charge?
    (iii) has the smallest mass?

2 In a nuclear reactor, energy is produced by the process of nuclear fission.

  Describe as fully as you can the process of nuclear fission.

  The answer has been started for you. Copy and complete:

  Atoms of uranium-235 are bombarded by neutrons. ....

3 Nuclear fusion is the process by which energy is released in stars.
  Describe as fully as you can the process of nuclear fusion.

EXAM-STYLE ANSWERS

1 a) Atoms of an element with same numbers of protons   *(1 mark)*
    but different numbers of neutrons.   *(1 mark)*

  b) i) 6   *(1 mark)*
    ii) 12 and 14   *(2 marks)*

  c) i) electron   *(1 mark)*
    ii) neutron   *(1 mark)*
    iii) electron   *(1 mark)*

2 A uranium-235 nucleus absorbs a neutron.   *(1 mark)*
  The nucleus splits into two smaller nuclei   *(1 mark)*
  and two or three neutrons   *(1 mark)*
  and energy is released.   *(1 mark)*
  The neutrons may go on to hit other nuclei   *(1 mark)*
  and start a chain reaction.   *(1 mark)*

3 The nuclei   *(1 mark)*
  of lighter elements join together   *(1 mark)*
  they form heavier elements   *(1 mark)*
  the process releases energy.   *(1 mark)*

4 a) $^{226}_{88}$Ra → $^{222}_{86}$Rn + $^{4}_{2}$α
  1 mark for each correct number   *(4 marks)*

  b) $^{14}_{6}$C → $^{14}_{7}$N + $^{0}_{-1}$β
  1 mark for each correct number   *(4 marks)*

  c) neutron becomes a proton and an electron   *(1 mark)*
  proton stays in the nucleus   *(1 mark)*
  electron is emitted as a beta particle   *(1 mark)*

5 a) e.g. food and drink, medical sources, nuclear accidents, cosmic rays   *(2 marks)*
  b) make measurements in different rooms   *(1 mark)*
  measure at different times of day   *(1 mark)*
  repeat all measurements and find an average   *(2 marks)*

  c) categoric variable   *(1 mark)*
  bar chart   *(1 mark)*

a) Radon is formed when radium-226 decays by the emission of an alpha particle.

Copy and complete the nuclear equation below.

$$^{226}_{88}\text{Ra} \longrightarrow \text{.......... Rn} + \text{..........} \alpha \quad (4)$$

b) Nitrogen is formed when carbon-14 decays by the emission of a beta particle.

Copy and complete the nuclear equation below.

$$^{14}_{6}\text{C} \longrightarrow \text{.......... N} + \text{..........} \beta \quad (4)$$

c) What changes take place in the carbon-14 nucleus when it decays by emitting a beta particle? (3)

Background radiation is with us all the time and comes from many different sources, such as radon gas.

a) Name two other sources of background radiation. (2)

b) Some scientists are measuring the amount of radon gas inside a house. The gas is released into the air from rocks in the ground. Suggest what the scientists could do to make their measurements as reliable as possible. (4)

c) The table gives some values for the dose of background radiation from the ground in different parts of the UK.

Area of UK	Dose in millisieverts per year
South west	0.35
South east	0.20
Midlands	0.25
North west	0.30
North east	0.23

(i) What type of variable is the 'Area of UK'? (1)

(ii) What would be the best way to represent this data on a bar chart or line graph? (1)

HOW SCIENCE WORKS QUESTIONS

Iodine-125 is a radioactive isotope used by doctors as a gamma emitter for measuring bone density in humans. It can also be used in the treatment of prostate cancer.

It is important to know how the activity of iodine-125 changes with time. The following measurements were taken in two identical tests of iodine-125.

Time (days)	0	50	100	150	200	250
Sample A (counts/min)	100	56	31	17	10	6
Sample B (counts/min)	100	55	31	18	9	5

a) Are the differences in activity between the two samples due to random or systematic variations? Explain your answer. (1)

b) The tests were carried on for several years and the results stayed more or less constant after a couple of years. This was said to be due to the ever-present background radiation.
Explain why the background radiation introduces a systematic error into the measurements. (1)

c) What are the environmental issues involved in using this isotope? (1)

PRESS RELEASE

Fifteen-year studies of prostate cancer patients using iodine-125 have been completed. The Medical Director from a US company confirmed that results show only 4% of patients had died from the prostate cancer. A British consultant urologist said that after 5 years, 93% of patients were disease-free.

d) Suggest two questions you might want to ask the scientists who gave this press release. (2)

HOW SCIENCE WORKS ANSWERS

a) The differences could be due to random variations as the differences show no pattern. However, radioactive decay is a random process, so there could be no error here.

b) The background radiation levels stay more or less constant in these time scales and so will affect each reading equally.

c) Environmental issues are that it must be used sensibly and stored safely to ensure as little as possible gets into the environment.

d) e.g. What did the people die from?
How many people were in the survey?
Do all prostate cancer patients get this treatment?
Was there a control group?
How many would have died anyway?

How science works teaching suggestions

- **Literacy guidance.** Key terms that should be understood: random error, systematic error, mean.

- **Gifted and talented.** Able students could explore the ways in which gamma radiation can be measured and suggest some units for the table.

- **How and when to use these questions.** When wishing to develop ideas around systematic and random error and the ways in which science can lead to technological development and environmental issues.
  The questions could be used in small discussion groups.

- **Homework.** The questions could be used for homework with more able students.

- **Special needs.** These students will need to be aware of the advantages and problems associated with using radioisotopes.

- **ICT link-up.** Students could use the Internet to research how gamma radiation can be detected. Search the web for 'detecting gamma radiation'.

Exam teaching suggestions

- In examinations students often confuse fission and fusion.

- In question 2 students might like to illustrate their answer with a diagram. They can get credit for this but the diagram needs to be clear, labelled and include several fissions, large and small nuclei and neutrons.

- There are many sources of background radiation. Students will gain credit for any sensible answer.

- Students should practise balancing nuclear equations for both alpha and beta decays.

P2 Examination-Style Questions

Answers to Questions

1 (a) Total momentum before = total momentum after
   (1 mark)

   $0 = 2\,\text{kg} \times v\,\text{m/s} + 0.0005\,\text{kg} \times 100\,\text{m/s}$ *(1 mark)*
   $0 = 2v\,\text{kg}\,\text{m/s} + 0.05\,\text{kg}\,\text{m/s}$
   $v = -0.05/2\,\text{m/s}$
   $v = -0.025\,\text{m/s}$ *(sign not essential for the mark)*
   (1 mark)

   (b) Change in momentum = force × time taken for the change.   *(1 mark)*
   If the force is applied for a longer time the gain in momentum is greater   *(1 mark)*
   so the velocity of the ball is greater.   *(1 mark)*
   [HT only]

2 (a) There is a drag force acting upwards on the ball.
   (1 mark)
   The drag force increases as the speed increases.
   (1 mark)
   Eventually drag force is equal to the weight (resultant force = zero).   *(1 mark)*

   (b) e.g. Eye at level of the ball.
   Take time as lower surface of the ball passes the mark each time.
   Repeat the test.   *(2 marks)*

   (c) Straight line, showing initial acceleration. *(1 mark)*
   Line curves.   *(1 mark)*
   Horizontal line to show terminal velocity. *(1 mark)*

3 (a) Negative electrons   *(1 mark)*
   stuck into a lump of positive matter.   *(1 mark)*

   (b) First explanation: Most of the atom is empty space.   *(1 mark)*
   Second explanation: The nucleus has a positive charge   *(1 mark)*
   and a large mass.   *(1 mark)*
   [HT only]

   continues opposite ❯

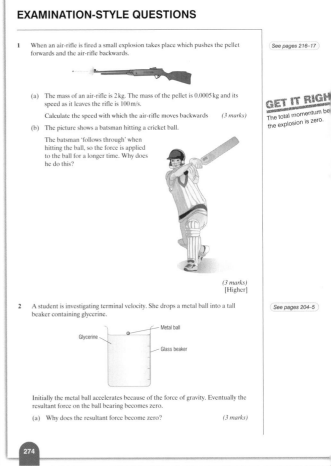

GET IT RIGHT!

Students should understand that the total momentum before the explosion is zero.

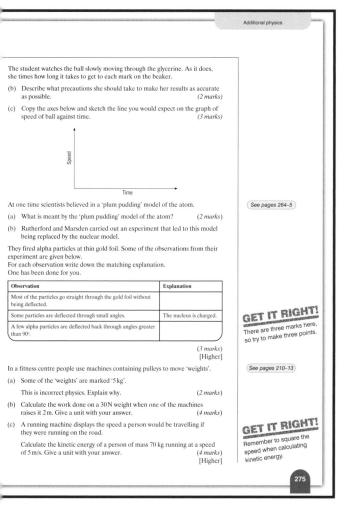

The student watches the ball slowly moving through the glycerine. As it does, she times how long it takes to get to each mark on the beaker.

(b) Describe what precautions she should take to make her results as accurate as possible. *(2 marks)*

(c) Copy the axes below and sketch the line you would expect on the graph of speed of ball against time. *(3 marks)*

At one time scientists believed in a 'plum pudding' model of the atom.

See pages 264–5

(a) What is meant by the 'plum pudding' model of the atom? *(2 marks)*

(b) Rutherford and Marsden carried out an experiment that led to this model being replaced by the nuclear model.

They fired alpha particles at thin gold foil. Some of the observations from their experiment are given below.
For each observation write down the matching explanation.
One has been done for you.

Observation	Explanation
Most of the particles go straight through the gold foil without being deflected.	
Some particles are deflected through small angles.	The nucleus is charged.
A few alpha particles are deflected back through angles greater than 90°.	

GET IT RIGHT!
There are three marks here, so try to make three points.

(3 marks)
[Higher]

In a fitness centre people use machines containing pulleys to move 'weights'.

See pages 210–13

(a) Some of the 'weights' are marked '5 kg'.

This is incorrect physics. Explain why. *(2 marks)*

(b) Calculate the work done on a 30 N weight when one of the machines raises it 2 m. Give a unit with your answer. *(4 marks)*

(c) A running machine displays the speed a person would be travelling if they were running on the road.

Calculate the kinetic energy of a person of mass 70 kg running at a speed of 5 m/s. Give a unit with your answer. *(4 marks)*
[Higher]

GET IT RIGHT!
Remember to square the speed when calculating kinetic energy.

> *continues from previous page*

4 (a) 5 kg is a mass. *(1 mark)*
Weight is measured in newtons. *(1 mark)*

(b) Work done = force × distance moved in the
direction of the force *(1 mark)*
Work done = 30 N × 2 m *(1 mark)*
Work done = 60 *(1 mark)*
Units of Nm or joules *(1 mark)*

(c) kinetic energy = $\frac{1}{2}$ × mass × velocity^2 *(1 mark)*
kinetic energy = $\frac{1}{2}$ × 70 kg × (5 m/s)^2 *(1 mark)*
kinetic energy = 875 J *(2 marks)*
[HT only]

How science works

How science works is treated here as an appendix to the Additional Science units. It is not intended that the 'thinking behind the doing' is taught here as a separate set of lessons. It is of course an integral part of the way students will learn about science and these skills must be nurtured throughout the course. It is anticipated that sections of this appendix will be taught as the opportunity presents itself during the teaching programme. The learning objectives and learning outcomes from the opening 'How Science Works' section in the GCSE Science Teacher Book are reproduced in this Appendix for your convenience. They can be integrated into your lesson plans as opportunities to teach concepts from 'How Science Works' arise throughout units B2, C2 and P2.

Teaching suggestions

Finding out what they know

Students should appreciate the 'thinking behind the doing' which was developed during Science 1 units. It would be useful to illustrate this by a simple demonstration (e.g. calcium carbonate into hydrochloric acid, catalase used to decompose hydrogen peroxide; or terminal velocity of a body falling through a liquid) and posing questions that build into a flow diagram of the way science progresses from observations to hypotheses, predictions, investigations and conclusions that relate to the original hypothesis. This could lead into recap questions to ascertain each individual student's progress.

The recap questions should identify each individual student's gaps in understanding. Therefore it is best carried out as an assessment. It might be appropriate to allow students to apply each of these terms to the particular example demonstrated to them.

Revealing to the students that they are using scientific method to solve problems during their everyday life can make their work in science more relevant.

Other situations could illustrate the importance of scientific research to everyday life and should be discussed in groups or as a class.

For example:

- The discovery of penicillin as an antibiotic.
- The discovery of microwaves.
- The discovery of polythene.

Able students could discuss what Isaac Newton meant by 'If I have seen further it is by standing on the shoulders of giants'. A description used by many subsequent scientists including Stephen Hawking.

Activity notes

Emphasise the importance of recognising the difference between myth or hearsay and science. Collect newspaper articles and news items from the television to illustrate good and poor uses of science. There are some excellent television programmes illustrating good and poor science. Have a competition for who can bring in the poorest example of science used to sell products – shampoo adverts are a very good starter!

Read the science behind the news at whyfiles.org. Search the Internet for 'good and bad science in advertising'.

Thinking scientifically

LEARNING OBJECTIVES

Students should learn:

- The relative importance of continuous, ordered and categoric measurements.
- That evidence needs to be valid and reliable.
- That variables can be linked causally, by association or by chance.
- To distinguish between opinion based on scientific evidence and non-scientific ideas.

LEARNING OUTCOMES

Students should be able to:

- Recognise measurements as continuous, ordered or categoric and state which of the three types of measurement is the most powerful.
- Suggest how an investigation might demonstrate its reliability and validity.
- State that variables can be linked causally, by association or by chance.
- Identify when an opinion does not have the support of valid and reliable science.

Deciding on what to measure

The demonstration chosen from the previous section could be developed to test a prediction. Choose an example that could include different types of variable so that their relative merits can be discussed. E.g. lumps of limestone versus mass of limestone or celery used as a source of catalase on hydrogen peroxide; or time taken for different objects to fall through oil.

Create a table for the results. Consider the use of preliminary work, controls, precision and what to do with anomalies.

Checking for misconceptions

Some common misconceptions that can be dealt with here and throughout the course are:

- The purpose of controls – some students believe that it is about making accurate measurements of the independent variable.
- The purpose of preliminary work – some believe that it is the first set of results.
- That the table of results is constructed after the practical work – students should be encouraged to produce the table before carrying out their work and complete it during their work.
- That precision is the number of places of decimals they can write down.
- That anomalies are identified after the analysis – they should preferably be identified during the practical work or at the latest before any calculation of a mean.
- They automatically extrapolate the graph to its origin.

Making your investigation reliable and valid

Students could be asked to design an investigation for homework and then pass this to a friend for criticism. This should be constructive and based on the need for validity, reliability and repeatability.

How might an independent variable be linked to a dependent variable?

It would be useful here to illustrate chance or association links which could masquerade as causal relationships. E.g. the number of schools and the number of pubs in different-sized towns.

Starting an investigation

LEARNING OBJECTIVES

Students should learn:

- How scientific knowledge can be used to observe the world around them.
- How good observations can be used to make hypotheses.
- How hypotheses can generate predictions that can be tested.
- That investigations must produce valid results.

LEARNING OUTCOMES

Students should be able to:

- State that observation can be the starting point for an investigation.
- State that observation can generate hypotheses.
- Recall that hypotheses can generate predictions and investigations.
- Show that the design of an investigation must allow results to be valid.

Observation

Use a simple investigation, such as the falling helicopter, split dandelion stems in different salt solutions or calcium dropped into water. Encourage students to make suggestions for any theory that they could use to help to explain their observations.

What is a hypothesis?

Each student could construct a hypothesis to suggest an explanation for their observation.

Starting to design a valid investigation

The hypothesis is put into terms that can be used as a prediction.

Dependent, independent and control variables are identified.

Building an investigation

LEARNING OBJECTIVES

Students should learn:

- How to design a fair test.
- The purpose of a trial run.
- How to ensure accuracy and precision.

LEARNING OUTCOMES

Students should be able to:

- Design a fair test and understand the use of control groups.
- Manage fieldwork investigations.
- Use trial runs to design valid investigations.
- Design accuracy into an investigation.
- Design precision into an investigation.

Fair testing

Students should now be able to describe how at least one control variable can be carried out, for example for the falling helicopter.

Choosing values of a variable

Constructing a table with units and suggestions for the range of the independent variable should now be possible.

Accuracy

Consideration should now be given as to how the independent variable can be used with accuracy and how the dependent variable can be measured accurately. Stress than an accurate measurement is one near the true value.

Precision

Repeats should be considered as one way to illustrate the precision of a set of measurements. Point out that precision is related to the smallest scale division on a measuring instrument.

Making measurements

LEARNING OBJECTIVES

Students should learn:

- That they can expect results to vary.
- That instruments vary in their accuracy.
- That instruments vary in their sensitivity.
- That human error can affect results.
- What to do with anomalies.

LEARNING OUTCOMES

Students should be able to:

- Differentiate between results that vary and anomalies.
- Explain why it is important to use equipment properly.
- Explain that instruments vary in their accuracy and sensitivity.
- State the difference between random and systematic errors.

Using instruments

It might be useful at this stage to set up a circus of instruments. This could be presented as a way of identifying the uses of the instruments, in terms of their accuracy and precision. Consideration should be given as to how easy they are to use and the likelihood of generating systematic or random errors.

Instruments could include: different thermometers, digital and analogue ammeters and voltmeters, measuring cylinders, gas syringes, burettes, pipettes, stopwatches, timing gates, various data logging devices, etc.

Anomalies

Sets of data could be given which illustrate clear anomalies and show the normal variation to be expected. Students should be asked to judge anomalies in the context in which they are presented and not as a strict routine. For example, a range of 10% in the oxygen collected in a photosynthesis investigation is less significant than a 10% range in a resistance investigation, using a multimeter to measure resistance. For this reason it would be useful to present data with which students are familiar. Graphs could be drawn to discover less obvious anomalies.

Presenting data

LEARNING OBJECTIVES

Students should learn:

- What is meant by the range and the mean of a set of data.
- How to use tables of data.
- How to display data.

LEARNING OUTCOMES

Students should be able to:

- Express accurately the range and mean of a set of data.
- Distinguish between the uses of bar charts and line graphs.
- Draw line graphs accurately.

Tables

Students could be given data in a very poor state of presentation and asked to organise it into a table.

The range of the data

They should identify the range of the independent and dependent variables.

The mean of the data

Calculate the mean.

Bar charts and line graphs

Decide on the style of presentation of the results. Perhaps using a spreadsheet to illustrate the many different ways for presentation and deciding on the best form.

Using data to draw conclusions

LEARNING OBJECTIVES

Students should learn:

- How to use charts and graphs to identify patterns.
- How to draw conclusions from relationships.
- How to improve the reliability and validity of an investigation.

LEARNING OUTCOMES

Students should be able to:

- Identify different relationships between variables from graphs.
- Draw conclusions from data.
- Evaluate the reliability and validity of investigations.

Identifying patterns and relationships

A range of graphs or data for graphs could be given to groups of students. Depending on their ability to use graphs, they could be presented with simple or complex relationships to identify. For example, data relating resistance to current or rate of photosynthesis in relation to light, with a limiting factor of carbon dioxide, or neutralisation of an acid and an alkali.

Evaluation

Students could be asked to draw conclusions about the graphs. They could then be subject to cross-examination by their friends to establish their justifications for their conclusions. Questions should be phrased to determine the validity and reliability of the data.

Drawing conclusions

The group, working together, produce a considered conclusion that takes into account all of the other possible interpretations of that data.

Scientific evidence and society

LEARNING OBJECTIVES

Students should learn:

- That science must be presented in a way that takes into account the reliability and the validity of the evidence.
- That science should be presented without bias from the experimenter.
- That evidence must be checked to appreciate whether there is any political influence.
- That the status of experimenter can influence the weight attached to a scientific report.
- That scientific enquiry can result in technological developments.
- That scientific and technological developments can be exploited by different people in different ways.
- That scientific and technological developments can raise ethical, social, economic and environmental issues.
- That different decisions concerning these issues are made by different groups of people.
- That there are many scientific questions unanswered and some questions that can never be answered by science.

LEARNING OUTCOMES

Students should be able to:

- Make judgements about the reliability and the validity of scientific evidence.
- Identify when scientific evidence might have been influenced by bias or political influence.
- Judge scientific evidence on its merits, taking into account the weight given to it by the status of the experimenter.
- Recognise links between science and technology.
- Recognise when people exploit scientific and technological developments.
- Recognise ethical, social, economic and environmental issues raised by scientific and technological developments.
- Show how scientific and technological developments raise different issues for different groups of people.
- Discuss how scientific questions remain unanswered and recognise the limitations of science for answering some questions.

Students should be given a topic to research. They should gather some relevant data. They should be asked to present a case for or against supporting the data. They could be asked to present it to the class, using as many of the key points in the Student Book as possible. They could role play a scientist or a politician.

For example:
- Data relating the incidence of thyroid cancer in children exposed to radiation at Chernobyl in 1986 as compared to those not exposed.
- The effectiveness of biological detergents.
- Efficient production of a meat product.
- The safety of background radiation.

Notes

Notes

Notes